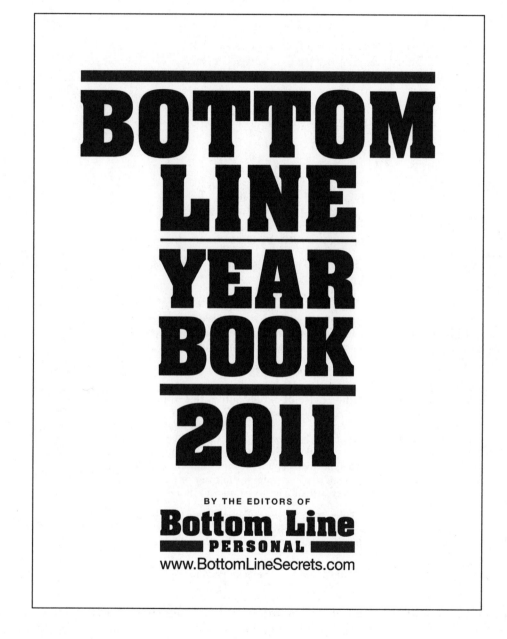

BOTTOM LINE YEAR BOOK 2011

BY THE EDITORS OF

Bottom Line
PERSONAL

www.BottomLineSecrets.com

Contents

6 • PERSONAL AND PRIVATE

PART TWO: YOUR MONEY

7 • MONEY MIRACLES

PART THREE: YOUR FINANCIAL FUTURE

12 • RETIREMENT RICHES

13 • ESTATE PLANNING ESSENTIALS

PART FOUR: YOUR LEISURE

14 • TERRIFIC TRAVEL

1

Health and Happiness

Health Rules You Can Break: Eat Cake…Blow Off Your Run…Stay Up Late…More!

ew of the so-called rules for healthful living—such as exercise every day and get annual checkups—are supported by scientific evidence. Yet millions of Americans feel guilty if they don't follow these and other specific do's and don'ts.

The fact is that people at either extreme in their health habits (those who totally neglect their health and those who behave obsessively about it) tend to be less healthy than those who occupy the middle ground.

What's hype and what's healthy…

Hype: **Annual physicals.** Healthy people who go to a doctor for an annual checkup every year are, on average, no more likely to avoid disease than those who never get annual checkups. The bottom line is that annual physicals do not change health outcomes.

I advise patients with existing health problems to see a doctor regularly to review medications, track changes in symptoms and so on. (Check with your doctor about how often you need to see him/her.) People without health problems can safely avoid the inconvenience and expense of yearly visits.

That said, some regular screenings are recommended even if you are otherwise healthy. Your blood pressure, for example, should be checked every two to three years and cholesterol, every five years.

Susan M. Love, MD, clinical professor of surgery at David Geffen School of Medicine at UCLA. She is president of the Dr. Susan Love Research Foundation and one of the country's foremost specialists in women's health. She is author of *Dr. Susan Love's Breast Book* (Da Capo) and coauthor, with Alice D. Domar, PhD, of *Live a Little! Breaking the Rules Won't Break Your Health* (Crown). Her Web site is *www.dslrf.org*.

Hype: **Eight hours of sleep.** A good night's sleep usually is defined as eight hours of continuous rest. The study most often cited in support of this was conducted in 1993 and focused on 16 volunteers who spent 14 consecutive hours in bed in a darkened room. At first, the volunteers slept an average of more than 12 hours a day. After a few weeks, most decreased their sleep time to seven-and-a-half to nine hours. The researchers concluded that the volunteers slept a lot at first because they were typical sleep-deprived Americans who needed to catch up and that the seven-and-a-half-to-nine-hour range was simply the optimal amount of sleep.

But the research really only indicates how much people will sleep when they have nothing else to do. If you get less sleep, is your health going to suffer?

Most studies that connect sleep loss with illness have focused on people who get only four hours of sleep or less for several consecutive nights. Other studies show that people who get six or seven hours of sleep each night live longer than those who get eight hours or more.

What's right for you? Listen to your body—and don't worry about not having the same amount each night. It's fine to get more sleep on some nights and less on others.

Hype: **Exercise is everything.** Millions of Americans are obsessive about exercise. They feel guilty if they miss their workouts or give up exercise altogether when they realize that they can't live up to an all-or-nothing ideal.

People who are fit clearly are healthier than those who are not, but this isn't the same as saying that everyone needs to exercise for 30 to 60 minutes most days of the week.

Proponents talk about studies that indicate that people who exercise have reduced rates of heart disease, cancer and other diseases. What they neglect to mention is that most of these studies are observational—they track behavior over time, typically through the use of questionnaires.

Observational studies are good for developing hypotheses, but they don't distinguish cause and effect. Perhaps people are healthier because they exercise...or maybe people exercise because they're healthier to begin with. The evidence is not clear.

This is particularly the case for younger adults, who typically incorporate a lot of natural movement into their daily lives, from chasing after young children to working in the yard and cleaning the house. No one really thinks of these activities as exercise, but people who do them usually are pretty fit.

After age 50, when people are less active in general, regular exercise makes more sense. People who exercise most days of the week do have a lower risk for heart disease, and they're less likely to get diabetes. Exercise also can help alleviate insomnia and depression.

Hype: **Thin is best.** Are you worried about your weight? Most American adults are. Yet there's not much evidence that people who are moderately overweight are more unhealthy than those with slim physiques.

Even if you're heavier than you would like to be, the odds that you can lose significant amounts of weight are against you. New research indicates that every individual is born with a genetically programmed weight range, give or take 10 to 20 pounds.

You might hover at the lower end of that range when you're watching your diet. You might drift toward the upper end around the holidays or when you're on vacation. But most people stay roughly within their natural range, regardless of how much or how little they eat or whether or not they exercise.

Of course, if people eat much too much for way too long, even those who are naturally slender can blow the ceiling off their weight range and become obese, which can lead to serious health problems, including diabetes, heart disease and cancer.

Whether you're naturally slender or rotund, your goal should be to stay roughly in the middle of your natural range. The danger is at the extremes. People who are too heavy or too thin tend to die sooner than those in the middle.

Hype: **Frequent mammograms.** More is not better. Most US health agencies advise women to get their first mammogram at age 40 and then have them annually.

Some doctors recommend a "baseline" mammogram at age 35 just in case a surgeon needs a reference point at some time in the future. This is reasonable advice for some women, but not for all women. Speaking as a surgeon, I can attest that doctors almost never consult a baseline mammogram.

It's true that annual mammograms in women over age 50 can reduce the death rate from breast cancer by 30%. Young women are different. Their overall risk from breast cancer is low, and their denser breast tissue makes mammograms less effective.

Also, mammograms have their own dangers. Younger women face higher risks from radiation than older women. And those who get mammograms every year in their 40s face a 20% to 56% risk of getting a false positive, a reading that suggests a problem when in fact no problem is present. This can lead to unnecessary biopsies or surgery.

For most women in their 40s who do not have a family history of breast cancer, a mammogram every two or three years is fine. If you do have a family history of breast cancer, however, you should have mammograms annually after the age of 40.

His and Hers Diseases: How Gender Affects Serious Health Conditions

Kathryn Sandberg, PhD, professor of medicine and director of the Center for the Study of Sex Differences in Health, Aging and Disease at Georgetown University Medical Center. She is a recipient of the Distinguished Scientist Award from the Washington Academy of Sciences and the Established Investigator Award from the American Heart Association.

Not that long ago, doctors assumed that women's and men's bodies reacted in more or less the same way to various diseases.

Now: Through several studies, researchers have discovered that more than half of the 30,000-plus genes in the human body behave very differently in women compared to men, affecting many vital organs.

Key gender-based variations…

PNEUMONIA IN MEN

Gender has a significant impact on infection-fighting immunity.

Important finding: The records of 1,136 men and 1,047 women who were treated at 28 hospital emergency departments for symptoms of pneumonia showed that men tended to be significantly sicker than women when admitted and had a 30% higher risk for death up to a year after the illness (even when the data were adjusted for such factors as age and other health problems).

No one knows exactly why women are better able to fight off bacterial and viral infections, including those that cause pneumonia. One theory suggests that women's two "X" chromosomes—compared with the "X" and "Y" chromosomes in men—may confer some level of protection against infection.

Self-defense: Everyone—and men, in particular—should be alert for symptoms of infection, including fever and fatigue, and seek prompt treatment.

STROKE IN WOMEN

Even though ischemic stroke (due to a blood clot) is slightly more common in men than in women, women account for about 60% of all stroke deaths. More research is needed to determine the reasons for this higher death rate. One possible factor is that women generally suffer strokes at an older age than men.

To minimize brain damage, it is crucial to recognize all symptoms of stroke. A clot-busting medication known as *tissue plasminogen activator* (tPA), the standard stroke treatment, should be administered within three hours of the onset of stroke symptoms (ideally, even sooner). However, female stroke victims frequently delay seeking treatment—in part because their symptoms may differ from men's.

Stroke symptoms that are widely known to affect both sexes strike suddenly. These symptoms include numbness or weakness of the face, arm or leg—especially on one side of the body…trouble speaking or understanding…difficulty seeing in one or both eyes…difficulty walking…dizziness, loss of balance…and/or severe headache with no known cause.

Women, however, are more likely than men to have other sudden-onset stroke symptoms, such as hiccups…nausea…chest pain, shortness of breath and/or heart palpitations.

Important new finding: In a recent analysis of 18 studies, Michigan State University researchers discovered that women admitted to hospitals while suffering stroke symptoms were 30% less likely to receive tPA than men experiencing such symptoms.

Self-defense: Discuss your stroke risk factors with your doctor, who will advise you what to do if you experience hiccups, nausea or other symptoms that less commonly signal a stroke.

If you suffer any of the classic symptoms (even briefly) described earlier—call 911 immediately. Anyone experiencing such stroke symptoms requires a prompt evaluation at a hospital to determine whether tPA should be given.

HIP FRACTURE IN MEN

Hip fracture is a leading cause of disability in both older men and women, but men are significantly more likely than women to get placed in a nursing home and about twice as likely to die from this injury. (Men's shorter average life expectancy may partly explain this disparity.)

Troubling finding: In a landmark study in the *Archives of Internal Medicine,* men hospitalized for hip fracture were reported to be significantly less likely than women to receive treatment for osteoporosis (a main cause of bone fractures) at the time of their hospital discharge.

Self-defense: If you are a man who has risk factors for hip fracture—such as age (over 65) and lack of physical activity—ask your doctor whether you should receive screening tests, including dual energy X-ray absorptiometry (DEXA), to assess your risk for hip fracture.

HEART DISEASE IN WOMEN

Heart disease is now America's number-one cause of death for both genders, but it actually kills more US women than men each year.

Because estrogen is believed to safeguard against the buildup of arterial plaque, men in their 40s are at much greater risk for a heart attack than women of the same age. When women's estrogen levels plummet throughout menopause, however, their heart attack rate equals that of men.

Recent research: Evidence suggests that women often exhibit a different pattern of arterial plaque buildup than men. While men tend to develop blockages at specific points in their arteries, women often develop plaque more evenly throughout their arteries, which makes it less detectable in screening tests.

Women also get less aggressive cardiac preventive care. While women over the age of 45 have higher cholesterol, on average, than their male counterparts, they are less likely to be prescribed cholesterol-lowering statin medication—or beta-blockers (a blood-pressure–lowering medication).

The surprising disparity: While one low-dose (81 mg) aspirin per day helps protect most men against heart attack, it doesn't give women any heart protection—but it does help protect most women (but not men) against ischemic stroke.

Women also are less likely than men to suffer classic heart attack symptoms, such as crushing chest pain, sweating and shortness of breath.

Less well-known heart attack symptoms, including pain in the jaw or shoulder, can occur in both sexes but are more common in women. Unusual fatigue for several days may precede a heart attack in women.

Self-defense: Beginning at age 40, women who are concerned about heart disease (due to family history, for example, or risk factors, such as high blood pressure) should consider consulting a cardiologist who specializes in women's cardiac health and ask which screening test for cardiovascular disease is most appropriate for them.

PARKINSON'S DISEASE IN MEN

This neurological disorder is nearly twice as common in men as it is in women ages 75 to 84, when the majority of cases occur.

Some experts believe that men might be more vulnerable to the disease because they are more likely to have been exposed to toxins, such as pesticides, in their jobs and/or to have suffered head injuries—both of which are believed to increase Parkinson's risk.

Self-defense: Anyone—and men, in particular—with Parkinson's symptoms, such as slowed gait and tremor, should see a doctor—especially if one of the risk factors described above is present.

When Cholesterol Just Won't Go Down: Treatment That Can Reduce LDL Up to 75%

Anne Carol Goldberg, MD, an associate professor of medicine in the division of endocrinology, metabolism and lipid research at the Washington University School of Medicine in St. Louis. A former president of the National Lipid Association, she has participated in numerous clinical trials involving the use of lipid-modifying agents, including the Lipid Research Clinic Coronary Primary Prevention Trial, which was one of the first to show that lowering blood cholesterol levels decreases risk for coronary artery disease.

Almost all of the estimated 42 million Americans with high cholesterol can successfully lower it with diet and exercise—or, when necessary, with statin drugs or other cholesterol-lowering drugs.

But what do you do if your cholesterol levels do not improve substantially with these standard therapies?

About one in every 500 Americans has an inherited (genetic) predisposition to high cholesterol—a condition known as *familial hypercholesterolemia* (FH), which is marked by LDL "bad" cholesterol levels ranging from 150 mg/dL to 1,000 mg/dL.

Dietary changes may have some positive effect on people with FH but typically do not lower LDL levels to a normal range. Cholesterol-lowering medication is sometimes sufficient for people with FH—but not always.

What most people do not know: A high-tech treatment that filters LDL from the blood (described on the next page) can reduce LDL levels by as much as 75% in people with FH

whose cholesterol is not controlled with standard treatments. The procedure also can be used by others, including people who cannot tolerate statin drugs due to side effects.

SKYROCKETING LDL

On the surfaces of a healthy person's cells, there are LDL receptors that remove LDL from the blood. Lower levels of LDL cholesterol reduce the risk for atherosclerosis (the accumulation of cholesterol and other fatty substances on artery walls). A genetic mutation in people with FH results in a greatly reduced number of LDL receptors—or none at all.

People who inherit a defective gene from one parent (the *heterozygous* form of FH) typically have cholesterol levels of 250 mg/dL to 500 mg/dL, while people with two defective copies of the gene (the *homozygous* form) can have cholesterol readings as high as 1,000 mg/dL. Genetic tests are available to detect the defective genes, but most doctors diagnose FH based on such factors as very high LDL levels and the presence of fatty deposits on certain parts of the body.

Important red flag: Cholesterol levels in people with FH may be so high that they develop *xanthomas* (deposits of cholesterol that accumulate). These occur most often in the Achilles tendons (backs of the ankles) but also over the knuckles, elbows, knees and bottom of the feet. They're most commonly seen in people with FH who have LDL levels above 200 mg/dL. If you have any such deposits, see a doctor for an evaluation.

MEDICATION TO TRY

Most people with FH can reach normal—or nearly normal—cholesterol levels with the use of medication. Typically, more potent statins are prescribed at the upper end of the daily dose range—for example, *simvastatin* (Zocor)—40 mg to 80 mg...*atorvastatin* (Lipitor)—80 mg...or *rosuvastatin* (Crestor)—40 mg.

Good news about side effects: Even though statin-related side effects, such as muscle pain, are more likely to occur when high doses are used, people with FH who take such doses of these drugs don't appear to have more side effects than individuals without FH who take lower doses.

Most patients with FH require combination therapy—treatment with a statin plus one or more additional cholesterol-lowering drugs, like *ezetimibe* (Zetia)…bile-acid resins, such as *cholestyramine* (Questran)…or high-dose niacin.

"DIALYSIS" FOR LDL

A relatively new procedure, known as *LDL apheresis,* filters LDL from the blood—similar to the way dialysis filters toxins from the blood when the kidneys are unable to do so. LDL apheresis can decrease LDL levels by at least 50% and sometimes by as much as 75%.

How it works: At an outpatient clinic, a needle attached to a catheter is inserted into a vein in the arm. Over a period of about 90 minutes, up to three quarts of blood are withdrawn from the body and passed through a series of filters that remove the LDL. The "cleansed" blood is then returned to the body through another vein.

Who can benefit: LDL apheresis is recommended for people who don't have atherosclerotic cardiovascular disease and whose LDL levels are 300 mg/dL or above and who can't significantly lower their LDL after maximum therapy, including medication. Additionally, if you have been diagnosed with atherosclerotic cardiovascular disease and your LDL level is 200 mg/dL or above after maximum treatment, you may benefit from LDL apheresis. Patients with cardiovascular disease whose LDL levels are above 200 mg/dL and who cannot tolerate the side effects of statins also are eligible.

The results from apheresis are immediate. Cholesterol levels are tested before and after the procedure. It is not uncommon for LDL to drop from levels greater than 300 mg/dL to as low as 35 mg/dL. This procedure also causes a reduction in C-reactive protein and fibrinogen, substances that increase the risk for blood clots.

Not a cure: Because apheresis does not eliminate the underlying genetic problem in people with FH, LDL levels start to rise immediately after the procedure is completed. Patients who opt for LDL apheresis must repeat the treatment every two weeks, possibly for the rest of their lives.

LDL apheresis is very safe. There is a potential risk for unwanted bleeding (both internally or from the needle site) because the blood thinner *heparin* is used to keep blood flowing during the procedure. However, this type of bleeding rarely occurs because the patient's "bleeding times" (how fast small blood vessels close to stop bleeding) are frequently tested and the dose of *heparin* is adjusted as needed.

Doctors don't yet know how effective LDL apheresis is at decreasing cardiovascular disease, but patients who receive the therapy often report a rapid reduction in cardiovascular symptoms, such as leg discomfort and chest pain from angina.

People who are eligible for LDL apheresis should ask their doctors where they need to go for the procedure. It is currently offered at more than 40 medical centers across the US. Each treatment costs, on average, $2,500 to $3,000* and is covered by Medicare and most insurance plans.

*Prices subject to change.

When "Good" Cholesterol Isn't So Good

Steven R. Jones, MD, an assistant professor of medicine and cardiology at Johns Hopkins University and director of inpatient cardiology at Johns Hopkins Hospital, both in Baltimore. He has presented several scientific papers on lipid research.

For years, we've heard about two forms of cholesterol—the "bad" low-density lipoprotein (LDL) and the "good" high-density lipoprotein (HDL). Higher levels of HDL cholesterol—50 mg/dL or above—are considered desirable because this form of cholesterol has long been associated with the cleanup of lipids (blood fats) from the arteries.

New thinking: HDL cholesterol readings that appear on blood tests may not always be a good indicator of a person's heart disease risk after all. In fact, some people with lower HDL cholesterol actually can be at lower risk than those with very high HDL numbers.

Why is this so? Most people don't realize that unwanted cholesterol is removed from the arteries through a process known as *reverse cholesterol transport.*

Cutting-edge research: The HDL that is measured on standard cholesterol tests does not necessarily indicate the *efficiency* of the reverse transport mechanism, researchers now are discovering. This means that some people with very high HDL, for example, could have inefficient disposal of unwanted cholesterol.

Result: Excess lipids remaining in the arteries and an increased risk for heart disease.

Bottom line: High HDL generally confers protection—but only when it accompanies a robust transport mechanism.

IDENTIFYING HEART DISEASE RISK WITH GREATER ACCURACY

Routine testing of cholesterol remains the mainstay of risk assessment for heart disease, along with consideration of any known cardiovascular risk factors, such as smoking, high blood pressure, family history and diet. Combined, these conventional risk factors identify most patients who are at risk for heart and vascular diseases.

Problem: About half of all heart attacks occur in people with so-called normal cholesterol levels.

Solution: There now are additional cholesterol tests that measure different types of LDL and HDL cholesterol, which may identify some people at risk for heart disease who are missed with conventional cholesterol testing and risk-factor assessment. These blood tests, which typically are covered by insurance, may give a more accurate assessment of your heart disease risk, when combined with standard measures.

You may want to ask your doctor about getting advanced tests, such as...

•**Lp(a).** *Lipoprotein (a)* is a small cholesterol particle that readily penetrates the artery wall, accelerating plaque formation. Lp(a) is associated with increased heart attack risk in most people.

•**Markers of abnormal LDL particle size, density or number.** Tests that measure these markers can help assess cardiovascular disease risk. For some patients, measurement of *apolipoprotein B* (another lipoprotein) levels may better represent the number of particles that cause *atherosclerosis* (fatty buildup located in the arteries).

LOWERING YOUR RISK

Although it's important to know your cholesterol levels, lifestyle changes and other strategies are crucial for decreasing heart disease risk. *They include...*

•**A Mediterranean-style diet,** which emphasizes fruits, vegetables, fish, whole grains and the use of olive oil as the main vegetable fat—and includes only small amounts of meat and saturated fats—is associated with very low cardiovascular disease risk. See page 100 for more on the Mediterranean diet.

•**Regular exercise** can increase HDL by up to 10%—and the weight loss that accompanies exercise can produce an added 20% to 30% increase.

•**Omega-3 fatty acids,** taken either by prescription or as high-dose fish oil, can lower triglycerides (one type of blood fat) by about 40%. This treatment often is combined with other lipid-lowering drugs under the care of a physician.

•**Statin drugs,** such as *simvastatin* (Zocor), *lovastatin* (Mevacor) and *atorvastatin* (Lipitor), which work primarily by lowering LDL cholesterol as well as inflammation, are among the most effective ways to lower cardiovascular risk. In general, every 1% reduction in LDL reduces the risk for heart attack by 1%.

•**Niacin.** *Nicotinic acid,* a form of niacin, has long been known to raise HDL by up to 30%.

But the real benefit of niacin now is thought to be due to improvements in reverse transport and its additional ability to lower levels of triglycerides and LDL. Niacin also makes LDL particles less toxic to the arteries by favorably changing the chemical properties of LDL and HDL—and is used to lower Lp(a) levels.

Caution: Because improper use of niacin can cause serious liver damage, it should be taken only in prescription form under a doctor's supervision.

Memory on the Blink? It May Be Due to Hypertension

High blood pressure can lead to memory problems in people over age 45. People whose diastolic pressure (bottom number) is 90 or above are more likely to have trouble with memory and thinking skills than people with normal diastolic readings of less than 80. Every 10-point increase in diastolic pressure raises the odds of cognitive problems by 7%. Talk with your doctor about maintaining a healthy blood pressure.

Georgios Tsivgoulis, MD, adjunct assistant professor of neurology at University of Alabama at Birmingham and a member of the American Academy of Neurology. He is lead author of a study of almost 20,000 people, published in *Neurology.*

A Virus That Causes High Blood Pressure

Recent research indicates that the *cytomegalovirus* (CMV), which more than 60% of adults have been infected by at some point in their lives, can cause high blood pressure. CMV was previously thought to be implicated in cardiovascular disease, but until now no causal relationship was known. The recent research found that healthy mice infected with CMV developed high blood pressure, and that when fed a high-cholesterol diet, such mice developed the highest blood pressure of all.

Implication: If a virus causes high blood pressure, an antiviral medication may be developed as a remedy.

Clyde Crumpacker, MD, Beth Israel Deaconess Medical Center and professor at Harvard Medical School and study coauthor.

Four Things Needed for An Accurate BP Reading

For an accurate blood pressure reading, sit with the back supported and both feet flat on the floor…wear short sleeves or ones that can be pushed up easily…avoid a large meal, alcohol and caffeine for at least 30 minutes before blood pressure is taken…be quiet and relaxed—do not rush to your appointment.

Mayo Clinic Health Letter, 200 First St. SW, Rochester, Minnesota 55905, *www.healthletter.mayoclinic.com.*

Nighttime Aspirin Lowers Blood Pressure

Although previous studies linked nighttime aspirin use with reduced blood pressure, there was no explanation for the drug's effect.

New research: Bedtime aspirin use was found to lower blood and urine levels of naturally occurring chemicals associated with high blood pressure in a study of 16 adults with untreated, mildly elevated blood pressure.

If your doctor has prescribed daily aspirin: Ask about taking the pill at night.

Jaapjan Snoep, MSc, researcher, department of clinical epidemiology, Leiden University Medical Center, the Netherlands.

A Vaccine That Does Double Duty

Pneumonia vaccine may protect the heart, as well. In one recent study, older adults with cardiovascular risk factors who were vaccinated against pneumonia at least two years earlier were 50% less likely to have a heart attack than the older adults who had not been vaccinated or who had been vaccinated within one year.

Study of 5,000 Canadian patients by researchers from Université de Sherbrook, Sherbrook, Quebec and McMaster University, Hamilton, Ontario, published in *Canadian Medical Association Journal.*

Best Treatment for Blood Pressure That Just Won't Lower

David A. Calhoun, MD, professor of medicine in the Vascular Biology and Hypertension Program at the University of Alabama in Birmingham. He was chair of the committee that wrote *Resistant Hypertension: Diagnosis, Evaluation, and Treatment,* published in *Hypertension.*

High blood pressure (hypertension) is widely known as a "silent" disease because it increases the risk for health problems ranging from stroke and heart attack to erectile dysfunction—often without causing symptoms. For this reason, half of people with hypertension don't even seek treatment.*

A more challenging health threat: There are many people who are trying to lower their blood pressure—but they are not successful. In fact, an estimated 20% to 30% of people being treated for high blood pressure are said to have *resistant hypertension* because blood pressure remains high although they are taking three or more medications at the same time. To prevent—or overcome—this problem...

WHY TREATMENT MAY NOT WORK

Resistant hypertension is on the rise in the US, in part due to the dramatic increase in overweight individuals and those with diabetes and chronic kidney disease—all of which render high blood pressure harder to treat. When other health problems are diagnosed and effectively treated, blood pressure usually drops.

Other conditions that can play a role in resistant hypertension...

*For most people, hypertension is defined as blood pressure of 140/90 mm Hg or higher. Optimal blood pressure is lower than 120/80 mm Hg. More than one reading is needed to make a determination.

• **Obstructive sleep apnea.** In one study, 83% of subjects with resistant hypertension suffered from sleep apnea (the airway relaxes and shuts during sleep, causing a temporary drop in oxygen).

Symptoms to watch for: Snoring, gasping for air during sleep and daytime drowsiness.

• **Aldosteronism.** This condition will occur when the adrenal glands put out too much of the hormone *aldosterone*, leading to fluid retention, which raises blood pressure. Aldosteronism is much more common than previously thought—it affects about 20% of people with resistant hypertension. Potassium levels often drop as a result of aldosteronism.

Symptoms to watch for: Weakness, muscle spasms and temporary paralysis—all of which can occur with low potassium.

DRUGS THAT MAY INTERFERE

Drugs taken for other health problems can interfere with blood pressure treatment. *For example...*

• **Nonsteroidal anti-inflammatory drugs (NSAIDs),** over-the-counter (OTC) painkillers such as *ibuprofen* (Motrin, Advil) and *naproxen* (Aleve), often are overlooked as a factor in resistant hypertension. NSAIDs promote fluid retention. If you have trouble controlling your blood pressure, *acetaminophen* (Tylenol) often is a better choice for pain relief.

• **Decongestants and diet pills,** including OTC versions, can raise blood pressure by causing *vasoconstriction* (narrowing of blood vessels).

• **Stimulants and amphetamines** may elevate blood pressure, also through vasoconstriction. The drugs—*methylphenidate* (Ritalin) and *dextroamphetamine* and *amphetamine* (Adderall), for example—are used for attention deficit disorder.

• **Oral contraceptives** could keep blood pressure high, likely by promoting retention of fluid.

LIFESTYLE CHANGES THAT HELP

Some factors that often contribute to resistant hypertension...

• **Salt is a double threat.** A high-sodium diet not only increases blood pressure in a lot of people, it also blunts the effectiveness of many antihypertensive drugs.

Not everyone with high blood pressure is sensitive to sodium, but nearly all people with resistant hypertension would benefit from cutting back to less than 2,300 mg daily.

• **Potassium in your bloodstream can become depleted** if you take a diuretic (water pill). If you develop symptoms of low potassium (described earlier), ask your doctor to check your potassium level with a blood test, and then take a potassium supplement if you need it.

Otherwise, add potassium-rich foods (such as citrus fruits, bananas, dried apricots and avocados) to your diet.

Caution: Chronic kidney disease patients, who are at higher risk for *hyperkalemia* (an abnormally high blood level of potassium), should ask their nephrologist (kidney disease specialist) about an appropriate diet.

• **Physical activity** has been shown to produce a small but significant drop in blood pressure—4 mm Hg in systolic (top number) pressure and 3 mm Hg in diastolic (bottom number) pressure, on average. Exercise for at least 30 minutes, most days of the week.

WHICH DRUGS ARE BEST?

Medicines work in different ways to lower blood pressure and may be tried in different combinations. For example, if an *angiotensin converting enzyme (ACE) inhibitor* doesn't do the job, a calcium channel blocker or diuretic, rather than another ACE inhibitor, might be added to the regimen. *Two kinds of medications that are particularly important for resistant hypertension...*

• **Thiazide diuretics** lower blood pressure by ridding the body of excess water and salt and also appear to increase the effectiveness of other types of blood pressure medications. If you take two or three blood pressure drugs, one should be a thiazide diuretic, such as hydrochlorothiazide or chlorthalidone.

• **Mineralocorticoid receptor antagonists,** such as *spironolactone* (Aldactone) and *eplerenone* (Inspra), have been shown to reduce blood pressure substantially when added to combinations of other drugs that haven't done the job.

Important: Even the most effective medications won't work if they stay in the bottle. If your blood pressure remains high despite treatment, make sure you take all the pills, all the time.

Smart idea: A pill-organizer box may help you stick to your medication schedule.

DO YOU NEED A SPECIALIST?

If your blood pressure is still high after six months of treatment by your regular doctor, it may be time to see a hypertension expert. The American Society of Hypertension (ASH) maintains a directory of clinical hypertension specialists at *www.ash-us.org.* Or call the ASH at 212-696-9099. Your doctor also may know of a cardiologist or nephrologist with expertise in treating resistant hypertension.

Keep trying until you've found a treatment that works. All too often, resistant hypertension remains untreated, causing steady, silent damage for years.

BP Drug Guidelines Behind the Times?

Current guidelines for treating hypertension (high blood pressure) advise starting with a diuretic to remove excess sodium and water from the body.

A study: Hypertension patients who took a single pill combining the calcium channel blocker *amlodipine* and the ACE inhibitor *benazepril*—both of which relax blood vessel walls—had 20% fewer cardiovascular events (such as angina, heart attack or stroke) than patients who took the diuretic alone or with benazepril.

Best: Ask your doctor about combination medication for hypertension.

Kenneth Jamerson, MD, professor of internal medicine, University of Michigan Medical School, Ann Arbor, and leader of a study of 11,506 people, published in *The New England Journal of Medicine.*

Generic Heart Drugs Are As Good as Brand Names

A review of 20 years of research revealed that, among medical journal editorials that discussed substituting generic for brand-name heart medications, 53% expressed a negative view of generics.

But: In 47 clinical trials, brand-name drugs were not found to be superior to the FDA-approved "bio-equivalent" generic heart drugs.

Thrifty: Ask your doctor about switching to generics, which cost less.

Aaron S. Kesselheim, MD, JD, Brigham and Women's Hospital, Harvard Medical School, Boston, and lead author of a review of studies on cardiovascular drugs.

Urine Test for Heart Disease 84% Accurate

Urine contains many different proteins, including some that are found only in people with *atherosclerosis* (fatty buildup in the arteries). An experimental urine test identified coronary artery disease with 84% accuracy.

American Heart Association, *www.americanheart. org.*

Best Cardiac Screening Tests

C. Noel Bairey Merz, MD, director of the Women's Heart Center and the Preventive and Rehabilitative Cardiac Center at Cedars-Sinai Heart Institute and professor of medicine at Cedars-Sinai Medical Center, all in Los Angeles. She is also chair of the National Institutes of Health–sponsored Women's Ischemic Syndrome Evaluation (WISE) study, which investigates various methods for more effective diagnosis and evaluation of heart disease in women.

Every adult should be assessed annually for heart health. How? During your routine physical, your doctor should record your height, weight, waist circumference and blood pressure...order fasting blood tests for glucose, cholesterol and triglyceride levels... and discuss your diet, exercise habits, alcohol consumption, cigarette use and family history. Based on these factors, your doctor calculates your risk for heart disease, heart attack and stroke.

If this annual evaluation indicates that your risk for heart disease may be elevated, your doctor may consider doing the following safe, radiation-free tests to get a clearer picture of your heart health...

• **Resting ECG.** This is an electrocardiogram taken while you lie quietly. It is able to identify atrial fibrillation, an irregular quivering of the heart muscle that increases stroke risk.

Insurance does pay if your physician orders this test for an approved indication. Unfortunately, many insurance companies now refuse to cover the test as part of a routine physical —so ask your doctor if you should consider getting it anyway and paying out-of-pocket.

Cost: $75 to $400,* depending on your location and provider.

• **Carotid intima-media thickness (C-IMT) measurement.** The test uses ultrasound to measure the thickness of the arterial wall in the carotid artery in the neck, which is an indicator of plaque buildup. Repeating this test as directed by your physician may help detect changes in your cardiovascular health.

The test works as well for women as for men and can help your doctor determine whether you would benefit from taking a daily aspirin or statin drug.

Cost: $250 to $500, usually not covered by insurance. If you are at intermediate risk, your doctor may advise you to pay for this test if the results could help determine the best course of action.

• **High-sensitivity C-reactive protein test (hs-CRP).** The regular CRP blood test measures levels of a protein linked to inflammation, which in turn is linked to heart disease. The high-sensitivity version more accurately reveals when the protein concentrations are only slightly elevated, so it is more useful in predicting a healthy person's heart disease risk.

*Prices subject to change.

Among people whose hs-CRP levels are in the high end of the normal range, heart attack risk is one-and-a-half to four times higher than in people whose CRP is at the low end.

Cost: Typically about $50, often covered by insurance.

Free self-assessment tool: To get an idea of your chances of developing heart disease within 10 years, check the online calculator from the National Heart, Lung and Blood Institute at *http://hp2010.nhlbihin.net/atpiii/cal culator.asp.*

Pulse Rate Can Predict Heart Attack Risk

Women's resting heart rate was measured in beats per minute (or BPM) after five minutes of inactivity. Those with rates of 76 BPM or higher were 26% more likely to have a heart attack or die from heart disease within eight years than those with rates of 62 BPM or lower. If your resting heart rate is higher than 76 BPM, tell your doctor.

Judith Hsia, MD, professor of medicine, George Washington University, Washington, DC, and lead author of a study of 129,135 women, published in *British Medical Journal*.

Heartburn Drug Danger

Don't mix heartburn drugs with the blood thinner *clopidogrel* (Plavix). Using Plavix along with certain drugs that reduce acid reflux, such as *omeprazole* (Prilosec) or *lansoprazole* (Prevacid), may raise the chance of a cardiac event, such as a heart attack or stroke, by 50%. But some doctors suggest taking this specific combination to lower the risk for stomach bleeding.

Self-defense: Ask your doctor about alternative heartburn drugs, such as *famotidine* (Mylanta and Pepcid) and *rantidine* (Zantac). Consider avoiding such medicines completely if your doctor says that your risk for stomach bleeding when taking Plavix is low.

David Flockhart, MD, PhD, chief, division of clinical pharmacology, Indiana University School of Medicine, Indianapolis.

The Great American Heart Hoax: Needless Cardiac Surgery

Michael D. Ozner, MD, cardiologist and medical director of Cardiovascular Prevention Institute of South Florida in Miami. Dr. Ozner is the symposium director for "Cardiovascular Disease Prevention," an annual international meeting highlighting advances in cardiology. He is author of *The Great American Heart Hoax: Lifesaving Advice Your Doctor Should Tell You About Heart Disease Prevention (But Probably Never Will)* (BenBella). His Web site is *www.drozner.com.*

Americans get more than 1.5 million cardiac bypass surgeries and angioplasty procedures a year, which makes heart surgery among the most commonly performed surgical procedures in the US.

Fact: These two procedures have not been proved to extend lives or to prevent future heart attacks except in a minority of patients (see "Who Really Needs Surgery" on page 14). More than one million people have needless cardiac surgery every year. Between 70% and 90% of angioplasties and bypass surgeries are unnecessary in stable patients with coronary artery disease.

While American patients are seven times more likely to undergo coronary angioplasty procedures and bypass surgery than patients in Canada and Sweden, the number of Canadians and Swedes who die from cardiovascular disease is nearly identical (per capita) to the number of people who die from heart disease in this country.

These are not harmless procedures. About 30% of angioplasties fail, requiring patients to repeat the procedure—and eventually, many of these angioplasty patients will undergo bypass surgery. People who have bypass surgery are nearly four times more likely to suffer a stroke at the time of surgery and are vulnerable to postsurgical infections. Between 3% and 5% of patients die from bypass surgery—that's 15,000 to 25,000 lives lost a year.

So why then do we keep performing these procedures?

A FLAWED MODEL

Cardiologists used to compare the coronary arteries to simple pipes under a sink. The thinking went that these arteries sometimes accumulated sludge, called plaque (cholesterol deposits within an artery wall), that impeded the flow of blood to the heart. Treating this sludge with angioplasty or shunting blood around it with bypass surgery seemed obvious.

That approach, however, is flawed. We now realize that the arteries are highly dynamic structures. And, what occurs within the artery wall is more significant than blockages that obstruct the *lumen* (arterial openings).

The majority of heart attacks can be linked to small, yet highly inflamed, plaques. These small plaques have no effect on circulation, because they take up little space within the lumen. Yet they may rupture and cause a sudden heart attack due to a clot that forms at the site of the rupture.

What happens: Cholesterol-carrying particles that enter an artery wall undergo oxidation and modification that trigger an immune response. White blood cells flood the area and engulf the oxidized cholesterol particles and cause plaque to form. Then the white blood cells secrete substances, such as *proteinases,* that break down the fibrous cap that covers the plaque. When the fibrous cap ruptures, blood enters the plaque and a blood clot forms that can block the artery.

Sudden clots that develop following plaque rupture are the cause of most heart attacks. Angioplasties and bypass surgery do nothing to prevent plaque rupture or clot formation.

HEART-SAVING STEPS

The following five steps may save lives. *Of course, always ask your doctor about the best heart-health strategies for you...*

•**Test for high sensitivity (hs)-C-reactive protein (CRP).** It's a "marker" that indicates simmering inflammation in blood vessel walls and can be measured with a simple blood test. Inflammation within arterial plaques contributes to plaque rupture and clot formation and subsequent heart attacks.

The landmark JUPITER research looked at more than 17,000 participants with elevated hs-CRP (above 2 mg/dL) and normal cholesterol. Those who were treated with medication to lower hs-CRP were significantly less likely to have a heart attack or stroke or to die than those in the control group. CRP can be lowered with lifestyle changes (diet, exercise, weight loss, smoking cessation) and medical therapy (including statin drugs).

•**Test for apolipoprotein B (apoB).** This is a better indicator of heart disease than standard cholesterol levels (including HDL, LDL and triglycerides). Even if your LDL "bad" cholesterol level is normal, you still could have elevated particle numbers, which means that your LDL cholesterol is distributed across a lot of very small, dense particles. These small, dense particles are the most dangerous kind—they are more likely to squeeze through the lining of the artery and more likely to become oxidized once they're there, leading to atherosclerosis (hardening of the arteries). You can check your "bad" particle number by testing for apoB. Blood tests for apoB are performed routinely in Europe and Canada but not in the US. Ask for this test when you have your usual cholesterol screening.

The optimal level of apoB is less than 90 mg/dL (or even lower for high-risk patients). To lower apoB, follow the recommendations for lowering CRP.

•**Choose an anti-inflammatory diet.** People who follow a Mediterranean-style diet—high in plant foods and cold-water fish (such as salmon) and low in red meat and processed foods—can reduce inflammation.

The Lyon Diet Heart Study compared the Mediterranean diet to a diet resembling the American Heart Association's cholesterol-lowering Step 1 Diet. Participants on the Mediterranean plan were 70% less likely to die from all causes and 73% less likely to have a recurrent cardiac event than those on the standard "healthy" diet.

The Mediterranean diet is effective partly because it limits saturated fat and does not contain trans fat. The fat present in the Mediterranean diet, primarily from olive oil and fish, has anti-inflammatory effects. Also, the antioxidants in fruits and vegetables decrease oxidation of cholesterol-containing particles within artery walls. See page 100 for more on the Mediterranean diet.

Avoid high-fructose corn syrup. This will go straight into the liver, where it causes an increase in triglycerides, a major risk factor for heart disease.

•**Laugh, pray, get a pet.** Anything that reduces stress can significantly reduce your risk for heart disease. Research at the University of Maryland Medical Center, for example, found that laughing is almost as effective as exercise at improving arterial health.

Laughter can relax blood vessels and improve circulation to the heart. And like other stress-control strategies, including prayer, loving relationships (with pets as well as people) and yoga, it decreases *cortisol*, a stress-related hormone.

•**Get moving.** There is a dose-response relationship between exercise and the heart—more exercise gives a greater benefit. Aim for 30 to 45 minutes of exercise most days of the week.

Good news: Walking for as little as 30 minutes five to seven days a week can significantly decrease the risk of dying from heart disease.

More from Dr. Michael Ozner...

Who Really Needs Surgery?

Americans often undergo unnecessary heart surgery, but stents or bypass surgery can be lifesavers for a select group of patients, including those with...

•**Unstable angina** that has increasing frequency and intensity of chest pain, often occurring at rest.

•**Disabling chest pain** that does not respond to lifestyle intervention or to optimal medical therapy.

•**Significant obstructions** in the left, right or other coronary arteries and a weak heart muscle.

•**Significant blockage** in the main trunk of the left coronary artery.

How to *Double* CPR Success

Double CPR success with chest compressions *alone*.

Study: Odds of surviving cardiac arrest outside of a hospital were 5% without CPR...6% with standard CPR (alternating chest compressions and mouth-to-mouth breaths)...and 11% with continuous compressions without mouth-to-mouth.

If someone needs CPR, call 911 and perform continuous chest compressions until medical help arrives.

Gordon A. Ewy, MD, director, University of Arizona Sarver Heart Center, Tucson, and presenter of an analysis of 4,850 cardiac arrest cases.

Taking a Daily Aspirin Isn't for Everyone

While taking an 81 mg "baby" aspirin each day may reduce risk for heart attack and stroke, it also increases risk for gastrointestinal (GI) bleeding for the same reason—it thins the blood.

Safety: Daily aspirin is not recommended for most men under age 45 and women under age 55, because among those younger age groups, risk of GI bleeding is much higher than risk for heart attack or stroke. Risk of GI bleeding also increases sharply after age 80.

Important: Consult with your doctor about the specifics of your own case before taking a daily aspirin.

Russell K. Portenoy, MD, professor, Albert Einstein College of Medicine, New York City, *www.stoppain.org*.

Stroke Risk: Little-Known Triggers That May Surprise You

Steven R. Messé, MD, assistant professor of neurology and director of the vascular neurology fellowship at the Hospital of the University of Pennsylvania in Philadelphia. Board-certified in neurology and vascular neurology, he has published scientific papers in *Stroke, Neurology* and the *Journal of Neurology, Neurosurgery and Psychiatry*.

Many risk factors for stroke are well known. For example, high blood pressure (hypertension), elevated cholesterol, diabetes, inactivity, smoking, a previous stroke or "mini-stroke" (also called a transient ischemic attack, or TIA) or a family history of stroke all increase your odds of suffering this potentially devastating condition.

What few people realize: There are many little-known risk factors for stroke, which also should be taken seriously, particularly if you have one or more of the risk factors mentioned above. Each additional risk factor increases your chance of having a stroke.

For example…

COLD WEATHER

High blood pressure can triple your risk for a stroke.

Recent development: A study of nearly 9,000 people found that cold weather raises blood pressure levels in people age 65 and older. One-third of those studied had hypertension in the winter, compared with about one-quarter during the summer.

Self-defense: If you have hypertension—a systolic (top number) reading of 140 mm Hg or higher and/or diastolic (bottom number) of 90 mm Hg or beyond—consider taking your blood pressure every day throughout the winter (at the same time of day) using an at-home device. Follow the same strategy if you have prehypertension (the stage before hypertension)—systolic reading of 120 mm Hg to 139 mm Hg and/or diastolic reading of 80 mm Hg to 89 mm Hg. If you have hypertension or prehypertension and your blood pressure rises in the winter, see your doctor.

SHINGLES

If you had chicken pox as a child, you're at risk for an outbreak of the same virus—a condition known as shingles—years later.

After a bout of chicken pox, the virus (*varicella-zoster*) becomes dormant in the sensory nerves along the spinal cord or near the brain. With shingles, the virus re-emerges, typically causing a painful rash that affects one side of the body. For example, the rash may wrap itself around the trunk from mid-back to one side of the chest. The trigger behind this reactivation is thought to be related to stress and suppression of the immune system.

New research: In a study of nearly 8,000 adults who had been treated for shingles and 23,000 who had not suffered the disease, the shingles patients were 31% more likely to have had a stroke in the year following the shingles outbreak. It's important to note that shingles often occurs in people who are already ill or have a suppressed immune system—factors that in themselves raise stroke risk.

Self-defense: There is not enough evidence to recommend that the shingles vaccine be given for stroke prevention. However, it's wise for older adults to receive the vaccine, since it's estimated that half of people who live to age 85 will suffer a shingles attack. If you have a history of shingles, follow your doctor's advice on stroke prevention, such as making lifestyle changes and taking medication to prevent or control hypertension, cholesterol levels and/or diabetes.

STRESS AND DEPRESSION

When researchers studied 600 people who had recently had a stroke and 600 people who hadn't, those who had experienced stress for one year or longer had a 3.5 times higher risk for ischemic stroke.

What happens: Unrelieved stress triggers secretion of the hormone *cortisol*. Continual secretion of cortisol can raise blood pressure, destabilize blood sugar levels and increase inflammation—all of which can raise stroke risk.

Self-defense: Chronic stress is often linked to clinical depression. If you suspect that you may be depressed (symptoms include change in weight and/or sleep habits), see your doctor. He/she may prescribe an antidepressant and/or recommend cognitive behavioral therapy (CBT), which research shows is as effective as medication in decreasing depression. Regular exercise, a healthful diet and sufficient sleep also help fight depression. If you are not depressed but regularly experience stress, follow the lifestyle changes described above.

MIGRAINE

People who suffer migraines with "auras" (visual disturbances such as jagged lines and flashes of light) have twice the risk for ischemic stroke as people without migraines, according to recent research. The increased risk is most apparent in women who smoke and take oral contraceptives.

Self-defense: If you suffer migraines with auras, talk about your stroke risk with your doctor.

CHIROPRACTIC ADJUSTMENT

Because chiropractic adjustments to the neck often involve physical manipulation of the cervical spine (neck region), neurologists and chiropractors have long debated whether such movements can lead to a rare form of ischemic stroke known as *vertebrobasilar artery* (VBA) stroke, which can be triggered by a tear in the vertebral arteries that run along the neck bones.

Latest research: A study with 818 people found that those under age 45 who had suffered VBA strokes and were hospitalized for that type of stroke were three times more likely to have seen a chiropractor or a primary care physician before the hospitalization than people without VBA strokes. In people over age 45, VBA stroke was associated with visits to primary care practitioners.

The researchers speculated that the visits to both practitioners occurred when people had symptoms of a VBA tear, such as neck pain or stiffness, but had not yet had a VBA stroke.

Self-defense: It is unlikely that a chiropractic adjustment of the neck will greatly increase your risk for a stroke. But since all medical treatments have some risks, you will need to decide whether the benefits of a chiropractic

manipulation of the neck outweigh the likely small risk for stroke.

Warning: You can trigger a VBA tear by bending your head backward over the sink while having your hair washed at a hair salon. If you've had a previous stroke or TIA, do not put your head in this position. If you have no history of stroke, make sure your neck is resting comfortably and securely on a towel and not on the sink itself.

FAST FOOD

People living in neighborhoods with the most fast-food restaurants had a 13% higher risk for ischemic stroke, according to a new study. This research does not prove that fast food causes stroke but shows a statistical association between the two factors. However, there is proof that high levels of saturated fat and salt—both commonly found in many fast-food meals—increase stroke risk.

Self-defense: Limit your intake of fast foods. If you go to a fast-food restaurant, choose more healthful menu items, such as salads.

Breakthroughs in Stroke Prevention and Treatment: Recent Findings Save Lives

Ralph L. Sacco, MD, professor and chairman of the department of neurology at University of Miami Leonard M. Miller School of Medicine. He is an international authority on the prevention and treatment of stroke and president-elect of the American Heart Association (AHA). Dr. Sacco also is the Olemberg Family Chair in Neurological Disorders and the Miller Professor of Neurology, Epidemiology and Human Genetics at the Miller School and neurologist-in-chief at Jackson Memorial Hospital, Miami.

Nearly 800,000 times a year—every 40 seconds—someone in the US suffers a stroke.

An ischemic stroke happens when a clot blocks the flow of blood to the brain. This accounts for 87% of strokes. A hemorrhagic stroke results when a blood vessel in the brain ruptures and accounts for 13% of strokes.

These "brain attacks" often are deadly or disabling. Stroke is the third-leading cause of death (after heart disease and cancer), killing more than 143,000 Americans yearly. It's the leading cause of disability and can result in paralysis, spasticity, pain, speech difficulties and memory loss.

Good news: Researchers are discovering more effective ways to prevent and treat stroke. In a recent 10-year span, the death rate from stroke has fallen by 30% and the actual number of stroke deaths has declined by 13.5%.

The latest findings…

DECREASE YOUR RISK

Scientists at Harvard School of Public Health identified five lifestyle factors that can cut the risk for ischemic stroke by 80% and all strokes by almost 50%—not smoking, maintaining a normal weight, eating a prudent diet, exercising regularly and moderate intake of alcohol. *Also…*

• **Consider statin medication.** A report in *The Lancet Neurology* analyzed the results of using LDL cholesterol–lowering statin medications to prevent stroke in 165,792 people. For every decrease in LDL of 39 mg/dL, there was a 21.1% decrease in the risk for stroke. Ask your doctor about whether a statin is right for you.

• **Eat more fish.** A study published in *Neurology* showed that people who ate tuna and other fish high in omega-3 fatty acids three times or more every week had a nearly 26% lower risk of having brain imaging findings of stroke, compared with people who didn't eat the fish regularly.

• **Drink tea.** Researchers at UCLA analyzed studies involving nearly 195,000 people and found that drinking six cups of green or black tea a day was associated with a 42% reduction in stroke risk. Drinking three cups was associated with a 21% reduction for stroke.

KNOW THE SYMPTOMS

Researchers from the Division for Heart Disease and Stroke Prevention at the Centers for Disease Control and Prevention surveyed 86,573 adults about the five warning signs of stroke (see below). They reported their results at the American Stroke Association's International Stroke Conference.

New finding: People at the highest risk for stroke—the elderly and those who have had a previous stroke—were the least likely to know the five stroke warning signs. Overall, only 37% of those surveyed knew all five signs and knew to call 911 immediately.

Here are the five signs of a stroke. If you experience one or more of these signs, call 911 immediately…

• **Sudden numbness or weakness** in the face, arm or leg, particularly if on only one side of the body.

• **Sudden, severe headache** with no known cause.

• **Sudden visual disturbance** in one or both eyes.

• **Sudden confusion** or difficulty speaking.

• **Sudden dizziness,** loss of balance, loss of coordination or difficulty walking.

IF YOU SUSPECT STROKE…

• **Don't call the doctor's office.** Calling a primary care doctor at the first sign of stroke delays patients from reaching the emergency room (ER), say researchers at West Virginia University-Morgantown. In their study, the researchers called primary care physicians' offices seeking advice for a hypothetical stroke or heart attack symptoms. Almost one-third of receptionists recommended scheduling an appointment for later in the day if symptoms continued.

• **Don't call the hospital help line if you're having stroke-like symptoms.** The operator may tell you to call your doctor. A study in *Stroke* showed that nearly one-quarter of hospital help-line operators mistakenly routed a caller describing classic stroke symptoms to primary care doctors rather than to 911.

RUSH TO THE ER

If you're having a stroke, the faster you call 911 and get to the emergency room…and the sooner you are treated with *tissue plasminogen activator* (tPA), the blood-thinning, clot-dissolving intravenous drug…the less amount of brain tissue is likely to die…and the better the probable outcome, in terms of preventing death and disability. But many people who are having a stroke don't get to the ER right away—mostly because they don't think they're having a stroke.

Mayo Clinic researchers reported in *Emergency Medicine Journal* that the average time of arrival at the ER was three hours or more *after* the onset of stroke, which was considered too late for tPA to be effective.

Recent finding #1: Researchers have found significant benefits—and no increased risk for brain injury—in people with stroke who were treated with tPA up to four-and-a-half hours after onset of stroke symptoms. Consequently, guidelines expanded the time to four-and-a-half hours that some patients can get the clot-busting drug.

Caution: It still is important to have treatment as soon as possible.

Recent finding #2: Three out of five stroke deaths occur in women. Women are 30% less likely than men to get tPA in the ER, reported researchers from Michigan State University at the International Stroke Conference.

Possible reason: Women may not have any of the five classic stroke symptoms. Instead, they may suffer a loss of consciousness or sudden body pain other than a headache. If you or a loved one experiences these symptoms, ask to be checked for stroke.

PREVENT A SECOND STOKE

Every year, of the 795,000 Americans who have a stroke, 185,000 will then suffer a second stroke. *To reduce your risk...*

Recent finding: A study reported at the American Academy of Neurology's 61st Annual Meeting in April 2009 demonstrated that stroke victims who achieve "optimal levels" of four risk factors—LDL cholesterol, HDL cholesterol, triglycerides (blood fats) and blood pressure—were 65% less likely to have another stroke, compared with people who did not reach an optimal level of any risk factor. Those who reached optimal levels of three risk factors were 38% less likely to have another stroke...two risk factors, 22% less...and one risk factor, 2% less.

Simple Test Gauges Stroke Risk

When researchers checked the blood flow at the ankle of 102 adults who had suffered a stroke or "ministroke," patients whose test results indicated *peripheral artery disease* (PAD)—narrowing of the blood vessels that carry blood to the legs, arms, stomach or kidneys—were three times more likely to suffer another stroke within two years than those without PAD.

If you've had a stroke or ministroke: Ask your doctor about the ankle brachial index test, which can be done in a doctor's office.

Souvik Sen, MD, professor and chair, department of neurology, University of South Carolina School of Medicine, Columbia.

Antidepressants Linked To Stroke

Postmenopausal women who began taking antidepressants during a six-year study had a 45% higher risk for stroke than women not on antidepressants.

But: Depression itself is a risk factor for cardiovascular problems, so do not stop taking antidepressants without first consulting with your doctor.

Sylvia Wassertheil-Smoller, PhD, professor of epidemiology, Albert Einstein College of Medicine, New York City, and coauthor of a study of 136,293 women.

Trouble Sleeping? You May Be at Risk For These Diseases

Women who take longer than 30 minutes to fall asleep have a higher risk for diabetes, heart disease and stroke.

Reason: These women tend to have higher levels of insulin...inflammatory proteins that are linked to heart disease...and *fibrinogen*, a protein that is associated with stroke and heart attack.

Best: If you often have difficulty sleeping, talk to your doctor about the risks and ways to fall asleep.

Edward Suarez, PhD, associate professor, department of psychiatry, Duke University Medical Center, Durham, North Carolina, and leader of a study of 210 people, published in *Brain, Behavior and Immunity*.

Surprising Symptoms of Prediabetes

Frederic J. Vagnini, MD, a cardiovascular surgeon and medical director of the Heart, Diabetes & Weight Loss Centers of New York in New York City. He is co-author of *The Weight Loss Plan for Beating Diabetes* (Fair Winds).

One of the best ways to avoid diabetes is to spot blood sugar (glucose) problems before the full-blown disease develops. But most people do not recognize that diabetes—and its precursor, prediabetes—can cause no symptoms at all or a wide range of symptoms that often are misinterpreted.

Common mistake: Because type 2 diabetes is strongly linked to excess body weight, many people who are a normal weight assume that they won't develop the disease. But that's not always true. About 15% of people who are diagnosed with diabetes are not overweight. And paradoxically, even weight loss can be a symptom of this complex disorder in people (normal weight or overweight) who have uncontrolled high glucose levels.

A shocking recent finding: The Centers for Disease Control and Prevention now estimates that 40% of Americans ages 40 to 74 have prediabetes, and nearly two out of three Americans over age 65 have prediabetes or diabetes—most likely due to the increasing numbers of people who are overweight and inactive, both of which boost diabetes risk.

However, most primary care physicians are not diagnosing and treating prediabetes early enough in their patients—often because they fail to prescribe the necessary screening tests. And because the symptoms of prediabetes can be subtle, especially in the early stages, most people are not reporting potential red flags to their doctors.

Fortunately, prediabetes can virtually always be prevented from progressing to diabetes if the condition is identified and treated in its early stages (by following a healthful diet, exercising regularly and taking nutritional supplements and medications, if necessary).

WHAT IS PREDIABETES?

Prediabetes occurs when the body's cells are no longer responding correctly to insulin, the hormone that regulates blood sugar. With prediabetes, levels of blood sugar are higher than normal but not high enough to warrant a diagnosis of diabetes.

Prediabetes affects about 57 million Americans—most of whom are unaware that they have the condition.

RED FLAGS FOR DIABETES

Being overweight (defined as having a body mass index, or a BMI, that is 25 or higher) is perhaps the best-known risk factor for type 2 diabetes.* The more excess body weight you have, the more resistant your cells become to the blood sugar–regulating effects of the hormone insulin, ultimately causing blood glucose levels to rise.

Greatest danger: Abdominal fat, in particular, further boosts diabetes risk. That's because belly (visceral) fat hinders the processing of insulin. The single biggest risk factor for prediabetes is having a waistline of 40 inches or more if you're a man...or 35 inches or more if you're a woman. *Lesser-known red flags for prediabetes (and diabetes)—if you have one of these symptoms, see your doctor...*

• **Increased thirst and need to urinate.** Because excess blood glucose draws water from the body's tissues, people with elevated blood glucose levels feel thirsty much of the

*For a BMI calculator, visit the Web site of the National Heart, Lung and Blood Institute, *www.nhlbisupport.com/bmi*.

time. Even when they drink fluids, their thirst is rarely quenched. Therefore, they drink even more, causing them to urinate more often than is normal for them.

• **Unexplained weight loss.** While being overweight is a significant risk factor for prediabetes, the condition also can paradoxically lead to unexplained weight loss resulting from a lack of energy supply to the body's cells and a loss of glucose-related calories due to excessive urination.

• **Dry, itchy skin.** Excess blood glucose also draws moisture from the skin, leaving it dry and prone to itching and cracking—especially on the legs, feet and elbows.

• **Blurred vision.** Glucose can change the shape of the eye lens, making it difficult to focus properly.

• **Slow-healing cuts, sores or bruises and frequent infections.** For unknown reasons, excess blood glucose appears to interfere with the body's healing processes and its ability to fight off infection. In particular, women with prediabetes and diabetes are prone to urinary tract and vaginal infections.

• **Red, swollen and tender gums.** Because the body's ability to heal can be compromised by prediabetes, gum inflammation, involving red, swollen, tender and/or bleeding gums, may develop.

• **Persistent feelings of hunger.** When the body's cells don't get enough glucose due to prediabetes, the cells send signals to the brain that are interpreted as hunger, typically about one hour after consuming a meal.

• **Lack of energy.** Because their cells are deficient of energy-boosting glucose, people with prediabetes often tire very quickly after even mild physical effort. Dehydration due to excess blood glucose also can contribute to fatigue.

• **Falling asleep after eating.** An hour or so after eating, our digestive systems convert the food we've eaten into glucose. In people who have prediabetes, the process gets exaggerated—blood glucose levels spike, triggering a surge of insulin as the body attempts to stabilize high glucose levels. This insulin surge is ineffective in lowering blood glucose,

causing the person to become drowsy. If you feel sleepy after meals, it can be a sign that your blood glucose levels are riding this prediabetic roller coaster.

• **Moodiness and irritability.** Lack of energy production in your cells, together with sharp rises and dips in blood glucose levels, can trigger feelings of restlessness, irritability and exaggerated emotional responses to stress.

• **Tingling or numbness in the hands and feet.** Excess blood glucose can damage small blood vessels feeding the body's peripheral nerves, often causing tingling, loss of sensation or burning pain in the hands, arms, legs or feet.

• **Loss of sex drive and erectile dysfunction in men.** Prediabetes is associated with low testosterone in men, which often reduces libido. In addition, glucose-related damage to the body's small blood vessels frequently impairs the ability of prediabetic men to have an erection.

Better Diabetes Screening—No Fasting

Six million Americans have undiagnosed diabetes. The current standard screening test requires a 10-hour fast, measures only the amount of glucose in the blood at the moment the sample is taken, and can be skewed by day-to-day changes in diet and exercise.

More accurate test: The *hemoglobin A1c* (HbA1c) test, which requires no fasting, reveals the average blood glucose level over the previous four months. Ask your doctor if HbA1c is an appropriate screening tool for you.

Christopher Saudek, MD, director of Johns Hopkins Comprehensive Diabetes Center, Baltimore, and lead author of a consensus statement from diabetes experts.

Nighttime Bathroom Trips May Signal Illness

In a study of 788 men and women (age 70 or older), those who typically got up at least twice during the night to urinate were 2.7 times more likely to die during the three-year study period than those who urinated once or not at all, on average.

Theory: Frequent nighttime urination could indicate a serious underlying health problem, such as diabetes or kidney or heart disease.

If you use the bathroom more than once nightly: Make an appointment with your doctor for an evaluation.

Haruo Nakagawa, MD, senior assistant professor, Tohoku University, Sendai, Japan.

You May Have Type 2 Diabetes...and Not Even Know It

With type 1 diabetes, the pancreas produces little or no insulin, the hormone required to convert sugar into fuel for cells. This soon leads to excessive thirst and hunger, frequent urination, weight loss, lethargy and blurry vision.

However, the more common type 2 diabetes—in which the body's cells do not use insulin properly—often causes no symptoms in the early stages. You could have the disease for five years or more before developing telltale signs, including those above plus slow-healing sores, frequent vaginal and/or bladder infections, and patches of dark, thickened skin.

Best: Talk to your physician about all diabetes risk factors—high cholesterol, high blood pressure, excess weight, history of gestational diabetes, family history of diabetes or being

of African American, Native American, Latino, Pacific Islander or Asian descent.

Steven Edelman, MD, professor of medicine at the University of California, San Diego, Veterans Affairs Medical Center, and founder and director of the not-for-profit education organization called Taking Control of Your Diabetes, both in San Diego, *www.tcoyd.org.*

Toxin in Plastics Linked To Diabetes

Bisphenol A (BPA), a chemical commonly found in hard plastics, such as water bottles and some baby bottles, already has been linked to cancer.

Recent finding: People who have higher amounts of BPA in their bloodstreams are more than twice as likely to have diabetes than people who have little or no BPA.

Theory: BPA acts like the hormone estrogen, which can increase levels of insulin and cause chronically elevated blood sugar, both of which are associated with diabetes.

Frederick vom Saal, PhD, curators' professor, division of biological sciences, University of Missouri, Columbia, and leader of a study of 1,455 adults, published in *The Journal of the American Medical Association.*

Arsenic in Water Exceeds EPA Standards

About 13 million Americans live in areas where arsenic levels in the water supply exceed EPA standards.

Study: Participants with type 2 diabetes had 26% more arsenic in their urine than those without diabetes.

Best: Have your water tested. If arsenic is above 10 micrograms per liter, install a filter that removes arsenic on your home's primary waterline.

Ana Navas-Acien, MD, PhD, assistant professor at Johns Hopkins Bloomberg School of Public Health, Baltimore, and leader of a study of 788 people.

The American Sugar Epidemic

Americans now have more than 22 tea-spoons of sugar a day. Soft drinks make up one-third of the additional sugar. One 12-ounce can of regular cola has about eight tea-spoons of sugar. Sweetened dairy products, fruit drinks, alcoholic beverages and candy account for 16%…cakes, cookies and pies, 13%.

New American Heart Association guidelines: Men should have no more than 150 calories of added sugar per day—about nine teaspoons. Women should have no more than 100 calories—about six teaspoons.

Rachel Johnson, PhD, RD, associate provost and professor of nutrition, University of Vermont in Burlington, and lead author of the American Heart Association Scientific Statement on Dietary Sugars and Cardiovascular Health, published in *Circulation*.

Don't Stand in Front of The Microwave…and Other Radiation Dangers In Your Home

Magda Havas, PhD, professor of environmental and resource studies at Trent University in Peterborough, Ontario, Canada. She is a leading expert on radio-frequency radiation, electromagnetic fields, dirty electricity and ground current. She is coauthor, with Camilla Rees, of *Public Health SOS: The Shadow Side of the Wireless Revolution* (CreateSpace).

Virtually everything with a cord or battery emits electromagnetic radiation—but some products put out much more than others do. The official exposure limit for electromagnetic radiation, set by the Federal Communications Commission, is based on old research that considered tissue heating to be the danger threshold.

New research: Radiation levels up to 1,000 times lower than the FCC's guidelines have been shown to affect our health.

Below, Magda Havas, PhD, one of the leading experts in this field, tells what to do…

CELL PHONES

In 2007, a study published in *The American Journal of Epidemiology* reported that use of a cell phone for more than 22 hours a month was associated with a 58% increased risk for tumors of the *parotid* (salivary) gland. Another study found that the risk for *gliomas* (a type of brain tumor) and acoustic tumors (where the ear meets the brain) doubled on the same side of the head after a decade of cell-phone use.

Studies funded by the telecommunications industry consistently have indicated that cell phones are safe.

Main flaws: These studies typically lasted six years or less, not long enough for tumors to develop. In addition, most of the studies defined "heavy use" as using a cell phone just a few times a week—far less than the hours that many people spend on their cell phones every day.

Self-defense: Use your cell phone only for emergencies or to retrieve messages. Return calls on a regular phone. *When you do use a cell phone…*

• **Regularly switch the phone from one side of your head to the other** to minimize one-side radiation exposure.

• **Turn off your cell phone when you're not expecting a call.** Even when you're not talking, cell phones send and receive signals to communicate with towers and satellites.

• **Never let the cell phone touch your ear or other body parts.** When talking, hold it at least one inch away from your head. Text-messaging is better than talking because the phone is farther away from your head. Blue-tooth (wireless technology) uses radiation, but generally, levels are lower than those from your cell phone. Turn off cell phones in shirt or pants pockets.

• **Use a pneumatic (plastic air-tube) earpiece to decrease the brain's exposure to radiation.** Mercola (877-985-2695, *http://prod ucts.mercola.com*) sells these headsets, which have a hollow tube near the head rather than a wire running to the ear.

• **Don't use a phone in the car.** Using a cell phone or any wireless device while driving (or while in a train, bus or plane) uses more power because the phone must continually be reconnecting with antennas. Also, the signal is reflected by the metal around you, so your exposure inside is higher than it is outside.

CORDLESS PHONES

Cordless phones, the kind with a base station and remote handsets that you can use anywhere in your house, use very similar frequencies to those used by cell phones. They pose the same risks.

Cordless phones with the designation Digitally Enhanced Cordless Telecommunications (or DECT) technology are the worst, because they constantly emit radiation whether you're using the phone or not. They're more dangerous than having a cell-phone antenna inside your home.

Self-defense: Replace all cordless phones with corded phones.

WIFI

The majority of newer computers, printers and similar devices now are equipped with WiFi (or wireless) capabilities. Wireless signals are a strong source of electromagnetic radiation. As long as you are using a device that is receiving and sending information to and from the Internet without wires (this includes BlackBerries and iPhones), then you are being exposed to radiation.

Self-defense: Use cables to connect your Internet service to your computers, not a wireless router. Similarly, it is safer to hardwire your printer to the computer than to use a WiFi connection. Hardwiring means that you won't be able to easily use a single computer throughout the house or to "beam" a signal to your printer from another room. Some people find this inconvenient, but the added safety is worth it. You can have additional Internet cables installed in multiple rooms.

If you do use a wireless router: Place it as close as possible to the devices that it controls. At greater distances, the router is forced to amplify its signal. Turn off the router when you're not using the computer.

If you don't use a wireless router: Find out how to disable the WiFi settings in your computer and printer. In the "on" position, these settings prompt the devices to put out electromagnetic energy in order to find the nearest available router.

MICROWAVE OVENS

Medical technicians leave the room when X-rays are taken. People should be just as cautious with microwave ovens.

Reason: Just about every microwave oven that I have tested, including the newest models, leaks radiation. In my home, I could detect electromagnetic radiation from the microwave 20 feet away.

Self-test: Put your cell phone inside the oven, and close the door (do not turn on the microwave). Call your cell-phone number. If you hear the phone ring, the cell-phone signal was able to pass through the walls of the oven—meaning that microwaves are able to pass out.

Self-defense: Leave the kitchen when the microwave is on.

DIRTY ELECTRICITY

Household electricity normally is delivered at 60 cycles per second. Along with this stable current, however, come higher frequencies—spikes in power that cause surges of radiation from appliances and even unused electrical outlets.

This so-called "dirty electricity" has been linked to fatigue, headaches, difficulty concentrating and even cardiac symptoms in people who are sensitive (known as electrohypersensitivity or EHS). It is recognized now as a functional impairment in Sweden.

Self-defense: Surge protectors, commonly used to protect computers and other electronic equipment, will "clean" household current to some extent.

Better: Graham-Stetzer Filters. These devices filter electrical "noise." You just plug them into wall outlets. They are designed to clean up entire circuits in the house. The average North American home needs about 20 filters. When you plug the filters in, you can use a microsurge meter to measure the levels of dirty electricity and try to get the levels below 40

GS units. The filters and meters are available at some hardware stores and online at *www.stetzerelectric.com* and *www.lessemf.com.*

Cost: About $35 for a filter, $125 for a meter.*

PLASMA TELEVISIONS

Plasma TVs generate high levels of dirty electricity. Using one filter will not solve the problem—people with plasma TVs might have to use three or more filters to clean up the power, compared with just one filter for an LCD TV.

Self-defense: LCDs produce nearly as good a picture and produce less dirty electricity than plasma TVs.

*Prices subject to change.

Alternatives to Cancer-Causing CT Scans

Computed tomography (CT) scans can be extremely valuable, but they expose patients to high radiation levels, which are linked to cancer.

Self-defense: If your doctor recommends a CT scan, find out why and whether there are other ways to get the same information, such as ultrasound, MRI or watchful waiting.

Rita F. Redberg, MD, MSc, editor of *Archives of Internal Medicine* and a cardiologist in the department of medicine at University of California, San Francisco.

How Allergies Reduce Cancer Risk

Cancers of the mouth, throat, digestive organs, colon, bladder, uterus, cervix, lung and skin were less common among allergy sufferers.

Theory: Sneezing, coughing and tearing eyes help the body expel environmental toxins that can trigger abnormal cell growth. More research is needed to see if allergy patients would benefit from discontinuing symptom-suppressing medication.

Paul Sherman, PhD, professor of neurobiology and behavior, Cornell University, Ithaca, New York, and leader of an analysis of 646 studies.

Alcohol Can Raise Pancreatic Cancer Risk

Consuming two or more drinks of any type of alcohol daily can raise risk for this cancer by 22%. One drink is 12 ounces of beer, four ounces of wine or one-and-a-half ounces of 80-proof distilled liquor.

Self-defense: Men should drink no more than two alcoholic beverages per day...women, no more than one.

Jeanine M. Genkinger, PhD, assistant professor, Lombardi Comprehensive Cancer Center, Georgetown University, Washington, DC, and leader of an analysis of 14 studies involving more than 862,664 people, published in *Cancer Epidemiology, Biomarkers & Prevention.*

Why You Should Let Tea Cool Four Minutes Before Drinking

Let your tea cool down a bit before drinking to reduce cancer risk.

Recent finding: People who drink hot tea within two minutes after it is poured are five times more likely to develop esophageal cancer than people who wait at least four minutes for the tea to cool down.

Also: Add lemon, not milk. Milk may lower tea's cardiovascular benefits...citrus increases absorption of antioxidants.

Paolo Boffetta, MD, professor of epidemiology, Tish Cancer Institute, Mount Sinai School of Medicine, New York City, and group head and cluster coordinator of a study of more than 48,000 people, reported in *British Medical Journal.*

Skip the Tanning Salon

Tanning beds can cause cancer. In a study, people who started using tanning beds or sunlamps before age 30 increased their risk for melanoma, the deadliest kind of skin cancer, by 75%. The International Agency for Research on Cancer recently classified tanning beds as "carcinogenic to humans."

UC Berkeley Wellness Letter, 500 Fifth Ave., New York City 10110, *www.wellnessletter.com.*

To Prevent Cancer, Take Good Care of Your Gums

Gum disease raises squamous cell cancer risk. Each millimeter of bone loss from chronic gum disease was linked to a fourfold increased risk for squamous cell carcinoma (a type of cancer) in the mouth and throat.

Best: Brush twice and floss once daily…get teeth professionally cleaned twice yearly…see your dentist if gums bleed, recede, swell, hurt or look purplish.

Mine Tezal, DDS, PhD, assistant professor, department of oral diagnostic sciences, State University of New York at Buffalo, and leader of a study of 433 people.

Use the Buddy System For Skin Cancer Checks

Melanoma has a five-year survival rate of about 99% when treated before it spreads to lymph nodes—compared with 18% for late-stage melanoma. Regular self-exams aid early detection. At-home exams are more effective when done with a partner, who can inspect your hard-to-see areas—such as the back of your neck, behind ears and buttocks—for suspicious spots.

June Robinson, MD, professor of clinical dermatology, Northwestern University Feinberg School of Medicine, Chicago, and author of a study of 130 people.

Better Melanoma Treatment

In a five-year study of 250 people (average age 57) with melanoma (a serious form of skin cancer) that had spread to lymph nodes, those who received radiation treatment after surgery were 40% less likely to experience a melanoma recurrence over the following two years than those who did not undergo radiation treatments. Radiation treatments destroy malignant cells that can remain after surgical removal of tumors.

If you have melanoma and are at high risk for recurrence: Ask your doctor whether radiation therapy would be appropriate for you.

Bryan Burmeister, MD, associate professor and director, radiation oncology, Princess Alexandra Hospital, Brisbane, Australia.

Test Detects Alzheimer's Early—87% Accurate

A new test can detect Alzheimer's early. The test measures proteins in the spinal fluid and is 87% accurate in predicting Alzheimer's in patients with early cognitive impairment but before full dementia symptoms appear. Early diagnosis allows doctors to provide medication to slow the progression of the disease.

Note: The test was also 95% accurate in ruling out Alzheimer's in those tested in a clinical study.

Leslie Shaw, PhD, professor, department of pathology and lab medicine, University of Pennsylvania Medical School, Philadelphia.

Secondhand Smoke May Damage the Brain

In a recent study of 4,809 nonsmoking adults, participants with the highest levels of *cotinine* (a nicotine by-product that can remain in saliva for up to 25 hours after exposure to secondhand smoke) were 44% more likely to show cognitive impairment (such as memory problems) than those with the lowest levels.

Theory: Secondhand smoke may damage the brain, as well as raise risk for heart disease and stroke.

David J. Llewellyn, PhD, research fellow, Peninsula Medical School, University of Exeter, England.

"Dementia" May Be a Drug Side Effect

Don't assume that a diagnosis of dementia is accurate. Up to 10% of seniors who are diagnosed with Alzheimer's or dementia may really be suffering from drug side effects.

Most likely culprits: Sleeping pills, tranquilizers and beta-blockers used to treat high blood pressure, among other ailments. When you take several drugs of any kind (including over-the-counter drugs), unexpected interactions can cause dementia-like symptoms.

Safety: Call your doctor at the first sign of memory problems after taking a new drug.

Samuel Gandy, MD, PhD, professor, Alzheimer's disease research, Mount Sinai School of Medicine, New York City, *www.mountsinai.org.*

Cell-Phone Waves May Protect Memory

Mice predisposed to Alzheimer's disease were exposed to cell phones' electromagnetic waves for two hours daily for seven to nine months. The younger mice did not get Alzheimer's...older mice who had the disease showed cognitive improvement.

Theory: Cell-phone waves reduce the *beta-amyloid protein plaques* believed to contribute to Alzheimer's.

Gary Arendash, PhD, research professor, Florida Alzheimer's Disease Research Center, University of South Florida, Tampa, and author of an animal study.

Early Signs of Parkinson's Disease

Long before people exhibit the tremors, slowness and stiffness of Parkinson's, they often have other problems. Some of the potential risk factors for Parkinson's are loss of smell (about 80% of Parkinson's patients lose most of their sense of smell before they have problems using their motor abilities)...chronic constipation...sleeping problems, in which patients act out violent dreams and may injure themselves or their partners...and feelings of fear and anxiety that surface for the first time in life.

Tanya Simuni, MD, associate professor of neurology, Northwestern University Feinberg School of Medicine, Chicago.

Constipation Concern

Constipation may indicate Parkinson's disease. In a study of 392 adults, those with Parkinson's disease were about twice as likely to report a history of constipation as those without the disease.

Theory: Parkinson's may begin to affect the autonomic nervous system—which controls digestion, bowel movements and other body functions—years or even decades before motor symptoms of the illness (such as tremors and rigid muscles) appear.

Self-defense: If you have a history of constipation and have Parkinson's-like symptoms, see your doctor.

Walter A. Rocca, MD, MPH, professor of epidemiology and neurology, College of Medicine, Mayo Clinic, Rochester, Minnesota.

Gum Disease Treatment Eases Arthritis

In a study of 40 patients with gum disease and moderate or severe rheumatoid arthritis (RA), those who received periodontal treatment had improvement in arthritis symptoms (including pain and swollen joints) with the greatest improvement seen in patients who also took arthritis medications known as anti-TNF (or *tumor necrosis factor*) drugs, such as *etanercept* (Enbrel) or *infliximab* (Remicade).

If you have RA or are at risk: Be sure to brush your teeth twice daily, floss once daily and see your dentist at least twice a year.

Nabil Bissada, DDS, chairman, department of periodontics, Case Western Reserve University School of Dental Medicine, Cleveland.

Vertigo Linked to Osteoporosis

In a study of 411 men and women, those with osteoporosis were three times more likely to have *benign positional vertigo* (BPV), an inner ear disorder that causes dizziness, than those with normal bone density.

Theory: Loose calcium carbonate crystals in the inner ear are thought to cause BPV, suggesting that people who have both osteoporosis and vertigo have difficulty metabolizing calcium.

If you suffer from BPV: Ask your doctor about getting tested for osteoporosis.

Ji Soo Kim, MD, PhD, associate professor, department of neurology, Seoul National University College of Medicine, Korea.

So Long, Soda!

Drinking soda may lead to kidney disease in women.

Recent finding: Women who drink more than two cans of regular soda each day (24 ounces) are nearly twice as likely to have *albuminuria,* a condition indicating an initial stage of kidney damage. Similar elevated risks weren't found for men or diet soda drinkers.

David Shoham, PhD, a researcher in the department of preventive medicine and epidemiology, Stritch School of Medicine, Loyola University, Chicago, and leader of a study published in *PLoS ONE.*

Do You Live in the "Kidney-Stone Belt"?

People living in warm climates are more likely to develop kidney stones. Kidney stones develop when salts crystallize in the kidneys, and that often is due to dehydration, which is more likely in warmer areas. States in the southeastern US report 50% more cases of kidney stones than do northeastern states.

New risk: Global warming could expand the "kidney-stone belt" to perhaps 56% of states by 2050 and 70% by 2095.

Margaret Pearle, MD, PhD, professor of urology, University of Texas Southwestern Medical School, Dallas, and coauthor of a study in *Proceedings of the National Academy of Sciences of the United States of America.*

Don't Ignore Head Injuries

Rebecca Shannonhouse, editor, *Bottom Line/Health,* Boardroom Inc., 281 Tresser Blvd., Stamford, Connecticut 06901.

The saddest part of actress Natasha Richardson's death last year from a skiing accident is that it may well have been prevented.

The condition that took her life was an *epidural hematoma* (bleeding between the skull and the lining of the brain), which can be corrected in about 90% of patients who receive a brain scan and surgery.

But Richardson, 45, apparently felt "fine" and reportedly declined to go to the hospital immediately after the injury—perhaps due to the so-called "lucid interval." It was only when she was said to have complained of a severe headache about one hour later that she was transported to a hospital.

That delay may have cost Richardson her life, explains Stephan M. Mayer, MD, a neurologist at Columbia University Medical Center in New York City. Chances are that Richardson felt briefly dazed or experienced other more subtle symptoms (see below) before the severe headache. It can take one to two hours for bleeding to generate enough pressure inside the skull to cause sustained symptoms, which can be quickly followed by coma and death.

About 2% of head-injury patients suffer an epidural hematoma—including many of whom think their injuries are minor. *Dr. Mayer says to call 911 if a head injury causes...*

• **A dazed feeling or a momentary lapse of consciousness.**

• **Any neurological symptoms,** including confusion, lethargy, vision changes or a severe headache.

Most important: Wear a helmet when engaging in any activity with a high risk for head injuries, such as bicycling, skiing, skating or riding a horse or a motorcycle.

Lasik Satisfaction High

In one recent finding, 95% of patients who had Lasik—elective laser eye surgery that reshapes the cornea to improve eyesight—reported being satisfied with the results. Only a small percentage of Lasik patients had adverse effects, such as blurry vision or dry eyes, which in some cases can be improved with

subsequent treatments. The American Society of Cataract and Refractive Surgery (at *www.ascrs.org*) can help you find a board-certified surgeon who can determine if Lasik is appropriate for you.

Kerry D. Solomon, MD, director, Magill Vision Center, Medical University of South Carolina, Charleston, and leader of a review of 19 studies involving 2,198 Lasik patients.

Sad Without Salt

Deficiencies of *sodium chloride* (table salt) seem to elicit feelings of depression, according to animal studies. Salt cravings have been likened to substance abusers' cravings for drugs.

University of Iowa, www.uiowa.edu.

Common Drugs That Increase Pneumonia Risk

Neil Schachter, MD, professor of medicine at Mount Sinai School of Medicine and the medical director of respiratory care at Mount Sinai Hospital, both in New York City. He's author of Life & Breath: Preventing, Treating and Reversing Chronic Obstructive Pulmonary Disease (Broadway) and also serves on the board of directors of the American Lung Association, www.lungusa.org.

There are several common medications that can increase your risk of contracting pneumonia. *See below...*

• **Use caution with all inhaled *corticosteroids*.** Treatments such as chemotherapy and *prednisone* are known to compromise the immune system, thereby increasing pneumonia risk. Now, research shows that extended use (24 weeks or more) of inhaled corticosteroids for COPD increases pneumonia risk by 50%. Among people age 65 and older, this figure jumps to almost 75%. However, the benefits of using an inhaled corticosteroid often outweigh the pneumonia risk. Monitor yourself closely with your physician's help.

• **Treat GERD, but follow your doctor's advice about medication.** *Gastroesophageal reflux disease* (GERD), in which stomach contents chronically wash back up the esophagus, boosts pneumonia risk by increasing the bacteria inhaled into the airways. However, treating GERD with acid-suppressing *proton-pump inhibitor* (PPI) medicine, such as *lansoprazole* (Prevacid) or *esomeprazole* (Nexium), also increases pneumonia risk by encouraging bacterial growth in the stomach.

New finding: While PPIs increase risk for community-acquired pneumonia only slightly, they appear to be a major factor in hospital-acquired pneumonia, which strikes up to 1% of all hospital patients in the US and kills 18% of its victims (in part because more virulent bacteria are present in hospitals).

One recent study estimates that PPIs and other acid blockers, such as *H2-receptor antagonists*—for example, *cimetidine* (Tagamet) and *ranitidine* (Zantac)—may bring on some 30,000 pneumonia-related deaths each year. The study also found that many patients were routinely given PPIs and other acid blockers despite not really needing them.

If you need to take one of these GERD drugs (even in an over-the-counter product) for more than two weeks, consult your doctor.

Statins Stave Off Pneumonia

Statins may lower risk for developing pneumonia. Studies have reported that patients who take cholesterol-lowering statins are less likely to develop pneumonia and pneumonia complications than those not taking statins.

Theory: Statins have an immune system–boosting effect.

Further research is needed.

Vineet Chopra, MD, assistant professor of medicine, University of Michigan Health System, Ann Arbor, and leader of a review of studies of the effect of statin use on pneumonia outcomes, published in *Chest*.

The Vaccine You May Need Now!

Whooping cough vaccine wears off after about 10 years.

Self-defense: Everyone ages 19 to 65 should be revaccinated for whooping cough (pertussis). The virus that causes whooping cough can lead to severe long-term coughing and pneumonia. Ask your doctor for a combination vaccine that also protects against tetanus and diphtheria, which also wears off after 10 years.

UC Berkeley Wellness Letter, 500 Fifth Ave., New York City 10110, *www.wellnessletter.com.*

Dangerous Microbes in Your Shower

Showerheads can cause lung disease. *Mycobacterium avium* grow inside showerheads and are released in water droplets that can be inhaled.

Vulnerable: Patients undergoing chemotherapy...recipients of transplants...people with AIDS or cystic fibrosis...and others with compromised immune systems.

Self-defense: Take baths, or use an old-fashioned metal tube showerhead. Microbes have a harder time clinging to metal than plastic, and these showerheads don't create aerosol droplets that can be inhaled. More tests are needed to determine if letting the water run dilutes bacteria.

Norman R. Pace, PhD, distinguished professor of molecular, cellular and developmental biology, University of Colorado, Boulder, and leader of a study published in *Proceedings of the National Academy of Sciences*.

MRSA at the Beach

You can catch MRSA anywhere—even at the beach. *Methicillin-resistant Staphylococcus aureus* (MRSA) is an antibiotic-resistant strain of bacteria that can cause difficult-to-treat skin and systemic infections. Staphylococcus bacteria are everywhere—many people carry them without realizing it. Beachgoers may pick up bacteria left behind in sand or water by other visitors.

Self-defense: Shower with soap after leaving the beach. Consider staying out of the water if you have an open cut or sore—these can be bacterial entry points.

Lisa Plano, MD, PhD, associate professor, departments of pediatrics and of microbiology and immunology, Miller School of Medicine, University of Miami, Florida, and leader of a study of 1,303 people.

Meat and Chicken Alert

Antibiotic-resistant bacteria can be found in meat and poultry. Foodborne *methicillin-resistant Staphylococcus aureus* (MRSA) is less virulent than the strains that occur in hospital patients—but it still can cause illness.

Self-defense: Wash hands with soap and warm water before and after handling raw meat or poultry. Clean food-preparation surfaces with bleach or alcohol after use. Cook meat and poultry thoroughly.

Stuart B. Levy, MD, director of Center for Adaptation Genetics and Drug Resistance at Tufts University School of Medicine, and president of Alliance for the Prudent Use of Antibiotics, both in Boston. He also is author of *The Antibiotic Paradox* (HarperCollins).

Heartburn Meds Raise Food-Poisoning Risk

Stomach-acid drugs boost food-poisoning risk. Medicines that decrease production of stomach acid, such as Prevacid and Prilosec, can increase food-poisoning risk by reducing the acid that is the body's natural defense.

Self-defense: If you use these drugs, be especially careful when handling raw meat and poultry, and avoid foods associated with food

poisoning, such as raw oysters, raw eggs and unpasteurized milk.

Leo Galland, MD, internist, founder and director, Foundation for Integrated Medicine in New York City, *www.mdheal.org.*

Over 60% of Chickens Have Harmful Bacteria

Two-thirds of chickens have potentially dangerous bacteria. *Campylobacter* was found in 62% of fresh whole broilers...salmonella in 14%...and both types in 9%.

Also: Most bacteria were resistant to at least one antibiotic. There's been modest improvement since 2007, when these pathogens were found in 80% of broilers, but findings suggest most companies' safeguards are inadequate.

Cleanest brand-name chicken: Perdue—56% of Perdue chickens were free of bacteria.

Self-defense: Thaw chicken in a refrigerator, inside its package and on a plate...in a bowl filled with cold water (change water every 30 minutes)...or defrost it on a plate in a microwave. Never thaw it on a counter—this can provide a breeding ground for bacteria. Cook chicken to at least 165°F.

Urvashi Rangan, PhD, director of technical policy, Consumers Union, Yonkers, New York, and leader of a study of 382 chickens, published in *Consumer Reports, www.consumerreports.org.*

Something Fishy

Unsafe levels of mercury were discovered in 27% of fish checked from US streams. The highest levels were in bass—largemouth, smallmouth and spotted. Lowest levels were in brown trout, rainbow-cutthroat trout and channel catfish. Mercury is a *neurotoxin* that is especially dangerous for infants and fetuses. For fish advisories, go to *www.epa.gov/water science/fish/advisories.*

Study by the US Geological Survey.

2

Doctors, Drugs, More

The Nice Way to Get Tough with Your Doctor

As the chief executive of a major medical center, I have reviewed dozens of situations in which patients thought something was wrong with their care but were too polite, too uncomfortable or too intimidated to speak up.

Example: One woman did not say anything when she was called by an incorrect name. She just went along—and wound up having extensive tests that were intended for another patient.

No serious harm was done in this case, but others aren't so lucky. I've seen people needlessly suffer severe pain because they didn't want to question their doctor's judgment...or risk a serious infection because they felt that it was rude to tell someone to wash his/her hands.

It's normal to feel intimidated in the authoritarian environment of a doctor's office or a medical center—but it's better to be tough. Studies show that so-called difficult patients, ones who demand the highest level of care, recover more quickly and with fewer complications than those who are passive.

Some common "sticky" situations, and how to respond...

UNWASHED HANDS

You may feel rude telling someone to wash his hands. Do it anyway. Every year, nearly two million infections are spread in hospitals. The Centers for Disease Control and Prevention (CDC) estimates that this number could

David J. Shulkin, MD, an internist and president and chief operating officer at Morristown Memorial Hospital in New Jersey. Previously, Dr. Shulkin was president and chief executive officer of Beth Israel Medical Center in New York City. He's also professor of medicine at Albert Einstein College of Medicine. He serves on the editorial boards of *Journal of Patient Safety* and *Journal of Clinical Outcomes Management* and is editor of the book *Questions Patients Need to Ask* (Xlibris).

be reduced by as much as 70% if health-care workers would consistently wash their hands before and after treating each patient.

Reducing infection, particularly from potentially deadly organisms such as *methicillin-resistant Staphylococcus aureus* (MRSA), is more important than not saying anything because you are embarrassed. *Don't let anyone in the hospital touch you until...*

• **You've seen him wash his hands, either in a sink or with an alcohol-based gel sanitizer.** You can say something like, "I'm sorry, but I'm really afraid of infections. Would you mind washing your hands before we start?"

• **You've seen him wash before he puts on gloves.** The gloves won't protect you if they're contaminated from unwashed hands.

• **He has wiped and sanitized instruments that will touch you,** including blood pressure cuffs and stethoscopes. Hospital staff use alcohol pads or cleaning cloths with disinfectants, such as ammonia, to clean equipment.

STOPPING A PROCEDURE

You are never required to continue a treatment or procedure that's going badly.

Examples: A nurse might fail to properly insert an intravenous (IV) needle after multiple attempts...or a resident might have a hard time doing a spinal tap.

When someone has a needle in your back, it might not feel like the best time to complain, but it's your right to do so...to ask someone else to take over...or even to stop the procedure.

At teaching hospitals, many procedures are done by residents. If a procedure or treatment is taking too long or causing too much pain, ask for a more experienced attending physician to take over. You could say something like, "This seems to be taking too long. I would appreciate having someone with more experience try." If the staff argues—or, worse, ignores you—ask to speak to a nursing supervisor.

Helpful: Ask a friend or a family member to be present during procedures. Patients understandably are reluctant to challenge their health-care team. An advocate, however, will be more dispassionate and watch out for your best interests. He might say something like, "I

think she has had enough. We need to take a break for a moment."

YOU SUSPECT A WRONG DIAGNOSIS

Suppose that you've been having headaches. Your physician might make the diagnosis of migraines and prescribe a strong prescription drug. That might be the correct decision—but what if later you wonder if the headaches are linked to something in your diet and that the medication might not be necessary?

• **Don't be silent.** The average patient knows more about his symptoms than the doctor. Most doctors welcome additional information, even when that information changes the original hypothesis. In this case, reporting a food sensitivity could be an important part of your treatment because migraines often are linked to dietary factors.

Important: If your doctor seems threatened by your questions or dismisses your ideas out of hand, get another doctor.

ASKING FOR MORE DRUGS

It's common for patients to needlessly suffer postsurgical pain because they don't want to seem like complainers or because they're afraid that their doctors will suspect they're drug abusers, but adequate pain control is so critical. Patients who experience little or no pain are more ambulatory, less likely to get pneumonia, have a lower risk for blood clots and leave the hospital, on average, one to two days sooner than those whose pain is managed poorly.

There are no tests that can accurately gauge a patient's pain, so self-reports are critical. Addiction is rare when drugs are used for temporary pain relief—and doctors know this. *What to do...*

• **Never assume that your level of pain is normal.** If you think the pain is intolerable, it needs to be treated. Make sure that your pain is taken seriously.

• **Request a pain assessment.** Pain is considered a vital sign, along with factors such as blood pressure, pulse and temperature. As soon as you notice pain, ask for a formal assessment. You'll probably be asked to rate your pain on a numeric scale, with zero indicating no pain and 10 representing the worst pain imaginable. Most patients can attain levels of two or below with the right medication.

•**If you need a higher dose, or more frequent dosing, say so.** Your doctor will understand if you say that the pain treatment isn't working. Everyone responds to painkillers in a different way.

Recommended: Patient-controlled analgesia (PCA). These devices deliver small regular doses of medication, usually intravenously, when you push a button. They now are the preferred method for controlling postsurgical pain.

DOORWAY VISITS

A hospital doctor sometimes will poke his head in your doorway, ask how you're doing and then rush off before you have a chance to discuss concerns.

Doorway visits are always inappropriate. If you are nervous about confronting the doctor directly—or he never sticks around long enough for you to say anything—you might keep a notebook by your bedside. Write down your questions and concerns. Then, when the doctor makes his rounds, hold up the notebook and say something like, "I'm glad you're here. I have just a few issues that I've written down. I'd like to go through them with you."

NEGOTIATING FEES

Don't be embarrassed to discuss financial issues with your doctor or the hospital, particularly if you don't have insurance. Negotiating fees and payment schedules is routine.

Example: Suppose that you have recently lost your job and health insurance. Bring it up the next time you see your doctor. Say something like, "I want to make sure that I get the best care, but I don't have health insurance right now. Cost is important, so I would be grateful if we could discuss it."

Doctors often reduce fees for patients who don't have insurance. They also can decrease costs in other ways, such as prescribing generic rather than brand-name drugs, ordering only essential tests and scheduling telephone follow-ups rather than office visits.

Exception: The health-care fees established by government insurance plans may not be negotiable. It is illegal, for example, for your physician to waive Medicare copayments or deductibles.

Are Doctor Rating Web Sites Reliable?

Web sites that provide doctor ratings can be reliable and useful—but it's important to check for clues to the Web site's objectivity. First, find out how a site determines the ratings. If doctors pay to be listed, the site won't be very objective. If a health insurance company sponsors the site, its ratings may be influenced by the reviewed physicians' fees. Next, examine the reviews themselves. If the ratings are anonymous, a spouse, a nurse or even the doctor might post a positive review, while a competitor could be behind a negative one. Still, it is possible to find useful information, such as how a doctor runs his/her practice. As these Web sites accumulate dozens or more ratings for each doctor, they will yield more reliable information about physicians.

No Web sites give comprehensive information, but *www.ucomparehealthcare.com* and *www.vitals.com* provide a good start.

Trisha Torrey, author, *You Bet Your Life! The 10 Mistakes Every Patient Makes* (Langdon Street).

Is Your Doctor an Addict? Warning Signs

Charles B. Inlander, a consumer advocate and healthcare consultant located in Fogelsville, Pennsylvania. He was the founding president of the nonprofit People's Medical Society, a consumer advocacy organization credited with key improvements in the quality of US health care in the 1980s and 1990s, and is the author of 20 books, including *Take This Book to the Hospital with You: A Consumer Guide to Surviving Your Hospital Stay* (St. Martin's).

An estimated one in five American physicians is impaired by alcohol and/or drug use, according to a startling report in *Virtual Mentor*, an American Medical

Association journal. These problems are estimated to be up to three times higher among anesthesiologists (who have easy access to narcotics) and in emergency room doctors (who work in a highly stressful environment).

Unfortunately, not enough is being done to protect patients from impaired doctors. Even though all but three states—California, North Dakota and Wisconsin—offer treatment programs for doctors who have problems with alcohol and/or drugs, unbelievably, impaired physicians often are allowed to continue their normal medical practices while in active treatment. What's more, alcohol and drug abuse are not the only reasons a doctor may be impaired. Mental illness and even old age also can prevent physicians from being able to perform their professional duties responsibly. *How to recognize if your doctor may be impaired—and what to do if you think there is a problem...*

• **Be alert for signs of impairment.** Experts point out that doctors with impairments often are able to cover them up, making it difficult for a patient to identify a problem. In addition, a recent study found that almost half of doctors surveyed say they do not report their impaired or incompetent colleagues to licensing boards.

• **Know what to watch for.** Smelling alcohol on a doctor's breath is an immediate red flag. Odd or erratic behavior may be another indicator of a problem. For example, when a relative of mine asked if an injection was going to hurt her, the doctor whipped out a syringe and stuck it in his own arm and said, "See, it doesn't bother me!" She got up and left, reported the incident to the state, and the doctor's license was yanked when its medical board determined that the doctor was mentally impaired. But symptoms of impairment can be subtle, such as repeatedly asking the same question or repeatedly calling you by a wrong name.

• **Report the problem.** If you suspect that your doctor is impaired in some way, get up and leave. If your doctor is in a group practice or on a hospital's staff, report your suspicions to one of the other doctors or the hospital's chief of medicine (check the switchboard for

his/her number). Follow up with a letter to whomever you spoke to explaining what happened. Also, report the problem to your state's medical licensing board. For a listing of all the boards, contact the Federation of State Medical Boards (see *www.fsmb.org/directory_smb.html*). By law, they are required to investigate any complaint related to impairment.

• **Consider legal action.** If you think you have been injured or otherwise harmed by an impaired physician, contact a medical malpractice attorney. Your local bar association can help you find a skilled lawyer.

Too often, the medical community doesn't do enough to protect patients from impaired doctors. That's why it is up to you to be the watchdog for you and your family.

More from Charles Inlander...

When It's Fine to Use an In-Store Health Clinic

An increasing number of retail establishments—including wholesale stores, drugstores and supermarkets—have now contracted with outside firms to offer on-site health services. In-store clinics typically are reliable and convenient for diagnosing and treating minor complaints, including colds, earaches, sore throats and urinary tract infections. They operate on a walk-in basis and typically are staffed by nurse practitioners, who can write prescriptions that can be filled on site. Most will accept insurance.

Also from Charles Inlander...

How to Get *Quick* Test Results And Specialist Appointments

An older woman in Philadelphia contacted me some time ago because her physician had told her to schedule heart-valve surgery with the surgeon he recommended, but she wasn't able to get an appointment to see this surgeon for three weeks. She didn't feel well and wondered why she couldn't get a quicker appointment. What should she do? I told her to call the referring doctor and have him call the surgeon. But before the referring doctor could intervene, the woman's daughter found her unconscious on the floor. She was rushed to the hospital for emergency heart-valve surgery—and survived. But not everyone is so lucky when such scheduling problems occur.

Waiting for appointments with specialists, long delays in getting scheduled for surgery and even interminable waits for test results are some of the most frequent complaints I hear from medical consumers. For example, the average waiting time to get an appointment with an orthopedic surgeon in Boston is 40 days…a gynecologist 70 days…and 21 days to see a cardiologist, according to a 2009 survey. The numbers are not much better across the country.

My advice on expediting appointments and test results…

• **Ask your doctor to make the appointment.** Anytime your doctor recommends that you see a specialist, you should ask if the doctor will call to make the appointment. The referring doctor usually can get you squeezed in if the problem needs quick attention. Even if your problem can wait, a delay of weeks often creates anxiety—so if you're still not satisfied with the appointment date, call the specialist's office and ask to be contacted if there is a cancellation. Then call the office as early as possible each week to ask if a cancellation has occurred. Chances are good that you'll get a quicker appointment.

• **Be willing to travel.** A friend of mine needed a series of neurological tests to determine if he had Parkinson's disease. He was told that he had to wait a month for one of the tests because of the backlog at the only testing facility in his area. I suggested that he call hospitals within 50 miles of where he lived to see if the test could be performed elsewhere. He found a facility about 40 miles away that could do the test in three days. The test confirmed that he did have Parkinson's. Because he was tested quickly, my friend was able to begin taking needed medication sooner. If you are flexible about when and where you receive medical tests (my father once had an outpatient MRI at midnight because the time was available), you'll have far less waiting time.

• **Choose the right day of the week.** Most medical labs are closed on weekends. To get your test or biopsy results sooner—without having to wait over the weekend—schedule your appointments on Mondays or Tuesdays whenever possible.

Insider secret: Since blood tests for cholesterol levels are usually scheduled early in the morning (because you are required to fast), those tests results are usually back the same day. Call your doctor's office that afternoon to see if your results are in.

Be Sure to Get Your Test Results

Doctors sometimes don't inform patients about abnormal test results.

Recent finding: In one out of 14 cases with abnormal test results, doctors either didn't notify the patients…or failed to document that they had notified them.

In fact, few physicians have explicit procedures for managing and disclosing test results to their patients.

Self-defense: If you have any test or procedure done and do not hear from your physician within two weeks, call and ask for your test results.

Lawrence P. Casalino, MD, PhD, chief, division of outcomes and effectiveness research, department of public health at Weill Cornell Medical College in New York City, and leader of a study of the records of 5,434 patients, published in *Archives of Internal Medicine*.

Diagnosis by Phone?

An iPhone or another mobile device equipped with specialized software can transmit images to radiologists from remote locations. One study of appendicitis patients found that diagnoses based on these images were as accurate as those made with traditional systems.

Radiological Society of North America, *www.rsna.org*.

Medical Imaging Test Self-Defense

Medical imaging procedures may be dangerous. *See below...*

Recent finding: Contrast agents, such as iodine—which allow doctors to see the blood vessel and tissue changes in cardiac angiography, computed tomography and other imaging tests—can adversely affect the kidneys and increase a person's heart attack and stroke risk for up to two years after the procedure.

Self-defense: Only contrast agents given intravenously have this effect (thus, not barium). Talk to your doctor about choosing the safest intravenous contrast agent (*iopamidol*) or avoiding having to use a contrast agent at all.

Richard Solomon, MD, professor of medicine, University of Vermont School of Medicine, Burlington, and leader of a study of 294 people, published in *Clinical Journal of the American Society of Nephrology.*

Blood Test Replacing Biopsy?

A blood test may replace biopsy for cancer detection. The test identifies tiny amounts of cancer-associated proteins. It has been tried only on blood cancers, but research on tumors has begun.

Dean W. Felsher, MD, PhD, associate professor of medicine–oncology and pathology, Stanford University, Stanford, California.

If You're Having Blood Taken...

Don't clench your fist while having blood drawn. Clenching might trigger excess release of potassium from skeletal muscles, which may prompt your doctor to prescribe unnecessary tests or treatments. High serum potassium is a sign of kidney disease and of heart problems. Also, high potassium may be a side effect of medication—so a doctor may stop a medicine or reduce the dosage.

Better: Close your hand lightly when the needle is being inserted—then open up your hand as blood is being drawn.

Vanessa R. Thurlow and Ian R. Bailey, Royal College of Pathologists, Princess Royal University Hospital, Farnborough, Kent, United Kingdom, and coauthors of a study published in *Annals of Clinical Biochemistry.*

The Best Advice My Doctor Ever Gave Me

Tamara Eberlein, editor of the e-letter *HealthyWoman from Bottom Line*, Boardroom Inc.

Dust, dander, mold—you name it, I'm allergic to it. And, sleeping away from home always sparked severe symptoms. Then my allergist told me to travel with my own pillow, which has an allergen-proof cover—an easy strategy that brought relief.

I asked colleagues to share several secrets they learned from their own doctors...

• **Dehydration causes so many common complaints—headache, nausea, dizziness, fatigue**—so drink a few glasses of water to see if symptoms abate.

• **To stop a severe nosebleed, roll a tissue into a cigarette shape,** gently insert it into the bleeding nostril as high as is comfortable, then squeeze the middle of the nose from the outside—this applies pressure from inside and out.

• **If breasts are lumpy and/or tender, consider giving up caffeine**—for some women, this seems to reduce lumps and tenderness associated with fibrocystic breasts.

• **Decrease the risk for urinary tract infections by urinating right after sex.**

• **To swallow pills more easily,** take them with warm water to relax your throat...and take sips before putting pills in your mouth.

Taking Medications? Timing Is Everything...

William J.M. Hrushesky, MD, principal investigator at the Chronobiology and Oncology Research Laboratory at the Dorn Research Institute VA Medical Center in Columbia, South Carolina. He also is a professor of cell development and biology at the University of South Carolina School of Medicine in Columbia and the author of *Circadian Cancer Therapy* (CRC).

Few doctors talk to their patients about the best time of day to take medication or undergo surgery, but it can make a big difference. *Examples...*

If you have high blood pressure, it's usually best to take a slow-release medication at bedtime. For osteoarthritis, your pain reliever needs to work hardest in the afternoon. Why does the timing matter?

Virtually every bodily function—including blood pressure, heart rate and body temperature—is influenced by our circadian (24-hour) clocks. Various external factors, like seasonal rhythms, also can play a role in certain medical conditions.

For optimal results when treating...

HIGH BLOOD PRESSURE

There are both daily and seasonal fluctuations in blood pressure. It's normal for systolic pressure (top number) to drop several points during the warm months, then to rise again in winter. Cold weather is thought to trigger the release of substances known as catecholamines, which may raise blood pressure.

Most people experience a sharp rise (about 10 to 25 points, systolic) in blood pressure when they first get up in the morning—this contributes to the morning peak in heart attack occurrences.

Research shows that heart attacks are 40% to 50% more likely to occur during the first six hours after a person awakens than later in the day or during sleep. Blood pressure declines at night and reaches its lowest point during sleep.

With standard treatments for high blood pressure, a patient might experience consistent reductions in pressure, including during times when the reduction isn't needed.

For best results: Ask your doctor about taking a drug that works in sync with the daily rhythms of your blood pressure. For example, the calcium channel blocker *verapamil* (such as Verelan PM) and timed-release *diltiazem* (Cardizem LA) as well as the beta-blocker *propranolol* (InnoPran XL) are all designed to be taken at bedtime.

With each of these slow-release, long-acting drugs, none of the active ingredient is released during the first four hours. Most of the drug effects occur between 6 am and noon, when blood pressure tends to be most elevated.

OSTEOARTHRITIS

Caused by inflammation due to wear and tear on the joints, osteoarthritis is almost always more painful late in the day after a full day of activity using damaged joints. A nonsteroidal anti-inflammatory drug (NSAID), like *ibuprofen* (Advil), is the most commonly recommended pain reliever, providing significant anti-inflammatory properties.

For best results: Ask your physician about taking one dose at noon...again in the afternoon...and at bedtime. This schedule allows drug levels to peak at about the same time that the symptoms are flaring.

Helpful: To help reduce the risk for NSAID side effects, such as gastrointestinal bleeding and ulcer, take each NSAID dose with food. Long-term use of NSAIDs has been linked to increased risk for heart attack, stroke and kidney disease, so if you regularly take an NSAID, discuss these potential risks with your physician. Also ask about taking occasional NSAID "drug holidays" (stopping use of the drug for a day or so each week). Do not discontinue any other drug without asking your doctor.

RHEUMATOID ARTHRITIS

NSAIDs also reduce pain caused by rheumatoid arthritis, an autoimmune disease in which the body's immune system "attacks" joints. This type of arthritis tends to hurt more in the morning. After the hormone cortisol, which suppresses the immune system, peaks at about 4 am each day, the immune system reactivates, inflaming joints by 8 am to 10 am.

For best results: Take your regular pain reliever dose at bedtime to help reduce morning pain and stiffness associated with rheumatoid arthritis. Taking the medication at night means that the drug reaches effective levels while you sleep, which helps decrease pain when you wake up. Keep one other dose on your nightstand to take before getting up in the morning if necessary. Eat a few crackers first to help prevent stomach distress.

DIABETES

Physiological reactions that are more detrimental at night than in the morning are believed to play a role in both type 2 diabetes and metabolic syndrome—a constellation of conditions that includes insulin resistance (in which the body's cells don't use insulin properly), abdominal obesity, high blood pressure and elevated LDL "bad" cholesterol.

The body produces and uses insulin most effectively in the daytime hours and its metabolism is most active during the day. The liver, pancreas and muscles are better able to utilize blood sugar (glucose) and burn calories when metabolism is high. Because metabolism slows at night, someone who eats a lot of snack foods, for example, at night will be unable to efficiently remove the resulting glucose and fats from the blood. Over time, this can cause a chronic rise in insulin and cholesterol and may lead to metabolic syndrome.

For best results: People with metabolic syndrome or diabetes (or those who are at increased risk for either condition due to obesity or high blood pressure) should synchronize all their meals with their metabolic rhythms. Consume most of your calories early in the day. Eat a relatively light supper—for example, a piece of fish, a green salad and vegetables—preferably at least a few hours before going to bed. Diabetes drugs, such as insulin, should be taken in anticipation of daytime calories and carbohydrates.

CANCER

Research has identified ways in which the circadian rhythm affects the toxicity and effectiveness of cancer treatments. *For example...*

•**Chemotherapy.** In an important study involving patients with colon cancer, researchers found a measurable response rate of more than 50% in those treated at an optimal time, com-

pared with only 32% in those treated at other times. Patients in both groups were given exactly the same drug and the same dose. The only difference was the timing of treatment.

What accounts for this difference? All cells undergo replication, repair and *apoptosis* (cell death) at predictable times during the day. By pinpointing these times, physicians can deliver chemotherapeutic drugs when cancer cells are most vulnerable—and when healthy cells are more resistant to toxic effects.

For best results: Discuss the optimal timing of your chemotherapy with your oncologist, who will determine this, in part, based on the anticancer drugs used.

•**Cancer surgery.** Several different studies have found that the timing of cancer surgery can significantly affect outcomes in women.

For example, research has discovered that performing breast cancer surgery in women shortly after ovulation can improve the cure frequency between two and two-and-a-half times. The explanation may be that elevated progesterone (which coincides with ovulation) may inhibit the production of enzymes that facilitate the *metastasis* (spread) of cancer.

Conversely, during the first half of the menstrual cycle (the follicular phase), there may be an increase in angiogenesis, the growth of blood vessels that supply tumors. There also may be delays in cancer-cell death or changes in immune activity.

For best results: If you are a woman facing cancer surgery, discuss its timing within your menstrual cycle with your doctor. The optimal timing depends on the type of cancer and the individual patient.

Medication Mix-Ups Can Be Deadly

Milap C. Nahata, PharmD, a professor and chairman of pharmacy practice and administration in the College of Pharmacy at Ohio State University and associate director of pharmacy at the Ohio State University Medical Center, both in Columbus. Nahata has authored or co-authored more than 470 peer-reviewed scientific papers and is a recipient of the Distinguished Pharmacy Educator Award from the American Association of Colleges of Pharmacy.

When you take a drug, you expect it to ease your symptoms or cure your medical problem. However, a medicine you take could sometimes cause serious harm—or even death—if there is a medication "error" (such as taking the wrong dose or an inappropriate drug).

Frightening statistic: Each year, up to 1.5 million Americans are impacted by preventable mistakes involving both prescription and over-the-counter (OTC) drugs, according to the Institute of Medicine. Most of these errors are minor and unlikely to cause serious problems—with dangerous exceptions.

Example: A baby in one hospital needed 0.5 mg of morphine for sedation and/or pain relief. The doctor who wrote the prescription did not put a "0" before the decimal point. A nurse who didn't see the decimal point gave the child 5 mg. This tenfold error was doubled when the child, who later died as a result of the overdose, was given an additional excessive dose.

WHAT'S GOING WRONG?

Medication errors can occur in several ways. Often, patients skip doses, stop a drug without medical advice or neglect to tell their doctors about other medicine and/or supplements they are taking, exposing themselves to the possibility of a dangerous interaction.

But health-care professionals also can play a role in medication errors. *Common reasons for medication errors that occur in doctors' offices and at pharmacies and hospitals...*

INCORRECT DOSES

Most prescription drugs come in standard doses, such as 10 mg or 100 mg. On occasion, doctors might accidentally omit a "0" or write down a decimal point that's difficult to see.

Self-defense: When your doctor hands you a prescription, confirm the dose (the specific number of milligrams, for example) before you leave his/her office.

ABBREVIATIONS

When writing prescriptions, physicians use abbreviations that could be easily misread by pharmacists.

Example: The abbreviation "QOD" signifies every other day..."QD" indicates every day..."BID" means twice a day...and "QID" is four times a day. If the pharmacist reads "QD" as "QID," the patient will be taking four times the recommended dose, which can lead to side effects.

Self-defense: Make sure you understand the intended dosing instructions (for example, once or twice daily) before leaving your doctor's office. Then confirm the drug and dose with the pharmacist before leaving the pharmacy to ensure that you're receiving both the correct medication and dose.

WRONG DRUGS

There are more than 10,000 prescription drugs and as many as 300,000 OTC medications on the market. Some of these drugs have similar names that are easily confused—either by the doctor who is writing the prescription or by the pharmacist who's filling it.

Example: It's easy to confuse *bupropion,* an antidepressant, with *buspirone,* the anti-anxiety drug.

Self-defense: Know the exact name of the drug you're supposed to be taking (both the generic name and the brand name)...why you are taking it...and what it looks like—consult the Physicians' Desk Reference online at *www.pdrhealth.com* to view photographs of commonly prescribed drugs.

Check the drug name before you leave your physician's office. Repeat the name out loud when you order the drug at the pharmacy. In the example above, bupropion is the generic name for the brand-name drug Wellbutrin. Buspirone is the generic name for Buspar.

Helpful: Prescription tablets and capsules are imprinted with numbers that are specific to particular drugs and doses from specific manufacturers. When you first fill a prescription, write down the manufacturer's number and keep it in a safe place. When you get the prescription refilled, double-check to ensure that it has the same number.

OTHER PRECAUTIONS TO TAKE

If you take medication...

• **Consult the pharmacist.** About 95% of patients don't ask questions about how to use their medication, according to research published by the California Board of Pharmacy and other groups. These patients may not understand not only how much of the medication to take or when and how often to take it, but also what side effects might occur or how to tell if the drug is working.

Self-defense: Consult with the pharmacist every time you start a new prescription—particularly if you're also taking other drugs with which it might interact.

Important: Many people who work behind the counter are pharmacy technicians. When asking questions about any medication, make sure that you're talking to a pharmacist. Look for the title "Pharmacist" or "RPh" (Registered Pharmacist) on the person's jacket (or nameplate)—or ask the person's title.

Helpful: A patient who takes multiple drugs can prevent many errors by buying them all at the same pharmacy. Virtually all pharmacies now have computers that track medications and will automatically give an alert if a patient adds a new drug that might interact with others that he is taking.

• **Tell your doctor about everything you take.** Adults over age 65 account for 13% of the US population but take one-third of all prescription drugs. Anyone taking numerous drugs may experience side effects and/or drug interactions—many of which could be avoided if patients periodically reviewed medication use with their doctors and/or pharmacists.

Doctors will usually ask patients what medications they are currently taking. They do not always ask about—or patients neglect to mention—supplements and/or OTC drugs.

Self-defense: Every time you see your doctor, bring a list that includes everything you're taking. Don't assume that supplements, including herbs, don't count. Many of these products can interact with prescription drugs.

Example: The husband of one of our employees was admitted to the hospital with a bleeding disorder. The condition had developed because he was taking the blood thinner *warfarin* (Coumadin) to prevent clots but hadn't told his doctor (or pharmacist) that he also was using the herbal supplement ginkgo biloba, which increases the risk of bleeding—especially when combined with warfarin.

Off-Label Drug Danger

Although the FDA allows doctors to prescribe drugs for conditions for which they were not originally given approval, a recent survey showed doctors knew the "approved" status of a drug only 50% of the time.

Problem: Many "off-label" uses for drugs are not supported by scientific evidence.

Safest: Ask your doctor if he/she is prescribing a drug off-label—if so, ask why he expects it to be effective.

G. Caleb Alexander, MD, assistant professor, department of medicine, University of Chicago Medical Center.

Avoid This Common Drug-Dosing Error

Rebecca Shannonhouse, editor, *Bottom Line/Health*, Boardroom Inc., 281 Tresser Blvd., Stamford, Connecticut 06901

If you take a spoonful of medicine, you may be getting more—or less—than you need.

Recent finding: When 195 cold and flu sufferers were asked to pour one teaspoon of medicine into kitchen spoons of differing sizes, they tended to underdose by as much as 8%...or overdose by up to 12%.

Because the average kitchen spoon holds more—or less—liquid than an official, 5-milliliter teaspoon, people who "guesstimate" the correct dose often get too much or too little of the active ingredient, says Jack M. Rosenberg, PharmD, PhD, professor of pharmacy and pharmacology at Long Island University in Brooklyn, New York. Such errors in dosing can have significant cumulative effects when a medicine is taken for several days.

To protect yourself, Dr. Rosenberg advises that you…

• **Talk with the pharmacist.** Ask him/her if it is okay to use a kitchen spoon to measure the dose of a liquid medicine. A kitchen spoon could be fine for some medicines, such as a liquid antacid, but for many others, you might think that you're pouring the correct amount—but you'll probably be wrong.

• **Use a precision device when needed.** Always use the calibrated cap or measuring device that's supplied with some medications. If no such device is provided, use a measuring teaspoon, oral syringe or a dropper.

• **Review the label.** Some over-the-counter medications have age and body-weight guidelines for dosing. Follow the label advice exactly, unless otherwise specified by your physician.

If You Take Aspirin for Your Heart, Avoid This…

Taking aspirin and ibuprofen together can block aspirin's beneficial effect on the cardiovascular system.

Self-defense: If you take aspirin daily to protect against heart attack and stroke, wait several hours before taking ibuprofen—and use ibuprofen only occasionally.

Russell K. Portenoy, MD, chairman of the department of pain medicine and palliative care, Beth Israel Medical Center, and professor of neurology and anesthesiology, Albert Einstein College of Medicine, both in New York City.

The Best Way to Get Rid Of Expired Drugs

Don't flush expired medications down the toilet—they can damage waterways and ecosystems.

Better: Remove them from their containers and mix them in a sealable plastic bag with coffee grounds, cat litter or sawdust to make them less appealing to children and pets. Put the bag in the trash.

Exception: The FDA recommends flushing certain highly addictive "controlled substances" (such as Percocet and Oxycontin) to be sure that nobody gets to them.

Alternative: Ask the pharmacist about any drug "return" programs in your area. For more information, visit *www.smarxtdisposal.net.*

Real Simple, 1271 Avenue of the Americas, New York City 10020, *www.realsimple.com.*

In the Hospital? Know Your Rights

Charles B. Inlander, a consumer advocate and healthcare consultant located in Fogelsville, Pennsylvania. He was the founding president of the nonprofit People's Medical Society, a consumer advocacy organization credited with key improvements in the quality of US health care in the 1980s and 1990s, and is the author of 20 books, including *Take This Book to the Hospital with You: A Consumer Guide to Surviving Your Hospital Stay* (St. Martin's).

If you are one of the roughly 35 million Americans who is admitted to a hospital this year due to a chronic illness, an emergency or a need for surgery, you may feel like you're in custody. Hospitals are so intimidating to most people that they don't realize that, thanks to federal and state laws, they have many rights as patients.

For example, when you're hospitalized, you can…

• **Say "No"!** You not only have the right to refuse any procedure or test you do not want, but also can say no to having a specific doctor, nurse or resident-physician treat you. (Of course, you may not have a choice if your case is an emergency.)

Bonus: My research has found that saying no is the best way to get hospital personnel to fully explain something you don't understand so that you can then make better-informed medical decisions.

•**Have a loved one with you.** Hospital visiting hours are not laws, but hospital-imposed restrictions. No matter what visiting hours the hospital lists, you have the right to have a personal advocate, such as a family member or friend, with you. However, visitation may be limited or barred in such areas as recovery rooms, trauma centers and quarantine areas.

Smart idea: In choosing someone to stay with you or nearby at all times, consider asking the person you've designated as your representative in a living will or medical durable power of attorney to make medical decisions for you if you are unable to do so.

•**See your medical records.** State and federal laws allow you to see and obtain copies of your medical records (except psychotherapy notes). But you—and, in general, your designated representative—also have the right to look at your medical chart (a detailed record of your medical care and status) while you are in the hospital. Just ask your nurse or doctor.

•**Check your bill.** State and federal consumer-protection laws give you the right to an itemized bill that includes every service, product, medication and procedure for which you are charged during your hospitalization.

Helpful: Since hospitals generally keep a running tab as charges occur, ask the billing office for a copy of your bill each day you are in the hospital. Hospital personnel may balk, but you have that right.

•**Insist on knowing who is treating you.** Doctors and nurses should wear nametags that include their medical degrees. You should know if your nurse is a registered nurse (RN) or licensed practical nurse (LPN). (RNs have more training.) You also have the right to ask anyone his or her job title and qualifications. Don't let uniforms fool you. A white coat and stethoscope hanging around the person's neck means nothing in terms of training or qualifications.

•**Check out.** By law, you can check yourself out of a hospital at anytime, even if your doctors don't recommend it. You must sign an "Against Medical Advice" form, but you can leave whenever you like—for example, if you disagree with the proposed treatment.

Top-Rated Hospitals In the US

The best hospitals in the US are Johns Hopkins in Baltimore…Mayo Clinic in Rochester, Minnesota…Ronald Reagan UCLA Medical Center, Los Angeles…Cleveland Clinic…Massachusetts General, Boston…New York-Presbyterian, New York City…University of California at San Francisco Medical Center…Hospital of the University of Pennsylvania, Philadelphia…Barnes-Jewish Hospital, Washington University, St. Louis…Brigham and Women's Hospital, Boston…Duke University Medical Center, Durham, North Carolina.

These hospitals achieved high scores in at least six specialties, such as cancer care, heart treatment and children's health. For the complete listing of hospitals, their specialties and their rankings, log on to *www.usnews.com/best hospitals.*

Rankings from *US News & World Report*, 1050 Thomas Jefferson St. NW, Washington, DC 20007

Looking for a Good Hospital? Find It Here…

Find a good hospital at *www.hospitalcom pare.hhs.gov.* This government-run Internet site compares hospitals around the nation based on 27 performance measures relating to certain medical conditions and/or surgical procedures, including patient satisfaction and discharge instruction. The site's goal is to improve quality of health care and drive down costs by providing patients with information so that they can choose the best hospital for their needs.

How to Get the Care You Need in an Emergency

Kathleen Clem, MD, associate professor and chair and chief of the department of emergency medicine at Loma Linda University Medical Center, Loma Linda, California. She also is a spokesperson for the American College of Emergency Physicians and a winner of its "Heroes of Emergency Medicine" award.

Overcrowding in the emergency room (ER) keeps growing worse. A recent study from Harvard Medical School discovered that, between 1997 and 2004, the number of ER patients in the US increased by 18%...the number of hospitals having 24-hour ERs fell by 12%...patients' average waiting time to see an ER doctor increased by 36%, to 30 minutes...and the average wait for heart attack patients increased by 150%, to 20 minutes.

A concern: Women wait, on average, 5.6% longer than men wait. It may not sound like much—but often a minute makes the difference between life and death.

One reason for the gender discrepancy is that doctors—and patients—do not always recognize how symptoms can differ between the sexes.

Example: Women with heart attacks are less likely than men to experience "classic" crushing chest pain. They are more likely to feel nauseated, dizzy and/or breathless, vague symptoms easily dismissed as indigestion or anxiety. Another issue is that women, brought up to give care rather than receive it, often are reluctant to demand attention.

How *everyone* can get the care they need...

LONG BEFORE YOU NEED THE ER

•**Ask your primary care doctor which hospital he/she prefers,** so that you are not forced to make this decision during a crisis.

You may be advised to go to the closest ER if your situation is potentially life-threatening... or to the hospital with which the doctor is affiliated if your condition is not as serious.

•**Create a written personal health record.**

Include: Your doctors' names, specialties and phone numbers...your current and past medical conditions and surgeries...the names and dosages of all prescription and nonprescription medications that you take (including supplements)...and family history of serious health problems. Always carry it with you.

Useful: To download a free personal health record form, log on to *www.BottomLineSecrets. com/Perk.*

•**Carry your medical insurance card.** ERs provide care regardless of patients' ability to pay, but having insurance information handy speeds the administrative process.

•**Talk to your doctor about your personal risk factors,** such as high cholesterol or blood sugar problems. Discuss warning signs that merit immediate care—for instance, decreased urination in someone who has chronic kidney disease.

THE INSTANT AN EMERGENCY ARISES

•**Decide if you need an ambulance.** Call 911 if you experience...

•Sudden onset of a severe headache or dizziness...severe abdominal pain...extreme shortness of breath not caused by exertion...numbness in a limb or trouble walking...or altered vision or speech.

•More than a few minutes of squeezing or burning pain in the neck or torso.

•An occurrence of uncontrolled bleeding... copious blood in vomit or stool...a broken bone penetrating the skin...or fainting not caused by emotional stress.

•If you do not need an ambulance—for instance, a cut requires stitches but is not bleeding profusely or you have twisted your ankle and may need X-rays to determine if a bone is broken—ask a relative or friend to drive you to the ER, or call a taxi. Do not drive yourself if you are in a lot of pain or feel woozy.

•**Drive yourself only if the problem is minor**—a condition that normally would be handled in your doctor's office (had it not occurred after hours or when you were out of town) but that should not go untended for many hours.

Example: A skin rash or other sign of a systemic allergic reaction that does not affect breathing.

BEFORE HEADING FOR THE ER

• **Call your own doctor if you are able,** or if your condition is too severe, ask someone to call for you. Your doctor may want to alert the ER to prepare for your arrival.

• **If you haven't made a list of your medications, put all your drug bottles in a bag** (or ask another person to) and take them with you. The ER staff needs to see what you take.

• **If you ingested someone else's medication or a toxic household product, bring the container.**

• **If a loved one is not accompanying you to the ER, try to arrange for someone to meet you there.** A companion can help you remember what the doctor says, provide emotional support and notify family.

• **Bring a pen and paper to write down the doctors' instructions.**

WHEN YOU ARRIVE AT THE ER

• **A nurse will assess you to determine how critical your condition is.** Don't downplay your symptoms!

• **Show the nurse the personal health record you created previously.** Share any suspicions—for instance, "My mother had blood clots. I'm worried that this lump in my leg might be a clot, too."

• **If you are or may be pregnant,** tell everyone who assesses or treats you.

• **If pain is severe, ask a nurse if you can have pain medication.**

WHILE YOU WAIT TO BE EXAMINED

• **If your symptoms change or worsen, tell the nurse** immediately.

• **In the waiting room, if someone near to you is coughing or vomiting, change your seat** and/or ask a nurse for a face mask.

• **Exercise patience.** Unless your situation is dire, other patients may be in more critical condition. The ER staff tries to attend to patients in order of patients' needs—not first-come, first-served.

WHEN YOU SEE THE DOCTOR

• **Again, describe all your symptoms and share your personal health record.** Don't assume that the doctor already knows everything you told the nurse who first assessed you.

• **Listen carefully, ask questions and take notes if you can.**

• **Discuss the risks and benefits of tests and treatments** that the doctor is considering.

• **If an ER physician suggests that you be admitted to the hospital for additional testing and/or overnight observation, consent.** Many patients refuse because they would rather go to their own doctors the next day—but staying at the hospital allows tests to be done quickly and gives you instant access to care if your condition worsens.

BEFORE LEAVING THE ER

• **Make sure that you understand your diagnosis** and instructions for care after discharge from the ER.

• **Review with the doctor or nurse any warning signs that merit an immediate return to the ER.**

• **Request that test results be sent to your primary care doctor.** (This is not necessary if your doctor is affiliated with the hospital.)

• **If you are told to see a specialist for follow-up, get a name.**

WHEN YOU GET HOME

• **Follow discharge instructions.**

• **Call the ER if questions or concerns arise.**

• **Contact your own doctor** during normal office hours to find out if a follow-up exam is recommended.

How to Not Regret Your Cosmetic Surgery

Any medical school graduate who completes a one-year internship can claim to be a "cosmetic surgeon"—even when his/her training in plastic surgery consisted solely of weekend courses. Yet in an ASPS poll, only 28% of cosmetic surgery patients checked out their doctor's credentials. Use a surgeon who is board-certified by the American Board of Plastic Surgery (215-587-9322, *www.abplsurg. org*)...or by another board that's listed at the American Board of Medical Specialties (312-436-2600, *www.abms.org*).

Once you've narrowed your candidate list to two or three surgeons, have a consultation with each. (Some doctors provide free consultations, while others charge up to several hundred dollars.)

Alan Engler, MD, assistant clinical professor of plastic surgery at Albert Einstein College of Medicine and a plastic surgeon in private practice, both in New York City. He is author of four books, including *BodySculpture* (Hudson). For more information on his book, go to *www.bodysculpture.com*.

What You Need to Know *Before* Having Surgery...

Thomas R. Russell, MD, FACS, executive director of the American College of Surgeons and an adjunct professor of surgery at the Northwestern University School of Medicine, both in Chicago. A former private practice general surgeon who specialized in colon and rectal surgery, he has published extensively on scientific and educational topics related to surgery. He is the author of *I Need an Operation...Now What?* (Thomson Healthcare).

Every year, about 20 million Americans undergo some type of surgery—and as many as one out of five of them experiences postoperative complications, including pneumonia and wound infection.

Surprising: Surgical patients spend an average of just one hour researching their operations—or carefully considering the surgeon.

About one out of three patients does not even check the surgeon's credentials.*

Surgery is inherently risky, but the majority of surgical procedures are elective (nonemergency), so patients can do more themselves to improve their odds of a favorable outcome. *To increase your chances of having a successful operation...*

•**Ask your surgeon the tough questions.** All surgeons have specialized training, but that doesn't mean that they're adequately trained for the procedure you are about to undergo.

Examples: A physician who's trained in eye surgery may augment his/her practice by performing plastic surgery—even though he did nothing more than take a weekend course in this. An orthopedic surgeon who does frequent spine surgeries might have inadequate experience in knee operations.

Before choosing a surgeon, ask if he does this particular procedure on a regular basis. Make it known that you are simply gathering the information you need to make informed decisions about your care. Surgeons improve with practice. Someone who does a particular procedure frequently usually will have better outcomes than someone who does it rarely. *Also...*

•**Ask about minimally invasive options.** Virtually every surgical procedure now has a less invasive alternative. Laparoscopic surgery, which involves a small incision and use of a laparoscope (an illuminated tube) to view the operative site, is routinely used for gallbladder removal, sinus operations, cardiovascular surgery and even some back procedures. Always find out if it is an option. Minimally invasive procedures are far less traumatic than "open" procedures. A gallbladder patient who has an open procedure, for example, might spend five days or more in the hospital, compared with just one or two days with a laparoscopic procedure.

•**Get in shape.** You're less likely to have complications if you eat well, lose weight (if

*Look for surgeons who are board-certified in their specialty and are fellows in the American College of Surgeons. This ensures that the surgeon has passed rigorous exams and completed accredited training.

necessary) and exercise regularly prior to your surgery.

Important: If you smoke, quit at least two weeks before the operation. Nicotine reduces the flow of blood to damaged tissues. Smokers are more likely to experience delayed wound healing as well as postsurgical pneumonia.

In addition, you should tell your surgeon about all medications and herbal supplements that you are taking and openly discuss alcohol consumption.

• **Schedule wisely.** Be cautious about scheduling a procedure just before the holidays, when the hospital may be short-staffed—and when your surgeon might be less available than usual.

In addition, try to ensure that your surgery is scheduled early in the morning so that you are not added on to the operating room schedule. Being the first patient of the day increases the odds that the surgical team will be fresh and fully engaged.

• **Discuss with your surgeon and the other surgical team members the site of the surgery.** The Joint Commission on the Accreditation of Healthcare Organizations, a nonprofit organization that evaluates and accredits more than 15,000 health organizations, recently estimated that more than 2,000 wrong-site events occur every year.

Examples: Operating on the right leg instead of the left leg…or removing the wrong kidney.

To prevent a wrong-site surgery, make sure that the correct location is identified with a marking pen prior to surgery. Don't mark the site yourself. It could cause confusion later. Instead, pay attention while the doctor or nurse marks the correct location. Make sure this is done before you're sedated and while you're in the presence of other members of the operating team.

• **Stay warm.** Patients often are told that operating rooms need to be cold to prevent infection. This isn't true. A cold operating room increases the risk for infection and also slows wound healing.

You want your body temperature to be normal. If you are cold, ask for a blanket in the staging area (where patients wait prior to surgery). If you're still cold, ask for another blanket.

In addition, be sure that a member of the surgical team will be monitoring your body temperature to ensure that it remains normal throughout the procedure—and will keep you warm, if necessary—if the procedure is expected to last for more than an hour.

• **Monitor glucose.** Most intravenous (IV) solutions contain significant amounts of sugar (glucose) to simulate body fluids. In patients with diabetes, this can cause dramatic blood sugar swings during surgery. Unstable glucose levels slow wound healing and increase the risk for infection.

If you have diabetes: Ask the anesthesiologist to monitor your glucose levels before, during and after surgery.

• **Breathe deeply and move.** Pneumonia is among the most serious postsurgical complications, particularly in patients who have had heart bypass surgery or other procedures that affect the chest and abdomen.

Deep breathing is the best way to prevent pneumonia after surgery. Every hour while you're awake, take a deep breath, hold it for three to five seconds and repeat two to 10 times.

Also important: Stand up periodically, or if you are confined to bed, sit up and move from side to side. Movement helps your lungs to expand and aerate (deliver oxygen to the blood).

• **Make sure pain will be managed aggressively.** Postoperative pain inhibits a patient's ability to move, breathe deeply and heal, and it increases the risk for infection and venous thrombosis (blood clots).

Ask your surgeon about his plans to arrange for preoperative medication to pre-empt pain. You should receive additional medication during the surgery, including injections of anesthetic into the incision. Also, ask your doctor about the possibility of using a patient-controlled analgesic after surgery so that you can manage your own pain by pushing a button.

If You Take Herbs… Read This Before Undergoing Surgery

David J. Rowe, MD, assistant professor in the department of plastic surgery at University Hospitals Case Medical Center in Cleveland.

Every patient is asked prior to surgery, "What medications do you take?" Yet 40% to 70% of all patients do not report their use of herbal supplements—typically because they don't think of their supplements as medication.

THE CONCERN

Although many herbs generally are safe, when you are undergoing or recovering from surgery—even a very minor procedure—certain herbs can lead to potentially serious side effects, such as…

BLEEDING PROBLEMS

Some herbs thin the blood, possibly complicating surgery and delaying healing. *These include…*

- **Dong quai,** commonly used for menstrual cramps and menopausal symptoms.
- **Feverfew,** for arthritis and headache.
- **Garlic,** helps stimulate the immune system.
- **Ginkgo biloba,** used for eye disorders, cognitive problems and vertigo.
- **Ginseng,** used for stress.

CARDIOVASCULAR SIDE EFFECTS

Postoperative hypertension, heart palpitations or other serious heart problems may develop if you are taking…

- **Feverfew,** for arthritis and headache.
- **Garlic,** for immune-strengthening.

DRUG INTERACTIONS

The actions and side effects of drugs commonly given before, during or after surgery —such as *lidocaine* (an anesthetic) and *midazolam* (a sedative)—may be intensified by…

- **Echinacea,** for cold and flu.
- **Goldenseal,** taken to relieve digestive and respiratory problems.

PHOTOSENSITIVITY

If you have laser surgery, you may develop a severe light-sensitivity rash if you're taking…

- **Dong quai,** for menstrual and menopausal symptoms.
- **St. John's wort,** for anxiety.
- **Reaction to anesthesia.**

Herbs that prolong sedation include…

- **Kava,** a sedative.
- **St. John's wort,** for anxiety, depression.
- **Valerian,** for insomnia.

SELF-DEFENSE

Follow these steps…

- **A month before any scheduled surgery,** give your doctor a list of every supplement and medication that you take.
- **Even if your doctor is not concerned,** it is safest to discontinue all supplements at least two weeks before surgery.
- **On the day of your operation,** remind your surgeon about any recent supplement use—and also show your list of drugs and supplements to the anesthesiologist.
- **Carry a personal health record that lists all supplements and drugs you take**—so that if you need emergency surgery, doctors can take precautions.
- **After surgery,** wait until your doctor declares you sufficiently healed before you resume supplementing.

EXCEPTIONS

Though clinical research is limited, anecdotal evidence suggests that recovery may be hastened by…

- **Arnica,** used for pain and inflammation.
- **Bromelain,** another analgesic and an anti-inflammatory.

With your doctor's okay, consider taking arnica and/or bromelain (following the dosage instructions on labels) starting the day after surgery.

Licorice Gargle Before Surgery Soothes Sore Throats and Coughs

A licorice gargle before surgery can reduce sore throat afterward. Patients who gargled with a licorice solution five minutes before an operation also had less postsurgical coughing. Sore throats and coughs are common after surgery involving general anesthesia with intubation. The licorice gargle is easy to make.

How to do it: Boil about one teaspoon of licorice powder in one-and-a-half cups of water, then filter. Gargle should stay at room temperature and be used within 24 hours. Licorice contains compounds with anti-inflammatory and anti-irritant effects. Ask your physician for more details.

Anil Agarwal, MD, department of anaesthesiology, Sanjay Gandhi Post Graduate Institute of Medical Sciences, Lucknow, India, and leader of a study published in *Anesthesia & Analgesia*.

Post-Surgery Blood Clot Prevention

D angerous blood clots are likely up to 12 weeks after surgery. Patients who have recently undergone a surgery are up to 110 times more likely to be admitted to a hospital because of potentially fatal *thromboses* (blood clots) than people who have not undergone surgery.

Self-defense: Anticlotting drugs and physical measures, such as compression stockings, can reduce risk.

Jane Green, MD, PhD, group head and principal investigator, Cancer Epidemiology Unit, University of Oxford, England, and coauthor of a study of thromboses in 947,454 women, published in *BMJ Online First*.

Supplements That *Speed* Healing After Surgery

S upplements can help to quicken recovery after an elective surgery by promoting the development of healthy tissues...decreasing inflammation, swelling and bruising...and/or minimizing scarring. Before you begin, consult your surgeon and have a nutrition-oriented physician prescribe dosages appropriate for you (even for over-the-counter products).

Reason: Some supplements can thin the blood, interact with medications or other supplements, or make you sensitive to lasers.

Supplements your doctor may recommend include sublingual vitamin B-12 (to dissolve under the tongue)...a vitamin B complex that includes B-1, B-2, B-3 and B-6...vitamin A... vitamin C...and/or selenium. Typically supplementation would begin about one month before surgery, then continue for several weeks afterward—but again, your physician should make this decision.

Andrew Rubman, ND, medical director of the Southbury Clinic for Traditional Medicines, located in Southbury, Connecticut.

Plant Therapy

P lants can help hospital patients recover more quickly.

Theory: Living plants and flowers reduce stress, as shown by patients' lowered blood pressure and heart rates, resulting in a decreased perception of pain.

Seong-Hyun Park, PhD, and Richard Mattson, PhD, horticultural therapy, Kansas State University, Manhattan, and leaders of a study published in *HortTechnology*.

Chew Gum After Surgery

C hewing gum may help to speed recovery from surgery.

Recent finding: Following abdominal surgery, patients who chewed gum required less time to return to normal bowel function, had fewer instances of blocked bowels and reported less nausea and vomiting.

Theory: Chewing gum helps the body release gastrointestinal hormones that promote recovery.

Analysis of five studies with a total of 158 patients by researchers at St. Mary's Hospital, London, UK, published in *Archives of Surgery*.

Tattoo You

Some people have tattoos to indicate health conditions, such as diabetes, in case they can't communicate during an emergency.

Example: A tattoo of the six-pointed star with a serpent, a symbol often seen on ambulances, with the word "Diabetic" inscribed below it.

Tattoos typically are located on the forearm, where a medical bracelet would be.

Saleh Aldasouqi, MD, clinical associate professor at Michigan State University College of Human Medicine, and medical director of the Diabetes Center at Saint Francis Medical Center, both in East Lansing, Michigan, and director of Cape Diabetes and Endocrinology and Cape Thyroid Center, both in Cape Girardeau, Missouri.

Alternative Medicine: Time to Give It a Try?

Marjory Abrams, president of Boardroom, Inc., 281 Tresser Blvd., Stamford, Connecticut 06901.

I was surprised when a sick friend poohpoohed my suggestion that "alternative" treatments might help. Like so many people, he thought that such treatments involve wacky therapies suitable only as a last resort. True natural medicine (commonly called *alternative medicine*) isn't wacky at all. It is used in place of, or in combination with, conventional medicine and often results in fewer side effects

and better health than more mainstream approaches.

Seattle's Bastyr University is a preeminent academic and treatment center. Kris Somol, ND, adjunct faculty member and primary care physician, told me about some of the conditions that can be effectively treated with natural remedies…

•**Allergies, asthma and eczema.** Dietary changes—such as eating less sugar, meat and fat—help to reduce the body's hyperimmune response at the root of these conditions. Dr. Somol often recommends the all-natural antihistamine *quercetin* and omega-3 fatty acids in the form of fish-oil capsules or flaxseed oil.

•**Diabetes.** A naturopathic doctor will find out why there is excess glucose in the blood. If it is a shortage of insulin, a natural antioxidant called *alpha-lipoic acid* can help remove the excess glucose. If the problem is that glucose can't get into the cells, chromium or magnesium supplements may help.

•**High blood pressure.** In addition to exercising more, eating less salt and other lifestyle changes, the natural diuretic *dandelion leaf extract* can help lower blood pressure.

•**Irritable bowel syndrome (or IBS).** Because stress is a major cause of IBS, natural medicine practitioners often suggest meditation, yoga, exercise and other stress-management techniques. *Peppermint oil* helps soothe the intestines.

Dietary changes are in order if tests show food allergies, such as to wheat or soy.

•**Natural medicine can help cancer patients,** too, enhancing quality of life and increasing survival, said Dr. Somol. The herb *Eleutherococcus* can increase white blood cell counts and improve the outcome of chemotherapy. Intravenous vitamins and minerals can restore energy and minimize *neuropathy* (peripheral nerve damage), which often accompanies chemotherapy.

Alternative and *complementary medicines* (therapies that are practiced with conventional medicine) also can be used for mental-health concerns. New York City psychiatrist Katherine Falk, MD, has developed a natural approach for treating depression. Some patients need to remain on medication, but others can be helped with a completely natural approach.

●**Depression.** Dr. Falk uses amino acids, herbs, vitamins and minerals that enable the patient's body to create more of its own neurotransmitters, which can affect mood and concentration. For example, the supplement *5-hydroxytryptophan* (5-HTP) is converted by the body into the mood-boosting neurotransmitter *serotonin*, usually without side effects.

The Awesome Healing Power of "Blended" Medicine

Brent A. Bauer, MD, director of the Complementary and Integrative Medicine Program and a physician in the department of internal medicine at the Mayo Clinic in Rochester, Minnesota. A professor of medicine at Mayo Medical School, also in Rochester, he has studied complementary medicine for 20 years and is medical editor of the *Mayo Clinic Book of Alternative Medicine* (Time).

The disciplines of conventional and so-called complementary medicine used to inhabit separate worlds.

Today: With more and more Americans embracing elements from both worlds, an increasing number of physicians are prescribing a combination of both conventional and complementary treatments—an approach known as "blended" medicine.

Blended treatments that you should know about…

HIGH CHOLESTEROL

Every year, about 1 million Americans have a heart attack, and nearly half a million die from heart disease—in part, because of uncontrolled high cholesterol.

Conventional approach: The use of cholesterol-lowering statin drugs, such as *pravastatin* (Pravachol) and *atorvastatin* (Lipitor). People who take these medicines and modify their diets can sometimes reduce their risk for a heart attack by 25% to 50%.

Drawbacks: Statins, particularly in higher doses, can cause severe muscle pain and other side effects in up to 30% of patients. Also, statins have little effect on triglycerides, another type of blood fat that's linked to heart disease.

Blended approach: By using plant stanols and sterols (modified plant extracts found in a number of "functional" foods, including butter substitutes such as Benecol and Promise activ Light), people with mildly elevated cholesterol often can control their cholesterol levels.

People with higher cholesterol levels can combine one of the butter substitutes described above with a statin drug for better results than from either treatment alone. In some cases, the medication dosage can be reduced, which lowers the risk for drug side effects.

For example, people who eat the equivalent of three pats of one of these butter substitutes daily can achieve reductions of 10% to 20% in LDL "bad" cholesterol—in addition to the reductions achieved with medications.

Helpful: So many people with high cholesterol also have elevated triglycerides—fish oil (1,000 mg to 3,000 mg per day from a supplement) can decrease triglycerides by up to 50% in some patients.*

Remember: When striving to reduce cholesterol levels, start out by exercising regularly and following a healthful diet, such as the Mediterranean diet.

For easy ways to adopt a Mediterranean eating plan, see page 100.

BACK PAIN

Four out of five Americans suffer from back pain (due to injury, back strain or a herniated disk, for example) at some time in their lives.

Conventional approach: A combination of short-term rest, mild exercise (such as stretching) and nonsteroidal anti-inflammatory drugs (NSAIDs), such as *ibuprofen* (Motrin). Less often, surgery is required for conditions such as a herniated disk.

Drawbacks: Conventional treatments are only modestly successful for most patients.

Blended approach: Acupuncture—combined with the use of other medical treatments, including physical therapy and pain medications. The patients who get six to eight acupuncture

---

*Consult your physician before trying any of the dietary supplements described in this article.

treatments, usually done once or twice a week, often achieve long-lasting relief—although some require monthly "tune-ups" to stay pain-free.

The National Institutes of Health has concluded that acupuncture is often effective for low-back pain.

Good news: Many insurance companies cover the cost of acupuncture as a treatment for back pain.

Also helpful: An herb known as devil's claw is very popular in Europe for low-back pain. Now, more than a dozen reputable studies show that it's effective—and it's less likely than ibuprofen or other drugs to cause side effects, including gastrointestinal upset. Follow the label directions.

To relieve osteoarthritis: Consider trying devil's claw by itself or in conjunction with heat and cold therapy…exercise…glucosamine and chondroitin supplements (*typical dose:* 1,500 mg of glucosamine and 1,200 mg of chondroitin daily)…and over-the-counter anti-inflammatory medication.

When buying devil's claw, look for a product that is standardized to contain 50 mg to 100 mg of *harpagoside* (that's the active anti-inflammatory ingredient). Check the product label for dosage instructions.

ANXIETY DISORDERS

One of the most common psychiatric problems in the US, anxiety disorders can lead to a variety of symptoms, including heart palpitations and a persistent fear and worry in situations that would not feel threatening to most people. Only a minority of patients ever seek treatment—and those who do often have limited success.

Conventional approach: In addition to counseling, some patients may be advised to take a benzodiazepine tranquilizer, such as *diazepam* (Valium) or *lorazepam* (Ativan). Or they might be given a prescription for an antidepressant, a beta-blocker or another drug to help relieve anxiety.

Drawbacks: Many psychiatric drugs cause side effects, including sedation, weight gain or problems with libido and sexual function. Anxiety medications can be addictive.

Blended approach: Meditation—with or without drug therapy—has a strong record of success in treating anxiety. Studies show that people who meditate for 20 minutes at least once a day experience less anxiety (and less depression).

Some breathing exercises also fight anxiety. One of the easiest involves taking a series of deep breaths, holding them briefly and then slowly exhaling.

What to do: Inhale through the nose for a count of four…hold your breath for a count of seven…then exhale through the mouth for a count of eight.

Important: Individuals who meditate or do breathing exercises for longer periods—and more often—tend to experience less anxiety overall than those who do it for less time.

Also helpful: Kava, an herbal supplement. Some studies show that it's about as effective as benzodiazepines for anxiety. Follow dosage instructions on the label.

Important: The FDA issued a warning in 2002 that kava had been linked to liver damage. Although it can be effective for many patients with anxiety disorders, kava should be used only under a doctor's supervision.

FATIGUE

Often due to stress or poor sleep habits, fatigue also can be caused by underlying health problems.

Conventional approach: Patients who experience severe and frequent fatigue should get a complete medical workup (your doctor will recommend specific tests) because it can be caused by literally hundreds of disorders.

Drawbacks: Unless your doctor can identify a specific underlying cause for fatigue, the treatment options are limited. People usually are advised to exercise more and get sufficient sleep—but that doesn't work for everyone.

Blended approach: Ginseng, an herb that has traditionally been used by athletes to improve stamina, seems to help many patients with fatigue.

Look for the American form of ginseng with at least 5% *ginsenosides* (the active chemical ingredient). Follow the dosage directions on the label.

Health Web Sites You Can Trust

Suzy Cohen, RPh, a pharmacist, syndicated health subject journalist, author of *The 24-Hour Pharmacist* (HarperCollins) and *Drug Muggers* (DPI). Her Web site features articles and videos on hundreds of health topics, streaming news on medical issues, and a special focus on the sensible use of medications and dietary and herbal supplements, *www.dearpharmacist.com.*

It can be very tricky to search the Internet for answers to health questions—because mixed in with a bounty of valid information are countless unsubstantiated claims and even some downright dangerous advice.

Best: Put your faith in the following reliable Web sites. *For information on...*

DIAGNOSIS AND TREATMENT
www.mayoclinic.com

• **Reports on symptoms,** causes, complications, tests, treatments and coping strategies for thousands of illnesses.

• **Multimedia presentations.**

• **Links to disease-specific organizations.**

Click-worthy: "Health Manager," a free personalized program for monitoring and managing your own and your family's health.

DRUGS AND SUPPLEMENTS
www.drugs.com

• **Consumer-friendly information** on uses, dosages, side effects and contraindications for prescription and nonprescription drugs, herbs and dietary supplements.

• **Interactions checker**—to see if the effect of a particular drug is altered when it is taken with another drug, supplement or food.

• **New drug approvals and alerts from the FDA.**

Click-worthy: The "Pill identifier" (including photos) that searches by color, shape and/or imprint.

INTEGRATIVE MEDICINE
www.naturalstandard.com

• **Free e-newsletter.**

• **Blogs and newsfeed.**

• **Comprehensive databases on thousands of herbs and supplements** (requires a paid subscription).

Click-worthy: Webinars on alternative medicine topics.

LIFESTYLE AND SPIRITUAL WELL-BEING
www.lifescript.com

• **Blogs from doctors,** psychologists, nutritionists, experts on fitness and alternative health-care providers.

• **Calculators for body mass index, calorie burn and more.**

• **Six free e-newsletters.**

Click-worthy: Quizzes that test your knowledge (for instance, on acupuncture or hygiene) or evaluate your risk (such as for cancer or depression).

NATURAL HEALTH AND HEALING
www.naturalnews.com

• **Breaking news reports.**

• **Cartoons and satire.**

• **"Citizen journalism" program** that invites articles from independent writers.

Click-worthy: Podcasts from author Mike Adams (aka "the Health Ranger") interviewing preeminent experts on alternative medicine.

SCIENTIFIC STUDIES
www.pubmed.gov

• **More than 19 million citations for biomedical articles** dating back to 1948.

• **Interactive tutorials** on newsworthy topics, such as flu outbreaks.

• **MedlinePlus, consumer-friendly articles on health-related subjects.**

Click-worthy: ClinicalTrials.gov, a locator for studies recruiting participants.

SYMPTOM IDENTIFICATION
www.healthcentral.com

• **Health and drug library.**

• **Expert Q & A.**

• **Community of members** who share experiences and advice.

Click-worthy: "Check a Symptom," a step-by-step function that leads you through a diagnostic process and treatment options.

3

Simple Solutions

Hooray! Home Remedies For Headaches

Next time your head begins to ache, instead of popping that pain pill, try all-natural remedies. Science cannot explain why these alternative approaches work—but they have stood the test of time, have no side effects and often work faster than drugs.

Caution: If headaches recur regularly or are severe, seek professional medical help.

Most of the categories below include several options. Try one or more remedies to see which work best for you. Products are sold in health-food stores.

•**Acupressure.** Clip a clothespin to the earlobe that is closest to your headache and leave on for one minute.

•**Stick out your tongue about one-half inch, and bite down as hard as you comfortably can**...continue for five minutes.

•**Ask your partner or a friend to slowly move one thumb down the right side of your back,** heading from your shoulder blade toward your waist and stopping to exert steady pressure for one minute on any tender spots.

•**Aromatherapy.** Rub a dab of rosemary or peppermint essential oil (properly diluted in a carrier oil) on your forehead, temples and behind the ears...and inhale the fumes from the open bottle four times.

Caution: Never place undiluted essential oil directly on the skin.

•**Crumple a fresh, clean mint leaf, roll it up and gently insert it into one nostril** (leaving a bit sticking out for easy removal)...remove after two to three minutes.

•**Boil one cup of water mixed with one cup of apple cider vinegar**...remove from

Joan Wilen and Lydia Wilen, folk-remedy experts based in New York City. The sisters are coauthors of many books, including *Bottom Line's Secret Food Cures* and *Bottom Line's Treasury of Home Remedies and Natural Cures* (both from Bottom Line Books, *www. bottomlinesecrets.com/store).*

53

heat...drape a towel over your head to trap steam and bend over the pot...breathe deeply through your nose for five minutes.

• **Compress.** Soak a white cotton scarf in distilled white vinegar and wring it out...tie it around your forehead as tightly as possible without causing discomfort...leave in place for 15 to 30 minutes.

• **Food.** Eat an apple, a cup of strawberries, a handful of raw almonds (chew thoroughly), one teaspoon of *gomasio* (Japanese sesame salt), or one teaspoon of honey mixed with one-half teaspoon of garlic juice.

• **Drink a cup of chamomile tea.**

• **Water.** Fill a sink with water that is as hot as you can tolerate and dunk your hands for one minute.

• **Fill a bathtub ankle-high with very cold water**...dress warmly but leave feet bare... walk around in the tub until feet start to feel warm (from one to a maximum of three minutes)...then get out, dry your feet, slip under the bedcovers and relax.

Natural Rx for Back Pain

Acupuncture relieves back pain better than standard treatment.

Recent finding: After receiving acupuncture for chronic back pain for eight weeks, 60% of study participants experienced significant improvement in their levels of functioning, compared with 39% who continued usual care, including medications and doctor visits.

Daniel C. Cherkin, PhD, senior scientific investigator, Group Health Research Institute, Seattle, and principal investigator on a study of acupuncture's effect on back pain, published in *Archives of Internal Medicine*.

Better Than Meds for Back Problems

Yoga is better than pills for low-back pain. Patients having mild-to-moderate chronic low-back pain took 90-minute classes twice a week of Iyengar yoga, doing 31 postures that relax and align the spine.

After 24 weeks: The yoga group reported significantly better function, mood and pain relief than patients who got standard care, including drugs.

Kimberly Williams, PhD, research assistant professor, department of community medicine, West Virginia University, Morgantown, and leader of a study of 90 people.

Surprising Places That Hide Cold and Flu Germs...and Other Dangerous Bacteria

Elizabeth Scott, PhD, assistant professor of biology and codirector of the Center for Hygiene & Health in Home & Community at Simmons College in Boston (see *www.simmons.edu/hygieneandhealth*). A member of the scientific advisory board of the International Forum on Home Hygiene, she is coauthor of *How to Prevent Food Poisoning: A Practical Guide to Safe Cooking, Eating and Food Handling* (Wiley).

Everyone recognizes that the virus that causes swine flu (H1N1) is easily transmitted person to person. As a protective measure, even hand shaking and "cheek kissing" have at times been temporarily banned in some churches, schools and other public places.

But the H1N1 and seasonal flu viruses can often be found in places that many people would never even suspect. This is also true of other harmful microbes, such as *methicillin-resistant Staphylococcus aureus* (MRSA) bacteria, and bacteria, including *Escherichia coli* and *salmonella*, that cause foodborne illness.

What you may not know: It's been estimated that about one in three Americans are carriers (and transmitters) of staph bacteria—usually in amounts so small that no infection occurs in the carrier.

Since it is impossible to completely avoid dangerous microbes, one of the best ways to stay healthy is to be aware of the germ "hot spots"—including ones that often are overlooked, such as...

•**Telephone receivers (and cell phones), TV remote controls, computer keyboards and copying machines.** Most of us know to wash our hands after touching public doorknobs or handrails, but we may not consider the microbes on telephone receivers (and cell phones), TV remote controls and computer keyboards in public places, at work or even in our own homes.

Other areas to be wary of include the control buttons on office copying machines, handles of communal coffeepots, elevator buttons and shared books or tools.

It's best to assume that any inanimate surface—such as Formica, stainless steel or even paper—that could have been touched by another person may be infected with viruses or bacteria. If you touch your mouth, nose and/or eyes (the body's main entry points for infectious organisms) after touching the infected surface, you may be exposed to the germ.

Cold viruses and many bacterial infections are primarily transmitted by such surface contact. Flu viruses—including the H1N1 and seasonal flu—tend to be transmitted through the air (via coughs and sneezes) but also can be passed through surface contact.

What you may not know: Since bacteria and cold and flu viruses can survive for up to several days on inanimate surfaces, you can be exposed to germs long after the infected person has contaminated the area. Scientists have estimated that 80% of all human infections are transmitted via hand-to-hand or surface contact.

Self-defense: After touching inanimate surfaces (such as those described earlier) in a public place—or at home, if someone in your household is sick—wash your hands thoroughly with plain soap for 20 seconds under running water. Then dry them off thoroughly with a paper towel or air dryer.

Or apply hand-sanitizing gel containing at least 62% alcohol, such as Purell Instant Hand Sanitizer or Germ-X, as soon as possible after touching such surfaces.

If someone in your home or office is sick: Each day, clean surfaces that are touched by others with a cleansing wipe or other product (such as those made by Lysol or Clorox) that is registered with the Environmental Protection Agency (EPA)—check the product label for an EPA registration number. This means the product can be used as a disinfectant. Or simply squirt alcohol-based hand sanitizer on a paper towel and wipe the surface.

Important: Use wipes and gels that kill bacteria and viruses. These broader-spectrum cleansers are sometimes labeled "antimicrobial"—not "antibacterial."

•**Paper money.** A recent Swiss study found that some strains of flu virus can survive on paper money for up to three days—and for up to 17 days when mixed with mucus.

In addition, a University of California researcher cultured 68 $1 bills and found that all but four had colonies of dangerous bacteria, including the variety that cause staph infections and pneumonia. Coins tend to have lower levels of bacteria and viruses—perhaps because they contain trace metals that help inhibit such microbes.

Self-defense: To reduce your exposure to germs, use credit or debit cards in place of paper currency as often as possible during daily transactions, and wash your hands with soap or use a hand sanitizer after touching paper money.

•**In doctors' waiting rooms.** Studies have found that germs are transmitted at a particularly high rate in the waiting areas of doctors' offices—especially by touching countertops, pens and even magazines.

Self-defense: As much as possible, avoid touching shared surfaces (such as those described above), and wash your hands immediately after your doctor visit.

If hand-washing is inconvenient, keep hand sanitizer in your pocket or purse and carry your own pen to sign papers at doctors' offices and stores.

●**Pets.** An increasing amount of evidence shows that dogs—and cats, especially—carry MRSA bacteria. It's believed that these animals are exposed to the germs by human carriers and that the bacteria contaminate the animals' coats, skin and saliva, where it can then be transmitted to other animals and people. MRSA bacteria can, of course, infect humans, but it also can make cats and dogs sick.

Important new finding: A recent random study conducted at the University of Guelph in Canada found that 2% to 3% of dogs carry MRSA bacteria. Meanwhile, in a study of 35 homes, researchers from Simmons College in Boston discovered that people who have cats in their homes are eight times more likely to have MRSA bacteria on household surfaces than those without household cats.

Self-defense: Wash your hands or use a hand sanitizer after touching your pet…make sure any cuts or abrasions you may have are covered with a bandage before touching an animal…do not let pets lick your face…wash pets' food and water bowls in a sink separate from the one used to prepare your own food…and wear gloves whenever touching an animal that has an open wound.

●**Microwave ovens, countertops and salt and pepper shakers.** Most of us know that we need to clean kitchen faucet handles and sinks, sponges and cutting boards to avoid exposure to foodborne microbes. However, some surfaces tend to be overlooked, such as microwave oven controls—which are touched frequently, often while the users are handling raw food—and countertops, which are high-contact areas for raw food. Research shows that salt and pepper shakers also are likely to be contaminated.

Self-defense: Immediately after preparing any raw food—including fruit and vegetables as well as meat, fish or poultry—wipe down any surfaces you may touch (such as microwave controls, countertops and salt and pepper shakers) with antimicrobial cleanser, or use a mixture of one part household bleach diluted in 10 parts water. Apply the cleanser

with paper towels or disposable rags. If you use sponges, put them in the dishwasher each time you run it—or rinse, then microwave them for one minute at high power several times a week. Do not place sponges that contain metal fibers in the microwave.

●**Bathroom sink handles.** In one survey of the homes of 30 adults with colds, bathroom sink handles were identified as the place most likely to harbor traces of cold virus.

Self-defense: If anyone in your family has a cold or flu—or any other respiratory, skin or gastrointestinal infection—clean bathroom sink handles (as well as other potentially contaminated objects, such as doorknobs and light switches) at least once daily with antimicrobial cleanser.

An Amazing Vitamin That Boosts Your Cold- And Flu-Fighting Defenses

In a study of 19,000 people, those with the lowest blood levels of vitamin D—less than 10 nanograms per milliliter (ng/mL)—were 36% more likely to report a recent respiratory infection (such as a cold or flu) than those with the highest levels—30 ng/mL or higher. People with lung disease (such as asthma or emphysema) were at greatest risk.

Theory: Vitamin D may play an important role in the body's immunity.

Self-defense: In addition to vitamin D from sun exposure, aim to get a total of 1,000 international units (IU) to 2,000 IU daily of vitamin D from food (such as eggs and fatty fish) and supplements.

Adit Ginde, MD, MPH, assistant professor, division of emergency medicine, University of Colorado Denver School of Medicine, Aurora.

A Simple Way to Combat Colds

The less sleep you have, the higher your chances of catching a cold. People who get fewer than seven hours of sleep a night are almost three times as likely to develop cold symptoms as people who sleep for eight hours or more. The percentage of time in bed spent asleep—known as sleep efficiency—matters, too. People with a sleep efficiency of 85% or less are five times as likely to develop cold symptoms as those with higher efficiency.

Sheldon Cohen, PhD, Robert E. Doherty Professor of Psychology, Carnegie Mellon University, Pittsburgh, and leader of a study of 153 people, published in *Archives of Internal Medicine*.

Think Twice Before Using Zinc

Zinc cold remedies can permanently damage sense of smell after just one use. Nasal gels containing zinc can damage the nerve at the top of the nose. Some people recover at least part of their sense of smell after discontinuing zinc nasal gels, but it could take five years or more.

Possibly helpful to restore sense of smell: Vitamins B-1 and folic acid—but studies are not conclusive.

Alan Hirsch, MD, founder and neurological director of the Smell & Taste Treatment and Research Foundation, Chicago, *www.smellandtaste.org*.

Sprouts Boost Antioxidants 200%!

In a recent study, it was found that people who ate seven ounces of broccoli sprouts daily for three days had up to a 200% increase in the production of antioxidant enzymes in the nasal passages. The antioxidants help to fight off the inflammation that contributes to allergy symptoms. Broccoli sprouts are very high in *sulforaphane*, which starts a process that leads to the antioxidant increase.

Marc A. Riedl, MD, researcher, department of medicine, section of clinical immunology and allergy at University of California, Los Angeles, and a coauthor of a study published in *Clinical Immunology*.

New Help for Chronic Sinus Infections: The Little-Known Cause 93% Of the Time!

Jordan S. Josephson, MD, an ear, nose and throat specialist in private practice in New York City. He is director of the New York Nasal and Sinus Center and an attending physician at Manhattan Eye, Ear and Throat Hospital, both in New York City. He is author of *Sinus Relief Now* (Perigee). His Web site is *www.drjjny.com*.

Chronic sinusitis is the most common of long-term diseases in the US. Even though more than half of all cases of sinusitis do clear up on their own within two weeks, about 40 million Americans develop the chronic variety.

What happens: The sinuses, four pairs of cavities in the skull that filter and warm air as it passes through the nose on its way to the lungs, are lined with mucus-producing tissue. The tissue typically produces more than a quart of mucus a day, which drains through tiny holes into the back of the throat. When these holes are blocked, mucus cannot drain properly. These holes often become blocked when the tissues swell during an allergy flare-up or an upper-respiratory infection.

Result: Facial pain, headache, fatigue, nasal and ear congestion, postnasal drip, cough, snoring, nosebleeds and a reduced sense of smell or taste, along with other coldlike symptoms. As mucus accumulates, it provides an optimal environment for bacterial or fungal growth. The resulting infection can further irritate and inflame sinus tissues.

DO ANTIBIOTICS WORK?

Sinusitis is defined as "chronic" when it lasts for more than four weeks or keeps coming back. For many patients, sinusitis is a lifelong disease. The symptoms might come and go, but the underlying problems persist. Patients need to manage it daily just as they would any other chronic disease, such as diabetes or arthritis. A total cure is unlikely—but with the right medical treatment, patients can expect a significant improvement in quality of life.

A short-term course of antibiotics usually will help eliminate a case of acute sinusitis (assuming that the infection is bacterial), but this rarely works for chronic sinusitis.

Reason: Most cases are multifactorial. Patients with a bacterial infection might simultaneously harbor viruses or mold, organisms that aren't affected by antibiotics. A Mayo Clinic study found that 93% of all chronic sinus disease cases are caused by fungus (mold) found in the nasal passages. The mold can cause persistent infection. Even in the absence of infection, mold spores can stimulate an allergic reaction that causes persistent congestion.

Antibiotics can make a difference in patients with chronic sinusitis, but only when they are used for three to eight weeks. The same is true of anti-fungal sprays or oral drugs. Long-term therapy (up to three months) usually is required.

Recommended: Regardless of the underlying cause, most patients can get some relief with prescription steroid nasal sprays. Decongestants (oral or spray) also can be helpful but should not be used for more than 48 hours without your doctor's approval. Nasal irrigation (see page 59) is among the best ways to promote mucus drainage and relieve sinusitis symptoms.

DAILY CARE

Every patient with a history of chronic sinusitis needs to be alert to lifestyle factors that increase congestion and symptom flare-ups. *Important...*

•**Track your diet.** Even patients without clear-cut food allergies may find that they produce more mucus when they eat certain foods, such as dairy or foods with gluten or certain sugars, including high-fructose corn syrup. I advise them to keep a food diary for a month or more. Write down everything that you eat and drink, and make a note when your sinuses feel worse. When you suspect that a certain food is causing problems, give it up for a few weeks and see if you feel better.

•**Take control of allergies,** as they are among the main triggers for sinusitis. When you have an allergy flare-up—whether from pollen, animal dander or anything else—treat it promptly with an antihistamine to keep mucus from building up.

•**Blow your nose gently.** Blow one nostril at a time. This is more effective than blowing both at once.

•**Clean your house and car.** Any area that's moist, such as the bathroom or under the refrigerator, can harbor mold spores that irritate sinus tissues. Clean these areas well with soap and water or a commercial mold-killing solution. Don't neglect your car. Cars trap humidity as well as heat, both of which encourage mold growth. Keep the seats and dashboard clean.

SINUS SURGERY

Some patients might require surgery to restore normal drainage. Endoscopic sinus surgery (or sinoscopy) is currently the standard approach. First, a thin tube is inserted through the nostrils. Then surgical instruments are used to remove blockages and sometimes to remove bone to enlarge the sinus openings. The procedure is done in an operating-room setting. Typically, you are home that night and back to work the next day with minimal discomfort that rarely requires more than Tylenol.

Recently, surgeons have added balloon sinuplasty to the standard procedure. A guide wire is used to position a deflated balloon inside the sinus openings. Then the balloon is inflated, which enlarges the openings and promotes better drainage, without removing tissue. It is appropriate in only about 10% or fewer of total cases—usually those involving a less severe condition.

Important: Most patients improve significantly after surgery, but few achieve a total remission of symptoms. Most still will need occasional help from steroid nasal sprays, decongestants, etc.

More from Dr. Jordan Josephson...

How to Cleanse Your Nasal Passages

Irrigating the nose once or twice per day is among the best ways to cause sinus drainage. This helps relieve symptoms, and it also can prevent sinusitis from getting started.

A neti pot (available at most pharmacies and health-food stores) is an effective irrigation tool. It's an ancient Indian device that has a tapered conical tip at the spout end. You also will need saline solution. You can buy prepared sterile saline from most pharmacies. Or you can make your own saline. Bring eight ounces of distilled water to a boil, add one-quarter teaspoon of salt to the water, and let the mixture cool.

Fill the pot with the cooled saline. Tilt your head to one side, and gently insert the spout of the neti pot into the raised upper nostril. Continue to breathe through your mouth, and slowly pour the saline into your upper nostril. The saline should pour through the upper nostril and out the other lower nostril into the sink (you also can try this in the shower).

When you're done, compress one nostril at a time by placing pressure on it with your finger and then blow your other nostril by exhaling firmly several times.

Then reverse the tilt of your head and repeat the process on the other side by pouring saline into the other nostril.

Swine Flu vs. Seasonal Flu

Rebecca Shannonhouse, editor, *Bottom Line/Health*, Boardroom Inc., 281 Tresser Blvd., Stamford, Connecticut 06901.

Swine flu can present a diagnostic challenge in hospital emergency rooms and doctors' offices.

Both swine flu and the normal, seasonal flu typically cause a cough, shortness of breath and other respiratory symptoms. Fever is another hallmark of flu, although it may occur less often with swine flu.

What's different: The seasonal flu is highly unlikely to cause gastrointestinal (GI) problems, such as diarrhea and nausea. But 20% to 40% of patients with swine flu exhibit such symptoms.

The quick tests (using nasal discharge samples) don't help. On average, they fail to detect 40% to 50% of flu cases. Even when a patient tests positive, the quick tests can't distinguish the different types of flu.

"You don't need tests," says Neil Schachter, MD, medical director of respiratory care for Mount Sinai Medical Center in New York City. "If it looks like flu, and the patient has been around other people who have the flu, then we assume that's what it is."

The antiviral drugs *oseltamivir* (Tamiflu) and *zanamivir* (Relenza) can be used for both types of flu, but doctors are more likely to prescribe them for swine flu because of fears that, if left untreated, the virus will become more lethal.

Important: Drug treatment should begin within 48 hours of the onset of flu symptoms. Patients should not wait if they suspect they have swine flu. Consult a doctor right away.

Folk Remedy More Effective Than Drugs For Swine Flu

Chemical compounds in a plant called *ferula asafoetida* were more effective against the swine flu (H1N1) virus than an antiviral drug in laboratory research. Ferula asafoetida has been used in folk medicine for so many years, including during the 1918 Spanish flu epidemic. Compounds in the plant could become the basis for new antiviral medicines.

Fang-Rong Chang, MD, and Yang-Chang Wu, MD, researchers, Kaohsiung Medical University, Taiwan, and correspondent authors of a study published in the American Chemical Society's *Journal of Natural Products*.

Statins Protect Against Flu Complications

Statins may help patients survive flu. People already taking cholesterol-lowering drugs when they were hospitalized with flu were half as likely to die as those not using these medicines.

Theory: Statins also reduce inflammation—and much of the damage from flu comes from inflammation.

Ann Thomas, MD, public health physician, Oregon Public Health Division, Portland, and leader of a study of 2,800 people, presented at a medical meeting in Philadelphia.

Five Signs the Flu Is Getting Worse

If you have the flu, be on the lookout for the following symptoms...trouble breathing, severe coughing, drinking much less than usual, less frequent urination, extreme irritability. See your doctor if these symptoms develop. If a child gets the flu, seems to recover and symptoms reappear, that could indicate complications, such as bacterial pneumonia—contact your pediatrician.

William Schaffner, MD, professor and chairman of the department of preventive medicine and professor of medicine in the division of infectious diseases, Vanderbilt University School of Medicine, Nashville. He also serves on the board of directors of the National Foundation for Infectious Diseases.

Aspirin May Cut Asthma Risk

Among healthy women age 45 and older, those who took a low dose of aspirin (100 mg) every other day were 10% less likely to develop asthma within 10 years than women who took a placebo.

But: In previous studies, aspirin worsened asthma symptoms in women who already had this condition.

Best: Discuss aspirin use with your doctor.

Tobias Kurth, MD, ScD, associate epidemiologist at Brigham and Women's Hospital, Boston, and leader of a study of 37,270 women.

Asthma Sufferers Get Relief from Antifungal Drug

Up to half of all adults with severe asthma are allergic to airborne fungi, which can worsen asthma.

Recent research: In a study of 58 patients with severe asthma and a fungal allergy (determined from skin and blood testing), one group took the oral antifungal drug *itraconazole* (Sporanax)—200 mg twice daily—and the rest took a placebo for 32 weeks.

Result: Within the drug group, 62% reported significant improvement in lung function, while the placebo group reported a worsening of lung function.

If you have both severe asthma and a fungal allergy: Ask your doctor if itraconazole is right for you.

David Denning, MD, professor of medicine and medical mycology, University of Manchester, UK.

Papaya Spells Relief

Reduce bloating, gas and indigestion with papain supplements. Papain, from papaya, can bring relief when the pancreas doesn't produce enough of the proteolytic enzymes needed to digest proteins. Take as directed at least 10 minutes prior to a meal.

Caution: Consult a physician before taking papain if you are taking a blood thinner. People who are allergic to latex also may be allergic to papaya.

Vegetarian Times, 300 N. Continental Blvd., El Segundo, California 90245, *www.vegetariantimes.com.*

Overindulged at The Buffet? Get Homeopathic Help

A good remedy to keep in your medicine cabinet is *nux vomica*. It effectively treats indigestion as well as constipation, especially when these two uncomfortable problems are caused by overindulgence. When you experience symptoms, dissolve three 30C pellets of nux vomica under your tongue. If you do not feel better within 45 minutes, repeat the dosage once or twice more. Do not exceed three doses in one day. Homeopathic remedies are sold at health-food stores and online.

Edward Shalts, MD, DHt (diplomate in homeotherapeutics), a private practitioner in New York City and the author of two books, including *Easy Homeopathy* (McGraw-Hill). His Web site is *www.homeopathynewyork.com.*

Beware of Medicated Creams and Gels: Common OTC Products Can Be Risky

Francesca Fusco, MD, a dermatologist in private practice and assistant clinical professor of dermatology at Mount Sinai School of Medicine, both in New York City.

Each day, we bombard our bodies with a variety of chemical-containing topical products—this includes most shampoos, bath soaps, moisturizing lotions, shaving gels, makeup products and colognes.

In addition, many of us compound the situation by applying a variety of medicated gels, creams and lotions to our bodies.

Problem: Even though our skin provides a barrier against most irritants, it naturally thins as we age—allowing for easier absorption of dangerous chemicals contained in seemingly harmless over-the-counter (OTC) products.

For people who have eczema, risk is even greater, as this skin condition causes microscopic cracks in the skin that allow chemicals to penetrate more easily and enter the bloodstream. Even the tiny cracks that occur in everyone with dry winter skin can provide entry points for chemicals. *What you need to know to safely use…*

MUSCLE CREAMS

Methyl salicylate, also known as wintergreen oil, is the active pain-killing ingredient in most OTC muscle creams, including Ben-Gay and Icy Hot. Used properly, these products can help alleviate sore muscles, but too much can be dangerous—or even deadly.

Frightening incident: A New York City high school track star died in 2007 after applying excessive amounts of methyl salicylate–containing ointment to her sore muscles.

The New York Medical Examiner's Office concluded that the methyl salicylate had accumulated due to its repeated use. Some doctors speculated that the methyl salicylate had possibly interacted with unidentified aspirin-based medications that she may have been using, leading to cardiac arrest.

For safe use: Apply a small amount (not to exceed the size of a quarter) onto the painful joint or muscle no more than three or four times a day.

Good rule of thumb: If you use more than a four-ounce tube within a week, that's probably too much.

Caution: The FDA warns that methyl salicylate–containing products should not be used for more than seven days and should not be applied to wounds or under a tight bandage. Also, watch your aspirin intake (do not exceed the daily dose on the label) and be aware that these creams may compound the effects of blood-thinning drugs, such as *clopidogrel*

(Plavix) or *warfarin* (Coumadin), and supplements with blood-thinning effects, including vitamin E, ginkgo biloba and fish oil.

ANTIBIOTIC OINTMENTS

We apply OTC *neomycin* and *bacitracin* to minor cuts, scrapes and burns to kill germs, but few people realize that up to 10% of users are actually allergic to such products.

The allergies are easily missed because the redness or rash that results may be mistaken for a worsening of the original problem. This often prompts the user to apply even more ointment.

For safe use: If your skin looks like it's getting worse or develops a rash, stop using the product and call your physician for treatment advice. If you have a cut, scrape or burn, you may be better off trying an ointment that contains vitamins A and D or products such as Vaseline or Aquaphor Healing Ointment—all of which keep the wound moist without irritating it.

NUMBING CREAMS

The numbing creams and patches are used as topical anesthetics for medical procedures (such as removing a mole) or cosmetic procedures (such as laser hair removal). Most OTC varieties contain small amounts (less than 5%) of the active ingredient—such as *lidocaine, benzocaine* or *tetracaine.*

When used according to package instructions, these products are safe, but if your skin becomes too numb, you're at risk for injury due to lack of sensation to trauma or heat. That is why you need to let your doctor or aesthetician know if you lose all feeling in the affected area during such a procedure.

Numbing creams also may cause an allergic reaction and can be absorbed systemically, leading to a toxic reaction, such as a slowed heart rate, a decrease in blood pressure, confusion, tremors or convulsions.

For safe use: Apply these creams sparingly.

AGE-SPOT CREAMS

The OTC age-spot fading creams promise to lighten age spots, but such products that contain *hydroquinone* actually may have the opposite effect in some individuals—especially those who have dark skin—causing *ochronosis* (darkening of the skin).

For safe use: If you use a topical product that contains hydroquinone, do so only under a doctor's supervision.

HYDROCORTISONE

Used as a topical product, *hydrocortisone* offers an anti-inflammatory effect that helps to relieve itching caused by chronic skin conditions (such as eczema), poison ivy, contact dermatitis, insect bites and hemorrhoids. OTC topical steroids typically contain just 1% hydrocortisone, which is usually safe.

However, these products often penetrate more deeply in such regions as the eyelids, armpits and groin, where skin is thinner and more folds exist, causing irritation and other local adverse effects, such as increased hair growth, acne or changes in pigmentation. If applied frequently and in excessive amounts, topical hydrocortisone can be absorbed into the bloodstream.

For safe use: If you notice any of the adverse effects described above in the areas to which you have applied hydrocortisone, stop using the product and see your doctor for treatment advice.

Bleach Baths Ease Eczema

Twice weekly, eczema patients soaked for five to 10 minutes in a tub of water mixed with very diluted bleach. After three months, 67% showed improvement, compared with 15% of patients who bathed in plain water.

Theory: Bleach kills the staph bacteria that often accompany eczema and cause painful lesions.

Safety: Use no more than one-half cup of bleach per 40 gallons of water...do not let any bleach bathwater enter the eyes or mouth... *never* apply undiluted bleach to skin.

Amy Paller, MD, chair, dermatology department, Northwestern University Feinberg School of Medicine, Chicago, and leader of a study of 31 eczema patients.

Wart Be Gone!

A natural remedy for warts is aloe vera. Use a cotton swab or cotton ball to dab the juice of the aloe vera plant on the wart. Do this daily until the wart disappears. Natural acids in aloe vera juice dissolve the wart and soften the skin.

Joan Wilen and Lydia Wilen, folk-remedy experts, New York City, and coauthors of *Secret Food Cures* and *Treasury of Home Remedies and Natural Cures* (Bottom Line Books, *www.bottomlinesecrets.com/store*).

How Video Games Can *Improve* Your Vision

In one study of 22 adults, participants who played an action video game for 50 hours during nine weeks had a 43% improvement in contrast sensitivity—one of the first visual abilities to decline with age—while those who played a slow-moving video game did not improve. The benefits lasted for several months after the study.

Theory: Action video games fine-tune the visual-processing pathways in the brain for challenging visual tasks, such as night driving.

Daphne Bavelier, PhD, professor of brain and cognitive sciences, University of Rochester, New York.

Tinnitus Prevention

Attending a *single* loud concert can cause tinnitus (ringing in the ears), especially if you are sitting or standing close to the powerful speakers placed near the stage and around the venue. Any exposure to noise above 115 decibels can cause tinnitus—or even permanent hearing loss. At a rock concert, you can be exposed to this level of noise for two to three hours.

Self-defense: Wear earplugs throughout the concert—but even they may not help if you are right in front of the speakers.

There is no definite treatment for tinnitus, but sometimes it disappears spontaneously. If the condition persists, see your doctor.

Murray Grossan, MD, otolaryngologist and head and neck surgeon at Tower Ear, Nose and Throat Clinic, Cedars-Sinai Medical Center, Los Angeles.

Eardrops Beat Antibiotics For Swimmer's Ear

Often prescribed for *otitis externa* (swimmer's ear infection), oral antibiotics can lead to rashes and drug-resistant infections.

Recent finding: Topical antibiotic or antiseptic eardrops effectively treat swimmer's ear, negating the need for additional oral antibiotics unless the infection spreads.

Prevention: Mix equal parts of white vinegar and water...place three drops in each ear after swimming.

Vivek Kaushik, MD, consultant otolaryngologist for Stockport NHS Foundation Trust, Stepping Hill Hospital, Stockport, England, and leader of a review of 19 studies involving 3,382 people.

Chewing Gums That Are *Good* for Teeth

Sugar-free chewing gums that are sweetened with *xylitol* suppress the growth of cavity-producing bacteria, reduce plaque acids and strengthen teeth.

Examples: Wrigley's brands Orbit, Extra and Eclipse sugarless gums.

Chewing gums that contain *CPP-ACP* (Recaldent)—calcium derived from milk—strengthen teeth by remineralizing tooth enamel more than regular gum when chewed for 20 minutes, four times a day, for two weeks.

Examples: Trident White and Xtra Care.

To eliminate bad breath, Wrigley's Eclipse is made with magnolia bark extract, proven to decrease bacteria that cause bad breath.

UC Berkeley Wellness Letter, 500 Fifth Ave., New York City 10110, *www.wellnessletter.com.*

vitamin B-12 supplement would be appropriate for you.

Ilia Volkov, MD, faculty of health sciences, department of family medicine, Ben-Gurion University, Beer-Sheva, Israel.

Fast Fix for Dull Teeth

If your teeth are too sensitive for whitening products, makeup make them look brighter. To brighten your smile no matter what your skin color, opt for cosmetics from the cool end of the color palette.

Lipstick: Wear pinks and reds that have bluish or purplish undertones, choosing relatively dark hues that provide contrast to your teeth. Stay away from orange, coral and peach tones, which make teeth look dingy. Stick to glossy lipstick—a matte finish will age your appearance.

Face makeup: Use a subtle bronzer in powder or liquid form, but avoid those with gold or orange flecks, which make teeth look yellow.

Jewelry: Follow the cool rule here, as well, skipping gold earrings and necklaces in favor of silver.

Cathy Highland, celebrity makeup artist, Aim Artists Agency, Los Angeles, *www.aimartist.com.*

Is This Popular Supplement Causing Your Sleep Troubles?

The popular dietary supplement CoQ10 can sometimes make it difficult to fall asleep. Some people take coenzyme Q10 to prevent migraines or alleviate hypertension, congestive heart failure or other conditions.

Insomnia self-defense: Consult your physician about taking CoQ10 with breakfast and/or lunch instead of later in the day. If falling asleep is still a problem, ask whether decreasing the dosage would help.

Mark A. Stengler, NMD, naturopathic medical doctor and founder/director, La Jolla Whole Health Clinic, La Jolla, California. He also is adjunct associate clinical professor, National College of Natural Medicine, Portland, Oregon, and author of the *Bottom Line/Natural Healing* newsletter.

B-12 Blasts Canker Sores

In a six-month study of 58 people who suffered from canker sores (shallow sores in the mouth), participants took oral vitamin B-12 supplements (1,000 micrograms) or placebos nightly.

Result: By the sixth month, 74.1% of the vitamin B-12 study participants no longer had canker sores, compared with 32% of the placebo group.

Self-defense: If you experience chronic canker sores, ask your physician whether a daily

How Much Sleep Do You Really Need?

To determine how much sleep you really need, go to bed at the same time every night for a week without setting an alarm. The number of hours you sleep on the fourth night is probably the number you need to feel really refreshed and to perform at your best—make that your goal every night. Most adults function best on seven and a half to eight hours of sleep.

James B. Maas, PhD, psychology professor, Cornell University in Ithaca, New York, and author of *Power Sleep: The Revolutionary Program That Prepares Your Mind for Peak Performance* (Harper Paperbacks).

Ahhh…Healing Baths for Insomnia, Flu and More

Jamison Starbuck, ND, a naturopathic physician in family practice in Missoula, Montana. She is past president of the American Association of Naturopathic Physicians and a contributing editor to *The Alternative Advisor: The Complete Guide to Natural Therapies and Alternative Treatments* (Time Life).

A lso known as *balneotherapy*, therapeutic bathing has long been used with many forms of water—for example, hot springs, cold pools, tap or even pond water. But mineral springs are among the most well-known for their healing powers. In the 1800s, bathing in the mineral springs (also known as "taking the waters") was very fashionable, and mineral water was even bottled and sold as a medicinal beverage. Scientific evidence proving that mineral spring therapy is helpful is limited. But scientists seem to agree that balneotherapy is not harmful, and it feels good. I know people who swear that regular mineral spring soakings cured their ailments, including arthritis and fibromyalgia.

Create your very own mineral spring soak at home with just one simple and inexpensive substance—Epsom salts. In fact, Epsom salts (a four-pound container is available from most drugstores and supermarkets for less than $4*) are a mainstay of my home-treatment recommendations for patients suffering from insomnia, arthritis, fibromyalgia, flu, back strain, acute sprains, itchy dermatitis, sunburn and shingles.

Epsom salts offer you magnesium sulfate. Magnesium is essential to human health (particularly heart and muscle function) and acts as a muscle relaxant. Because magnesium is often depleted with the processing of foods, magnesium deficiency is common—it is estimated to affect more than half of Americans—and can contribute to fatigue, muscle spasm, weakness, irritability, insomnia, high blood pressure, sugar cravings and anxiety. Magnesium-rich foods, such as nuts, whole grains and blackstrap molasses…and magnesium supplements (*typical dosage:* 300 mg daily) are your best options to

*Price subject to change.

keep your magnesium levels adequate. However, soaking in a hot tub of Epsom salt water also provides some magnesium.

To create your own healing bath: Add two cups of Epsom salts to a tub of comfortably hot water, and soak for 20 minutes. At the end of your soak, moisten a washcloth with cool water and rub it all over your arms, legs and trunk for 30 seconds—to prevent chilling and promote blood circulation. Towel off and then relax by lying down for at least 30 minutes. To complete the healing environment, use low lights and/or candles, drink cool water throughout the bath and ask not to be disturbed.

People with high blood pressure or arterial disease should avoid hot mineral soaks—the hot water can aggravate these conditions. For this reason, pregnant women should consult a doctor before trying a hot mineral bath.

Aromatherapy's Amazing Effects on Your Mind and Mood

Alan Hirsch, MD, founder and neurological director of the Smell & Taste Treatment and Research Foundation and an assistant professor in the departments of neurology and psychiatry at Rush-Presbyterian-St. Luke's Medical Center, both in Chicago. Dr. Hirsch has done more than 200 studies on smell and taste disorders and is the author of eight books, including *Life's a Smelling Success* (Authors of Unity) and *Sensa Weight-Loss Program* (Hilton). His Web site is *www.smellandtaste.org*.

S cents can have subtle yet amazing effects on emotions—boosting confidence, easing stress, triggering fond memories and more. *Here's how to use your sense of smell to manage your moods…and other people's, too!*

•**Increase mental sharpness with fresh flowers.** When you really need to focus—for instance, to memorize a speech or balance a checkbook—keep a vase of mixed fragrant flowers nearby. Take periodic breaks to consciously "stop and smell the roses."

For kids: This helps when doing homework or studying for a test.

•**Promote harmonious family interaction with garlic.** Serve garlic bread at dinner. In studies, this scent reduced negative dinner-time remarks by 22.7% and increased pleasantries by 7.4%. You don't even have to eat the bread to reap the benefits.

• **Feel younger with pink grapefruit.** To make others perceive you as youthful (so you feel that way, too), apply a grapefruit-scented or other citrusy body lotion or spray right after your shower.

Avoid: Lavender—it's too granny-ish.

• **Feel more secure with baby powder.** Keep a small bottle or resealable plastic bag of baby powder in your purse or briefcase. Before heading into a challenging situation (a meeting with your ex, a job interview), open the container slightly and take a small whiff. Don't inhale too deeply—you may sneeze or get powder all over your face.

• **Curb food cravings with banana or peppermint.** You needn't eat a banana—just smell it (peeled or unpeeled). Or, place two drops of peppermint essential oil on a cotton ball, stick it in a plastic bag and take a whiff...or try sugar-free peppermint gum or hard candy.

• **Fight claustrophobia with evergreens.** Keep a small vial of evergreen essential oil in your pocket or purse. When in a cramped space (an elevator, a crowd), hold the vial near your nose and inhale two or three times. Repeat every 10 minutes as needed.

• **Assuage anger with cucumber.** Hold a sliced cucumber one-half inch from your face and level with your lips...inhale deeply, continuing for several minutes. To reduce road rage, use a cucumber-melon air freshener.

Avoid: Barbecuing or roasting meat when you're angry—the scent stirs up fiery feelings that heighten aggression.

• **Relax and wind down with lavender.** Lie down and place a lavender-scented eye pillow over your eyes...breathe slowly and deeply for several minutes.

Avoid: Jasmine, which promotes alertness.

• **Rev up a man's libido with pumpkin pie or black licorice.** Bake a pumpkin pie for maximum effect...or use a reed diffuser (a stick that wicks the aroma from a bottle of scented oil).

On a date: Nibble on black licorice.

Noteworthy: Perfume is only 3% effective at arousing a man's romantic feelings...versus 40% for pumpkin pie and 13% for licorice.

Kiss to Lower Stress

When couples kissed, it set off a multitude of chemical reactions, including a reduction in levels of the stress hormone cortisol.

Also effective: Holding hands while talking together.

Wendy L. Hill, PhD, professor of psychology, Lafayette College, Easton, Pennsylvania, and her student Carey Wilson, author of a thesis on kissing.

Ouch! Better First Aid For a Burn

Don't put ice on a burn. Several published studies have shown that putting ice on a burn can damage the skin further, even causing frostbite. It is much better to run the burn under cold water, take a pain reliever and cover the burn with gauze.

The New York Times, www.nytimes.com.

How to Ice an Injury

Apply ice to an injury as soon as possible, and leave it on for 15 to 20 minutes. Taking the ice off too soon reduces its effectiveness...leaving it on too long can cause frostbite. Apply ice five times the first day following an injury, with at least 45 minutes in between sessions. Never apply ice right before you participate in sports or exercise—numbing a body part may block pain signals to your brain. See a doctor if the injury worsens.

Runner's World, 33 E. Minor St., Emmaus, Pennsylvania 18098, *www.runnersworld.com.*

4

Fitness Fast

Your Lucky 13— The Best Secrets for Losing Weight Without Feeling Hungry!

**W**hen your stomach is sending out insistent and incessant "feed me!" messages, it is almost impossible to stick to a strict diet. That's why the real key to weight-loss success is to shut down hunger and to short-circuit food cravings—because then it is easier to cut down on calories. *Here are 13 simple strategies for slimming down without making yourself feel deprived...*

1. Have two servings of protein at breakfast. Proteins are natural appetite suppressants. This means that even if eating more protein ups your usual morning calorie count, you will feel fuller longer—so over the course of the day, you'll wind up eating less.

Breakfast combinations: An egg scrambled with an ounce of shredded cheese...or eight ounces of low-fat yogurt mixed with an ounce of slivered almonds. Do not just have coffee for breakfast—you'll feel ravenous later.

2. At lunch and dinner, consume items in order of least-to-most calories. Start the meal with your salad and vegetables...eat the grains next...and then work your way around the plate to the heavier foods, such as meat. By the time you get there, you're already starting to feel full—so it is easier to control your portions of those calorie-dense items.

Interactive tool: Gauge proper portion sizes based on your weight, height and exercise level at *www.mypyramid.gov* (click "My Pyramid Plan").

Keith-Thomas Ayoob, EdD, RD, a nutritionist and associate clinical professor at Albert Einstein College of Medicine, Bronx, New York. He is coauthor of *The Uncle Sam Diet: The 4-Week Eating Plan for a Thinner, Healthier America* (St. Martin's).

3. Don't think of snacking as cheating. Wisely chosen snacks keep hunger pangs at bay, so you won't overindulge later in the day. Have a midafternoon and an evening snack every day, combining two food groups.

Examples: Pair a vegetable with a whole grain (hummus or salsa with whole-wheat pita or crackers)…or pair fruit and dairy (pineapple with low-fat cottage cheese, a smoothie made with blueberries and low-fat yogurt). Prepare some healthful snacks ahead of time so you'll reach for them—not candy and chips—when your stomach grumbles.

4. Choose foods that you can't eat quickly. Labor-intensive foods—pistachios in the shell, edamame in the pod, peel-and-eat shrimp—force you to savor each bite instead of shoveling everything down. This leisurely pace fools your brain into thinking that you're consuming much more than you actually are.

5. Drink water to squelch the munchies. People often mistake thirst for hunger—so downing eight ounces of water may quickly quell food cravings.

Also helpful: Make sure that your diet includes high-water–content foods, such as cucumbers, lettuce, zucchini…oranges, peaches, strawberries, watermelon…low-fat broth and tomato-based soups.

6. Cut down on caffeine intake. True, caffeine gives a short-term energy buzz—but it also contributes to hunger.

Reason: Caffeine stimulates insulin secretion…which reduces blood sugar…which tells your brain that it's time to eat. Limit caffeinated coffee, tea and cola to two cups daily, consumed with meals, to see if this eases food cravings. Cut back further if you suffer from insomnia.

7. Chew some sugarless cinnamon gum. Of course, when there's gum in your mouth, you won't be tempted to put food in there, too—but there's more to this strategy. Chewing gum helps improve mental focus, so that you stay engaged in your activity and are less apt to hear the call of the refrigerator. Also, chewing gum helps relieve the stress that can lead to overeating. Why choose cinnamon? It retains its flavor longest.

8. Fill up on fiber. Soluble and insoluble fibers hold water and expand in your stomach, making you feel fuller longer.

Daily goals: Four cups of fruits and vegetables (assuming foods are small, such as berries, or chopped)…one-half cup of beans (which are highly nutritious yet underappreciated) or other legumes…and three servings of whole grains (try brown rice, oatmeal, whole-wheat bread).

Party trick: Eat half an oat-bran muffin before you go out. Those 100 calories will save you hundreds more because you'll feel less enticed by the hors d'oeuvres.

9. Indulge in chocolate for dessert. One ounce of dark chocolate with 70% or more cocoa content has only about 150 calories. Savor it with a cup of decaf coffee or herbal tea—its big taste contradicts its relatively modest calorie count.

Delectable brands: Scharffen Berger (866-972-6879, *www.scharffenberger.com*)…and Valrhona (888-682-5746, *www.valrhona.com*).

10. Fool the hunger hormone. Ghrelin, a hormone that stimulates hunger, drops about a half-hour after you eat—so nibble on a half-ounce of nutrient-rich nuts 30 minutes before dinner to make it easier to keep meal portions modest. If you're going out, carry nuts in your purse. (Recycle an Altoids mint tin—it's the perfect size for your portable nut stash.)

11. Shake your booty—or simply take a brisk walk. Aerobic exercise lowers hunger-triggering *ghrelin*…increases amounts of the appetite-suppressing hormone *peptide YY*…burns calories…and relieves stress.

Goal: At least 30 minutes of aerobic exercise (such as quick-paced walking) every day.

12. Retrain your palate. When you habitually consume lots of sugar, salt or fat, your taste buds become desensitized. Like addicts, they require a bigger and bigger "fix" to feel satisfied. But when you cut down on those three troublemakers, within a few weeks you regain the ability to detect and enjoy subtler flavors—and sugary, salty and fatty foods lose their appeal.

13. Move up your bedtime. People who sleep less than five hours a night have higher ghrelin levels—causing them to feel near-constant hunger. Sleeping for about eight hours per night helps normalize ghrelin levels. Also, fatigue can increase stress and compromise judgment—so by getting more rest, you become better able to make sensible decisions about food.

Bonus: An early bedtime means that you won't be tempted to have a midnight snack, so you're likely to wake up weighing less—and feeling proud.

How a "Foodie" Lost 42 Pounds—No Dieting

Pam Anderson, a monthly food columnist for *USA Weekend* and *Better Homes & Gardens* and a contributing editor to *Fine Cooking*. Based in Darien, Connecticut, she teaches cooking classes across the country. Her latest book is *The Perfect Recipe for Losing Weight & Eating Great* (Houghton Mifflin Harcourt).

Pam Anderson, the food columnist and cookbook author, faces challenges that would stress any dieter. She tests—and tastes—every single recipe that she develops. She spends two or more days a week in the test kitchen, where she might sample three dozen versions of a chocolate cake or 16 versions of a pot roast recipe. That led her to her top weight of 192 pounds.

Over the years, she tried dozens of different diets, including Atkins and South Beach. She lost weight initially, but the pounds always came back.

• **Her "mirror moment."** In 2002, Anderson took an exercise class that was held in a mirrored room. She did not like the look of the overweight food writer looking back at her. At the same time, she experienced an intense longing for what she would like to become— thinner and healthier.

That morning in front of the mirror represented her first step in the healthier direction. It was another two years before she fully dedicated herself to healthier living. When she did, the results were striking. She lost 42 pounds

in about eight months, without dieting, and has not gained it back.

The approach that worked for her…

• **Focus on your life, not your weight.** A few years after my "mirror moment," I saw an acupuncturist for shoulder pain. During my sessions, I would lie in a meditative state for nearly an hour. I left the sessions feeling centered and refreshed. That's when I realized that my weight was secondary. Changing my life was a necessary first step.

I started weekly therapy sessions with a psychologist, during which I came to understand that I have always shouldered too many responsibilities. As a working parent, I brought home a big chunk of the bacon, and I took on most of the household responsibilities. So in addition to my job, I shopped, cooked, oversaw the child care and housecleaning, took charge of all the finances, planned vacations and organized the social calendar. It was too much. I unconsciously used food to build up my body to "support" the many responsibilities that I carried.

Food was always one of my comforts—but the heavier I got, the more insecure I felt. So I overcompensated by taking on even more responsibilities, thinking that this would make up for my not being fit.

Therapy didn't cause me to lose weight, but it did help me to understand that my life was out of balance. It helped me feel more in control and sure of myself, which allowed me to reduce the responsibilities that I had taken on.

• **Get physical.** I never exercised regularly until my husband and I took a trip to Italy in the summer of 2004. We walked miles every day. I was surprised to discover that daily exercise made me less hungry. At the same time, those daily walks burned a lot of calories. I wasn't trying to lose weight—I ate all the bread, pasta and desserts that I wanted—but by the time we returned, after two weeks, my clothes were looser.

After that, I kept up the habit of walking every day. I would walk briskly for several miles in the morning and sometimes again in the afternoon. As I got stronger, I alternated walking with bursts of running. I kept losing weight.

•**Opt for casual calorie counting.** Most diets incorporate nutritional rules. You're supposed to eat this many calories or limit yourself to these portion sizes. I don't bother with that. I've learned that food restriction only creates cravings and that strict portion control can leave you feeling hungry all the time.

I do have a sense of what I should and shouldn't eat and how much I should eat in a given day. I know from experience that I can maintain my current weight (about 150 pounds) on 2,000 to 2,500 calories a day. I'm in that range when I eat a big breakfast, a healthy salad for lunch and a light meal at supper, along with a few snacks. If I've been tasting a lot of new recipes, I cut back on calories somewhere else. I don't think about it very much. Calorie control becomes second nature once you know what "healthy" feels like. Now I'm rarely tempted to overindulge, because I feel so much better when I don't.

That's as specific as I get. I've developed a heightened awareness of what my body does and doesn't need at any given time. As long as I stay in this general calorie range—and burn roughly 450 calories a day with exercise—my weight naturally takes care of itself.

•**Eat often.** Most people do get hungry every three to four hours. This is why doctors recommend "grazing," in which you eat five or six times a day. It's good for energy and healthy blood sugar levels, as well as appetite control.

I haven't given up my three main meals, but I supplement them with snacks whenever I'm feeling hungry. I make a ritual of afternoon tea, in which I'll have a cup of tea and something sweet, such as a small cookie. Then, before supper, I will have an hors d'oeuvre—a deviled egg or a handful of nuts—along with a glass of wine.

•**Look good, feel good.** I got rid of the ugly sweatpants I used to exercise in. Now I have smart-looking spandex. After my workouts, I don't just shower—I fix my hair and put on makeup. The way we present ourselves indicates how we feel about ourselves. Looking good made me feel good—and the better I felt, the better I wanted to look.

I also go through my closet periodically and get rid of my "fat" clothes. I used to hang on to everything, probably because I knew in the back of my mind that my diets weren't going to stick. This new approach was different. I wasn't merely dieting, I was changing my life. I knew I wasn't going back.

•**Personalize.** One of the big issues with weight-loss diets is that they force different people to follow exactly the same plan. But in fact, everyone has to figure out what works for him/her.

Example: I'm not about to give up my before-supper glass of wine, no matter how many calories it has.

I go to bed earlier than a lot of people, so I'm unlikely to snack after supper. But if you happen to be a night owl, you'll probably want to have a snack between supper and bedtime. Similarly, we all have our own favorites. I love pasta and couldn't stick with a diet that forced me to give it up. Maybe you crave a daily dessert or full-fat cream in your coffee. Don't give it up! Just make the necessary adjustments.

Supplement Speeds Weight Loss

In one recent study, obese women with diabetes supplemented with 6.4 g daily of the fatty acid *conjugated linoleic acid* (CLA). In 16 weeks, they lost three pounds of fat, on average…and their body mass index (a calculation based on height and weight) fell by about half a point.

Reassuring: Earlier animal studies raised concerns that CLA might decrease beneficial lean muscle mass—but patients in this study did not lose any lean muscle.

Martha Belury, PhD, RD, professor of nutrition at Ohio State University, Columbus, and leader of a study of 35 women.

The Fat Blocker You Probably Have In Your Cupboard...

Vinegar is high in the chemical *acetic acid*. During six weeks, researchers gave either water or vinegar to mice on an otherwise identical high-fat diet. Mice given the highest-concentration of acetic acid gained 6% less weight than those given water.

Theory: Acetic acid stimulates proteins that help break down fats, limiting weight gain.

Tomoo Kondo, researcher, Central Research Institute, Mizkan Group, Nakamura, Japan, and leader of an animal study.

Dieting? Don't Drop Dairy

Contrary to popular belief, dieters do not have to skip dairy products.

Recent research: Thirty-four overweight men and women drank 20 ounces of skim milk or a fruit drink with breakfast (two slices of toast with jam and margarine), followed by lunch (a sandwich) four hours later.

Result: The skim milk group ate 50 fewer calories, on average, at lunchtime compared with the fruit-drink group, and reported feeling fuller.

Theory: Milk's high protein content, lactose (natural sugar) and/or thickness may contribute to feelings of fullness.

If you are trying to manage your weight: Consider drinking a glass of skim milk with your breakfast.

Emma R. Dove, MD, research associate, School of Medicine and Pharmacology, University of Western Australia, Perth.

Tea Time for the Weight Conscious

German researchers performing laboratory tests on human fat cells have found that white tea extract—less processed than other teas—inhibits the generation of new fat cells. Researchers theorize that substances, including caffeine, in white tea are responsible for this effect.

BioMed Central, *www.biomedcentral.com.*

Natural and Artificial Sweeteners—Latest Research

Karen Collins, RD, a registered dietitian in private practice in Jamestown, New York, and nutrition adviser to the Washington, DC–based American Institute for Cancer Research, *www.aicr.org.* She is the author of two weekly syndicated newspaper columns, "Nutrition Notes" and "Nutrition Wise."

There are so many natural and artificial sweeteners on the market today. It is more important than ever to know the risks—and benefits—of the product you use most often.

Important new development: In a recent report, the American Heart Association stated that a growing (though inconclusive) body of evidence suggests that consuming too much "added sugar" (sugars and syrups added to foods during processing or preparation) may increase blood pressure—which, in turn, raises the risk for heart disease. What's more, diets high in added sugar can lead to weight gain (possibly resulting in diabetes) and elevated levels of blood fats known as triglycerides (a risk factor for heart disease)—and perhaps even increase risk for some cancers.

Best advice: To help avoid any increased health risks, most women should limit their daily intake of added sugar to six teaspoons (about 25 grams [g], 100 calories)...most men should limit intake to nine teaspoons (about

38 g and 150 calories). If you have an active lifestyle, you can consume up to an additional three to five teaspoons daily.

That's still significantly less than the 22 teaspoons of added sugar that the average American consumes each day.

People with diabetes can include any type of sweetener in their diets as long as they count these carbohydrates (compounds broken down in the body to form energy-producing sugar, or glucose) as part of the total daily carbohydrate limit that's recommended by their doctor or registered dietitian. *What you need to know about sweeteners…*

TRADITIONAL SWEETENERS

•**White and brown sugars.** White sugar is derived from sugarcane or beet sugar. Brown sugar is a combination of white sugar and molasses. Both white and brown sugars are refined (processed).

White sugar contains about 16 calories per teaspoon…brown sugar about 17 calories per teaspoon. Using brown sugar in baked goods makes them moister than white sugar does and adds a hint of caramel flavor.

How safe? There's no evidence that sugar leads to weight gain or an increased risk for cancer when consumed in modest amounts.

•**Honey.** This sticky, unrefined sweetener is flower nectar that has been concentrated by bees. Honey is about 25% to 50% sweeter than sugar. Honey also has slightly more calories (21 calories per teaspoon) and carbohydrates than a similar amount of sugar. Honey contains trace amounts of minerals (such as potassium and calcium), but its nutritional value is not significantly different from that of table sugar.

How safe? Honey should never be given to babies under one year of age—it could contain bacterial spores that may produce a toxin that causes infant botulism, a serious form of food poisoning. Honey's stickiness also may promote cavities—especially in young children.

•**Molasses.** This syrupy liquid is created from the juice of sugarcane and beet sugar during the refining process. The type of molasses is determined by the degree of boiling that occurs—light molasses, which is typically very light in color, is derived from the initial boiling…dark molasses, which is darker and thicker, comes from the second boiling…and blackstrap molasses, which is quite thick and dark, comes from the third boiling.

How safe? Dark and blackstrap molasses are rich sources of disease-fighting antioxidants. Blackstrap molasses is a good source of iron.

PRESERVATIVE/SWEETENER

•**High fructose corn syrup (HFCS).** This processed sweetener, derived from cornstarch, is found in many processed foods and sweetened beverages.

How safe? Research has shown mixed results. Several studies have linked the trend toward increased intake of HFCS-containing beverages to increased rates of obesity in the US, but this association might have more to do with the increased consumption—both in frequency and portion size—of high-calorie sweetened drinks than with the form of sugar that they contain. By avoiding these beverages and limiting intake of processed foods, Americans can substantially cut their overall sugar and calorie consumption.

LOW- OR NO-CALORIE SWEETENERS

Although reports have been circulated that some of these sweeteners can lead to serious health problems, such as lupus and even Alzheimer's disease, there is no credible scientific evidence to support those claims.

Low- or zero-calorie sweeteners can help people avoid all the calories and dental cavity concern that come with traditional sweeteners. And, because these sweeteners have no effect on blood sugar, they can all be used by people with diabetes. In addition to use on the table, many of these sweeteners could be used in cooking and baking—check the product label for instructions.

•**Aspartame.** This artificial sweetener is made by combining two amino acids—*aspartic acid* and *phenylalanine* (one of the protein building blocks used to make the sweetener). Sold in a light blue packet as NutraSweet or Equal, the white crystalline powder has no calories and is about 200 times sweeter than white or brown sugar.

How safe? People with *phenylketonuria*, a rare genetic disorder, need to avoid aspartame completely since this condition makes it difficult to metabolize *phenylalanine*. Although animal studies have linked aspartame to cancer, human research conducted by the National Cancer Institute showed no such association. Some people get such symptoms as headaches and/or dizziness when they have too much aspartame.

•**Saccharin.** The oldest of all the artificial sweeteners, saccharin is found in a pink packet and sold as Sweet'N Low. It is 200 to 700 times sweeter than sugar. Saccharin has less than four calories per packet.

How safe? Since there's some evidence that saccharin can cross the placenta, some (but not all) experts advise women to limit the use of saccharin during pregnancy. Despite concerns about saccharin causing bladder cancer in male rats, many human studies have shown no link with cancer risk. Still, the watchdog group Center for Science in the Public Interest believes more research is needed and recommends against its use.

•**Stevia.** Extracted from the leaves of a South American shrub, stevia (sold as PureVia and Truvia) has zero calories per packet and is about 200 times sweeter than sugar. In late 2008, the FDA allowed manufacturers to use some forms of stevia in foods and beverages.

How safe? Concerns have been raised as a result of some studies in rats linking stevia with DNA damage and genetic mutations, changes that can lead to cancer. However, US and international expert panels that reviewed a wide range of studies concluded that stevia is safe.

Stevia has been used safely in Japan for decades and in South America for centuries. But people in these regions tend to consume a much smaller quantity of sweetener than Americans do, so it's unclear whether larger amounts might be a health hazard.

•**Sucralose.** Known as Splenda and sold in a yellow packet, it contains four calories per packet and tastes about 600 times sweeter than white or brown sugar.

If you substitute sucralose for sugar in baked goods, it will not produce the same texture or brown in the same way, so it's best to substitute sucralose for only half the sugar in many baking recipes. (Check the label.)

How safe? Sucralose has been well studied, and there's no evidence that it raises risk for cancer or any other disease.

WHICH SWEETENER DO I USE?

I try to limit my use of added sweeteners. But I do use white and brown sugars, honey and molasses in small amounts based on what tastes best in the food I am preparing. If I want to reduce the sugar in a recipe, I usually substitute sucralose for some of the sugar.

Just Say No! to Second Helpings

People consume 65% more calories when eating with someone who takes a second helping than when eating with someone who doesn't.

Self-defense: Have a cup of herbal tea after you finish your main course. It has no calories and keeps your mouth busy, so you will be less tempted to take seconds or order dessert even if your companion does.

Jonny Bowden, PhD, nutrition adviser, *Men's Health*, 33 E. Minor St., Emmaus, Pennsylvania 18098, *www.menshealth.com*.

Body Fat That *Burns* Calories

Brown adipose tissue, also called brown fat, burns calories to help small mammals stay warm. Recent research shows that some people have brown fat located above the collarbone and in the upper chest. If drugs could be developed to activate brown fat, people might be able to burn calories more quickly—aiding in weight loss. Research is very preliminary.

Study of 1,972 people by researchers at Joslin Diabetes Center, Boston, published in *The New England Journal of Medicine*.

Eating Fast Contributes To Weight Gain

There is truth to the long-held notion that eating fast promotes weight gain say researchers, and we may now know why.

Possible reason: The release of hormones that help regulate appetite may be reduced by fast eating.

Journal of Clinical Endocrinology & Metabolism, http://jcem.endojournals.org.

Worst Time of Day to Eat For Weight Loss

Late-night eating causes more weight gain than eating during the day.

Recent finding: Mice that ate when they would normally have been sleeping gained 2.5 times more weight than mice that ate during their usual waking hours.

Fred Turek, PhD, professor of biology and circadian biology, Northwestern University, Evanston, Illinois, and principal investigator of an animal study published in *Obesity*.

How the Food Industry Is Causing You to Overeat

David A. Kessler, MD, former head of the Food and Drug Administration and onetime dean of the Yale School of Medicine. A professor at the University of California, San Francisco, he is author of *The New York Times* best seller *The End of Overeating: Taking Control of the American Appetite* (Rodale).

Take a moment and think of a food that is irresistible to you. You probably can see it vividly in your mind's eye...and you even may start to salivate.

Chances are that the food you imagined is not a vegetable or fruit but rather a processed food made with a precise combination of ingredients that trigger repeated cravings similar to those of addicts who can't resist a drug or alcohol.

Can our taste buds really be so easily tricked by food manufacturers?

Absolutely, says David Kessler, MD, former head of the Food and Drug Administration (FDA). Dr. Kessler, who has extensively researched the eating habits of Americans, recently answered questions about the ways the food industry is controlling our appetites.

• **It's widely reported that about one-third of American adults weigh too much. Why has this occurred in the US?** There should be a balance between the food we consume and the energy we expend. All the evidence says that it's the amount we eat that's gotten out of hand.

It's useful to note that in 1960, the average 40- to 49-year-old American woman weighed 142 pounds. By 2000, the average weight in that age group had jumped to 169 pounds. Research shows that also during this period, American adults were gaining more from ages 20 to 40. Instead of just a few pounds, the average man gained more than 12 pounds during these ages.

• **Why are Americans now eating so much more?** While past generations ate most of their food at mealtimes, processed foods that are highly "palatable"—meaning that they stimulate the appetite and prompt us to eat more—are now available 24/7. With such ready access, it has become socially acceptable to eat these foods at any hour of the day. For many people, they're impossible to resist.

• **Can't a person use willpower to resist such foods?** Not necessarily. It's not a question of people lacking self-control or being lazy. What is really happening is that their brain circuitry has been "hijacked."

Considerable animal and human research shows that foods are made palatable by three ingredients—fat, sugar and salt. Sugar is the main driver of food appeal. Fat and salt work synergistically with sugar.

Get the proportions right, and you hit what might be called the "blisspoint." Candy bars, buffalo wings, Big Macs, cheese fries—they all combine fat, sugar and salt. The "white chocolate mocha frappuccino" served at Starbucks is coffee diluted with a mix of sugar, fat and salt.

• How do these foods hijack our brain circuits? Foods that taste good are reinforcing—that is, they keep us coming back for more. But highly palatable—or so-called "hyperpalatable"—foods do even more.

They stimulate brain circuits that release *dopamine*, the neurotransmitter that focuses attention and increases motivation. It can take only a single taste of a hyperpalatable food to set this process in motion.

After you've eaten such a food several times, you become more sensitive to cues surrounding the experience—for example, the sight of the wrapper and the name of the food arouses your memory of how it felt to eat the food and focuses your attention on getting it.

Every time you repeat the experience by eating the food, you strengthen the neural circuits involved, making yourself ever more sensitive to anticipation cues—literally rewiring your brain.

• What is the food industry's role in all this? The basic business plan of the typical modern food company is to sell foods loaded with fat, sugar and salt.

Take buffalo wings. They're the fatty part of chicken, fried and refried and covered with red sauce that's full of salt and sugar. Fat on fat, on fat, on sugar and salt.

You'll find similar combinations in many appetizers, snacks and fast foods, such as chocolate-covered pretzels and cinnamon rolls.

"The three points of the compass" is what one high-level food industry executive calls sugar, fat and salt. "They make food compelling," he noted. "They make it indulgent, and they make us want to eat more."

• But it's easy for consumers to tell when a food is fatty, salty and sugary—it's not like the food industry can hide it. Actually, experts in the food industry have found additional, sneakier ways to increase what they call the "craveability" of food products.

They've learned how to combine ingredients, including chemical enhancers (such as artificial sweeteners, hickory smoke flavoring and cheese flavoring) to create the complex series of flavors and textures that can magnify sensory appeal.

Food manufacturers even have spent considerable effort making their creations easier to swallow. It used to be that the average bite of food in the American diet required 20 chews before swallowing—now it's only two or three chews.

As soon as that fleeting taste and oral stimulation fade, you reach for more. Through careful engineering by food companies, you're led to eat quickly enough to override your body's "I'm full" signals.

On top of that, incessant advertising adds pleasurable associations to the sensory experience—it pairs foods with images of parties, barbecues and friends having fun. The combined effect is very powerful.

People in the food industry would argue that they're just giving consumers what they want. But we now know this means excessively activating our brains to overeat. It's not what most consumers would want once they understood what was happening.

• Why not go on a diet? Diets alone won't work, because they can't change the brain circuitry that's been created by all the food cues put forth by the food industry. You can try to fight these forces by depriving yourself—and you may even lose weight for 30, 60 or 90 days. But if you're still living in the same environment, you'll be surrounded by all the same food cues you've been trained to respond to.

You can keep foods full of sugar, fat and salt out of the house, but every time you walk down the street, you'll be bombarded. Sooner or later, you'll gain back the weight. A diet alone doesn't get at the root of the problem—the way your behavior has been shaped by changes in your brain circuitry.

• What can we do to defend ourselves? Simply knowing that the food industry has created many of its products in a way that is calculated to take control of your eating behavior will go a long way toward helping you see hyperpalatable foods for what they are—which is not at all appealing.

When you are armed with this knowledge, you can take some concrete steps to replace one set of automatic behaviors with another set that is much more healthful.

For example, for people who are overweight and those who may not be overweight but want to avoid unhealthful processed foods, I suggest that they establish their own rules and enforce them ruthlessly. Identify the foods that you know are uncontrollably appealing and decide that they're absolutely off limits.

For a while at least, plan all your eating. Decide what you want to eat and when, and limit it to three meals a day, with a midmorning and midafternoon snack.

•**What if I start to lose my resolve?** If you feel yourself slipping into a mental dialogue of "This looks great, but I know I shouldn't have it…maybe just this once…" then reframe your thoughts and remind yourself of your goals. Tell yourself, for example, "If I don't give in to my desire for this food, I'll feel a lot better about myself tomorrow."

Many of us have gotten so caught up by the stimulation of food that we have lost touch with how much we really need to eat to feel satisfied. How much will it take to keep you from getting hungry until the next meal? Try increasingly smaller portions—you may be surprised by what you find out.

Dear Diary…

Writing in a food diary helps to promote weight loss.

Recent finding: As part of one three-year study with nearly 1,700 men and women who followed a diet emphasizing fruit, vegetables and low-fat or nonfat dairy foods, participants who kept daily food diaries lost twice as much weight as those who kept no diaries.

Theory: Keeping track of what you eat (and the total daily calories) makes you more aware of your dietary choices.

If you're trying to lose weight: Keep a food diary. It can take several forms—for example, take notes, send e-mails to yourself or keep a more formal journal.

Jack Hollis, PhD, senior investigator, Kaiser Permanente Center for Health Research, Portland, Oregon.

Too Busy to Go to the Gym? Get Fit in Just a Few Minutes

Joan Price, a certified fitness instructor and motivational speaker based in Sebastopol, California, and author of six books, including *The Anytime, Anywhere Exercise Book* (iUniverse). She credits her commitment to exercise for her success in twice regaining the ability to walk and dance after two head-on car crashes. Her Web site is *www.joanprice.com.*

Lack of time is a primary reason people give for failing to get the recommended 30 to 60 minutes of moderate-intensity exercise most days of the week. Admittedly, it can be tough to find such a big chunk of time in your busy schedule.

What helps: Instead of feeling compelled to cram an entire day's worth of exercise into a single block of time, commit to fitting in little bursts of physical activity—two minutes, five minutes or 10 minutes—throughout the day. The more these "fitness minutes" add up, the more you reap the benefits of exercise, including improved health, better weight control, increased energy and a sense of well-being.

IN THE MORNING

•**When your alarm clock rings—instead of pressing the snooze button, get up** and use those extra minutes to do some gentle yoga poses.

•**While brushing your teeth—fit in calf raises.** Standing, slowly rise onto the balls of your feet…hold for several seconds…return to the starting position. Repeat, continuing for two minutes.

•**In the shower—give your upper back muscles a workout.** Squeeze your shoulder blades together…hold for five to 10 seconds… rest for a moment. Repeat 10 to 15 times.

- **While you style your hair, squeeze your buttocks muscles as hard as you can for 10 seconds…**rest for several seconds…repeat five to 10 times.

- **When going down stairs—turn around at the bottom and go back up,** making one or more extra up-and-down trips.

- **As the coffee is brewing—hop on your right foot 10 times…**then hop on the left foot. Repeat twice.

- **When letting the dog out—go with him for a short walk.**

OUT AND ABOUT

- **At the gas station—walk inside to pay rather than swiping a credit card at the pump.** Instead of sitting in your car as the gas flows, clean all your windows, alternating the hand that holds the squeegee.

- **At every red light—do shoulder shrugs and roll your shoulders…**repeatedly tighten and release your thigh muscles…rotate one wrist, then the other wrist.

- **When parking—instead of finding a spot close to your destination, get one a few blocks away.**

- **Upon entering a store—if all the items you need will fit in a shopping basket, get a basket instead of a cart.**

- **As you shop—if you need a cart, do 10 bicep curls with weightier items—**soup cans, juice jugs—before placing them in your cart. (If you feel silly doing this in public, do your bicep curls at home as you put the items in the pantry.)

- **While waiting in line—work your abdominal muscles.** Suck in your belly and tighten your abs…hold for 10 seconds…relax. Repeat five to 10 times.

- **On a long car trip—stop every 50 miles or so, and take a walk around a rest stop or scenic area.**

- **When traveling by bus, plane or train—walk up and down the aisle for at least five minutes every hour.**

AT YOUR DESK

- **While on the phone—march in place or pace around your office.**

- **As you read e-mail—lift your right foot several inches off the floor…**rotate your ankle clockwise several times, then rotate your ankle counterclockwise. Repeat on the left side.

- **If you need to talk with a coworker—walk over to her office instead of phoning.** When you get back to your own desk, hold your arms out to the side and circle them forward 15 times, then circle them backward.

- **Each time you finish a task—do "chair dips."** With feet flat on the floor, place your hands on the armrests and push your body up…hold for several seconds…lower yourself back into the chair. Repeat 10 times. (Skip this if your chair has wheels.)

- **During your lunch break—take a walk through the office complex.**

- **If you drop a pencil, do a variation on toe touches.** Stand up, bend down, pick up the pencil, then straighten up…drop the pencil again. Repeat 10 times.

IN THE EVENING

- **Before starting dinner—take one quick bike ride around the neighborhood.**

- **At the dinner table—do leg lifts.** Sit with feet flat on the floor. Straighten your right leg to hold your right foot out in front of you…lift your right thigh a few inches off the chair and hold for several seconds…lower the foot. Repeat 10 times, then switch to the left leg.

- **Doing laundry—when you grab a basket of clothes, tighten abdominal muscles** and, with your back straight, lift the basket from hip height to chest height five times.

- **Listening to a CD, dance around for one entire song.** Repeat several times.

- **While watching TV—pop an exercise video or DVD in your player.** Every time the TV show cuts to a commercial break, turn on the player and follow along with the workout for several minutes.

- **Climbing the stairs—take the steps two at a time.** (Do not do this if you have balance problems.)

- **After washing your face—tilt your head slowly from side to side,** feeling a good stretch along your neck…try to touch your chin to your chest to stretch the back of your neck.

• **Before climbing into bed—raise your arms overhead**...tilt gently to the right, feeling the stretch along the left side of your torso...then tilt to the left. Repeat five times.

• **When you lie down—do knee hugs.** Lie on your back with your knees bent, feet flat on the mattress. Raise one leg, place your hands behind the thigh and draw the leg toward your chest. Hold for 30 seconds...return to starting position. Repeat with the other leg.

• **Closing your eyes—breathe in and out deeply 10 times,** feeling grateful for all that your body was capable of doing during the day.

Charge Up Your Energy: The Best Food to Eat Before and After Exercise

Tammy Lakatos Shames, RD, and Elysse Lakatos, RD, owners of The Nutrition Twins, a nutrition counseling practice, New York City. They're the "Sideline Reporters" at *The Weekend Workout*, a syndicated radio show, and authors of *Fire Up Your Metabolism* (Fireside) and *The Secret to Skinny* (HCI). Their Web site is *www.nutritiontwins.com*.

What you eat before and after exercise makes a significant difference in how you feel and how well you perform...

BEFORE/DURING WORKOUTS

During exercise, the body gets energy from *glycogen*, a type of carbohydrate that's stored in muscles and the liver. Being hungry going into a workout rapidly depletes glycogen and can cause premature fatigue. *Recommended...*

• **Combine protein with carbohydrates.** For example, have a hard-boiled egg (for protein) and half a bagel (for carbs) about one hour before a workout. Protein makes carbohydrates a slower-burning (longer-lasting) energy source.

If it will be more than an hour until you can exercise, eat something substantial, such as a peanut butter sandwich or a wrap with turkey breast, lettuce and tomato. This larger meal takes longer to digest and will stay with you longer so that you will have enough energy for your workout.

Note: It isn't necessary to eat first thing in the morning before exercising as long as you have a good dinner that includes carbs the night before.

• **Remember the "90-minute rule."** It takes about 90 minutes of hard exercise to deplete stored glycogen. If you engage in extended cardiovascular workouts, you'll need to replenish glycogen while you exercise. You can munch on a protein/carbohydrate bar or sip a sports drink (such as Gatorade).

AFTER WORKOUTS

If you're trying to lose weight, schedule your workouts so that you'll have lunch or dinner when you're done. The increased expenditure of calories that occurs during exercise persists for about an hour afterward. Eating right after a workout allows you to take advantage of the increased calorie burning.

• **Get sufficient protein.** Muscle cells are very receptive to amino acids (the individual building blocks of protein) 30 minutes to one hour after exercise. Consuming protein right after exercise accelerates both muscle repair and muscle growth. You want to consume 15 grams (g) to 20 g of lean protein.

Examples: Two ounces of chicken provides about 12 g of protein. An egg has about 6 g.

• **Add a complex carbohydrate to replace glycogen.** Muscle cells quickly absorb carbohydrates after exercise. The optimal ratio is four parts carbohydrate to one part protein. A turkey sandwich and a nonfat fruit yogurt has this ratio with 75 g of carbs and 18 g of protein.

• **Eat fruit.** There's an increase in muscle-damaging free radicals during and after exercise. The antioxidants in fruit reduce muscle damage and accelerate muscle repair. Also, the sugars in fruit quickly replete glycogen stores.

• **Check your water level.** Weigh yourself immediately before and after exercise—and drink enough water to make up the difference. If you weigh a pound less after exercising, drink at least 16 ounces of water.

Weight Lifting vs. Running—What's Best For Weight Loss?

In a recent study, on separate days, 11 men engaged in treadmill running for 60 minutes or weight lifting for 90 minutes.

Result: The men reported feeling less hungry while they ran on a treadmill than when they lifted weights.

Theory: While both running and weight lifting suppress *ghrelin*, a hormone that stimulates appetite, only vigorous aerobic exercise increases blood levels of *peptide YY*, a hormone that suppresses appetite.

If weight loss is one goal of your exercise routine: Aim to do aerobic exercise (such as brisk walking, running, cycling or swimming) for at least 30 minutes five days a week.

David J. Stensel, PhD, senior lecturer at the School of Sport and Exercise Sciences, Loughborough University, Leicestershire, UK.

A Good Excuse to Skip The Sit-Ups!

Sit-ups can hurt your back. The abdominal muscles are designed to keep your spine straight and secure. Sit-ups put an unhealthy strain on your back at its weakest point and can damage spinal discs. The best exercises for a firmer stomach and back health are ones that exercise your abdominals while holding your spine straight.

Examples: Lie on the floor, and raise your shoulders and head slightly without bending your back. Hold for 10 seconds. Push-ups also are good.

Stuart M. McGill, PhD, professor of spine biomechanics, University of Waterloo, Ontario, and author of *Ultimate Back Fitness and Performance* (*www.backfit pro.com*).

Three Simple Steps to Sleeker Thighs

Karen Burke, MD, PhD, a dermatologist in private practice in New York City and author of *Thin Thighs: Exercises and Recipes for Trim, Toned Thighs* (Hamlyn).

Lumpy cellulite can plague women of all sizes. Though it is composed of ordinary fat, cellulite gives a distinctive dimpled appearance.

Why women have it worse: Women have sacs of soft, spongy fat cells divided by connective tissues arranged in a series of arches that point outward, rippling the skin's surface, especially on hips and thighs. In men, fat sacs are smaller...connective tissues are more net-like...and the skin is thicker—so the surface is smoother. *Helpful...*

•**Adopt an anti-cellulite diet.** Losing excess weight shrinks fat cells—but what you eat is as important as how much (even if you are slim).

Best: Eat less fat—dietary fat converts easily into body fat and triggers production of *galanin*, a hormone that increases cravings for yet more fatty food. Avoid sugar and alcohol—these increase insulin levels, inhibiting fat breakdown and facilitating fat storage. Get more fiber and protein—these digest slowly, so you feel fuller longer.

•**Do the right type of exercise.** Stretching and toning activities (yoga, tai chi, ballet) and isometrics (in which you hold contracted muscles in a static position) lengthen and smooth muscles, giving thighs a sleeker appearance.

Try this: Stand up with feet shoulder-width apart. Contract your abdominal muscles, and squeeze buttocks together...hold for 10 seconds...release...repeat 10 times.

•**Use daily self-massage.** Physically manipulating cellulite improves circulation, inhibiting blood vessel constriction that exacerbates lumpiness...and makes massaged areas swell slightly, so skin looks smoother for about a day. Some research suggests that anti-cellulite creams with caffeine and vitamin E help break down stored fat and promote skin elasticity (though no human studies confirm this). Try these creams if you choose to...or apply any lotion or oil to your thighs so your hands glide smoothly. Massage for five to 15 minutes, applying firm pressure with the heels of your hands and stroking from the toes toward the tops of the legs, following the direction that blood flows as it returns to the heart.

Do Yoga and Stand Tall

Elderly women who spent nine weeks doing yoga gained an average of one centimeter in height because they stood more upright and crouched less. They also walked faster, used longer strides and could balance longer on one leg by the end of the program.

Jinsup Song, DPM, PhD, assistant professor, Temple University, Philadelphia.

Amazing Juice Relieves Muscle Pain

In a recent finding, runners who drank pure tart cherry juice immediately after a long run had 23% less pain than those who drank a placebo cherry drink. Tart cherry juice has strong anti-inflammatory properties that also could help fight arthritis and heart disease. Tart cherry juice comes from the Montmorency, or sour pie, cherry and may have properties similar to anti-inflammatory medications.

Study by researchers at Oregon Health & Science University, Portland, Oregon, presented at the American College of Sports Medicine Conference.

The Secret to Better Workout Recovery

After your workout, take a hot shower for five minutes, then turn the water as cold as you can stand for one minute. Repeat this for at least three cycles, and end with cold water. Alternating between hot and cold water dilates your blood vessels and helps facilitate circulation, reducing inflammation and pain, which helps you recover faster.

Men's Journal, 1290 Avenue of the Americas, New York City 10104, www.mensjournal.com.

Joining a Gym Can Save You Money

The typical obese American spent $1,429 more on health care than a typical person who maintained a healthy weight in 2006—the latest year for which statistics are available. A health-club membership costs roughly $775 a year*—so buying one and using the club regularly could reduce your total annual expenses.

What to do: Look for a club whose facilities make you more likely to attend regularly.

Money, Time-Life Bldg., Rockefeller Center, New York City 10020, http://money.cnn.com.

*Price subject to change.

Before You Join a Gym...

When considering a gym membership, be especially leery of clubs that push you to pay the entire year's membership up front. That could be a sign of the club's questionable financial health. Understand what "free" means. At the end of a free trial month, if you choose not to join the gym, you may have to officially cancel the membership or be billed for the next month. Also, be sure to visit the gym at the times you are most likely to use it so that you can see how crowded it is. And, know the terms of the agreement—are you allowed to use only a certain location...which services cost extra? Finally, don't sign up on the spot. Take the promotional materials and a copy of the agreement, and read them thoroughly when you are not under any pressure.

The New York Times, www.nytimes.com.

5

Natural News

Lessons for Living Longer from the People Who Live the *Longest*

The average life expectancy in the US is 78.2 years, an age that is far less than our potential maximum for life span.

On the Japanese island of Okinawa, there are approximately 50 centenarians (those who reach 100 years or more) per 100,000 people. In the US, at most 20 per 100,000 people reach this impressive milestone.

A long life is not an accident. Writer and longevity expert Dan Buettner, in conjunction with the National Institute on Aging and the nation's top gerontologists, has studied what he calls the world's Blue Zones, areas where people live unexpectedly long and healthy lives. In addition to Okinawa, the Blue Zones include Sardinia, Italy…Loma Linda, California

(home to many Seventh-day Adventists)…and the Nicoya Peninsula in Costa Rica.

An important finding: Only about 25% of longevity is determined by genetics. The other 75% is largely determined by the choices that we make every day.

The average American could live up to 14 more good years by putting the following habits to work…

CHOOSE ACTIVITY, NOT "EXERCISE"

In Sardinia, where the rate of centenarians is 208 per 100,000, many men work as shepherds. They hike for miles every day. Similarly, people in Okinawa get hours of daily exercise in their gardens. California's Seventh-day Adventists, one of the longest-living groups in the US, take frequent nature walks.

Dan Buettner, founder of Blue Zones, an organization that studies the regions of the world where people commonly live active lives past the age of 100, *www. bluezones.com*. Based in Minneapolis, he is a writer for *National Geographic* and author of *The Blue Zones: Lessons for Living Longer from the People Who've Lived the Longest* (National Geographic).

What these groups have in common is regular, low-intensity physical exercise. They don't necessarily lift weights or run in marathons. They merely stay active—and they do it every day throughout their lives.

Everyday physical activity improves balance and reduces the risk for falls, a common cause of death among seniors. It also lowers blood pressure and improves cardiovascular health. It increases the odds that people will be functionally independent in their later years.

Recommended: 30 to 60 minutes of moderate physical activity daily. This could include riding a bicycle or walking instead of driving.

EAT LESS

Okinawan elders intone this adage before eating—*hara hachi bu*—a reminder to stop eating when their stomachs are 80% full.

People who quit eating when they're no longer hungry (rather than eating until they feel full) find it easy to maintain a healthy weight, which reduces the risk for heart disease. This approach is more natural than conventional diets. *Helpful…*

• **Serve yourself at the kitchen counter, then put the food away.** People who do this tend to eat about 14% less than those who don't.

• **Use smaller plates and bowls.** Doing so makes servings look larger, which helps you eat less. In one study, people who ate from a 34-ounce bowl took in 31% more than those who used a 17-ounce bowl. Similarly, people drink at least 25% more when they use short, wide glasses instead of tall, narrow ones.

• **Buy small.** Most people consume about 150 more calories when they take food from large packages than when they take it from smaller ones.

LIMIT MEAT

In every Blue Zone, meat is consumed, at most, a few times per month. People in these communities live primarily on beans, whole grains, vegetables and other plant foods. All of these foods are high in fiber, antioxidants and anticancer compounds. All traditional Sardinians, Nicoyans and Okinawans eat what is produced in their gardens supplemented by staples—durum wheat (Sardinia), sweet potato (Okinawa) and maize (Nicoya). Strict Adventists avoid meat entirely.

Studies of Seventh-day Adventists show that a relatively high proportion eat nuts (any kind). Those who eat about two ounces of nuts five or more times a week have heart disease rates that are only half those who rarely eat nuts.

CONSIDER WINE

Studies of long-lived people suggest that drinking alcohol in moderation is a powerful factor in living longer. It is consumed in three of the Blue Zones (Okinawa, Sardinia and Costa Rica). In Sardinia, the shepherds drink about one-quarter bottle of red wine a day. Their wine has two to three times more flavonoids than other wines (because of the hot climate and the way the wine is made). Flavonoids reduce arterial inflammation. Inflammation has been linked to atherosclerosis, diabetes and Alzheimer's disease.

CULTIVATE A SENSE OF PURPOSE

A study funded by the National Institutes of Health (NIH) found that people who are excited by life and feel that they're making a difference tend to live longer (and healthier) lives than those who just "get by."

Okinawans call it *ikigai* and Nicoyans call it *plan de vida*, but in both cultures, the phrase essentially translates to why I wake up in the morning. Anything that gives you a sense of purpose—even something as simple as taking pleasure in watching your children or grandchildren grow up well—can add years to your life.

DE-STRESS

Many people don't recognize that the 24/7 American lifestyle is literally toxic. It produces a chronic increase in stress hormones that triggers inflammation throughout the body.

Most of the world's longest-lived people incorporate some form of meaningful downtime into their daily lives. Nicoyans take a break every afternoon to socialize with friends. For Adventists, the Saturday Sabbath is a time to rest.

EMBRACE YOUR SPIRITUAL SIDE

Faith is a key element that most centenarians have in common. The Sardinians and Nicoyans are primarily Catholic. Okinawans have a blended religion that stresses ancestor worship. The Adventists provide a strong religious community. People who attend religious services are about one-third less likely to die in a given period than those who don't. Even among people who don't go to church, those with spiritual beliefs have less depression, better immunity and lower rates of heart disease.

PUT FAMILY FIRST

In the Blue Zones, a great emphasis is placed on family—and people who live with or maintain close ties with their families get sick less often than those without these ties. They also are more likely to maintain better mental and social skills throughout their lives.

tives of about 100,000 women (age 50 and older) found that those who were "cynically hostile"—highly mistrustful and resentful of others—were 16% more likely to die from any cause during the eight-year study period than those who were the least cynically hostile.

Theory: Negative attitudes may contribute to high blood pressure, heart disease and other health problems.

If you tend to be cynical and mistrustful: In addition to eating well and exercising, consider extending your social network...and, if necessary, talk with a therapist to help change your thinking.

Hilary A. Tindle, MD, assistant professor of medicine at the University of Pittsburgh School of Medicine in Pennsylvania.

Here's to Long Life! Wine Extends Life Span For Men

In a study of 1,373 men, those who drank wine—on average, less than one-half glass daily—lived an average of five years longer than abstainers of alcohol and two-and-a-half years longer than beer and spirits drinkers.

Theory: The cardiovascular benefits of wine may account for the added longevity. More research is needed to assess whether these findings would also apply to women.

Marinette Streppel, PhD, researcher, division of human nutrition, Wageningen University, Wageningen, the Netherlands.

For a Longer Life, Drop The Negativity Now

Mental attitudes may affect life span. *See below...*

Recent study: Researchers who analyzed results that measured attitudes and perspec-

Aging Reversed for Real! (Anyone Can Do It)

Paul McGlothin and Meredith Averill, who have both practiced calorie restriction for 17 years. They are the directors of the CR Way Longevity Center in Ossining, New York, and leaders of the CR Society International. They are the authors of *The CR Way: Using the Secrets of Calorie Restriction for a Longer, Healthier Life* (HarperCollins) and the online e-book *The CR Way to Happy Dieting*, a guide to changing your biochemistry so that you feel optimistic most of the time. Their Web site is *www.livingthecrway.com*.

Seventy years of scientific research shows that restricting calories to 30% below normal intake can extend life span by up to 50% in laboratory animals. Recent research shows that calorie restriction may extend the life span of human beings as well.

Here, Paul McGlothin and Meredith Averill, internationally recognized experts on calorie restriction and authors of *The CR Way: Using the Secrets of Calorie Restriction for a Longer, Healthier Life* describe some of their important findings...

LATEST RESEARCH

Reporting in *Science* in 2009, researchers from the University of Wisconsin revealed all the results of a study on calorie restriction in rhesus monkeys, our closest "relatives." The researchers studied 76 adult rhesus monkeys (which live an average of 27 years and a maximum of 40), dividing them into two groups. One group ate a calorie-restricted diet, and one didn't. After 20 years, 37% of the monkeys in the nonrestricted group had died, compared with only 13% in the calorie-restricted group. The calorie-restricted monkeys also had fewer incidences of heart disease, diabetes, cancer and brain disease.

In research published in 2007, scientists at Washington University School of Medicine in St. Louis studied the biomarkers of aging of 33 people, average age 51, who ate a calorie-restricted diet for an average of six years. Compared with another group of people who ate a typical American diet, the calorie-restricted practitioners had lab results that are typical of people much younger than themselves. They had lower cholesterol, lower blood pressure, less body fat and lower glucose (blood sugar) levels.

The study participants also had lower levels of *insulin* (the hormone that regulates blood sugar)…*C-reactive protein* (a biomarker for disease-causing inflammation)…*tumor necrosis factor* (a biomarker for an overactive immune system)…and *thyroid hormone T3* (lower levels indicate a slower, cell-preserving metabolic rate).

WHY IT WORKS

There are several theories as to why calorie restriction improves health and may increase life span. *It may…*

• **Reduce DNA damage.**

• **Reduce daily energy expenditure,** the most basic of metabolic processes, thereby reducing *oxidative stress*, the internal "rust" that damages cells.

• **Decrease core body temperature.** The higher your normal body temperature is, the faster you age.

• **Improve how the body's cells handle insulin,** which controls glucose. Poor glucose regulation damages cells.

• **Improve your *neuroendocrine* system,** the crucial link between the brain and the hormones that regulate many of the body's functions.

• **Activate a type of gene called *sirtuins*,** which protect *mitochondria*, tiny energy factories in the cells. Mitochondrial failure speeds aging.

EASY WAY TO CUT BACK

The level of calorie restriction probably required to extend life in humans—about 20% to 30% of typical intake—is more than most people are willing to do on a regular basis, but reducing calories by even 5% can produce significant health benefits.

Estimated calorie requirements for a moderately active person age 51 or older are 2,200 to 2,400 calories a day for a man and 1,800 for a woman. Reducing calories by 5% would mean cutting between 110 and 120 daily calories for a man and 90 for a woman.

With just a few changes in your dietary routine, you easily can reduce calories by 5% or more and improve your health…

• **Favor nutrient-dense foods.** A nutrient-dense food has a high amount of nutrients per calorie. They're the healthiest foods to eat. *They include…*

Animal protein: Salmon (Alaskan wild—canned, fresh or frozen), sardines, tuna.

Good fats: Nuts…avocados…grapeseed oil, extra-virgin olive oil.

Beans: Adzuki, pinto, soy, black-eyed peas, black turtle beans, garbanzos (chickpeas), lentils (red or green), mung, lima.

Veggies: Arugula, beets, bok choy, broccoli, cabbage, carrots, chard, collard greens, garlic, kale, kohlrabi, leeks, mushrooms (maitake, portobello, shiitake), mustard greens, onions, romaine lettuce, spinach, squash (butternut, summer), sweet potatoes, tomatoes.

Grains: Barley, quinoa, wild rice, sprouted-grain breads.

Fruit: Apricots, blackberries, blueberries, cantaloupe, cranberries, kiwi, lemons, limes, oranges, peaches, raspberries, strawberries, tangerines.

Spices and herbs: Season foods with herbs and spices rather than salt, butter or sugar. Examples include basil, chives, ginger, parsley and turmeric.

• **Focus on foods with low-to-moderate *Glycemic Index* rankings.** High levels of glucose and insulin are linked to faster aging and disease. It's just as important to limit glucose as it is to limit calories.

The best way to regulate glucose and insulin is to choose carbohydrates with a low-to-moderate score on the Glycemic Index (GI)—carbohydrates that digest slowly so that glucose and insulin levels don't suddenly skyrocket.

The beans, veggies, grains and fruits that are nutrient-dense (listed above) have low-to-moderate GIs.

Other ways to keep glucose low...

• Start your meal with one cup of water with one tablespoon of lemon juice, which lowers glucose.

• Finish your last meal of the day as early as possible, eating complex carbohydrates and a fat source.

• After your evening meal, take a 45-minute or longer walk.

• **Keep protein intake moderate.** Excess protein can increase blood levels of the hormone *Insulin-Like Growth Factor-I* (or IGF-I), which deactivates a sirtuin gene and accelerates aging.

Each day, consume 0.36 grams of protein per pound of body weight—at your healthiest, ideal body weight. That's 43 grams of protein a day for a woman whose ideal weight is 120 pounds and 55 grams of protein a day for a man whose ideal weight is 154 pounds. For comparison, typical intake for US adults is 65 grams to 90 grams. One ounce of meat or fish contains about seven grams of protein.

• **Stop eating before you are full.** Always leave the table slightly hungry. This helps you cut calories and prompts the *hypothalamus*— the emotion-generating part of the brain—to produce the hormone *orexin*, which increases feelings of happiness. The Japanese created a concept for this healthful practice—*hara hachi bu*—which means eat until you're 80% full.

Web Site Calculates Your Chance of Living to 100

Estimate your chance of living to 100 by visiting *www.livingto100.com* and answering 40 questions about family history, health, diet and lifestyle. Have your cholesterol and blood-pressure numbers handy—you need to enter them. The site, created by Thomas Perls, MD, who is the founder of the New England Centenarian Study, lets you see how your answers influence longevity, so you can change life-shortening habits if you want to.

The Science of Staying Young: Six Simple Ways to Add Years to Your Life

John E. Morley, MD, the Dammert Professor of Gerontology and director of the division of geriatric medicine at Saint Louis University School of Medicine. He also is director of geriatric research at the Saint Louis Veterans Affairs Medical Center and is coauthor, with Sheri R. Colberg, PhD, of *The Science of Staying Young* (McGraw-Hill).

If someone asked you to predict how long you will live, chances are you would base your answer, in part, on the life span of your parents. Undoubtedly, genetics do play a powerful role in longevity.

What you might not realize: Anywhere from 50% to 80% of a person's longevity is determined by factors within our control.

Even though you may be surprised to learn that the lifestyle choices you make each day have such a profound impact on how long you live, there is a simple principle to keep in mind if you want to extend your life span.

How to live as long as possible: Improve the health of the cells in your body. With each decade we live, our cells divide less rapidly. This slowdown is associated with declines in muscle mass and bone strength and with the onset of chronic diseases, such as heart disease.

We can't stop this process altogether, but we can slow the rate at which it occurs. Research shows that by eating a healthful diet, exercising regularly, avoiding dangerous behaviors (such as smoking) and taking particular steps to protect general health, many people could add a decade or even more to their lives.

Specific actions that can give you a longer—and healthier—life…

1. Keep your balance. Falling is among the strongest predictors of premature disability and death. Most falls are due to impaired balance, which is caused by declines in muscle strength, decreased flexibility and degeneration of nerves.

Try the dance test: To assess a patient's balance, I dance with him/her in my office. If the patient has difficulty following dance steps…cannot lift his feet off the ground…or has trouble balancing during turns, there may be a potentially dangerous problem with gait and/or balance.

My recommendation: Perform balance-specific exercises once a day (for 15 to 30 seconds per exercise).* *Examples*…

•Stand in different ways—with your eyes closed…with your head tilted to one side…or with your hands held away from your body.

•While standing in bare feet, put a towel on the floor and practice gripping it with the toes of one foot and then the other.

2. Increase your "SPA." People who exercise tend to live longer and remain healthier—but it's possible to gain even greater benefits by getting more *spontaneous physical activity* (SPA), daily physical exertions that complement "formal" exercise routines.

Suppose you burn 200 calories daily by walking about an hour at a leisurely pace. That's a good start, but you'll do better if you find ways to stay active the *rest* of the time. A study of older adults ages 70 to 82 found that for every 287 calories expended per day during physical activities (primarily SPA), they increased their chances of living longer by 68%.

My recommendation: Boost your SPA by doing housework, for example, or gardening.

*Make sure that someone is with you to monitor your balance when you first try these exercises.

3. Supplement with *testosterone*. Traditionally, replacement of testosterone has been recommended only for men who have extremely low levels of the hormone. Yet there is good evidence that millions of American men—and women—with even slightly low testosterone levels could benefit from replacement therapy.

Men with low testosterone have an increased risk for cardiovascular disease and are more likely to suffer from depression and fatigue. In addition, there appears to be a link between low testosterone and Alzheimer's disease. In women, low testosterone is a leading cause of low libido along with declines in muscle mass and bone density.

My recommendation: Get tested for bio-available testosterone (the form that is available to the body's tissues) if you suffer from chronic fatigue, moodiness or depression—or if you've noticed a decline in libido and/or sexual function. Low testosterone can be treated with a gel or patch (usually at a starting dose of 5 mg for men) or with twice-monthly injections. (Women typically are prescribed a lower dose.)

New alternative for men: A small, tablet-like testosterone-replacement product that is held between the cheek and gum.

Important: There has been some concern that long-term testosterone replacement might increase the risk for prostate cancer in some men. Although the research has not definitively found this association, I suggest that men using testosterone play it safe and get an annual prostate examination and prostate-specific antigen (PSA) blood test.

The safety of long-term testosterone use in women is also of concern. Any patient who chooses this treatment should be closely monitored by a doctor.

4. Get more *alpha lipoic acid*. It's a very powerful antioxidant (more potent than vitamin E) that reduces free-radical damage within the *mitochondria*—energy-producing parts of cells. Damage to mitochondria is thought to be a main cause of cellular aging.

My recommendation: Eat more foods that are high in alpha lipoic acid (such as spinach, broccoli, tomatoes, potatoes, green peas and brussels sprouts). If you have diabetic neuropathy, painful nerve damage that often occurs in people with diabetes, take 600 mg of alpha lipoic acid daily. The same dose also may improve memory and slow the progression of Alzheimer's disease.

5. Consume alcohol. Red wine is widely recognized for its heart-protective effects, but recent research has found that *any* alcoholic beverage, including hard liquor (such as vodka or whiskey) and beer, can help you live longer.

Why is this so? Cell membranes get more rigid with age, impairing the ability of molecules to effectively communicate with one another. Alcohol is thought to make the cell membranes less rigid and to improve cellular functions.

My recommendation: Men should imbibe no more than two drinks daily…and women no more than one drink daily.

Important: Even one daily drink has been associated with an increased risk for breast cancer.

6. Drink green tea. It has a five- to tenfold higher concentration of polyphenol antioxidants than black tea. One such antioxidant, *epigallocatechin*, improves the liver's ability to break down potential carcinogens, potentially reducing cancer risk. People who drink three or more cups of green tea daily also are less likely to experience age-related cognitive declines.

My recommendation: For cancer-fighting and brain-protective effects, consume three or more cups of green tea daily.

Why a Bad Economy Can Be *Good* for Your Health

US death rates dropped during the 1974 and 1982 recessions and rose during the recovery of the 1980s.

Theory: Time is more valuable when the economy is good, so people work more and spend less time exercising and with family,

leading to stress, which can be bad for health. During downturns, people spend more time taking care of themselves and their children, which is good for health.

Christopher J. Ruhm, PhD, Jefferson-Pilot Excellence Professor of Economics, University of North Carolina, Greensboro, and author of a study of economic conditions and health, published in The Quarterly Journal of Economics.

Still Trying to Be Perfect? Why You Should Stop Now

Older individuals who expressed a strong motivation to be perfect were 51% more likely to die during a six-and-a-half-year study than people who had considerably lower self-expectations.

Prem S. Fry, PhD, research professor, graduate psychology program, Trinity Western University, Langley, British Columbia, Canada, and leader of a study of 450 people, published in Journal of Health Psychology.

Take a Stand to Live Longer

Spending more time standing can help you to live longer. People who spend the most time sitting have increased risk for premature death from cardiovascular disease and other causes—even if they exercise regularly.

Self-defense: Even if you have a desk job, get up as often as possible.

Peter Katzmarzyk, PhD, associate executive director of population science, Pennington Biomedical Research Center, Baton Rouge, Louisiana, and coauthor of a 12-year study of more than 17,000 people, reported in Medicine & Science in Sports & Exercise.

The Simple Supplement That May Prevent Killer Diseases

Joseph Maroon, MD, professor, neurological surgery and Heindl Scholar in Neuroscience at the University of Pittsburgh School of Medicine and team neurosurgeon for the Pittsburgh Steelers. He is the author of *The Longevity Factor: How Resveratrol and Red Wine Activate Genes for a Longer and Healthier Life* (Atria). His Web site is *www.josephmaroon.com*.

When it comes to "hot" supplements, resveratrol is high on the list. Multiple studies conducted on laboratory animals have demonstrated the highly beneficial effects of this *polyphenol* (a class of plant chemicals), which is found most abundantly in the skins of grapes and in red wine—and now is available in supplement form.

Key animal findings: Resveratrol has been shown not only to enhance muscle strength and decrease fatigue, but also to help prevent heart disease, stroke, diabetes and cancer... clear away the toxic proteins that cause Alzheimer's disease...and even lengthen life span by 25%.

But can this substance do the same for human beings?

AN IMPORTANT DISCOVERY

Resveratrol's first emergence as an antiaging and disease-fighting powerhouse began in the 1930s with a seemingly unrelated finding —that severe calorie restriction extended the lives of rodents by 40% to 50%.

It wasn't until the 1990s, however, that researchers at Harvard Medical School discovered the genetic basis for the beneficial effect of calorie restriction. Through various experiments in animal studies, calorie restriction was shown to trigger a kind of chain reaction that activates "survival genes" (*sirtuins*), which, in turn, energize an enzyme called SIR2 that stabilizes DNA. This process slows cellular aging. In further studies, researchers discovered that resveratrol is one of the most potent sources of the molecules that activate these survival genes.

CURRENT EVIDENCE

To further test resveratrol's power, researchers conducted other animal studies—this time without restriction of calories. Resveratrol and other polyphenols were found to increase the life span of fish by 60%...worms and flies by 30%...and mice by 25%—benefits attributed to improved cellular health.

Resveratrol-enhanced cells are believed to help fight...

• **Heart disease and stroke.** Resveratrol appears to decrease harmful inflammation, which contributes to cardiovascular disease.

Breakthrough research: A human study showed that drinking one-and-a-half glasses of red wine a day lowered, by 40%, levels of *lipid peroxide*, a by-product of inflammation that damages arteries. This and other health benefits are believed to be due to resveratrol and several other polyphenols in red wine.

Through various animal studies, resveratrol was found to help spark the production of the beneficial gas nitric oxide, which gives blood vessels more flexibility. Resveratrol also thins the blood, reducing the risk for an artery-clogging clot. In studies of animals with induced heart attacks, those given resveratrol had a significantly lower fatality rate. In similar studies on stroke, resveratrol prevented paralysis and limited brain injury in animals.

• **Cancer.** Eighteen different cancer types— including lung, colon, skin, liver and pancreatic—have been markedly inhibited by resveratrol in laboratory studies using animal and human cells.

• **Diabetes.** In animals, resveratrol helps to normalize blood sugar (or glucose) levels by moving glucose out of the bloodstream and into cells. Laboratory research also shows that resveratrol reduces diabetic neuropathy (nerve pain that often occurs in the legs and feet).

Recent finding: In a human study, a synthetic, resveratrol-like compound was shown to give people the same type of glucose control that resveratrol gives mice.

• **Alzheimer's disease.** In animal studies, resveratrol helps remove the amyloid-beta protein that has been associated with Alzheimer's disease.

Recent finding: In a study of 90 healthy people, researchers at Marywood University in Scranton found that a supplement containing resveratrol and other polyphenols improved memory and sped up reaction time.

RESVERATROL SOURCES

Even though the preliminary research is so promising, there is a caveat. You would have to drink up to 1,150 bottles of red wine daily to get the amount of resveratrol used in most animal studies.

Since that's not very feasible, I recommend a more practical approach that includes two things—a regular diet using resveratrol- and polyphenol-rich foods (the resveratrol is much lower than the doses used in animal studies, but these foods contain other beneficial compounds that may enhance absorption of resveratrol from food and/or supplements)...and the use of a mixed polyphenol supplement or a resveratrol supplement.

That strategy—along with regular exercise and a lifestyle that includes the health-promoting effects of close emotional bonds with family and friends—is your best bet for fighting off chronic disease and living longer. *My advice...*

•**Eat a polyphenol-rich diet.** Resveratrol is the superstar of polyphenols, but many scientists think that a *combination* of polyphenols—ingesting them together, as they are in nature—is the better way to activate survival genes.

The foods richest in resveratrol and a variety of other polyphenols...

•Red wine or red grape juice. These two are the top dietary sources of resveratrol. *Important:* Wine grapes offering the most resveratrol include pinot noir, merlot, grenache, cabernet sauvignon and tempranillo. (These wines also deliver up to about 500 different polyphenols along with resveratrol.) *Suggested daily intake:* Four to 16 ounces of red grape juice daily (be mindful of the sugar content). Up to 12 ounces of red wine daily for men...and no more than six ounces daily for women (the potential health benefit of daily wine consumption by women must be weighed against a possible increase in breast cancer risk).

•Pomegranate juice. It is a good source of resveratrol and many other antioxidants. *Suggested daily intake:* Three to five ounces.

•Dark chocolate. It is a rich source of concentrated *flavonols*, a potent type of polyphenol. Select unsweetened or semisweetened varieties with at least 70% cocoa. *Suggested daily intake:* One bite-sized square.

•Green tea. Green tea contains resveratrol and is rich in epigallocatechin gallate (EGCG) and other polyphenols. *Suggested daily intake:* Three eight-ounce cups. Decaffeinated green tea contains EGCG but relatively little resveratrol.

•Blueberries. They are rich in procyanidins and other polyphenols. *Suggested daily intake:* At least one cup (fresh or frozen).

•**Take a mixed-polyphenol supplement.** I recommend the mixed polyphenol supplement Vindure 900, a product developed by Vinomis Laboratories based on Harvard University research. Vindure is available from Vinomis Laboratories (877-484-6664 or *www.vinomis.com*).

Cost: $40* for 30 tablets. Follow the dosage recommendation on the label.

Because resveratrol absorption is thought to be enhanced when combined with other natural polyphenols, a mixed-polyphenol supplement is best.

However, an alternative is to...

•**Take a resveratrol supplement.** There are now more than 300 resveratrol-containing products available. All the better products are made with trans-resveratrol (the active form of the substance shown by professional testing to activate the sirtuin "survival genes")...and produced by manufacturers who comply with "Good Manufacturing Practices" (GMP), which ensures that the product contains no major contaminants.

My favorite resveratrol products are manufactured by...

•Longevinex, *www.longevinex.com* or 866-405-4000...30 capsules for $37.

•RevGenetics, *www.myrevgenetics.com* or 888-738-4363...30 capsules for $43.

Suggested intake for most resveratrol supplements: 250 mg to 500 mg daily.

*Prices subject to change.

A Tasty Way to Reduce Inflammation

People who drank 17 ounces of skim milk with 40 grams of unsweetened cocoa every day for four weeks had significantly lower levels of inflammation and higher levels of HDL (good) cholesterol, potentially slowing or preventing the development of atherosclerosis. Cocoa is rich in flavonoids, which may help to reduce inflammation.

Ramón Estruch, MD, PhD, senior consultant, department of internal medicine at University of Barcelona, Spain, and senior author of a study published in *The American Journal of Clinical Nutrition*.

The Case *Against* Statins: You Can Reduce Heart Disease Risk Without These Dangerous Drugs

Mark A. Stengler, NMD, naturopathic medical doctor in private practice, La Jolla, California...adjunct associate clinical professor at the National College of Natural Medicine, Portland, Oregon...the author of many books, including *The Natural Physician's Healing Therapies* and coauthor of *Prescription for Natural Cures* (both from Bottom Line Books)...and author of the *Bottom Line/Natural Healing* newsletter.

Statins—a group of medications used to decrease LDL (bad) cholesterol levels in the blood—are among the most popular drugs ever developed. You might recognize them by the names Lipitor (*atorvastatin*), Crestor (*rosuvastatin*) and Zocor (*simvastatin*), among others.

The number of people who might consider taking this type of medication has grown, thanks to a recent study showing that statins also might help to reduce inflammation—another important risk factor for heart attack and stroke. The JUPITER study (which stands for Justification for the Use of Statins in Primary Prevention: An Intervention Trial Evaluating Rosuvastatin) indicated that statins benefited people with *normal* cholesterol levels who had elevated levels of *C-reactive protein* (CRP), a sign of inflammation.

Statins do have a role in treating people with a history of heart attacks or other acute cardiovascular concerns, as well as those with extremely high total cholesterol (beyond 350 mg/dL) or very high LDL cholesterol (above 200 mg/dL) that cannot be treated with natural therapies. But for those people with only moderately elevated cholesterol or CRP, the scientific record and my clinical experience tell me that the dangers of statins outweigh their benefits. People within this group are better off avoiding these drugs and pursuing several safe, easy alternative ways to lower cholesterol and reduce inflammation.

EXAGGERATED UPSIDE

While statins have been shown to lower the statistical risk of heart attack and stroke, this effect is less impressive when you look at the number of people who actually benefit from the drugs.

Example: The JUPITER study reported that Crestor lowered the risk of heart attack or stroke by 50% in people with normal cholesterol and elevated CRP—a striking amount, until you discover that this number translates into preventing a single heart attack over two years' time for every 120 people on statins. A benefit, yes—but not enough to justify taking a lifetime regimen of costly drugs that may have dangerous side effects, especially when the same benefits can be attained naturally.

UNDERREPORTED DOWNSIDE

Statins block the activity of a liver enzyme that is crucial to the production of cholesterol and additional natural substances. By stifling this natural function of the liver—one of the body's most important organs—statins could cause a number of unwanted side effects, including liver damage, muscle pain, memory impairment and depletion of coenzyme Q10, an antioxidant that's needed for heart health. They also may reduce immune response, increase risk for diabetes and possibly elevate cancer risk.

Better way: Most people with moderately elevated cholesterol (total cholesterol of 200 to

239 mg/dL and/or LDL above 130 mg/dL) are better off trying to lower their cholesterol and CRP naturally.

HELP FROM DIET

Many of my patients have been able to bring their cholesterol levels into normal range and reduce CRP through diet. *How...*

• **Reduce saturated fat to 7% of your daily calories** by cutting back on all types of meat and whole-fat dairy products.

• **Avoid trans fats contained in deep-fried foods,** commercial baked goods, packaged snack foods, crackers, and anything with "partially hydrogenated" on the label.

• **Use health-promoting cooking oils,** such as extra-virgin olive oil, macadamia nut oil and avocado oil. These monounsaturated fats contain antioxidants and have been shown to reduce total and LDL cholesterol.

• **Consume two servings a week of omega-3–rich fish,** such as herring, sardines and salmon.

• **Eat five to seven servings a day of fruits and vegetables.**

• **Consume foods high in soluble fiber,** such as oats, beans, peas, apples and oranges. A daily bowl of oatmeal alone can reduce total cholesterol by up to 23%.

HELP FROM NATURAL SUBSTANCES

Natural substances can also help you lower cholesterol and reduce CRP levels.

To lower cholesterol: If a change in diet does not bring down your cholesterol sufficiently, try each of the natural substances below (one at a time), in the order in which they are described. If, in eight to 12 weeks, your cholesterol level has not improved, try the next supplement.

• **Red yeast rice extract.** This fermented rice product contains *monacolin K,* which inhibits the same liver enzyme involved in the synthesis of cholesterol that statins do. Studies show that it is effective for treating moderately elevated levels of total and LDL cholesterol, as well as triglycerides (a type of blood fat). Take 1,200 mg twice daily. Side effects, although rare and mild, may include heartburn, dizziness and gas. Do not take this supplement if

you have a liver disorder, particularly hepatitis, or are pregnant or breast-feeding.

Also recommended: Take 50 mg to 100 mg daily of coenzyme Q10, since red yeast rice may inhibit the body's natural production of this nutrient.

• **The plant sterols.** These plant membrane components can lower LDL by reducing cholesterol absorption in the small bowel. Use several teaspoons daily of a margarine substitute spread, such as Benecol. But, because sterols reduce the body's levels of beta-carotene, be sure to eat foods high in carotenoids, such as carrots, tomatoes and cantaloupe, and take a multivitamin containing beta-carotene.

• **Niacin.** This water-soluble vitamin (also known as vitamin B-3) increases HDL (good) cholesterol and lowers LDL cholesterol and triglycerides. It works by reducing production of proteins that transport cholesterol and triglycerides in the bloodstream. Niacin is recommended for people who have HDLs below 40 mg/dL, particularly if they have a history of heart disease. Take 1,500 to 3,000 mg daily. It can cause stomach upset if not taken with food. Some people do experience temporary warmth and/or flushing in the neck, ears and face. Try "flush-free" forms of niacin available over the counter. Women who are pregnant or breast-feeding should not take niacin.

To lower CRP: Diet alone can't always reduce CRP levels. Many of my patients also rely on anti-inflammatory nutrients. *Nutrients that can help...*

• **Multivitamins.** In one study, a daily multivitamin was shown to reduce CRP levels by 14%.

• **Vitamin D.** Recent research suggests that this vitamin protects the heart over the long term. Take 2,000 international units daily (including the amount in the multivitamin).

• **Omega-3 fish oils.** These can benefit the heart in a number of ways by mildly thinning the blood, lowering triglyceride levels and improving blood vessel flexibility. Take fish oil with a combined total of 1,500 mg to 2,000 mg of *eicosapentaenoic acid* (EPA) and *docosahexaenoic acid* (DHA).

To lower both cholesterol and CRP: Take both the red yeast rice and the omega-3 fish oils (in the amounts described above). If you do not see a benefit in about three months, don't continue taking them.

The Power of Peas

Purified proteins extracted from yellow garden peas lowered blood pressure by 20%, on average, in recent animal studies. The proteins also improved urine output, important for healthy kidney function.

American Chemical Society, *www.acs.org*.

Happy Music as Good For Your Heart as Aerobics

Joyful music promotes heart health, according to the latest research.

Recent study: When 10 men and women spent 30 minutes listening to music that they deemed joyful, their blood vessels widened by 26%, on average—an effect similar to that from aerobic exercise. When the participants heard music that caused anxiety, their blood vessels narrowed by 6%, on average.

Theory: Pleasurable music triggers the release of brain chemicals that promote the production of nitric oxide, which causes blood vessels to relax.

For heart health: Listen to whatever music you find joyful.

Michael Miller, MD, director, Center for Preventive Cardiology at University of Maryland Heart Center in Baltimore.

Chickpeas Curb Cholesterol

In recent research, 45 adults with high total cholesterol levels (250 mg/dL, on average) ate at least 25 ounces (about three cups) of canned chickpeas (garbanzo beans) per week for 12 weeks.

Result: The participants' total cholesterol levels dropped by 7.7 points, on average.

Theory: Chickpeas are high in fiber and polyunsaturated fats, which help reduce total cholesterol when they replace saturated fats.

Self-defense: Enjoy chickpeas in hummus, salads and other dishes.

J.K. Pittaway, researcher and lecturer in health and biomedical science, University of Tasmania, Launceston, Tasmania, Australia.

Fatty Fish Fights Heart Failure

Eating fatty fish just once a week lowers men's risk for heart failure.

Reason: Fatty fish such as salmon, herring, mackerel, whitefish and char contain omega-3 fatty acids.

One weekly three-ounce serving of any of these fish reduced heart failure risk by 12%.

Emily Levitan, ScD, research fellow, Cardiovascular Epidemiology Research Unit at Beth Israel Deaconess Medical Center, Boston, and lead author of a study of 39,367 men, published in the online edition of *European Heart Journal*.

Get More Shut Eye to Protect Your Arteries

Lack of sleep is linked to hardening of the arteries. In a recent study of 495 men and women, 27% of those who slept fewer than five hours nightly developed coronary artery calcification (hardening of the arteries) over a five-year period. The rate was 11% for those who slept five to seven hours...and 6% for those who slept more than seven hours.

Theory: People who get insufficient sleep might have a higher average blood pressure than people who get adequate sleep, raising the risk for artery calcification.

Self-defense: Aim to get at least six hours of uninterrupted sleep nightly.

Diane Lauderdale, PhD, associate professor of epidemiology, University of Chicago.

Nuts Now to Prevent Heart Disease

In a recent study among women who have type-2 diabetes (which puts them at high risk for heart disease), those who ate five or more servings a week of nuts or peanut butter had a 44% lower risk for heart disease than those who rarely or never ate these foods.

Theory: Monounsaturated fat in nuts reduces cholesterol and inflammation.

Best: At least five times weekly, have one ounce of nuts or one tablespoon of peanut butter.

Frank Hu, MD, PhD, professor of nutrition and epidemiology, Harvard School of Public Health, Boston, and lead author of a 22-year study of 6,309 women.

Early to Bed for a Healthy Heart

A late bedtime is linked to higher heart disease risk.

Recent finding: In a study of 251 healthy men, those who typically went to bed after midnight were more likely to exhibit arterial stiffening, which is an early stage of *athero-*

sclerosis (hardening of the arteries)—a heart disease risk factor.

Theory: A late bedtime may promote insulin resistance (a condition in which the body is less able to respond to insulin), which can lead to atherosclerosis and heart disease.

Yu Misao, MD, PhD, chief researcher, laboratory of disease prevention, department of medicine, Misao Health Clinic, Gifu, Japan.

Wine Boosts Healthy Omega-3s

Moderate wine consumption increases the body's levels of heart-healthy omega-3s. The increase was greater for wine drinkers than for those drinking other alcoholic beverages. This means components other than alcohol are likely responsible for the boost in omega-3s. The results apply only to moderate wine consumption—up to two glasses a day for men and one glass a day for women.

Romina di Giuseppe, a doctor in food science and technology and researcher in nutritional epidemiology, Catholic University, Campobasso, Italy, and leader of a study of 1,604 people, published in *The American Journal of Clinical Nutrition.*

No More Fishy Burps

To prevent fish oil's aftertaste and fishy burps, take these capsules *frozen*—they will break down more slowly and still be fully digested. Or, take a capsule at the start of a meal—food mixes with the capsule in the stomach, reducing the fishy burp. You could also try a capsule with enteric coating that lets it pass through the stomach and dissolve in the intestines. Switching brands might work as well—better-purified capsules have fewer side effects, although they usually cost more.

Mayo Clinic Health Letter, 200 First St. SW, Rochester, Minnesota 55905, *www.healthletter.mayoclinic.com.*

Ommm...Meditation Lowers Heart Risk 47%

Patients with coronary heart disease practiced transcendental meditation (TM) for 20 minutes twice a day for five years, on average...or got instruction in heart-protecting diet and exercise habits. Meditators were 47% less likely than nonmeditators to have a heart attack or stroke, or to die.

Information: www.tm.org.

Robert Schneider, MD, director, Institute for Natural Medicine and Prevention, Maharishi University of Management, Fairfield, Iowa, and leader of a study of 201 heart patients.

Sweet Treat for Heart Attack Patients

The survivors of a first heart attack who ate chocolate at least twice weekly were 66% less likely to die from heart disease than those who never ate chocolate. Other sweets were not linked to reduced mortality.

Theory: Antioxidants from cocoa improve blood pressure and blood flow.

If you eat dessert, consider chocolate—but keep portions small to avoid weight gain.

Imre Janszky, MD, PhD, postdoctoral research fellow, department of public health sciences, Karolinska Institute, Stockholm, Sweden, and leader of an eight-year study of 1,169 people.

A Common Drink That Reduces Stroke Risk 21%

A recent analysis of nine studies involving nearly 195,000 adults found that for each additional three cups of black or green tea consumed daily, stroke risk dropped by 21%.

Theory: The antioxidant *epigallocatechin gallate* or the amino acid *theanine*, both found in tea, may provide anti-inflammatory effects that protect the heart and brain. (The processing for decaffeinated tea may remove these ingredients.)

Lenore Arab, PhD, professor of medicine and biological chemistry, David Geffen School of Medicine, University of California, Los Angeles.

Popular Foods Increase Diabetes Risk

Among middle-aged nondiabetic patients, those who ate the most red meat, refined grains, fried potatoes, tomato-based products (lasagna, enchiladas), eggs and cheese were four times more likely to get type 2 diabetes within five years than those who ate the least of these—regardless of body weight.

Best: Eat fruits, vegetables, whole grains, low-fat dairy and beneficial fats, such as olive oil and nuts.

Angela D. Liese, PhD, associate professor, department of epidemiology and biostatistics, University of South Carolina, Columbia, and leader of a study of 880 people.

Great Medicine for Diabetics—Laughter!

Researchers recently looked at laughter's effect on people who have diabetes. In this one-year study, 20 diabetes patients received medication for their diabetic condition, including *glipizide* (Glucotrol), but the other group also watched humorous movies (which they selected) for 30 minutes daily. After one year, 26% of the "laughter group" patients had higher levels of HDL "good" cholesterol, compared with 3% of patients in the other group. The laughter group also had lower levels of inflammatory chemicals (such as *C-reactive protein*) linked with cardiovascular disease. Based on this research, people who have diabetes or are at risk for the disease may benefit from treating themselves to a good dose of laughter every day. If you follow this advice, choose any form of humor or comedy that appeals to you (such as movies, TV shows or books) and that produces joyful laughter.

Lee Berk, DrPH, MPH, a preventive care specialist and psychoneuroimmunologist, Loma Linda University, Loma Linda, California.

What Your Reflexes Say About Your Health

Jamison Starbuck, ND, a naturopathic physician in family practice in Missoula, Montana. She is past president of the American Association of Naturopathic Physicians and a contributing editor to *The Alternative Advisor: The Complete Guide to Natural Therapies and Alternative Treatments* (Time Life).

When you're getting a physical exam, chances are you don't give it much thought if the doctor taps on your knees, ankles and other parts of your body with a small, hammerlike device (known as a reflex hammer). This type of reflex testing is crucial to assessing the health of your spinal cord and even may offer clues about a hidden illness. Unfortunately, this testing is often neglected during routine physicals.

Failure to perform this test is a problem, particularly for patients over age 65. Research has found that about 26% of adults ages 65 to 74 who receive the test have a *neurologic deficit* (a deficiency in nerve function), such as diminished reflexes or response to pain, and 54% of people over age 85 exhibit such a disorder. At the same time, statistics indicate that in adults over age 65, the presence of a neurologic deficit is associated with an increased risk for dying, even in the absence of a specific disease.

It would be useful if you could test your reflexes yourself, but you cannot—the mind inevitably creates a biased response. That is why it's important to make sure that your doctor does the complete test (described below) when you get a physical exam. During the reflex test, your doctor should tap various tendons either with the reflex hammer or by putting his finger over your tendon and then tapping his finger.

The five parts of the body most commonly included in a reflex test are the biceps (the muscle extending from the shoulder joint to the elbow)...triceps (the muscle on the back of the arm)...just below the knees...the heels (the Achilles tendons)...and the soles of the feet. Each of these corresponds to a portion of the spine. For each of these sites, the reflex response is graded according to five categories—absent, underactive, normal, hyperactive (brisk) and hyperactive with spasm.

Here's what the results may mean...

• **A diminished reflex response can point to a variety of neurologic diseases or non-neurologic conditions,** including metabolic disturbances such as low potassium or hypothyroidism (underactive thyroid), drug toxicity or a deficiency of vitamin B-12. Or, it can be a normal variant. Hyperthyroidism (overactive thyroid), hypocalcemia (low blood calcium), Parkinson's, drug toxicity, muscle spasms or chronic pain can cause a "brisk," or hyperactive, response.

• **When one of my patients shows an abnormal reflex response, I check for other signs of illness or injury.** For example, I test blood levels of vitamin B-12 and order a metabolic panel (including various electrolytes, calcium and blood sugar). Or I might refer the person to a specialist, such as a neurologist. If I can't identify a specific problem, I might prescribe yoga, walking or a stretching program and re-examine the patient in six weeks. Movement and improved circulation frequently normalize reflex responses.

To keep your nervous system healthy: Eat mineral-rich foods (such as leafy greens and whole grains) and take a daily B-complex supplement (including 50 mg of vitamin B-6 and a total of 800 micrograms of vitamin B-12—take a separate B-12 supplement, if necessary).

What Your Feet Tell About the Rest Of Your Body

Johanna S. Youner, DPM, a board-certified podiatrist in private practice, *www.healthyfeetny.com*, and an attending podiatric surgeon at New York University Downtown Hospital, both in New York City. She serves as a spokesperson for the American Podiatric Medical Association.

During a foot exam, your podiatrist also will look for any signs of medical conditions that affect other parts of your body, and if any of the following are present, perhaps refer you to a specialist (such as a neurologist or oncologist)…

• **Circulatory problems.** The podiatrist may squeeze one of your toes until it turns very white to see how quickly the toe regains its normal color, indicating that blood has flowed back into the capillaries. If the color doesn't return within a few seconds, you may have impaired blood flow, which could signal arterial blockages in other parts of the body.

• **Neurological disorders.** If you pull your feet away because you're oversensitive to your podiatrist's touch (such as when he/she cuts your toenails), this may be a sign of *hyperreflexia*. This condition can be an early indicator of Parkinson's disease or multiple sclerosis.

• **Diabetes.** If your feet are insensitive to the podiatrist's touch, this may signal neuropathy—damage to the nerves in the feet that often is an early sign of diabetes.

• **Melanoma.** Your podiatrist should check your soles and between your toes for abnormal moles that could indicate melanoma. These often-overlooked areas get very little sun exposure, yet they can hide a melanoma tumor.

Biblical Oil Fights Cancer

Frankincense oil, an herb-derived oil referenced in the Bible, appears to selectively kill bladder cancer cells without harming normal cells. This finding suggests that the oil may be used in the future as a therapy for bladder cancer.

BioMed Central, *www.biomedcentral.com.*

Grab a Handful of These Tasty Nuts to Curb Cancer Risk

Pistachios may cut risk of cancer. They are high in *gamma-tocopherol*, a form of vitamin E shown to be protective against lung cancer and other cancers.

Recent study: Participants who ate approximately two ounces (about 100 nuts) a day for four weeks showed a significant increase in gamma-tocopherol.

Best: A few handfuls daily.

Ladia Hernandez, PhD, senior research dietitian, department of epidemiology, University of Texas MD Anderson Cancer Center, Houston, and lead investigator of a study presented at a recent American Association for Cancer Research conference.

Wristbands Reduce Nausea from Radiation Treatment

In a study, cancer patients undergoing radiation wore wristbands that press on an acupuncture point which, according to traditional Chinese medicine, relieves nausea. Half were told that wristbands eased nausea…the others were not told. Patients in both groups experienced a 24% decrease in nausea, on average—compared with a 5% decrease among patients not given wristbands. Acupressure wristbands cost $5 to $10 per pair at drugstores.*

Joseph Roscoe, PhD, research associate professor, department of radiation oncology, University of Rochester Medical Center, New York, and leader of a study of 88 people.

*Prices subject to change.

Marijuana Café

The Cannabis Café in Portland, Oregon, is one of the first public places where patients who have been approved to use marijuana for medical purposes can smoke "pot." Oregon is one of 13 states that now permit marijuana to be grown and used for medical purposes (such as reducing the nausea from chemotherapy).

USA Today, www.usatoday.com.

Cheers! Red Wine Reduces Lung Cancer Risk

Red wine may lower men's lung cancer risk. Smokers who drink one to two glasses of red wine a day have a 60% lower rate of lung cancer, compared with smokers who do not drink red wine. But even these men face higher lung cancer risk than nonsmokers, so quitting smoking remains the most effective way to lower lung cancer risk. Red wine may help reduce risk because of its high levels of antioxidants. No similar effects were found for white wine, beer or liquor.

Chun Chao, PhD, research scientist, Kaiser Permanente Southern California Department of Research and Evaluation, Pasadena, California, and leader of an analysis of data from more than 84,000 men, published in *Cancer Epidemiology, Biomarkers & Prevention.*

Moderate Drinking May Reduce Arthritis Risk

In a recent finding, risk for rheumatoid arthritis was about 40% to 50% lower among people who consumed more than three alcoholic beverages per week than among those who consumed less or no alcohol.

Henrik Kallberg, PhD, researcher, Karolinska Institute, Stockholm, and leader of an analysis of Swedish and Danish studies of 2,750 people, published in *Annals of the Rheumatic Diseases.*

A Very Cherry Arthritis Treatment

Cherry pills ease arthritis pain. In a recent study of 20 patients with osteoarthritis of the knee, more than half the patients experienced significant improvement in knee pain after taking tart-cherry supplements daily for eight weeks.

Theory: Cherry extracts contain *flavonoids* and *anthocyanins*, which have been shown to have anti-inflammatory effects.

If you have osteoarthritis: Ask your doctor about trying tart-cherry supplements.

John J. Cush, MD, rheumatologist, Baylor Research Institute, Dallas.

A Healthy Juice

Pomegranate juice is healthier than the fruit itself.

Reason: Most of the fruit's antioxidants are found in the inedible rind of the fruit—but the rind is typically used to create the juice. Pomegranate juice helps protect the heart and prevent arthritis and gingivitis.

Best: Choose pure pomegranate juice with no added sugars or fillers (such as apple or pear juice).

Steven Pratt, MD, ophthalmologist, Scripps Memorial Hospital, La Jolla, California, and author of *SuperHealth* (Signet) and *SuperFoods Rx* (Bottom Line Books).

Treat Gums to Ease Arthritis

Patients with rheumatoid arthritis and gum disease had tartar beneath gums scraped away so that gums could heal. After six weeks, patients had significantly less joint pain, stiffness and swelling. Patients whose gums were not treated did not improve. Decreasing oral bacteria could ease inflammation elsewhere. See your dentist if gums bleed—and especially if joints ache, too.

Nabil Bissada, DDS, chair, department of periodontics, Case Western Reserve University School of Dental Medicine, Cleveland, and leader of a study of 40 people.

The Beer/Bone Connection

Beer is high in dietary silicon which has been linked to bone health. Beers with the highest levels of malted barley and hops are richest in silicon. The silicon content of 100 commercially available beers was found to range from 6.4 to 56.4 milligrams per liter. The India pale ale category generally had the most silicon.

Charles Bamforth, PhD, professor, department of food science and technology, University of California, Davis, and leader of a study of the silicon in beer, published in *Journal of the Science of Food and Agriculture*.

Pet Therapy for Pain

Pet therapy can reduce the need to take pain medicine.

In a recent finding, patients who received pet therapy after joint-replacement surgery required 50% less pain medication than those who didn't. Animal-assisted therapy—typically performed in five- to 15-minute sessions during which the patient may talk to the animal or perhaps take the dog for a walk—improves patients' emotional and physical health.

Julia Havey, RN, senior systems analyst, department of medical center information systems, Loyola University Health System, Maywood, Illinois, and leader of a study presented at the 18th annual conference of the International Society of Anthrozoology and the First Human Animal Interaction Conference.

Curse to Reduce Pain... But Don't Overdo It!

Swearing is a common response to an injury—and one recent study suggests why. Volunteers were asked to keep their hands in ice water for as long as possible while repeating either a neutral word or the swear word of their choice.

Results: Swearers tolerated the discomfort for longer, perhaps because cursing triggers a fight-or-flight response that decreases pain perception.

But: Don't make it a habit—swearing more often may make it less effective at relieving pain.

Richard Stephens, PhD, lecturer, school of psychology, Keele University, Staffordshire, UK, and leader of a study of 64 people.

Got Pain? Get Your Vitamin D Checked

Chronic pain is the leading cause of disability in the US. In a recent study, it was found that patients with low vitamin D levels required twice as much narcotic pain medication to manage symptoms as those with adequate levels.

Theory: Vitamin D deficiency leads to low bone density, which can promote achy pain throughout the body.

Best: Ask your doctor about testing your blood level of vitamin D and supplementing if it is below 20 nanograms per milliliter.

Michael Turner, MD, department of physical medicine and rehabilitation, Mayo Clinic, Rochester, Minnesota, and lead author of a study of 267 people.

Looking for Pain Relief? Try Prolotherapy

Allan Magaziner, DO, director of Magaziner Center for Wellness in Cherry Hill, New Jersey, and a clinical instructor at University of Medicine and Dentistry of New Jersey in New Brunswick. His Web site is *www.drmagaziner.com.*

A medical procedure that can "trick" the body into healing itself, *prolotherapy* treats acute or chronic pain from damaged ligaments, tendons and cartilage. Some studies show significant improvement in patients with injuries or arthritis, especially in the joints, back, neck or jaw. Prolotherapy is utilized as a first-line therapy or when other treatments fail.

•**How it works.** A physician injects a solution, typically of *dextrose* (a sugar) and *lidocaine* (an anesthetic), into a painful area. This provokes a minor, temporary inflammation... causing the body to send more blood and nutrients to the spot...which hastens healing.

•**What to expect.** Each session lasts 15 to 30 minutes and includes from one to 20 injections, depending on the areas treated. Patients experience slight discomfort during injection and mild soreness for several days after. Minor pain might need one session...severe pain might require 10 sessions spread over several months.

•**Cautions.** Your physician may advise you to temporarily decrease or discontinue anti-inflammatory drugs—like aspirin, *ibuprofen* (Motrin), *naproxen* (Aleve)—while undergoing prolotherapy. *Acetaminophen* (Tylenol) is okay. If you take blood thinners or other drugs, tell your doctor, as extra precautions may be warranted.

•**Looking for a practitioner.** Prolotherapy should be administered by a physician trained in the procedure—preferably by the American Association of Orthopaedic Medicine (800-992-2063, *www.aaomed.org*) or Hackett Hemwall Foundation (*www.hacketthemwall.org*). Go to these Web sites for referrals.

Cost: $100 to $400 each session.* Because prolotherapy is considered experimental, insurance seldom covers it.

*Prices subject to change.

Want to Lower Alzheimer's Risk 76%? Drink This...

Fruit juice may lower the risk for Alzheimer's disease.

Recent finding: People who report drinking at least three servings of juice a week are 76% less likely to develop Alzheimer's than those who drink juice less than once a week. The research is not conclusive—juice drinkers may lead a more healthful life in general.

Qi Dai, MD, PhD, assistant professor of medicine in the division of general internal medicine and public health, Vanderbilt School of Medicine, Nashville, and leader of a study of 1,836 people of Japanese descent, published in *The American Journal of Medicine.*

Put On Another Pot— Coffee Protects Against Alzheimer's

Drinking three large cups of coffee a day may help protect against Alzheimer's.

The latest research: Mice with genetically impaired memories that were given caffeine (equal to about five cups of coffee or 500 milligrams of caffeine daily) performed far better on memory tests and thinking skills than genetically impaired mice not given caffeine.

Gary Arendash, PhD, research professor at Florida Alzheimer's Disease Research Center in Tampa, *www.floridaadrc.org.*

Calm Disposition = Reduced Dementia Risk

Calm people are less likely to develop dementia, a recent study says.

Recent finding: In a study of 506 older adults (median age 82), researchers found that those with calm, easygoing personalities were 50% less likely to develop dementia than those who were prone to distress.

Theory: Chronic stress can affect the *hippocampus*—the part of the brain that helps regulate memory and emotion—possibly leading to dementia.

To guard against this ill effect of stress: Participate often in physical, social and mentally challenging activities.

Hui-Xin Wang, PhD, research scientist, Aging Research Center, Karolinska Institute, Stockholm, Sweden.

Fast Weight Loss May Indicate Dementia

In an eight-year study of 1,836 women and men (average age 72), subjects who unintentionally lost weight at a "fast" rate were nearly three times more likely to develop dementia than those who lost weight more slowly. Fast weight loss was described as dropping more than one body mass index (BMI) point every year.

Theory: Weight loss in older adults may be an early physical sign of dementia that occurs before the disease affects memory function.

If you are an older adult who has experienced unexplained rapid weight loss: See your doctor for an evaluation.

Tiffany Hughes, PhD, MPH, researcher, department of psychiatry at the University of Pittsburgh School of Medicine.

Eating the Mediterranean Way: Delicious, Easy and Healthy

Wendy Kohatsu, MD, assistant clinical professor of family medicine at the University of California in San Francisco, and director of the Integrative Medicine Fellowship at the Santa Rosa Family Medicine Residency Program in Santa Rosa, California. Dr. Kohatsu is also a graduate of the Oregon Culinary Institute.

There is abundant scientific evidence on the health benefits of the so-called Mediterranean diet, which promotes the traditional eating habits of long-lived people in such countries as Greece and Italy.

The landmark research: Among the most compelling evidence is one long-term European study of healthy men and women ages 70 to 90.

It found that following the Mediterranean diet as part of an overall healthful lifestyle, including regular exercise, was associated with a more than 50% lower rate of death from all causes over a decade. Numerous studies have associated this type of eating with a reduced chance for heart disease, cancer, cognitive decline, diabetes and obesity.

But many Americans are reluctant to try the Mediterranean diet for fear that it will be difficult or costly to follow because it emphasizes such foods as omega-3–rich fish, vegetables and nuts.

Surprising findings: Mediterranean eating does not increase food costs, according to a recent study—and this style of eating need not be complicated.

Below, Wendy Kohatsu, MD, assistant clinical professor of family medicine at the University of California, San Francisco, and a chef who conducts cooking demonstrations for patients and doctors, explains the best ways to incorporate Mediterranean eating into your daily diet...

EASY WAYS TO GET STARTED

To effectively tap into the Mediterranean diet's powerful health benefits, it's important to know exactly which foods should be eaten —and in what quantities.

Start by getting four to five daily servings of whole grains (one serving equals one-half cup of cooked quinoa, brown rice or whole-wheat noodles, for example, or one slice of whole-wheat bread) and two to three daily servings of low- or nonfat dairy products (such as yogurt, cottage cheese and milk), which are an important source of bone-protecting calcium. *In addition, be sure to consume...*

•**Oily fish.** This high-quality protein contains abundant omega-3 fatty acids, which can help fight the inflammation that plays a role in cardiovascular disease, Alzheimer's disease and asthma.

Best choices: Follow the acronym SMASH—salmon (wild)...mackerel (Spanish, not king, which tends to have higher levels of mercury) ...anchovies...sardines...and herring.

How much: Three ounces (the size of a deck of cards), twice a week.

Chef's secret: Drain canned sardines (the large size), grill briefly, sprinkle with fresh lemon juice and chopped parsley.

Beware: Some fish—such as shark, swordfish, golden bass (tilefish), king mackerel and albacore tuna—can be high in mercury. Avoid these. If you eat tuna, choose the "light" version, which contains less mercury than albacore tuna does.

If you don't like fish: Take a fish oil supplement (1,000 mg daily). Choose a brand that guarantees that no lead or mercury is present.

My favorite brands: Carlson's and Nordic Naturals.

Vegetarians can obtain their omega-3s from flaxseed, walnuts and other nonfish sources. However, nonfish food sources of omega-3s are largely in the form of *alpha-linolenic acid* (ALA), which is not as potent as the more biologically powerful fatty acids found in fish. Algae-derived *docosahexaenoic acid* (DHA) capsules contain the omega-3s found in fish. The recommended dose of DHA capsules is 1,000 mg daily.

What most people don't know: A small but important study shows that eating oily fish with beans, such as lentils and chickpeas (also known as garbanzo beans), improves absorption of the iron found in beans.

•**Olive oil.** Olive oil contains about 77% healthful monounsaturated fats. Olive oil is also high in sterols, plant extracts that help reduce LDL "bad" cholesterol and increase HDL "good" cholesterol.

Best choice: Look for extra-virgin (or "first-press") olive oil. ("Extra virgin" indicates that the oil is derived from the first pressing of the olives.)

How much: Use olive oil as your primary fat—in salad dressings, marinades and sautées. To minimize your total daily intake of fat, do not exceed 18 g to 20 g of saturated fat and 0 g of trans fat from all food sources.

Chef's secret: If you dislike the "grassy" taste of some extra-virgin olive oils, look for Spanish and Moroccan versions, which tend to be more mellow. One good choice is olive oil made from the arbequina olive, which has a buttery taste.

What most people don't know: Nutrients in extra-virgin olive oil may offer some pain-relieving qualities over the long term.

•**Nuts.** Like extra-virgin olive oil, nuts are high in healthful monounsaturated fats. In fact, a recent Spanish study found that a Mediterranean diet that included walnuts significantly lowered risk for heart disease.

What kinds: Besides walnuts, best choices include almonds and peanuts. Choose plain raw nuts—not salted or honey-roasted.

How much: One-quarter cup daily.

Beware: One-quarter cup of nuts contains about 200 calories. Eat only a small handful daily—for example, about 23 almonds or 35 peanuts. If you're allergic to nuts, try pumpkin, sunflower or sesame seeds instead.

Chef's secret: Store nuts in your freezer to prevent them from going rancid.

•**Fruits and vegetables.** Many of the most healthful vegetables—including those of the brassica family, such as cabbage, kale, broccoli and cauliflower—originated in the Mediterranean area.

What kinds: Choose brightly colored fruit, such as citrus and berries, and vegetables, such as spinach, watercress, beets, carrots and broccoli.

How much: Five to nine servings daily. (A serving is one-half cup of cooked vegetables, one cup of leafy greens, one medium orange or one-half cup of berries.)

Contrary to popular belief, frozen vegetables, which are often far less costly than fresh produce, are just as nutritious—if not more so because they're frozen at their peak level of freshness and don't spoil in the freezer.

Chef's secret: Cooking tomatoes in olive oil concentrates the tomatoes' levels of lycopene, a powerful antioxidant that has been associated with a decreased risk for prostate, lung and stomach cancers.

Suicide by Sugar: It's More Addictive Than Cocaine...but You Can Break the Habit

Nancy Appleton, PhD, a clinical nutritionist in San Diego. She is author, with G.N. Jacobs, of *Suicide by Sugar: A Startling Look at Our #1 National Addiction* (Square One). Her Web site is *www.nancyappleton.com.*

The words "addictive white powder" may make you think of illegal drugs. Add in sugar to that addictive group. Americans consume enormous amounts—and suffer withdrawal symptoms when they don't have it. In fact, animal studies indicate that sugar is more addictive than cocaine.

Excess sugar has been linked to obesity, cancer, diabetes and dementia. *What to do...*

SUGAR, SUGAR EVERYWHERE

In the US, an average person will consume about 142 pounds of sugar each year, that's the equivalent of 48 teaspoons a day. Of that amount, 74 pounds is "added" sugar—about 23 teaspoons every day. Added sugars are defined as those sugars added to foods and beverages during processing or home preparation as opposed to sugars that occur naturally.

People who want to cut back on sweeteners usually start with the sugar bowl. They spoon less sugar on their breakfast cereal, for example, or use a sugar substitute in their coffee.

This doesn't help very much. The vast majority of added sugar in the diet comes from packaged foods, including foods that we think are healthful.

For example, eight ounces of one brand of sweetened apple yogurt contains 44 grams of sugar, according to the nutrition facts label. Four grams equals one teaspoon, so that's 11 teaspoons of sugar. (You cannot tell from the label how much sugar is from the yogurt, how much is from the apples and how much is added sugar.)

Most of the added sugar that we consume comes from carbonated soft drinks (there are about 10 teaspoons of sugar in 12 ounces of nondiet soda), candy, pies, cookies, cakes, fruit drinks and milk-based desserts and products (ice cream, sweetened yogurt).

If you look carefully at ingredients labels, which list ingredients in order of quantity, you will see that the first two or three ingredients often are forms of sugar, but many have innocuous-sounding names, such as barley malt, galactose and agave nectar. Other forms of sugar include honey, maple syrup, corn syrup, corn sweetener, dextrine, rice syrup, glucose, sucrose and dextrose.

DANGEROUS IMBALANCE

The difference between sickness and health lies in the body's ability to maintain homeostasis, the proper balance and performance of all of the internal functions. Excess sugar disturbs this balance by impairing immunity, disrupting the production and release of hormones and creating an acidic internal environment.

It's not healthy to maintain a highly acidic state. The body will try to offset this by making itself more alkaline. It does this, in part, by removing calcium and other minerals from the bones.

Result: People who have too much sugar experience disruptions in insulin and other hormones. They have an elevated risk for osteoporosis due to depletion of calcium. They also tend to have elevated levels of cholesterol and triglycerides (blood fats), which increase the risk for heart disease.

BREAK THE CYCLE

A sweet tooth is not the same as a sugar addiction. We are genetically programmed to enjoy sweets on occasion. It becomes an addiction when sweet foods make you crave even more sugar and your consumption increases over time...you experience withdrawal (in the form of mood changes, such as irritability or feeling "down") when you briefly go without sugar...and you experience intense cravings when sweet foods aren't available.

Sugar, like drugs and alcohol, is addictive because it briefly elevates levels of *serotonin*, a neurotransmitter that produces positive feelings. When a sugar addict doesn't eat sugar, serotonin declines to low levels. This makes the person feel even worse than before. He/she then eats more sugar to try to feel better—and the vicious cycle goes on.

For the best chance of breaking a sugar addiction, you need to ease out of it. This usually is more effective than going cold turkey. Once you've given up sugar entirely and the addiction is past, you'll be able to enjoy small amounts of sugar if you choose to, although some people find that they lose their taste for it. *How to break the habit...*

• **Divide sugar from all sources in half.** Do this for one week.

Examples: If you've been drinking two soft drinks a day, cut back to one. Eat half as much dessert. Eat a breakfast cereal that has only half as much sugar as your usual brand, or mix a low-sugar brand in with your higher-sugar brand.

• **Limit yourself to one sweet bite.** The second week, allow yourself to have only one taste of only one very sweet food daily. Then push the dish away. This might be ice cream, sweetened cereal or a breakfast muffin. That small "hit" of sugar will stop your serotonin from dropping too low, too fast. This is important because low serotonin can make you feel so poorly, physically and emotionally, that you'll want to self-medicate with more sugar.

After about two weeks with little or no sugar, your internal chemistry, including levels of serotonin and other neurotransmitters, will stabilize at a healthier level.

• **Eat fresh fruits and vegetables.** These foods help restore the body's natural acid-alkaline balance. This will help reduce sugar cravings and promote better digestion. Be sure to substitute fresh fruits for juices. Whole fruit is better because the fiber slows the absorption of sugars into the bloodstream. The fiber also is filling, which is why few people will sit down and eat four oranges—the number you would need to squeeze to get one eight-ounce glass of juice.

Helpful: All fruits are healthful, but melons and berries have less sugar than other fruits.

Pumpkin Seeds Pump Up Mood

Pumpkin seeds boost mood. Like chocolate, pumpkin seeds are a good source of the amino acid *tryptophan*, which improves mood—but pumpkin seeds do not have the sugar that chocolate does, and one ounce of pumpkin seeds contains about half the daily requirement of magnesium, which strengthens bones. Sprinkle toasted seeds on soups and salads, or put raw, unsalted seeds on the tops of muffins before baking.

Melina Jampolis, MD, physician nutrition specialist, San Francisco, and author of *The Busy Person's Guide to Permanent Weight Loss* (Thomas Nelson). Her Web site is *www.drmelina.com.*

The Most Healthful Way To Eat Garlic

One of the healthful chemicals in garlic is *allicin*. Allicin is destroyed by heat, so cooking with garlic gives little benefit. Allicin also breaks down when garlic is simply left standing, as in jars of peeled garlic cloves available in supermarkets. The chemical is present only when garlic is chopped up, so you can consume it by chopping cloves of raw garlic and adding them to salad or other foods. Alternatively, and to avoid bad breath and body odor, buy a garlic supplement and take it daily. Choose one with guaranteed high amounts of allicin—avoid supplements that do not list allicin content on the label.

Mark A. Stengler, NMD, naturopathic medical doctor in private practice, La Jolla, California, and author of many books and the *Bottom Line/Natural Healing* newsletter.

Beans: The Ultimate Health Food

Jo-Ann Heslin, RD, CDN, a Douglaston, New York–based registered dietitian. She is coauthor of 30 books, including *The Healthy Wholefoods Counter* (Pocket) and two college textbooks on nutrition. A previous faculty member of the State University of New York, Downstate Medical Center, in New York City, she was the editor of the *Journal of Nutrition for the Elderly* for 23 years.

Ask someone to name the food that is richest in disease-fighting antioxidants, and you're likely to hear "blueberries" or "cranberries." Few people are aware that red beans actually provide more antioxidants than these nutritional-powerhouse berries. *See the list below created by the US Department of Agriculture...*

TOP 10 ANTIOXIDANT FOODS

(1) Red beans...(2) Wild blueberries...(3) Red kidney beans...(4) Pinto beans...(5) Cultivated blueberries...(6) Cranberries...(7) Artichokes... (8) Blackberries...(9) Prunes...(10) Raspberries.

WHAT MAKES BEANS SO SPECIAL?

Some foods are rich in protein, while others provide healthful unsaturated fats, vitamins and minerals or fiber.

Beans (in a class of vegetables known as legumes) are all of the above—the ultimate "combination food," providing maximum nutritional value, including about 15 g of protein and about 13 g of fiber per cup cooked. (A typical serving is one-half cup cooked.)

Compelling scientific evidence: In a landmark study of nearly 800 people (ages 70 and over) from Japan, Sweden, Greece and Australia, the risk for death over a seven-year period dropped by 7% to 8% for each 0.7 ounces (about one-quarter cup cooked) of beans consumed daily.

Bonus: It's especially important to eat beans as we grow older. As we age, our metabolism slows, and we tend to eat less—even though we need more vitamins, minerals and other food-based chemicals to support a weakening immune system...fiber to keep digestion functioning smoothly...and protein to slow the age-related loss of muscle tissue. Beans provide all of these benefits—and they're economical and easy to eat for those who have difficulty with chewing or swallowing.

WHAT NUTRITIONISTS HAVE LONG KNOWN

For people who are trying to improve their diets, beans are an excellent—though underutilized—food source. Long known by nutritionists for their exceptionally high nutritional value, beans are now the focus of more and more scientific research.

Important recent studies show that beans help fight...

• **Cancer.** Phytochemicals in beans may alter biochemistry to keep cells from becoming malignant.

• **Diabetes.** The complex carbohydrates in beans are digested slowly, which helps maintain steady levels of blood sugar.

• **Heart disease.** The healthful unsaturated fats in beans help slow the body's production of artery-clogging cholesterol.

• **Obesity.** The protein and fiber in beans satisfy the appetite more quickly and for a longer time than simple carbohydrate foods, reducing overall calorie consumption.

BEAN STANDOUTS

More than 100 types of beans are grown worldwide and offer similar basic nutritional advantages. *However, some varieties do stand out...*

• **Red beans** not only have more antioxidants than blueberries, but also are a good source of iron (5.2 mg iron per cup cooked).

• **Kidney beans** are also rich in antioxidants and are an especially good source of fiber (13 g fiber per cup cooked).

104

• **Pinto beans** have been shown to reduce the markers for heart disease, including total cholesterol, when one-half cup cooked was consumed daily for eight weeks, according to research published in the *Journal of the American College of Nutrition.*

• **Lima beans** are a good source of potassium and have been shown to reduce blood glucose levels.

• **Navy beans,** which also are a rich source of potassium as well as calcium and magnesium, have been linked to reduced risk for high blood pressure and heart attack.

• **Black beans** are another excellent source of antioxidants—one cup cooked offers the same antioxidant levels as a six-ounce glass of red wine.

• **Garbanzo beans** (also known as chickpeas) have been shown to reduce LDL "bad" cholesterol by nearly 5%.

• **Soybeans** have higher-quality protein—it closely matches that of eggs, meat and milk—and more of it (60% of your daily needs in a single cup) than other types of beans.

Important: Soybeans are the richest source of isoflavones—phytochemicals with estrogen-like properties. Although research findings have been mixed, there is some concern that high intake of isoflavones may promote the growth of precancerous or malignant breast cancer cells. The American Cancer Society recommends that women who are at a high risk for breast cancer or with a history of the disease eat no more than moderate amounts of soy foods and avoid isoflavone supplements.

BEST WAYS TO ADD BEANS TO YOUR DIET

Aim for at least three cups of cooked beans (six servings) per week. *For example, you can try...*

• **Garbanzo or kidney beans** in a lettuce salad.

• **Navy beans or black beans** in soups.

• **Roasted soybeans** (soy nuts) and edamame (fresh soybeans) as convenient snack foods.

• **Three-bean salad** containing more dried beans (such as chickpeas and kidney beans) than yellow or green string beans.

For even more variety: Try adzuki beans in rice dishes...anasazi beans in Southwestern soups...and fava beans in stews.

NO MORE GAS!

Many people avoid beans because they can produce intestinal gas. To minimize gas, add beans to your diet gradually—start with one-quarter cup on top of a salad, for example... and increase your intake to half-cup and full-cup servings over a period of weeks.

Other gas-control secrets: Get dried beans when they're fresh (otherwise, the beans' natural starches degrade and become more difficult to digest). Look for a "best by" date or buy dried beans at a store where business is brisk. Soak them overnight, then rinse them thoroughly before cooking.

SODIUM-REDUCING TRICKS

The very high salt content of canned beans (it's added to preserve texture) is a problem if you are on a low-sodium diet. Canned beans typically contain 300 mg of sodium per one-cup serving. By washing the beans, you can lower their sodium content by 40% or more. Rinsing canned beans thoroughly also helps prevent intestinal gas.

When cooking dried beans, it is not necessary to add salt. However, seasonings, including salt (in moderation), can be added once the beans are cooked. For convenience, freeze serving-size portions for later use. Frozen cooked beans also are becoming increasingly available at supermarkets and are nearly sodium-free.

Raisins *More* Healthful Than Grapes

Raisins are better for you than grapes. A recent finding showed that raisins have nearly three times more antioxidants than red or green grapes, making them one of the best sources of antioxidants. When fruits are dried, their compounds become very concentrated.

Raisins are a good source of fiber, potassium and some minerals.

But: Raisins also have a higher concentration of sugar and more calories than grapes. One-half cup of grapes has nearly 50 calories, while one-half cup of raisins has about 220 calories.

Best: 60 raisins, or one ounce, once a day is a healthy snack with just 85 calories.

UC Berkeley Wellness Letter, 500 Fifth Ave., New York City 10110, *www.wellnessletter.com.*

Best Way to Cook Carrots—for Health And Taste

Cook carrots whole before chopping them to retain their nutrients. Chopping before cooking increases the surface area of carrots, so more of the nutrients, including vitamin C, disappear into the water. Cooking carrots whole keeps them tasty as well—80% of people preferred the flavor of carrots cooked whole over the flavor of ones chopped before cooking.

Kirsten Brandt, PhD, senior lecturer, department of food and rural development, School of Agriculture, Newcastle University, UK, and lead researcher of a study reported in *Tufts University Health & Nutrition Letter.*

Surprise! Popcorn Is Good for You

In a recent study, researchers reported that popcorn is the richest source for antioxidants among whole-grain snack foods, including tortilla chips and crackers.

Self-defense: In addition to regularly consuming fruits and vegetables, you can increase your antioxidant intake by enjoying popcorn as a snack (with little or no salt and no butter).

Joe Vinson, PhD, professor of chemistry, University of Scranton, Pennsylvania.

To Keep Produce Fresh...

David Grotto, RD, registered dietitian and author of *101 Foods That Could Save Your Life* (Bantam).

Leave fruits and vegetables in their whole, unwashed state until shortly before eating them. Washing can strip away protective man-made waxes and natural coverings that delay spoiling.

Keep fresh avocados, bananas, tomatoes, winter squash at room temperature on your kitchen counter—but refrigerate tomatoes and winter squash after cooking or cutting. With avocados and bananas, peel only what you intend to eat at that time.

To slow the ripening process, you can store most fruits and vegetables in the refrigerator. Crisper drawers are best for celery, peppers, ripe fruits, summer squash and leafy vegetables. Place berries and grapes uncovered on a shelf in your refrigerator. You can leave strawberries in their store-bought boxes, but transfer blackberries, blueberries and raspberries to shallow bowls lined with paper towels. Keeping those berries dry can prevent mold.

Store dried beans, root vegetables and tubers (carrots, garlic, onions, potatoes, radishes and rutabagas) in a dark pantry. Refrigerate them in airtight containers after they've been peeled, cut or cooked.

Common Kitchen Spices Fight Deadly E. Coli

The food-borne bacterium *Escherichia coli O157* causes severe cramps, bloody diarrhea and kidney failure. Researchers studied the effects of extracts of 20 different spices on the bacterium. Allspice significantly decreased E. coli O157 toxin growth...to a lesser degree, so did cloves.

Worth a try: Add ground allspice and/or cloves to burgers, vegetables and salads.

Kumio Yokoigawa, PhD, professor of food microbiology, University of Tokushima, Japan.

6

Personal and Private

How to Have Great Sex at *Any Age...* Get Healthier, Too!

espite what the movies would have us believe, sex is not limited only to people under age 40. In fact, recent research indicates that a sizable percentage of Americans are remaining sexually active into their 70s, 80s and beyond. But let's be honest—there are obstacles, both physical and psychological, to maintaining a healthy sex life as we age.

Very good news: After years of research and clinical practice as a specialist in longevity, I have found six key principles that, taken together, can help the vast majority of couples—no matter what age—have a good sex life. And when a couple has a satisfying sex life, their feelings of fondness and intimacy can grow

stronger—and that improves every aspect of their lives. *For a great sex life at any age...*

•**Realize that sex and intimacy can literally add years to your life.** Numerous studies have shown that close relationships are a key to maintaining good mental and physical health as we get older. Of course, emotional closeness can exist without sexual intimacy—but to the degree that sexuality helps enrich our closest relationships, it can be an important contributor to a long, healthy life.

Bottom line: If you give up on a good sex life, you may die sooner.

•**Ignore what society tells us about aging and sex.** The idea of older people having sex is thought of as a rarity. This stereotype could not be further from the truth. A 2007 study about sexual activity among older

The late Robert N. Butler, MD, former professor, geriatrics, Mount Sinai School of Medicine in New York City and president and CEO of the International Longevity Center, *www.ilcusa.org*. He was the founding director of the National Institute on Aging and coauthored *The New Love and Sex After 60* (Ballantine).

Americans, published in the *New England Journal of Medicine*, showed that more than one-half of men and women between the ages of 65 and 74 and more than one-quarter of those between 75 and 85 had been sexually active within the previous 12 months. And among those who reported that they were in good or excellent health, these figures were considerably higher.

Bottom line: Don't let society's false stereotype keep you from one of the great joys of life.

•**Take control of your health.** A healthy blood flow to the sexual organs is essential for sexual response. That's why maintaining good cardiovascular health—including managing cholesterol levels and blood pressure as well as exercising—is key to a good sex life. *Also vital...*

•If you have diabetes, control it. Diabetes is a killer of sexuality because it damages the cardiovascular system and the body's peripheral nerves.

•Discuss with your physician whether any medications you take might be impacting your sexual desire or response. *Examples:* An antidepressant can significantly reduce libido, while diuretics and beta-blockers used for high blood pressure can bring on erectile dysfunction. Ask about alternative drugs and/or drugs that might counter the sexual side effects.

•**Steer clear of alcohol.** A character in *Macbeth* famously said of alcohol, "It provokes the desire, but it takes away the performance." He was right. Alcohol can make us want sex more—and some women, in particular, claim that their sexual pleasure is increased after drinking, most likely because alcohol reduces psychological inhibition. But even one drink can reduce a woman's vaginal blood flow and lubrication and intensity of orgasm. For men, intoxication can severely reduce the ability to achieve an erection and the intensity of orgasm—and regular alcohol consumption (even without intoxication) lowers testosterone levels, affecting quality of erection and orgasm.

Bottom line: A little alcohol might help—or at least not hurt your sex life. But it's best to save any imbibing for after sex.

•**Take advantage of the medications and sex-related personal-care products.** For older people, the introduction of the oral medications *sildenafil citrate* (Viagra), *vardenafil* (Levitra) and *tadalafil* (Cialis), which help men maintain their erections, has been an important development.

Reason: Erectile dysfunction is one of the most frequently cited reasons that older couples are no longer sexually active. While they are safe and effective for most men, talk with your doctor about potential side effects before trying any of these drugs.

What many couples don't realize: It is normal for an older man to need to have his penis physically stimulated to achieve an erection—just thinking about sex, or even kissing and other foreplay, often isn't enough. Ladies, this is not an indication of diminished desire.

As we all know, hormones play a great role in sex...

For men: If you are not happy with your sexual response after following all the advice throughout this article, see an endocrinologist for a check on your levels of testosterone and thyroid hormones. A low level of either can dampen sexual desire and ability. Hormone supplements can be prescribed.

For women: Older women can often experience vaginal dryness, which can make intercourse much less enjoyable or sometimes impossible. This problem can be remedied by applying an over-the-counter, non–oil-based lubricant, such as K-Y Jelly, Astroglide, or Slip, just before sex...or, to allow for more spontaneity, by using a moisturizing insert such as Lubrin (which lasts several hours) or Replens gel, which lasts several days. (Avoid oil-based lubricants, such as petroleum jelly and baby oil, which tend to remain in the vagina and create a breeding ground for infections.)

Alternative: If a lubricant isn't enough to make sex comfortable, ask your doctor about a topical form of the hormone estrogen, which can be applied to the vagina to increase your body's ability to lubricate itself.

•**Keep all the flames burning.** If you're in a long-term relationship and you want a satisfying sex life, it's important to purposely set aside time for nonsexual intimacy on a regular basis.

Perfect example: Years ago, I lived next door to a couple who had a weekly candlelight dinner in their backyard. This kind of intimate encounter may not always lead into sex—but it creates a psychological closeness that encourages physical intimacy.

More from Dr. Robert Butler...

If You Are Single, Divorced, Widowed...

For older unmarried people, finding an appropriate sexual (and life) partner is a challenge. This is especially true for older women, whose longer life span means they outnumber older men by about two to one.

But remember: The loss of a sexual partner wouldn't stop a 30-year-old from seeking a new relationship, so why should it stop you at age 60, 70, 80 or older?

To find a wonderful partner: The key is to frequently participate in activities that will expose you to potential partners, especially activities in which you have a strong interest, such as dancing, politics or sports. This will give you the best chance of meeting someone you're attracted to and who shares your interests, an ideal starting place for developing a more intimate bond.

Vibrator Use Linked to Sexual Health

More than 52% of US women questioned had used a vibrator...24.3% had done so within the previous month. Compared with nonusers, vibrator users reported more sexual desire, arousal, lubrication and orgasms...had less pain...and were more likely to have had a recent gynecologic checkup.

Debra Herbenick, PhD, MPH, research scientist, department of applied health science, Indiana University, Bloomington, and leader of a survey of 2,056 women ages 18 to 60.

Yoga Leads to More Enjoyable Sex for Women

Yoga may improve sex for women. Some women have trouble focusing when making love. In yoga, you are encouraged to concentrate on how the body responds to each pose. This can make it easier to tune in to sexual sensations as well. Most types of yoga can provide this benefit.

Lori Brotto, PhD, assistant professor of obstetrics and gynecology, and director, Sexual Health Laboratory, University of British Columbia, Vancouver, Canada, and leader of an article published in *The Journal of Sexual Medicine.*

Sex Drive Not What It Used to Be? Check Your Meds

Your sex drive can be affected by different medications. Talk to your prescribing doctor about changing medications if you think this might apply to you.

Several antidepressants, including *bupropion* (Wellbutrin) and *duloxetine* (Cymbalta), might cause fewer sexual side effects than others. If switching is not recommended, your physician may prescribe a second drug that counteracts your antidepressant's sexual side effects, such as the antianxiety medication *buspirone* (Buspar).

Oral contraceptives sometimes cause sexual dysfunction—so if you are taking both an antidepressant and the Pill, your risk for low libido is further increased. In this case, consider a different form of birth control.

Anita H. Clayton, MD, professor of psychiatry and neurobehavioral sciences, University of Virginia Health System, Charlottesville, and the author of *Satisfaction: Women, Sex and the Quest for Intimacy* (Ballantine).

High Cholesterol Dampens Women's Sex Lives

In a recent study of 556 women, researchers found that women with *hyperlipidemia* (elevated cholesterol levels in the blood) reported significantly lower sexual satisfaction than those without the condition.

Theory: Accumulation of fats in blood vessel walls (already linked to erectile dysfunction in men) also may reduce blood flow to female genitals.

If you have experienced a loss of sexual function: Ask your doctor to check your total cholesterol levels.

Katherine Esposito, MD, PhD, researcher, department of geriatrics and metabolic disease, Second University of Naples, Italy.

More Sex = Lower Risk For Heart Disease

In a recent finding, men who had sex once a month or less were approximately 50% more likely to suffer cardiovascular events, such as heart attack, stroke or heart failure, than men who had sex at least twice a week. Further research is needed. The frequency of sex may simply indicate a man's overall health. In the meantime, men should discuss with their doctors any sexual problems.

Susan A. Hall, PhD, a research scientist, department of epidemiology, New England Research Institutes, Watertown, Massachusetts, and lead author of a study of 1,165 men, published in *The American Journal of Cardiology.*

Sexual Problems Linked To Plastic?

There could be a risk of sexual problems from plastic.

Recent finding: Male factory workers in China exposed to very high doses of *bisphenol A* (BPA), commonly used in hard plastic bottles, had higher rates of sexual problems, including reduced sexual desire and erectile and ejaculation problems. Though this is more exposure than a typical American man would face, there is a possible risk from even low-level exposure. More research is needed.

Self-defense: Avoid hard plastic bottles that carry the recycling symbol with the number 7.

De-Kun Li, MD, PhD, senior research scientist at the division of research, Kaiser Foundation Research Institute of Kaiser Permanente, Oakland, California. He led a study of 164 factory workers in China exposed to high BPA levels, published in *Human Reproduction.*

Top Way to Prevent and Reverse ED

The best way for men to prevent and reverse sexual dysfunction is the same way to reduce heart disease risk. Erectile dysfunction (ED) results from diminished blood flow and can be an early warning sign for heart disease. Men who have ED are 80% more likely to develop heart disease than other men.

Self-defense: Exercise regularly, eat a nutritious diet and maintain a healthy weight. And, try to keep your blood pressure, cholesterol and blood sugar under control.

Joshua Green, MD, urologist specializing in male sexual dysfunction and infertility, and medical director, Urology Treatment Center of Southwest Florida, Sarasota, and clinical assistant professor of medicine, Florida State University, Sarasota.

Use It or Lose It

The more sex men have in middle age, the more likely they are to maintain erectile function as they age.

Recent finding: Men who do not have intercourse at least once a week in middle age are twice as likely to develop erectile dysfunction as men who have sex once a week.

Study of 989 men ages 55 to 75 by researchers at the University of Tampere, Finland, published in *The American Journal of Medicine.*

ED Supplement Alert

"All-natural" supplements used for erectile dysfunction (ED) could be dangerous. The ingredients in products such as "Blue Steel" and "Hero," two dietary supplements offered online as natural ED treatments, may dangerously lower blood pressure, especially among men who take medication to control diabetes, blood pressure, cholesterol or heart disease. These supplements have not been proved safe and are not approved by the FDA.

Best: If you are having ED problems, see your doctor.

Elizabeth Miller, PharmD, acting team leader of the Internet and health fraud team, US Food and Drug Administration Center for Drug Evaluation and Research, Silver Spring, Maryland.

What You Must Do *Now* If You Think Your Partner's Cheating

If you suspect your partner is being unfaithful, be tested for all common sexually transmitted infections. These include HIV, the virus responsible for AIDS...human papillomavirus (HPV)...chlamydia...gonorrhea...syphilis... and herpes simplex. A test for *mycoplasma—*

a respiratory illness caused from contact with an infected person—also may be worthwhile. Ask your gynecologist or urologist what other tests would be appropriate for you.

Helpful: The Web site of the Centers for Disease Control and Prevention at *www.cdc. gov/std.*

Barbara Bartlik, MD, medical sex therapist and psychiatrist, and assistant professor of psychiatry, Weill Cornell Medical College, New York City.

Pregnant? Be Sure to Limit Cell-Phone Use

Children of women who use cell phones two to three times a day while pregnant may be more likely to develop various behavioral problems.

Recent finding: Children born to women who frequently used cell phones were 54% more likely than other children to be hyperactive and have difficulties with conduct, emotions and relationships.

Reason: Unknown.

These results should be viewed with caution. More research is needed.

Leeka Kheifets, PhD, professor of epidemiology at UCLA and one of the leaders of a study of 13,159 children, published in *Epidemiology.*

Dads-to-Be: Avoid Heated Car Seats!

Men who sit on a heated car seat for 90 minutes have a significant rise in scrotal temperature. Heat can damage sperm. It is not proven that these short-term temperature changes affect sperm production or quality, but men who are concerned about their fertility may want to avoid using heated car seats.

Study by researchers at Justus Liebig University, Giessen, Germany, published in *Fertility and Sterility.*

Early Menopause May Raise Stroke Risk

When researchers followed 1,430 women for an average of 22 years, they found that those who experienced natural menopause (cessation of menstruation for one year) before age 42 were twice as likely to suffer strokes as women whose natural menopause occurred at a later age.

Theory: Decreased estrogen levels due to early menopause may affect the arteries, thus promoting cardiovascular disease.

If you experienced natural menopause before age 42: Tell your doctor and ask him/her to evaluate your stroke risk.

Lynda D. Lisabeth, PhD, assistant professor of epidemiology, University of Michigan, Ann Arbor.

The Menopause/ Cholesterol Link

Menopause raises cholesterol, increasing risk for heart disease. The average LDL (bad) cholesterol count jumps by about 9% in the two-year window that surrounds the final menstrual period. Total cholesterol levels also increase by about 6.5%.

Important: Women in menopause should take steps to keep cholesterol under control.

Among the strategies: Regular exercise... maintaining a healthy weight...not smoking... taking cholesterol-lowering medications.

Karen A. Matthews, PhD, distinguished professor of psychiatry and professor of epidemiology and psychology, University of Pittsburgh School of Medicine. She is lead author of a study of menopausal transition in 1,054 women, published in *Journal of the American College of Cardiology.*

Hormone Therapy: Recent News

JoAnn E. Manson, MD, DrPH, a professor of medicine and women's health at Harvard Medical School and chief of the division of preventive medicine at Brigham and Women's Hospital, both in Boston. She is one of the lead investigators for two highly influential studies on women's health—the Harvard Nurses' Health Study and the Women's Health Initiative. Dr. Manson is the author, with Shari Bassuk, ScD, of *Hot Flashes, Hormones & Your Health* (McGraw-Hill).

What happens to a woman's health risks after she stops using hormone therapy (HT) following five to seven years of use? Until recently, there was little rigorous scientific data to address this question.

Now: Recent findings from the Women's Health Initiative (WHI) study provide us with an answer.

At the start of the WHI, in the mid-1990s, more than 16,000 women ages 50 to 79 were assigned to take either a combination of estrogen plus *progestin* (Prempro) or a placebo for 5.6 years. After they stopped taking the pills, the women were tracked for three more years.

Good news: The risks for heart attack, stroke and blood clots, which rose while women were taking HT, quickly dropped back toward normal after HT was stopped.

Bad news: The benefits of HT—relief from hot flashes, protection against bone loss and fractures—also dissipated quickly...a slightly higher risk for breast cancer persisted...and there was a suggestion of a higher risk to get various cancers and for death in the post-HT years.

Significance: These findings reinforce current guidelines advising women to consider HT only for short-term relief from moderate-to-severe menopausal hot flashes and/or night sweats that significantly disrupt their quality of life and/or sleep. Ideally, treatment should be limited to two to three years or, at most, five years.

Although HT does help prevent fractures, it is no longer recommended as a first line of defense against osteoporosis.

Reason: The average age of women who break a hip is close to 80 years, so women would need to take HT for many, many years to maintain good bone protection when risk for fracture is greatest.

Keys to safety: Health status and timing. HT-related heart attack, stroke and blood clot risks are low for women in good cardiovascular health whose periods ended less than 10 years ago, but higher in those who are older and/or in poorer cardiovascular health.

Example: Among women who entered the WHI trial with better cholesterol levels, those assigned to HT had a 40% lower risk for coronary heart disease than those on a placebo...but among women who entered with worse cholesterol levels, HT users had a 73% higher risk.

The balance of benefits and risks of HT appears quite favorable for younger women. Among WHI participants in their 50s, HT use was linked to a 30% reduction in mortality. This does not indicate that healthy, recently menopausal women should take HT specifically to prevent health problems—rather, when taking HT for short-term symptom management, such women need not be overly concerned about risks.

What's next: More research is needed to determine if lower doses of oral HT or transdermal patches or gels can further minimize risk.

Spray Relieves Severe Hot Flashes

When 454 postmenopausal women who suffered from moderate to severe hot flashes used *estradiol* (Evamist)—a spray-on product that contains estrogen—or a placebo spray for 12 weeks, the estradiol group had an average of eight fewer hot flashes per day, compared with an average of four fewer hot flashes daily for the placebo group. Unlike oral estrogen therapy, the spray form does not appear to increase risk for side effects, such as blood clots. See *www.evamist.com.*

John E. Buster, MD, division of reproductive endocrinology and infertility at Women & Infants Hospital, Providence and Tufts Medical Center, Boston.

Seven Ways to Protect Yourself from Ovarian Cancer

Robert P. Edwards, MD, professor of obstetrics, gynecology and reproductive sciences at University of Pittsburgh School of Medicine.

Ovarian cancer is tough to battle, because it often goes undiagnosed until it has spread to other parts of the body. *Self-defense always starts with prevention strategies...*

1. Drink coffee. In a recent study, women who drank more than four cups of coffee daily had a 49% lower risk for ovarian cancer than women who did not drink coffee.

2. Take ginkgo biloba. Women who regularly took an extract of this herb had about a 60% lower ovarian cancer risk than those who did not take it. If you take a blood thinner, such as aspirin or *warfarin* (Coumadin), *don't* take ginkgo.

3. Cut dietary fat. Postmenopausal women who cut their fat intake to 20% of their daily calories for eight years had a 40% lower risk for ovarian cancer.

4. Lose weight if necessary. A study found that being overweight was associated with a 20% increased risk for ovarian cancer...obesity increased risk by 30%. To evaluate your weight using body mass index—a mathematical formula based on height and weight—visit *www.nhlbisupport.com/bmi.*

5. Exercise—but don't overdo it. Women who regularly engaged in moderately intense physical activity, such as walking and golfing, were at lower risk for ovarian cancer than sedentary women.

But: Vigorous activity (such as running and racquetball) did not lower risk—perhaps because excessive exercise can suppress the immune system.

Best: Do moderate exercise for 30 to 60 minutes three times per week.

6. Consider the Pill if you are premenopausal. Studies show that five years or more of oral contraceptive use is linked to a 30% to 50% reduced ovarian cancer risk.

7. Weigh pros and cons of hormone therapy (HT) if you are menopausal. HT reduces hot flashes but increases lifetime ovarian cancer risk somewhat.

Best: Use the lowest effective dose of HT for the shortest amount of time possible.

Pour Another Cup: Coffee Cuts Risk of Cancer

Women who consumed at least two cups of caffeinated coffee daily were 22% less likely to develop cancer of the endometrium (uterine lining) than women who drank one cup or less per day…among those who drank four or more cups daily, risk decreased by 25%. (Decaffeinated coffee was not studied.) For overweight and obese women, who typically are at highest risk for endometrial cancer, coffee's benefits were greatest.

Theory: Coffee and/or caffeine has beneficial effects on blood sugar, fat cells and estrogen, all of which play a role in endometrial cancer.

Best: Have several cups of coffee daily—preferably before mid-afternoon so that the caffeine won't interfere with sleep.

Emilie Friberg, PhD, nutritional epidemiologist, National Institute of Environmental Medicine, Karolinska Institute, Sweden, and leader of a study of 60,634 women.

The Power of Yogurt

Yogurt reduces risk for bladder cancer. A recent study found that consuming two or more servings of yogurt per day was associated with a 45% reduction in bladder cancer for women and a 36% reduction in men, compared with people who didn't consume yogurt.

Theory: The researchers believe that lactic acid bacteria in yogurt may destroy harmful carcinogens that otherwise may form in the bladder.

Susanna C. Larsson, PhD, division of nutritional epidemiology, National Institute of Environmental Medicine, Karolinska Institutet, Stockholm, Sweden.

How to Reduce Breast Cancer Risk by 43%! Recent Breakthroughs In Prevention and Treatment

Shannon Puhalla, MD, assistant professor of medicine at the Magee-Womens Hospital of The University of Pittsburgh School of Medicine and a breast cancer specialist in the division of hematology/oncology at UPMC Cancer Centers. Her scientific articles about breast cancer and other cancers have appeared in several medical journals, including the *Journal of Clinical Oncology* and *The American Journal of Hematology/Oncology.*

In 2009, doctors told more than 260,000 American women they had breast cancer. Of these women, more than 40,000 died from the disease—it's the second-leading cause of cancer-related deaths in women, after lung cancer.

Good news: Scientific breakthroughs offer women new hope in the battle against breast cancer—hope for effective prevention, early detection and life-extending treatments…

PREVENTION BREAKTHROUGHS

• **HRT update.** In 2002, the Women's Health Initiative (or WHI)—a scientific study designed to demonstrate the many benefits of hormone replacement therapy (HRT) for postmenopausal women—found that those taking a combination of the drugs estrogen and progestin increased their risk of developing breast cancer by 26% (and increased their risk for a heart attack by 29% and stroke by 41%). This unexpected result changed the opinion of doctors and patients regarding HRT. Prescriptions for the therapy declined from 60 million in 2001 to 20 million in 2005—and breast cancer rates also declined. But some authorities questioned the connection, saying that the drop in cancer rates was too rapid to have been caused by women stopping HRT.

Recent study: Scientists at Stanford School of Medicine looked at data from more than 56,000 women—15,000 from the original WHI study and 41,449 others. *They found that...*

• A 50% decrease in hormone use between 2000 and 2003 was correlated with a 43% reduction in breast cancer rates in 2002 and 2003.

• Among women who stopped taking HRT, rates of breast cancer declined by 28%—within one year.

• Women who stayed on HRT for five years doubled their annual risk for breast cancer.

All these results appeared in the February 5, 2009, issue of *The New England Journal of Medicine.*

What to do: Women at high risk for breast cancer and those who have been diagnosed with breast cancer should avoid HRT. Women at low risk for breast cancer can use HRT to control menopausal symptoms but only as a last resort and for the shortest possible duration and at the lowest possible dosage (which varies per individual).

Your risk for breast cancer depends on a lot of factors, such as your age and the number of your first-degree relatives (mother, sister, daughter) with a history of breast cancer.

Helpful: Use the National Cancer Institute's Breast Cancer Risk Assessment Tool at *www. cancer.gov/bcrisktool.*

• **The power of exercise.** Scientists in England analyzed 62 studies on physical activity and the risk for breast cancer—and found that the most active women had 25% lower risk than the least active. *They also found...*

• Regular recreational activity, such as brisk walking, lowered risk more than doing household chores.

• Physical activity throughout life was the most protective, but exercising after menopause was more protective than exercising only earlier in life.

The study appeared in 2008 in *British Journal of Sports Medicine.*

What to do: Researchers are now determining the exact type and amount of exercise that may help protect against breast cancer. In the meantime, a sensible recommendation is to exercise for at least 20 minutes five days a week. Most people find brisk walking is the easiest way to exercise regularly.

• **Weight control.** Losing weight may help you decrease risk for breast cancer—and stay alive after a diagnosis.

Recent study: Researchers at the National Cancer Institute analyzed five years of health data from more than 99,000 postmenopausal women. They reported that women who were not overweight at age 18 but who were overweight at ages 35 and 50 were at a 40% higher risk of developing breast cancer, compared to women who maintained a normal weight or lost weight.

Theory: An estrogen buildup in fat tissue may trigger the growth of cancer cells in the breast.

Other recent studies show that overweight women diagnosed with breast cancer have faster-growing tumors, are more likely to have a recurrence and have lower survival rates.

What to do: If you have weight to lose, talk to a dietician about eating a low-fat diet similar to that used in the Women's Intervention Nutrition Study (WINS), which showed that a diet limited to 33 grams of fat a day or less lowered the recurrence rates of breast cancer. You can achieve that fat level by emphasizing fruits and vegetables, whole grains, legumes (beans, lentils) and lean meats...and avoiding red meat and full-fat dairy products.

TREATMENT BREAKTHROUGHS

• **Bone-saving medicine—for breasts.** The bone-building drug *zoledronic acid* (Zometa) routinely is used in women with breast cancer that has metastasized to the bones to help protect the skeleton and stop fractures. Now it's being used to treat breast cancer itself.

Recent study: Researchers in Austria studied 1,803 premenopausal women with estrogen-responsive early-stage breast cancer. They treated half with conventional estrogen-blocking anticancer drugs and the other half with those medicines and Zometa. After four years, the women also receiving Zometa had a 36% slower progression of tumor growth, on average. The study appeared in the February 12, 2009, issue of *The New England Journal of Medicine*.

Scientists theorize that Zometa's antitumor mechanisms may encompass reducing blood supply to the tumor (*antiangiogenesis*) or increasing the immune system's cancer-fighting power. Side effects include joint and muscle aches.

What to do: Zometa is not routinely prescribed for breast cancer. If you have breast cancer, ask your oncologist about participating in a clinical trial of the drug. You can find a list of clinical trials for Zometa and breast cancer at *www.druglib.com/druginfo/zometa/trials*.

• **Better, safer radiation.** In a study published in the March 15, 2009, issue of *Cancer*, researchers at University of Michigan Comprehensive Cancer Center found that one in five women with breast cancer who are at high risk for a recurrence after a mastectomy did not receive radiation. And that's a shame, because radiation can help prevent a recurrence—and now it can be delivered in ways that are safer and faster.

The international standard for delivering radiation therapy for breast cancer is a regimen of 25 doses of 2 Gy (a unit of absorbed radiation) for a total of 50 Gy over five to seven weeks. But for the past 10 years, researchers in England and Holland have studied a treatment that delivers fewer, bigger doses for an overall smaller dose—40 Gy—in three weeks.

A study in *The Lancet* in 2008 found that the faster regimen is just as effective at stopping tumors from returning—with fewer side effects.

Also, during September 2008, at the annual meeting of the American Society for Thera-

peutic Radiology and Oncology, Canadian researchers announced similar findings after a 12-year study. At the same meeting, researchers presented a study showing that a technique called *accelerated partial breast irradiation* (or APBI)—using radioactive-seed implants or localized radiation, which shortens radiation therapy to one week—is just as effective as standard "external beam" radiation.

What to do: Talk to your oncologist about whether a shorter schedule and APBI are right for you.

Dreading Your Next Mammogram? How to Be Much More Comfortable

Ellen Mendelson, MD, a professor of radiology at Northwestern University Feinberg School of Medicine and section chief of breast and women's imaging at Northwestern Memorial Hospital, both in Chicago.

Many women dread the brief breast-squishing discomfort during mammograms—sometimes to the point that they delay or skip the test. This is unfortunate, because mammography is the one screening test proven to decrease mortality from breast cancer. Why the big squeeze? Compressing the breast allows X-rays to penetrate better, reducing your radiation absorption and producing clearer images. *What minimizes discomfort…*

• **Breast cushions.** In studies, about 70% of the patients indicated significantly less pain when single-use, adhesive-backed foam cushions were attached to the mammography machine's compression plates. The cushions do not affect mammogram image quality. To find a facility that uses cushions, visit *http://locator. mammopad.com*.

• **Good timing.** Schedule your mammogram for the week after your period—premenstrual hormonal fluctuations trigger fluid retention, making breasts tender. If you are postmenopausal, timing doesn't matter unless you are on cyclical hormone treatment, in which case schedule your mammogram for the first half of the cycle.

- **Limiting caffeine.** For some women, caffeine increases breast sensitivity. Avoid coffee, tea, cola and chocolate for three days before your mammogram.

- **Nonprescription pain reliever.** Take one or two tablets of *ibuprofen* (Motrin) one hour before your mammogram. Avoid aspirin—it can lead to bruising.

Caution: Some radiology centers provide a topical lidocaine cream to numb breasts. This anesthetic carries a slight risk for causing cardiac problems, however—so use it only if you really need it and wash it off when the test is done.

Grapefruit Warning

Grapefruit may be linked to cancer of the breast.

Recent finding: Women who ate the equivalent of half a grapefruit every other day had a 30% increase in breast cancer risk.

Possible reason: The compound in grapefruit that changes blood levels of some drugs also may increase estrogen levels.

More research is needed—but women at high risk for breast cancer may want to avoid grapefruit. Other citrus fruits appear to be safe.

Kristine R. Monroe, PhD, assistant professor, department of preventive medicine, University of Southern California, Los Angeles, and lead author of a study of 46,080 postmenopausal women, published in *British Journal of Cancer.*

Lots of Lentils Fight Breast Cancer

In a recent study, women who ate one-half cup of lentils at least twice per week were 24% less likely to develop breast cancer, com-

pared with women who ate the same amount of lentils less than once a month or not at all.

Theory: Lentils' protective effects may be due to particular types of phytochemicals. One-half cup of lentils has 9 grams (g) of protein, 8 g of fiber, 3 milligrams of iron and only 115 calories. And they are inexpensive. Add lentils while cooking soups and whole grains, and use cooked lentils in salads.

Clement A. Adebamowo, MD, ScD, professor, department of epidemiology and preventive medicine, Institute of Human Virology, member of the Greenebaum Cancer Center, School of Medicine, University of Maryland, Baltimore, and coauthor of a study of 90,630 women, published in *International Journal of Cancer.*

Soy Reduces Breast Cancer Recurrence By 32%

Soy decreases breast cancer recurrence. A recent study with breast cancer survivors indicated that diets high in soy protein (up to 11 grams per day) were associated with a 32% lower risk for breast cancer recurrence and a 29% lower risk for death. Soy is controversial because it contains estrogen-like compounds shown to increase breast cancer cell growth, but this new study shows that soy may help women at risk for breast cancer recurrence.

Xiao-Ou Shu, MD, PhD, professor of medicine, Vanderbilt University Medical Center, Nashville, and leader of a study of 5,042 women, published in *The Journal of the American Medical Association.*

For Cancer Protection... Keep It Dark at Night

Nighttime light contributes to cancer of the breast and prostate.

Reason: The hormone melatonin can inhibit cancer cell growth. It is produced at night, and exposure to even just a little light can suppress melatonin production.

117

Best: When preparing for sleep, make the room as dark as possible. Buy a night-light for the bathroom so that you won't have to turn on the bright overhead light in the night...or consider red lightbulbs for the bathroom, as they impact melatonin production less than regular bulbs.

Richard Stevens, PhD, professor and cancer epidemiologist, department of community medicine and health care, University of Connecticut Health Center, Farmington, and coauthor of a study published in *Chronobiology International*.

Tasty Juice Slows Down Cancer

Pomegranate juice may slow the development of prostate cancer.

Recent research: In a study of 48 men who had undergone surgery or radiation treatment for prostate cancer, those who consumed eight ounces of pomegranate juice per day for six years prolonged their "doubling time" from 15 months up to 54 months. Doubling time is the amount of time it takes for levels of *prostate-specific antigen* (PSA) to double—an indication of prostate cancer progression.

Theory: The juice's antioxidants and/or anti-inflammatory substances may help slow down cancer progression.

Allan J. Pantuck, MD, associate professor of urology, University of California, Los Angeles.

HPV: The Killer That No One Talks About

Diane M. Harper, MD, MPH, director of the Gynecologic Cancer Prevention Research Group and professor of community and family medicine and women's and gender studies, Dartmouth College. She is one of the country's leading experts on the human papillomavirus (HPV)

There was lots of media coverage of actress Farrah Fawcett's death in 2009 of anal cancer. *Below is important information on this deadly disease...*

Little-known fact: The majority of anal and cervical cancers—and most cancers affecting the penis and oral cavity (mouth, throat and sinus cavities)—are linked to the *human papillomavirus* (HPV), the most common sexually transmitted infection in the US.

Each year, about 5,000 Americans are diagnosed with anal cancer...approximately 11,000 women are found to have cervical cancer...an estimated 1,500 American men are diagnosed with penile cancer...and some 34,000 Americans are found to have oral cancer.

Why you should be informed about HPV: Even if you have been in a monogamous sexual relationship for years, you may unknowingly be carrying the potentially deadly virus. At least *half* of all sexually active men and women in the US will be infected with HPV at some point in their lives, and an estimated 20 million Americans are currently carrying the virus.

CANCER-CAUSING HPVs

There are more than 100 strains of viruses in the papilloma family. HPV is a well-known cause of warts on the genitals and elsewhere on the body (such as on the hands or feet). Two varieties of HPV—known as type 6 and type 11—can cause genital warts, while more than 30 strains can cause warts on other parts of the body.

Important: Even though genital warts may be emotionally disturbing, they do not turn into cancer.

All the remaining types of HPV have cancer-causing (*oncogenic*) potential. Of the high-risk strains, two—known as type 16 and type 18—account for about 70% of all cases of cervical cancer, as well as most cases of anal cancer. These strains of HPV also can infect the penis, the vagina and the mouth.

A HIDDEN THREAT

Infections due to cancer-causing strains of HPV usually go undetected because they do not cause warts or any other symptoms.

Both women and men who are infected can unknowingly transmit the virus—usually during sexual encounters (vaginal, anal or oral sex). The virus enters the body through cuts or tiny tears in the outer layer of the skin in the vagina, cervix, penis, anus and mouth. Because HPV is spread through skin-to-skin contact, it is possible that kissing is another route of transmission, but the virus is usually transmitted sexually.

The good news is that the body's immune system effectively eliminates the cancer-causing virus in about 90% of HPV infections—usually within two years. When the virus stays in the body beyond two years, it is considered chronic, and the risk for cancer of the genitals, cervix, anus or oral cavity rises.

ARE YOU AT RISK?

Most HPV infections are transmitted during sexual activity, but about 10% to 15% of the population become infected from nonsexual sources that have not yet been identified. In general, the risk for HPV infection is higher for people who have impaired immunity—for example, anyone undergoing chemotherapy or those with diabetes or an autoimmune disease, such as lupus or rheumatoid arthritis, and for people who have many sexual partners or who use devices that cause tears (even very tiny ones) in the skin of the genitals, anus or mouth.

Startling new finding: A common ingredient in many vaginal spermicides, *nonoxynol-9,* triples a woman's risk for HPV infection. It damages the lining of the vagina and makes it easier for the virus to enter through the skin.

TESTING AND DIAGNOSIS

Precancerous changes to cells in the cervix can be detected by a Pap smear. If a woman's Pap results are described as atypical, she is advised to undergo a test that checks for one or more of 13 cancer-causing HPV types.

Recent finding: A study of 130,000 women published in *The New England Journal of Medicine* showed that a test used to check for HPV could replace the Pap test at some point. Women who got the HPV test were 37% less likely to die due to cervical cancer than those who received Pap tests, suggesting that the HPV test identifies cervical cancer sooner than a Pap test.

THE HPV VACCINE

Gardasil, a vaccine that prevents infection from four strains of HPV—the high-cancer-risk types 16 and 18, as well as the genital wart–causing 6 and 11—was approved by the FDA in 2006.

How it is used: The Centers for Disease Control and Prevention (or CDC) recommends vaccination for girls/young women ages nine through 26. There has been a movement to recommend the vaccine for young men to protect both them and their future partners. But recent data found that Gardasil protected men only from the genital wart–causing 6 and 11 types of HPV—but not from the cancer-causing strains.

Latest development: A recent controversial study published in the *Journal of the American Medical Association* found some serious adverse effects, including death, after Gardasil use. Discuss the risks and benefits of the vaccine with your physician.

OTHER PREVENTIVE STEPS

Using a condom reduces—but it does not eliminate—risk for HPV infection in women and men. This is because the virus can occur in areas that aren't covered by a condom, and it can be spread by hand-to-mouth contact. Being in a mutually monogamous relationship with someone who has had few or no previous partners also curbs risk.

To protect yourself: Women are advised to have Pap tests to identify cervical cell changes—every three years if the last test results were normal. If abnormal, an annual Pap test is recommended until the results are normal for three consecutive years.

Women who use spermicides that contain nonoxynol-9 (including condoms that use this ingredient) to prevent pregnancy should consider switching from this form of birth control to some other method, such as oral contraceptives or cervical caps. Both men and women should ask for an oral cancer check during each dental visit. And men should regularly check for signs of penile cancer, such as visible bumps or ulcers.

Should You Get a "Virtual" Colonoscopy?

David H. Kim, MD, associate professor of radiology and the residency program director at the University of Wisconsin School of Medicine and Public Health in Madison. He is a researcher in computed tomographic colonography and the lead author of multiple studies, including recent analyses published in *The New England Journal of Medicine* and the February 2010 issue of *Radiology*.

A large study recently reported in *The New England Journal of Medicine* discovered that computed tomographic (CT) colonography—also known as "virtual" colonoscopy—might be just as effective as a colorectal screening tool as conventional colonoscopy—without carrying the risk for colon perforation (damage to the intestinal wall).

What you need to know about your options for colonoscopy...*

PROS AND CONS OF SCREENING TESTS

Any pain related to conventional colonoscopy is typically well controlled by sedation, but the exam requires a 24-hour bowel preparation, including a liquid diet and medications that cause diarrhea to cleanse the colon. When receiving conventional colonoscopy, most patients spend about half a day at a hospital or clinic, and they must arrange transportation because they're not allowed to drive after being sedated.

CT colonography also requires the colon cleanse, but the test itself takes only about 15 to 20 minutes. No sedation is given, so people who drive can take themselves home.

For these reasons, many medical experts believe that many more Americans will undergo screening for colorectal cancer when CT colonography becomes more widely available—about 17% of US hospitals currently offer CT colonography services. The American Cancer Society now includes CT colonography as one

*Men and women at average risk of developing colorectal cancer should start screening for colorectal cancer at age 50, or earlier if they have a personal history of colorectal cancer or polyps, a history of chronic inflammatory bowel disease, a strong family history of colorectal cancer or polyps, or a known family history of hereditary colorectal cancer syndromes.

of its recommended tests for colorectal cancer screening.

Key issues that influence the effectiveness of colonoscopy—and how each method stacks up...

• **"Hidden" polyps.** Conventional colonoscopy is very effective, but there are problem areas that the camera can't see, including the back side of folds and the right side of the colon. Skilled doctors can often minimize these "blind spots" during conventional colonoscopy, but those areas appear to be easier to view with CT colonography.

• **Polyp size.** The high-definition cameras and computer monitors that are often used in conventional colonoscopy allow the doctor to examine the intestinal lining in crisp detail.

Small polyps (less than 5/16 inch) can be more difficult to see on a CT scan compared with conventional colonoscopy. Some experts argue that any missed growth is unacceptable—that conventional colonoscopy, at least for now, is superior because it's more likely to detect the small polyps and possibly flat lesions that can lead to colon cancer.

It's important to note, however, that fewer than three in 10,000 growths smaller than 3/16 inch are cancerous. Moreover, the few small polyps that could develop into cancer in the future could be removed at a later screening, when they have grown larger and before they change to cancer.

• **Incidental findings.** Conventional colonoscopy examines only the intestinal wall. Since a CT scan has a field of view that encompasses tissues and organs beyond the intestine, 7.4% to 11.4% of people who undergo CT colonography are found to have abnormalities, including life-threatening conditions, such as an aortic aneurysm (an abnormal swelling in the wall of the body's main artery), that might have gone undetected without the test.

However, incidental findings can lead to batteries of expensive tests to investigate abnormalities that usually turn out to be harmless. About 2% of screened people have findings beyond the colon that turn out to be significant and require treatment.

• **Repeat testing.** With CT colonography, patients who have growths that need to be biopsied or removed require a subsequent conventional colonoscopy.

My advice: People who have normal colon cancer risk factors are good candidates to get CT colonography. Among average-risk people, about 10% require conventional colonoscopy as well. If you're at known high risk for polyps and/or cancer (due to a personal history of an inflammatory bowel disease, for example), it's usually better to have the conventional test.

Before scheduling a CT test: Ask the doctor whether a subsequent colonoscopy, if it is needed, can be performed the same day. This saves you from having to repeat the bowel-prep procedure.

• **The risks.** With conventional colonoscopy, perforation—which typically leads to surgical removal of part of the injured colon and can, in rare instances, cause death—occurs in about one in 1,000 procedures. A CT colonography doesn't require the insertion of a lengthy optical tube, although a small tube is inserted a few inches into the rectum to inflate the colon with carbon dioxide gas so that the intestinal wall can be easily viewed. There's virtually no risk for perforation during the CT procedure.

Recent finding: With conventional colonoscopy, research shows that the complication risk (including perforation) rises with age in adults age 65 and older.

• **Radiation.** If you're concerned about the radiation exposure, you may choose to avoid CT colonography. Depending on the imaging machine, patients are exposed to 50 to 100 times the radiation that they would get from a single chest X-ray. But, to put this into perspective, someone who lives in Denver is exposed to about the same amount of radiation each year—from cosmic rays and radon—as is used in two CT colonographies.

• **Cost and insurance.** Medicare currently does not cover CT colonography (*cost:* about $400 to $800*) as a mass screening procedure, but that may change considering recent data. Conventional colonoscopy (*cost:* about $1,500) is covered by most insurance policies. While conventional colonoscopy is usually repeated every 10 years, CT colonography is typically performed every five years.

*Prices subject to change.

Folic Acid Folly

Recent studies have shown that people who regularly consume large amounts of folic acid may increase their risk for several forms of cancer, including colorectal and prostate. The government-recommended tolerable upper limit is 1,000 micrograms (mcg) a day.

At risk: People who take in a lot without realizing it.

Example: A daily multivitamin with 400 mcg of folic acid...a B-complex supplement with another 400 mcg...cereal with 400 mcg to 800 mcg...and flour-based products with 100 mcg to 200 mcg.

Joel Mason, MD, director, Vitamins and Carcinogenesis Laboratory, Jean Mayer USDA Human Nutrition Research Center on Aging, Tufts University, Boston.

Colon Cleansing Con

Stay away from "colon cleansing" products. "Colonic irrigation" is a scam and can be dangerous. Do not believe ads that say colon cleansing will remove toxins. Any weight loss that accompanies colon cleansing results only from dehydration or from eating less during the process. Your colon does an excellent job of cleansing itself and does not need expensive products to assist.

UC Berkeley Wellness Letter, 500 Fifth Ave., New York City 10110, *www.wellnessletter.com*.

Psyllium Soothes IBS

In a 12-week study, 275 men and women with irritable bowel syndrome (chronic abdominal pain with diarrhea and/or constipation) took 10 g daily of psyllium (a vegetable fiber), bran or a placebo. Using a standard scale, the severity of symptoms dropped by 90 points, on average, in the psyllium group, compared with 58 points, on average, for the bran and placebo groups.

Theory: Psyllium is a soluble fiber, which slows the rate at which the stomach empties—an effect that reduces IBS symptoms.

If you have IBS: Ask your doctor about taking 10 g (about two tablespoons) daily of psyllium, which can be mixed with water, taken in capsule form or added to foods, such as yogurt.

C.J. Bijkerk, MD, PhD, researcher, University Medical Center, Utrecht, the Netherlands.

Are You Drinking Too Much?

Lisa M. Najavits, PhD, professor of psychiatry at Boston University School of Medicine, and lecturer at Harvard Medical School, Boston. She is president-elect of the Division on Addictions of the American Psychological Association and author of *Seeking Safety: A Treatment Manual for PTSD and Substance Abuse* (Guilford). For more, go to *www.seekingsafety.org.*

People often are surprised to realize that they drink more than is safe. "Low-risk" drinking is no more than seven drinks a week (no more than three on any given day) for most women, and no more than 14 a week (no more than four on any day) for men. Also, most people find it surprising that "one drink" is smaller than they think—five ounces of wine, 1.5 ounces of 80-proof liquor or 12 ounces of beer. For some people, such as those with a family history of alcoholism, the only safe limit is no drinking.

About 30% of Americans drink more than the low-risk limits and are considered "at risk." This means that they are likely to develop a substance-abuse problem or may already have one. Heavy drinking also increases the risk for many health problems, including liver disease and cancer, as well as car accidents.

If you suspect you may need help with a drinking problem, go to *www.samhsa.gov* for a government listing of facilities or call 800-662-4357.

How to Tell If You Smell—and What to Do...

William P. Coleman III, MD, clinical professor of dermatology and adjunct professor of surgery, Tulane University School of Medicine, New Orleans, and editor-in-chief of *Dermatologic Surgery.*

Raise your arm and take a whiff...smell the shirt you wore today...ask a friend if your odor offends.

Basics: Body odor happens when bacteria interact with sweat. For people with *hyperhidrosis*—excessive perspiring, generally due to genes—odor can be extreme. *Helpful...*

• **Bathe twice daily.** Use a deodorant soap, pay extra attention to where sweat glands are plentiful—underarms, nipples, genitals, feet.

• **Put on a combination antiperspirant/deodorant.** Apply to underarms twice daily after bathing and toweling off. Antiperspirants prevent sweating by blocking pores...deodorants mask smells and kill bacteria.

Safety: Despite rumors, there is no convincing evidence that links aluminum (the active ingredient) in antiperspirants to cancer or to neurological problems. If you prefer natural deodorants, try witch hazel or baking soda... Tom's of Maine...or Crystal Body Deodorant (*www.thecrystal.com*), made of mineral salts.

If body odor persists: See your dermatologist. If diagnosed with hyperhidrosis, try...

• **Prescription antiperspirant.** Drysol and Xerac have higher aluminum concentrations. Apply at bedtime. These work overnight, typically reducing perspiration within seven days. Cost is about $30 to $50.*

• **Botox injections.** These block off chemical signals from the nerves that stimulate sweat glands. Underarm treatment requires multiple injections...effects last eight months on average. The cost is $1,000 to $2,000.

• **Liposuction.** A dermatologist removes fat from the armpits—which also removes sweat glands. Bruising and swelling subside in a few days...occasionally, scarring or numbness occurs. Effectiveness varies, but some patients get permanent relief. Cost is $2,500 to $3,500.

*Prices subject to change.

7

Money Miracles

How the Rich Get Rich— And You Can, Too!

Most people would like to live like a millionaire, but so few understand what that really means. The marketers of luxury products foster the impression that millionaires drive fancy cars, live in mansions and surround themselves with expensive luxury goods.

The reality is that most millionaires live surprisingly modest lives far from the fast lane. And most people who act rich are not rich. That's what Thomas J. Stanley, PhD, America's foremost authority on the affluent, discovered during extensive research for his book titled *Stop Acting Rich…and Start Living Like a Real Millionaire.**

*Dr. Stanley defines a millionaire as someone with investments of $1 million or more, not including equity in one's home, motor vehicles, furniture, etc.

Below, Dr. Stanley describes how to live like a real millionaire and become a millionaire in the process…

• **Own a modest home, and use the money you save to invest wisely.** Three times more millionaires live in homes valued at less than $300,000 than more than $1 million.

What's wrong with living in a big, fancy house? Though many Americans believe luxury real estate is a great long-term investment— recent years aside—a big home is much more likely to prevent you from becoming a millionaire than to help you become one. While it's true that real estate tends to increase in value, big homes also have big costs, including big mortgage payments, property taxes, heating and cooling bills, and insurance and maintenance bills.

Thomas J. Stanley, PhD, who has studied the wealthy in America for more than 30 years. Based in Atlanta, he is author of the mega–best sellers *The Millionaire Next Door* and *The Millionaire Mind*. His most recent best seller is *Stop Acting Rich…and Start Living Like a Real Millionaire* (Wiley). His Web site is *www.thomas jstanley.com.*

Also, expensive homes tend to be surrounded by other expensive homes that are owned by people who buy expensive things. That creates social pressure to spend to fit in. It is better to buy a modest home that you can easily afford in a neighborhood where you are more successful than most of your neighbors, minimizing the pressure to overspend.

Invest the money that you save in the stock market. Stocks, not real estate, are the true investment path to wealth despite big pullbacks in stock prices from time to time.

• **Drive a modest car.** When I conducted my research, I found that about 11% of vehicle purchases by US millionaires were Toyotas. Although that is less than the roughly 17% market share that Toyota has had among US car buyers overall, it still makes Toyota the most popular of auto brands among millionaires. Toyotas and several other brands, such as Ford, Chevrolet and Honda, provide reliability at reasonable prices (although Toyota's recent safety-related recalls have tarnished its image).

Fully 86% of people driving luxury brands (BMW, Mercedes, Lexus, Jaguar and the like) are not millionaires. All of these brands tend to attract high earners who also are status-conscious overspenders—this prevents them from ever accumulating significant assets.

• **Don't buy a second home or a boat.** Most millionaires (64%) have never owned a vacation home. They understand the real cost (in terms of dollars and time) of buying, furnishing, maintaining, commuting to, renting and possibly selling a second home. And most don't want to be "tied down" to one vacation spot.

Even more millionaires (70%) have never owned a boat. Of those millionaires who actually purchased a boat sometime during their lifetime, most sold it and never bought another one.

• **Avoid aspirational brands.** People buy elite brands of clothes, jewelry and consumer goods because they want to look rich. Actual millionaires know better than to waste money on labels.

When millionaires shop for clothes, they are more likely to head to Kohl's, JCPenney and Target than to Saks and Brooks Brothers. (If a millionaire does wear a Brooks Brothers garment, he/she probably bought it on sale.)

When millionaires buy a watch, their choice is Seiko, not Rolex. Paying thousands is just showing off, something true millionaires rarely do. (Of those who wear a Rolex, 46% received it as a gift.)

When millionaires uncork wine for guests, the median price they paid for the bottle is just $13. Only 7% of millionaires own a bottle that cost more than $100.

Exception: Many male millionaires are willing to pay $100 to $300 for a pair of shoes. They aren't anteing up to get a flashy brand name, however. The most popular millionaire shoe brands include Allen Edmonds, Cole Haan and Johnston & Murphy—the shoemakers known for providing comfort, quality construction and timeless styling. When these shoes wear out, millionaires (70%) have them resoled instead of replaced.

• **Spend time without spending money.** Ultrarich "deca-millionaires"—those with more than $10 million—could afford to do almost anything, yet the leisure activities that they engage in most often include socializing with their kids and grandkids...watching those kids or grandkids play sports...entertaining close friends...studying art...attending religious services...fund-raising for noble causes...jogging ...praying...attending lectures...and caring for elderly relatives.

• **Befriend all the right people.** Surround yourself with people who excel at converting a high percentage of their income to wealth, the single most important millionaire skill. Engineers, educators and managers of supermarkets and discount department stores tend to do this extremely well. Why?

Engineers tend to be analytical thinkers who value quality and substance. They ignore marketing hype and focus on things that matter.

Example: An engineer is more likely to pay extra for a garment with a high thread count—an objective measure of quality—than one with a prestige label.

The culture at most educational institutions esteems saving for retirement over spending on elite consumer goods. Few educators earn flashy salaries, yet teachers and professors often manage to amass seven-figure savings.

Managers of supermarkets and discount department stores look at consumer products not as symbols of economic success but merely as a way to make a living.

• **Choose a tightwad spouse.** My research has shown that when a wife covets the trappings of wealth, it doesn't matter how much the couple earns—the family is likely to wind up living above its means and saving little. Meanwhile, in millionaire households, the husband often reports, "I just can't get my wife to spend much money."

If you already have married someone who likes to spend, try to hang out as a couple with your more frugal friends. This should dampen your partner's impulse to spend to fit in.

Where to Turn *First* for Emergency Cash

Jim Holtzman, CPA, CFP, Legend Financial Advisors in Pittsburgh, *www.legend-financial.com*. The fee-only firm has been named 15 times as one of the country's top wealth advisers by *Worth* magazine.

Every household should strive to keep an emergency fund that is big enough to cover expenses for at least six months, especially in these turbulent times. But if that money runs out, you need to know where to turn first to raise cash while avoiding penalties and/or taxes on that money. *The best order...*

• **Sell stuff that you don't want or need.** Lots of people have valuable items in their homes that they can turn into cash. The easiest way is to advertise on the classified ad Web site Craigslist.org—listings are free.

• **Redeem long-term certificates of deposit (CDs).** Many banks impose a penalty of six months in interest for early withdrawal on a one-year CD, but with interest rates as low as they have been lately—typically less than 2%*—that's not much of a penalty.

*Prices and rates subject to change.

• **Stop reinvesting interest and dividends that you earn on your savings and investments.** This is a relatively painless way to restock your emergency fund, although it could deprive you of the opportunity to buy more shares of stock or bonds cheaply.

• **Borrow from a relative or friend.** Tread lightly here, because an unpaid debt can poison a treasured relationship. Have an attorney draw up a promissory note spelling out the terms of the loan, including an agreed-upon interest rate. Such rates are usually based on the "applicable federal rate," published monthly by the IRS. In August 2010, the rate ranged from 0.53% a year for loans of less than three years to about 3.79% a year for loans longer than nine years.

• **Borrow against your home equity.** Many banks and credit unions continue to provide home equity lines of credit (or HELOCs). However, you may now need 20% or more equity in your home and a FICO credit score of 660 or better (out of 850) to qualify...and to merit the lowest interest rates, you may need a stellar score of 750 or higher. If you meet these criteria, you may be able to borrow at initial rates as low as 4.8%. HELOCs have no closing costs and low up-front charges (about $400), though you may pay an additional annual fee of about $50 to maintain the line.

• **Sell stocks.** If your shares have lost value since you bought them, you can use the capital loss now or in a later year to offset capital gains and up to $3,000 of ordinary income and thus reduce your taxes. You can also consider selling bonds now, but one result of the credit crisis is that the market for individual bonds is highly illiquid, meaning that there are few buyers out there for individual bonds. Even if you find a buyer, you'll probably wind up selling at a discount.

• **Borrow from life insurance.** Many whole-life policies allow you to borrow up to 90% of the cash value at favorable interest rates, and such borrowed amounts are tax free.

Caution: If you die before repaying, the death benefit to your beneficiaries is reduced by the amount of the loan plus interest owed.

●**Consider tapping your IRA.** Uncle Sam imposes a 10% penalty on IRA assets that are withdrawn before age 59½, on top of ordinary income taxes. But under the IRS's 72(t) rule, you may receive "substantially equal periodic payments" penalty free before age 59½, provided they run a minimum of five years. You may also take an early distribution if you are unemployed and use the money to pay health insurance premiums and in several other circumstances. You may withdraw IRA contributions made for the year if the contributions, plus earnings, are withdrawn by the due date of your return (including extensions). Roth IRA contributions can be withdrawn at any time (they were made with after-tax money). Earnings on Roth IRA contributions can be withdrawn free of taxes and penalties only after age 59½, on account of disability, or for first-time home buying, provided that the account has been established for at least five years.

Helpful: If you can pay yourself back within 60 days, you may borrow from a traditional IRA for any reason without paying taxes or penalties.

More information: See IRS Publication 590, *Individual Retirement Arrangements* (IRAs), at *www.irs.gov.*

●**Turn to a 401(k) plan as a last resort.** The strictest rules apply to withdrawals from 401(k)s. You pay income tax and a 10% penalty even for hardship withdrawals—generally, similar situations to those that are described in the IRA section above.

Exception: If you retire or lose your job at age 55 or later, you may begin taking distributions penalty free.

Another alternative is borrowing from your 401(k). Loans are typically limited to 50% of your vested balance up to a limit of $50,000, and you must repay them within five years. But interest rates are low—generally just a percentage point or two above the prime rate. If you lose your job, you must repay the loan, usually within 30 or 60 days, or be taxed on the unpaid balance, as well as pay a 10% penalty if you are under age 59½.

Easy Way to Wire Money Internationally

Wire money internationally from a computer using new services from MoneyGram, Western Union and other companies. You can send money whenever you like—but only from a bank account or by using a credit card. To use cash, you must still work with an agent. The cost to send, say, $200 to Mexico using your computer ranges from $5 to $20*— but there may be an additional charge of up to $25 the first time. Using an agent for the same transaction costs $8 to $15.

Coming soon: Sending money using your cell phone—this is already possible in some countries.

What to do: Decide how often you need to send money out of the US, then shop around for the best deal based on your likely frequency of use.

Ben Woolsey, spokesperson, CreditCards.com, Austin, Texas.

*Prices subject to change.

No-Stress Way to Pay Bills

Leo Babauta, author of *The Power of Less* (Hyperion). He created and runs the popular Internet blog ZenHabits (*www.zenhabits.net*), which has more than 137,000 subscribers and two million visitors a month. *Time* magazine selected the blog as one of the 25 best of 2009.

It's amazing how people let the simple, predictable chore of paying monthly bills create so much tension, with paperwork getting lost, deadlines being missed and mad dashes to the post office.

I used to think that waiting to pay all my bills once a month was efficient and financially advantageous, because it allowed my money to sit in an interest-bearing account a bit longer each month.

Reality: Whenever you create such a "system" to simplify your life, it's important to do what's easiest in practice, not theory. For me, the longer a bill sits around, the easier it is to forget about or lose. And just one late-payment penalty can negate several years of extra interest you might earn by waiting until the last minute to pay.

So now, I keep my checkbook and stamps handy and pay each new bill with the next day's mail. It is quick and easy—and there's never any stress.

Simple Secrets of Living Debt-Free from Those Who Don't Owe a Penny

Jeff Yeager, dubbed "The Ultimate Cheapskate" by NBC's *Today* show, honed his cheapskating skills during 25 years working with underfunded nonprofit agencies. He lives in Accokeek, Maryland, and is author of *The Ultimate Cheapskate's Road Map to True Riches* and *The Cheapskate Next Door* (both from Broadway). His Web site is *www.ultimatecheapskate.com.*

My grandfather frequently said, "If you can't afford to pay for it now, you can't afford it." When he first told me that 40 years ago, it did not sound nearly as radical as it does today. Grandpa borrowed money only once in his life—to buy a house—and even then he paid it off long before the bank required.

Of course, times are different now. Everything costs so much more. There's no way you can live comfortably these days without borrowing money and going into debt.

Wait one minute! If you believe those last three sentences, then have we got an article for you. Those three sentences are as false as Grandpa's teeth.

I picked the brains of some leading personal finance experts and my own network of volunteer "Miser Advisers" to gather their thoughts on living comfortably without going into debt—or at least without borrowing to the extent that most Americans do today. *Here are their secrets…*

●**Be afraid, be very afraid, of credit cards.** To paraphrase Jack Nicholson's character in the movie *A Few Good Men,* "Credit cards? You can't handle the credit cards!" Roughly 60% of active credit card accounts are not paid off every month. Many people think that they can game the system—earn lots of bonus points or cash back by frequently using a credit card—and pay it off every month. In reality, most people just end up in debt.

●**Pay in cash, and you certainly will spend a lot less.** According to Bankrate.com, the average credit card purchase now ends up costing 112% more than the purchase price (that's right, more than twice as much) because we fail to pay it off right away.

To me, there are only a few wise uses of a credit card. These include establishing your credit history…actual emergencies…and transactions such as car rentals that require a card.

●**Practice the art of procrastination.** When it comes to living free of debt, procrastination can be a virtue, not a vice. We've all had buyer's remorse. That is the feeling of regret you get when you buy something that disappoints you. Buyer's remorse often is compounded by a sense of guilt when you buy something on credit. A purchase has disappointed you, and you haven't even paid for it yet.

Practice procrastination when it comes to all discretionary purchases, particularly if you plan to use your credit card. Wait at least one week between the time you see an item in a store or online and the time you go back to buy it. Chances are good that you will decide that you don't want it after all. And whenever you do buy, save your receipts so that you can return items you regret for a full refund.

●**Shine up that used car.** When it comes to buying an automobile, the smart money is almost always on buying a used (but not abused) vehicle, so you let the guy who buys the new auto pay the 20% or more in value that most new cars lose in their first year of ownership.

Still have that urge-to-splurge on a new car? Anthony Manganiello, author of *The Debt-Free Millionaire* (Wiley), has this simple advice that helps him resist the call—keep your car really clean. He says that a sparkling used car feels like a new car and helps him resist the unending barrage of car commercials.

•**Buy a home, not a castle.** Granted, few people can afford to buy a home without taking out a mortgage, but that does not mean that you need to live your entire life with a mortgage hanging over your head, as many Americans do. The secret is to choose a house costing no more than 75% of the maximum amount you can qualify to borrow and then aggressively paying off your mortgage early.

"The priority is to get into something you can afford and then work on trading up or improving the house you have," says personal finance columnist Gregory Karp in his book *Living Rich by Spending Smart* (FT Press).

Once you're in that affordable home, begin making extra principal payments to pay off the loan early. If in the course of a year you make just one additional monthly payment, you can knock years and many thousands of dollars in interest off your mortgage.

•**Ask yourself, "When is Christmas next year?"** That sounds like a strange question, but as Heather Wagenhals of the Unlock Your Wealth Foundation points out, many people are financially blindsided every year by holidays, vacations and other "spending events" that can be planned for well in advance.

The same goes for "emergencies." Certainly it is possible to have a truly unanticipated financial emergency, but for too many people, almost everything is an emergency because they have failed to plan—and save—for even the things that can be anticipated. A car with 100,000 miles on it needing repairs shouldn't be an emergency. You know it's going to need repairs…you just don't know exactly when.

•**Figure out what Grandpa would do.** If you still aren't convinced that it's possible to live debt free, or nearly so, like previous generations of Americans did, keep track of everything you spend money on for one month. Then look over that list, and ask yourself one simple question, "Did my grandparents spend money on that?" A second or third automobile? Unlikely. More than one TV? Doubtful. Meals in restaurants, other than for very special occasions? Rarely. Pet-grooming services? Not a chance. Bottled water? Are you crazy? Tanning salons? Forget about it!

Digging Out of Debt: Six Strategies That Work

Gerri Detweiler, credit adviser for the credit education Web site Credit.com, located in San Francisco. She is former executive director of Bankcard Holders of America, a nonprofit consumer education and advocacy group. Based in Sarasota, Florida, she is the author or coauthor of several books, including the e-book *Reduce Debt, Reduce Stress* (Good Advice Press, go to *www.reduce-debt-reduce-stress.com*).

T he average American adult carries more than $16,000 in debt (excluding home mortgages)—and that figure is likely to climb higher.

The best paths out of debt, starting with those most appealing to the largest numbers of debtors…

CREDIT COUNSELING

A nonprofit credit-counseling agency might be able to help you set up a three- to five-year debt-repayment plan. Anyone struggling with debts should give this a try. The agency will negotiate with your creditors to try and lower your interest rates and perhaps get some fees waived. Unfortunately, not all of your creditors are likely to agree to do this, but at least some will. Once this repayment plan is put in place, you send a single debt-payment check to the agency each month, and it distributes the money to your creditors. Credit-counseling agencies also provide useful money-management advice.

How to get started: Choose a credit-counseling agency that has been in business for at least 10 years and that has been approved by the US Trustee's office. (On the Department of Justice Web site, *www.usdoj.gov*, click on "A-Z Index" at the bottom of the page, then "Credit Counseling and Debtor Education," then "Approved Credit Counseling Agencies.") Expect to pay an initial charge of perhaps $50* and a monthly fee of $30 to $50.

Drawbacks: If your debts are so great that there is no feasible way for you to pay them back within three to five years…or you have lost your job and cannot pay off your debts at all in the near term, a credit-counseling

*Prices and rates subject to change.

organization will not be able to construct a debt-repayment plan that you can afford.

Helpful for home owners: The US Department of Housing and Urban Development (HUD) sponsors free counseling agencies that provide advice on credit concerns, mortgage loan defaults and foreclosures. For agencies in your state, go to *www.hud.gov/offices/hsg* (click on "Single Family," then on "Housing Counseling").

RETIREMENT ACCOUNT LOAN

If you have a 401(k) or 403(b) retirement account or a pension plan where you work, it's likely that you can borrow against the value of your account or plan so that you can pay off other debts. These retirement-account loans generally are capped at either $50,000 or 50% of the amount in the account, whichever is less, and need to be repaid within five years. You might be allowed to borrow up to $10,000 even if this represents more than half of your account balance. (If you have a defined-benefit pension plan, the amount you can borrow may be determined by the number of years you have worked for your employer or some other formula.) Interest is charged—typically 6% to 8%—but this interest is paid to your own retirement account. Ask your employer's retirement-plan administrator whether you can borrow.

Retirement-account loans do not require a credit check, which makes them particularly attractive for people with low credit scores.

Drawbacks: Retirement-account loans that are not repaid within five years are treated as distributions, triggering income taxes and a 10% IRS penalty. If you change or lose your job—a big concern in today's economy—your employer might require you to pay back the loan immediately. Money borrowed from your retirement account misses out on tax-deferred growth until it is repaid.

PERSONAL LOAN

Personal loans are unsecured loans with interest rates that can be well below typical credit card rates. Consolidating credit card debt into a personal loan can lower debt costs so that debts can be paid off sooner.

Many banks have stopped issuing personal loans in this credit crunch. Try local credit unions or a "social lending" company instead. Social lenders bring together borrowers with investors who wish to make loans to earn interest. Some reputable social-lending companies include Lending Club (866-754-4094, *www.lendingclub.com*) and Prosper (866-615-6319, *www.prosper.com*). Borrowers typically pay interest rates of 7.5% to 12% for three-year fixed-rate loans of up to $15,000.

Drawbacks: Only borrowers with credit scores above 660 to 680 are likely to qualify. Loans rarely exceed $5,000 to $15,000, which is not enough for many people who are deep in debt. Loans typically last just 36 months, so sizable monthly payments are required.

HOME-EQUITY LOAN

Home-equity loans and home-equity lines of credit (HELOCs) let home owners borrow against the equity that they have in their property—assuming that they have any equity left after the recent real estate declines. (A home-equity loan will provide cash in a lump sum, while a HELOC will provide revolving credit.) This money can be used to pay down high-rate debt. Falling property values and increasingly cautious lenders have made these loans difficult to obtain, but most home-equity loans typically have interest rates of about 5% to 9%, and the interest paid on these loans usually is tax deductible.

Drawbacks: If you pay off credit card debt with a home-equity loan or HELOC, you are trading unsecured debt for secured debt (your home is the collateral)—you could lose your home if you fall behind on debt payments. Adding to the amount that you owe on your home could make it harder to sell the home and move.

DEBT-SETTLEMENT FIRM

A debt-settlement company will attempt to convince your creditors to settle for less than you owe, perhaps 50 to 60 cents on the dollar. That's very different from a credit-counseling company, which will attempt to help you pay back the full amount that you owe but with lower fees and interest. Your creditors might accept these terms if they believe that you will otherwise default on your loans. To increase its leverage, the debt-settlement company often will instruct you to stop making debt payments while it negotiates.

Choosing your debt-settlement company: Reputable companies charge primarily based on the amount that they save you—not the amount you owe—with only modest up-front fees. That might be a set-up charge of a few hundred dollars and 15% to 25% of the amount you will save. Reputable companies also warn clients about the downsides of debt settlement (see below). The firm should propose a plan that will have you out of debt in less than 36 months—any longer and creditors are more likely to sue than accept the terms. It's a good sign if the debt-settlement company has been in business at least 10 years and belongs to the Association of Settlement Companies (*www. tascsite.org*).

Drawbacks: You are likely to be besieged by calls from collection agencies and might be sued by your lenders when you stop making loan payments. There are any number of disreputable debt-settlement companies that charge high fees but do little for their clients. You may owe income taxes on any debt that is forgiven. Working with a debt-settlement company will harm your credit rating—perhaps severely. The size of the hit depends on the current status of your debts. If you already are behind on payments to multiple creditors, entering debt settlement might not make a huge difference. If you have not missed any payments yet, debt settlement is the equivalent of defaulting on all of your loans and your credit score could drop by more than 100 points.

Bottom line: Debt settlement is a viable option only if your debt problems are so substantial that you see no other way to pay off your debts and if you take extreme care to use an honest debt-settlement company.

BANKRUPTCY

It might be possible to cancel your debts through a Chapter 7 bankruptcy...or to reorganize your debts through a Chapter 13 bankruptcy despite the hurdles recently added to the bankruptcy process. Discuss all your options with a bankruptcy attorney—bankruptcy laws are too complex to sort out on your own. Select an attorney who is a member of the National Association of Consumer Bankruptcy Attorneys (at *www.nacba.org*). The initial consultation typically is free. Expect legal costs of around $900 to $2,000 if you do file. If you cannot afford this, contact your state's bar association and ask if there's a state legal aid society that can provide a lawyer for less or for free.

Drawbacks: Bankruptcy will devastate your credit rating and remain on your credit report for 10 years, compared with a maximum of seven years for other credit missteps. Certain debts—including child support, alimony and student loans—might not be discharged in a bankruptcy. The recent changes to bankruptcy laws make it impossible for some debtors who have large amounts of disposable income to qualify for Chapter 7 bankruptcy at all. Many of your assets could be seized.

Considering Bankruptcy? First Read This...

Prior to filing for bankruptcy, be sure you consider every possible alternative. Bankruptcy is a major black mark on your credit for years.

What to do: Get free credit reports at Equifax (800-685-1111, *www.equifax.com*)...Experian (888-397-3742, *www.experian.com*)... and TransUnion (800-888-4213, *www.transunion. com*). Make sure all information is accurate. Consider such options as negotiating with creditors, using a credit-counseling agency to reduce interest rates or using a debt-resolution firm to try to reduce principal owed.

Ethan Ewing, president of Bills.com, a personal finance information source, San Mateo, California.

Checkup for Your Bank

Anew site from the Investigative Reporting Workshop of American University (*http://banktracker.investigativereportingworkshop.org*) can tell you whether your bank is in danger of failing. The site analyzes data from the FDIC on hundreds of banks, comparing such key points as total assets, provisions for loan losses, total deposits, etc. According to its research, the number of banks with more troubled loans than assets to cover them continues to rise. In 2007, only 10 banks were in this position. That number rose to 165 by the end of 2008...and 391 by the end of 2009.*

Linda Sherry, director of national priorities, Consumer Action, Washington, DC, *www.consumer-action.org*.

*Latest date for which figures are available.

How to Get a Bank's Best Interest Rates

Abank's best interest rates might not be offered at its local branch. Major banks sometimes make on their Web sites high-interest-rate investment and other "special" offers that aren't available in local branches. So, when looking for the best interest rate on a certificate of deposit (CD) or other savings option, look at both what's offered on the bank's Web site and in your local branch. Compare online offers at *www.bankrate.com*.

Greg McBride, CFA, senior financial analyst, Bankrate.com, North Palm Beach, Florida.

Secret to Getting Higher CD and Bank Rates

Higher rates on certificates of deposit (CDs) and bank accounts are available through some organizations and buying clubs. Groups such as AAA, Costco and USAA offer special rates on financial products to their members.

Example: Members of AAA get slightly higher interest than the published rates at Discover Bank. And some groups may add benefits, such as no minimum deposit or a waiver of early-withdrawal penalties.

What to do: Check with organizations to which you already belong to find out if they offer special savings on banking rates or products. But be wary of joining a group simply to get special financial deals—the cost of membership may be higher than any benefit the group offers. Check an online CD calculator, such as the one at Bankrate.com, to compare the difference.

Patricia Seaman, director of marketing and communications, National Endowment for Financial Education, a nonprofit financial-literacy organization, Denver, Colorado, *http://nefe.org*.

"Indexed" CDs Boost Returns

Mark Cortazzo, CFP, senior partner at Macro Consulting Group, a financial planning firm in Parsippany, New Jersey, *www.macroconsultinggroup.com*.

There's one type of certificate of deposit (CD) that can help boost your returns without sacrificing safety. That is why investors have been scooping them up. These indexed CDs, offered by banks and protected by the Federal Deposit Insurance Corporation (FDIC), may be linked to a stock index, such as the Standard & Poor's 500...to Treasury bond rates...or to an index of foreign currencies or commodities. To guarantee that you will get back at least the full principal from your initial investment—even if the index falls—you must keep the CD until maturity, which might be three years or longer. And your returns may be limited to a predetermined portion of any gains in the index rather than the full gains.

Example: Harris Bank (*www4.harrisbank.com*) is offering a five-year CD that matches gains in the S&P 500 stock index up to 10% a year for five years.* For more options, consult your financial adviser.

Caution: An indexed CD is best for tax-deferred accounts, such as IRAs, because the CD might generate "phantom" income each year that requires payment of a small, predetermined minimum tax imposed by the IRS.

*Offer and rate subject to change.

Have Banks Fight for *Your* CD Business

MoneyAisle.com is a free Web service that deals only with FDIC-insured banks. You type in the dollar amount you want to deposit, the length of the certificate of deposit (CD) you want and the state in which you live. Then click "start." All the participating banks begin bidding immediately by offering you interest rates. MoneyAisle monitors the bidding, notes the best bid and then contacts all the other bidding banks to find out if they wish to improve their offers. You are then notified of the final best bid, but you're not required to accept.

The process takes only a few minutes. I ran a test in which I entered $10,000 for a 24-month CD. Ninety-one banks bid with the highest bid being 2.03%.* I was given 29 minutes in which to accept or reject the bid.

Nancy Dunnan, a New York City–based financial and travel adviser and author or coauthor of 25 books, including *How to Invest $50–$5,000* (HarperCollins).

*Offer and rate subject to change.

Yippee! No-Penalty CDs

No-penalty certificates of deposit (CDs) can provide higher yields than various other savings alternatives. The CDs usually pay less interest than standard CDs of the same term. But they let you take out your money without penalty—so if you need to use the funds or if rates go up, you can withdraw your funds

for use or reinvest them at a higher rate. No-penalty CDs also provide extra flexibility for money that you do not expect to need during the CD's term…but just might have to tap.

Jonathan Wilk, deposit balance growth executive at Bank of America, Charlotte, North Carolina, *www.bank ofamerica.com.*

How a High Credit Score Can Hurt You

Having a credit score that is "too high" could mean fewer card offers and lower credit limits. If your score is 820 or higher (out of 850), which usually means that you pay off all your credit cards on time and in full each month, issuers may view you as unprofitable.

What to do: Make at least one small purchase on each of your credit cards every few months to keep a variety of cards active so that your overall credit availability remains ample even if limits on some cards are cut back.

Adam Jusko, founder of IndexCreditCards.com, based in Lakewood, Ohio, which compares more than 1,200 credit cards.

Don't Let Your Credit Card Rewards Disappear

Your credit card rewards may disappear if you make payments late. More card issuers are reducing or eliminating rewards as a penalty for late payments.

An example: Some Capital One reward packages cancel miles earned in a period during which a late fee is charged.

Best: Read mailings from card issuers to find out about changes in terms and conditions. Always pay credit card bills on time to preserve rewards.

Curtis Arnold, founder, CardRatings.com, North Little Rock, Arkansas.

Warning: Think Twice Before Asking for a Rate Reduction

In the past, calling your credit card company for an interest rate reduction was almost a slam dunk strategy. Now, many people are finding that the call actually leads to lower credit limits or a closed account. Credit card issuers are using the call as a way to interrogate the cardholder for details that might indicate an elevated credit risk. Before you call, ask yourself if you really deserve a lower rate. If the answer is no, leave the phone on the hook.

John Ulzheimer, president of consumer education for Credit.com, Inc., a credit information Web site, San Francisco.

"Protection Plans" Not Worth the Cost

Credit card "protection plans" from credit card issuers, which promise to pay all or a portion of your credit card bill if you become disabled, lose your job or die, are especially popular during this time of high unemployment and mounting debts—but there are so many loopholes. The plan may not kick in if you lose your job for performance reasons…if you are disabled but can do some other kind of work…or if you have other disability coverage. The monthly fee ranges from 35 cents to 99 cents per $100 of debt.*

Better: Build up an emergency fund or purchase extra life insurance.

Sandy Shore, senior counselor at Novadebt, a nonprofit credit-counseling agency in Freehold, New Jersey, *www.novadebt.org*.

*Prices subject to change.

Downside of Debit Cards

Debit cards provide less protection than credit cards. If your credit card is lost or stolen, you are not liable for more than $50 of unauthorized charges. But if thieves steal your debit card number, you must report any misuse within two days to be protected at the $50 level. From then until 60 days, you may be liable for $500—and after 60 days, your liability is unlimited. Read debit card agreements carefully. Visa and MasterCard advertise zero-liability policies for their cards—but those policies apply only when their networks process the transactions using your signature. If you use a PIN, another network may process the transaction and the policy does not apply.

Best: Consider paying cash for small purchases instead of using a debit card. Use credit cards and ATM-only cards for larger purchases. Ask your bank to replace your debit card with an ATM-only card.

Paul Stephens, director of policy and advocacy, Privacy Rights Clearinghouse, San Diego.

Best Way to Dispose of Credit Cards

Shred unwanted credit cards or cut them into many small pieces, and dispose of the bits in separate garbage bags. The old recommendation to cut an old card in half is no longer enough.

Reason: Some cards give the entire credit card number on both the front and the back. A crook who finds only one half of the card might be able to figure out the complete number by combining the numbers on the back with those on the front.

Edgar Dworsky, founder of ConsumerWorld.org in Boston.

Claim Your Property Now!

Learn if a state is holding unclaimed property for you. Every year, state governments take possession of billions of dollars worth of unclaimed property, such as utility deposits, unclaimed state tax refunds, uncashed paychecks and dividend checks, and other kinds of items. To learn more and check the online databases of unclaimed property held by 38 states, go to the MissingMoney.com Web site. Or reach the appropriate government office in your state through the Web site of the National Association of Unclaimed Property Administrators, *www.naupa.org.*

National Association of Unclaimed Property Administrators, *www.naupa.org.*

Whose Name Should Go on Your Home and Auto? The Wrong Choice Can Cost You BIG

Clay Stevens, Esq., an estate-planning attorney based in Los Angeles. He is director of strategic planning for Aspiriant, a financial advisory company in San Francisco and Los Angeles (*www.aspiriant.com*) and is an adjunct professor of law at Chapman University Law School in Orange, California.

You may spend a lot of time deciding which home and car to buy. You likely spend much less time deciding whose name or names to put on the home title and vehicle title, insurance policies and loan documents. But the wrong choices could imperil your financial future.

Examples: Married couples will often list both their names on the home title—unaware that this can create unnecessary capital gains taxes and estate taxes. Parents often put their own names and their college kids' names on the titles of the children's vehicles—unaware that doing this could put their personal assets

at unnecessary risk. Single people who share their homes with widowed, elderly parents often list these parents as co-owners—unaware that this means that the home might have to be sold to pay nursing home bills before Medicaid will cover the costs if the parent requires an extended nursing home stay.

The good news: If you chose the wrong name(s) when you're titling any of your assets, it often is possible to retitle, assuming that the error is caught before one of the listed owners dies, is sued or is pursued by creditors. Retitling might entail additional fees and legal bills—well worth it. *What you need to know when signing for...*

A CAR TITLE

When two people buy a car together, they typically put both names on the title...or only the name of the buyer who pays most or all of the cost of the car. Neither approach is necessarily the best if the co-owners are not married...or are married but have separate assets. That's because if the vehicle later is involved in a car accident, any owner(s) of the vehicle could be liable for property damage and injuries along with the driver.

Best strategy: Use only the name of the vehicle's primary driver on the title. This approach restricts liability to that person.

Exceptions: Keep the title in your name if you are not sure how much you can trust the primary driver with full ownership—say, a 16-year-old child. Also, list both spouses' names on titles if both jointly own most assets, which means it does not matter if one or both of you are liable in lawsuits. That way, insurers are more likely to allow the family's vehicles to be grouped together on one policy, which is generally cheaper than insuring each separately.

A CAR LOAN

Put the automobile loan in one partner's name if the other partner has weaker credit scores (so you improve your chances of getting the lowest interest rate on the loan) or if there's a chance that you will default on the loan (so you don't hurt both your credit ratings). List both partners if that results in better loan terms.

A HOME

One reason often given for listing more than one person as a home's owner is to avoid probate—the court process in which a will's instructions are carried out—when one owner dies. Listing two names on your home's title as "joint tenants" does avoid the costs and delays of probate—the home simply passes to the surviving owner or owners—but it does not necessarily provide maximum tax savings or asset protection. *Best strategies...*

●**If your goal is to avoid estate taxes, name a "living trust"**—a legal entity that is given control over the assets it holds—as owner of the home, with the names of both partners as trustees. A lawyer should be able to set up a trust for $1,500 to $5,000 or so.

Example: A married couple has $4 million in assets, all held in both partners' names. When one partner dies, the assets pass to the surviving partner without probate and estate taxes. When the second partner dies, however, perhaps half the family's wealth will face steep estate taxes. (*Note:* There is no estate tax in 2010, but it will be back in 2011.) Had the couple's home (along with any other major assets) been held in the name of a type of living trust known as a "bypass trust," the couple could have left the entire estate to their heirs without estate taxes.

●**If you or someone who shares your home is at particular risk of bankruptcy,** divorce, lawsuits or a long stay in a nursing home, your main goal in choosing a name or names for the title might be protecting assets.

Best strategy: Listing someone other than this high-risk individual on the home's title might provide a degree of asset protection.

Exceptions: Listing just one owner could create complications...

●The home might have to pass through probate when one partner dies. That could cost thousands in fees.

●The person listed as sole owner could sell the property or force the other from it if the relationship sours. *Note:* A spouse might be considered a co-owner of the home even if not listed on the title, particularly in a community property state. Ask your attorney what's best for you.

●The asset protection provided by placing a shared home in one name is not ironclad, particularly between married partners. This should not be considered a substitute for adequate business, professional, liability or umbrella insurance.

●Civil and criminal penalties could result if you shift assets to someone else's name after legal claims occur.

HOMEOWNER'S INSURANCE

The name(s) on your homeowner's insurance should match the name(s) on your home's title.

Reason: Having a different name on the policy could undermine your estate planning.

Example: A man places his home in a trust, but his homeowner's insurance is inadvertently left in his name, not the trust's name. If this man dies in a home fire, his homeowner's insurance will pay the claim to his estate, rather than to his trust, subjecting the payout to probate and estate taxes—exactly what the trust was created to avoid.

A MORTGAGE

Two-income couples will typically receive the best mortgage terms when they list both names as borrowers. If one partner provides most or all of the family's income and has a far superior credit score, however, the couple might qualify for better terms if they include only this partner's name.

Note: Some lenders require that every name on the title appear on the mortgage.

Foreclosure Know-How

If you want to buy a foreclosed home, look for listings on specialized Web sites, such as *www.realtytrac.com* and *www.foreclosurepoint. com*. Buy from a bank if possible—banks will clear outstanding liens, and you can inspect their foreclosed homes before purchase. Before you bid, ask a contractor for an estimate of how much renovations will cost. Bid low— perhaps 20% below market price, even if the bank is asking for more. Finally, be prepared to wait, as the process can take up to three months.

Helpful: Have multiple properties in mind, and get financing preapproved before making a bid.

Money, Time-Life Bldg., Rockefeller Center, New York City 10020, *http://money.cnn.com.*

Mortgage Red Flags

Be on the lookout for five red flags when seeking a mortgage...

•**Excessive points**—you should not normally be charged more than one point, which is 1% of the loan amount.

•**Prepayment penalties** that require a fee if you pay off the mortgage quickly.

•**Adjustable interest rates** that can skyrocket within two to three years.

•**Loans that have balloon payments**—large amounts that need to be repaid after a fairly short period of time.

•**Failure to count taxes and insurance**—omitting them can make payments seem artificially low.

What to do: Shop around for a mortgage, and compare offers carefully.

Center for Responsible Lending, Durham, North Carolina, www.responsiblelending.org.

Keep Your Adjustable-Rate Mortgage or Refinance?

Generally, stay with your adjustable rate mortgage (ARM) if you plan to move before it adjusts or can handle a modest increase in payments. Refinance to a fixed-rate loan if you expect to stay put for at least three years or if you owe more on your home than it is

worth and qualify for the government's Home Affordable Refinance Program (HARP). To see if you qualify, go to *http://makinghomeafford able.gov* and click on "Eligibility" and then on "Home Affordable Refinancing."

Greg McBride, CFA, senior financial analyst, Bankrate. com, North Palm Beach, Florida.

New Mortgage Form Helps Consumers

The more understandable mortgage form gives home buyers better estimates of the many costs associated with home loans. Lenders and brokers now are required to use a new standard three-page "Good Faith Estimate" form—and the form itself urges consumers to shop around for better deals. Lenders must wrap all fees they charge into a single origination fee so that consumers can compare total costs from different lenders. And the origination fee cannot be increased after the form is prepared—although some costs, such as title services and recording charges, can go up by as much as 10%.

What to do: Be sure to get the new form when obtaining a mortgage. And do comparison shop—get the same form from multiple lenders.

Vicki Bott, deputy assistant secretary for US Department of Housing and Urban Development, Washington, DC, www.hud.gov.

Don't Panic If Your Home's Value Goes "Under Water"

Mary Hunt, editor, Debt-Proof Living, Box 2135, Paramount, California 90723, www.debtproofliving.com.

If you bought your home to live in for the long term, the value that matters most is its "use value"—not its market value.

Therefore, if the price you paid was worth it for you, it was a good purchase and still is—even if the home's market value has since fallen.

In fact, it really doesn't matter even if the home's value has fallen to "under water"—less than the mortgage's current balance. You are in the same position you would have been in if the value hadn't fallen, living in the same home and making the same payments.

Look at it this way: If you bought a car or television that you were happy with and the seller later lowered its price to less than you paid—you wouldn't sell or junk your car or television, would you?

What to do: If your home's price has fallen "under water," you should probably do nothing, except to enjoy living in it as you would have otherwise. Certainly, if you enjoy living in it, you shouldn't default on the mortgage and ruin your credit rating.

Improve Your Home: Uncle Sam Foots the Bill!

Improve your home and increase its value with money from the government and local utilities. The federal government's "stimulus" package expanded tax credits for energy-saving appliances and home improvements. Also, many states and local utilities provide their own credits of as much as 20%.

Example: A $10,000 new central air-conditioning system could cost as little as $6,500* after federal, state, local and utility credits.

Check out all the available credits in your area and learn what best qualifies for them—it can be well worth the effort. (For details visit *www.energystar.gov.*)

Craig Perkins, executive director, The Energy Coalition, San Francisco, *www.energycoalition.org.*

*Price subject to change.

High-Payback Home Improvements

Decks can offer the best payback among home improvements. At resale, a deck returns 85% of what it cost to build.

More high-payback home improvements: Any home improvements that increase energy efficiency, such as installing a new furnace or upgrading attic insulation, return 85% of their costs…siding replacement and minor kitchen remodeling return 83%…window replacement, 81%.

Worst projects for getting back what they cost: A bathroom addition, 66%…sunroom, 59%…home office, 57%.

Bill Keith, remodeling expert in St. John, Indiana, and host of *Quick Tips* on Chicago-area PBS TV. He is president of SunRise Solar, a designer of solar-powered attic fans, *www.sunrisesolar.net.*

Simple Ways to Get a Much Faster Home Sale

To make your home easier to sell, increase its curb appeal by upgrading your mailbox, house numbers, doorbell and knocker… edging and mulching beds…and fertilizing the lawn so that it is greener. Inside, update bathrooms using stylish faucets and regrout tile floors…paint the interior and install new lighting fixtures…paint dark kitchen cabinets white and replace old knobs and pulls.

Bottom line: Make sure your home is the best-looking one in its price range.

Money, Time-Life Bldg., Rockefeller Center, New York City 10020, *http://money.cnn.com.*

For Students Who Don't Need Financial Aid...

Students who do not require financial aid should apply to colleges that may seem out of their reach academically. Due to the tough economy, many students have to turn down their top college choices even after they have been accepted because their families cannot afford the bills. If you are able to make the payments, encourage your child to apply to schools that may be a stretch. Spots may open up for those who can afford it.

Raymond D. Loewe, CLU, ChFC, founder of College Money, and president, Financial Resources Network, both in Marlton, New Jersey.

More from Raymond Loewe...

Kids Nearing College Age? Time to Clean Up Your Credit

If your child is reaching college age, clean up your credit history. While federal student loans will not require a credit check, federal Parent Loans (PLUS) and alternative student loans do. Applying for these loans is becoming more competitive because lending agents are reviewing applicants' credit reports more closely. Furthermore, a better credit score can reduce the interest rate on the alternative student loans.

Grandparents Contributing Tuition? How to Do It Right

Money, Time-Life Bldg., Rockefeller Center, New York City 10020, *http://money.cnn.com*.

Tuition help from the grandparents can decrease the financial aid to which the grandchild is entitled. Money given directly to the student is considered income and must be reported on the Free Application for

Federal Student Aid (FAFSA). This can reduce an aid award by up to 50%.

What to do: Have the check given to you, the parent—then it is not counted as student income. Or ask a grandparent to open a tax-favored 529 account with the grandparent as owner—then it is not counted as the student's asset, although distributions are considered student income and may affect aid. If a grandparent wants to mail a check directly to the tuition office to cover the expense, the university may reduce a financial-aid package by the amount of the contribution. Also, monetary gifts to a grandchild must be reported on financial-aid applications.

For more information, talk to your financial adviser.

Don't Let Financial Fights Ruin Your Marriage: Strategies That Really Work

Olivia Mellan, a psychotherapist based in Washington, DC, who specializes in couples' financial issues. She is author or coauthor of five books, including *Overcoming Overspending: A Winning Plan for Spenders and Their Partners* (Money Harmony).

Marital money arguments increase in tough financial times such as these. Even the closest couples don't always see eye to eye on money matters. Couples argue over what to buy...how much to save... how aggressively to invest...and anything else involving dollars and cents.

Most married couples are not as far apart in their financial thinking as they imagine. The problem is that they tend to see only their money differences and ignore the similarities. Rather than judge our partners' financial beliefs and habits against an objective standard, we tend to consider them in comparison with our own habits—then cast our partner as our polar opposite. This can make minor differences in opinion seem like major schisms.

Example: A wife saves 35% of her salary, while her husband, who has a higher salary, saves "only" 20% of his. Though this husband is a responsible saver by any objective standard, the wife may feel that she is carrying an unfair share of the burden and that the husband is spending too freely.

FINANCIAL BATTLE LINES

The first step in overcoming financial friction in a marriage is identifying areas of conflict and the opposing financial roles that each partner is forced into. Here are six common battle lines. Do you see your relationship described here?

• **Spender vs. hoarder.** One spouse considers the other an overspender...while the second sees the first as a hoarder or miser. This leaves neither one happy. The spender feels forced to defend or cover up purchases...while the hoarder feels saddled with full responsibility for reaching the family's savings goals. Even if both partners are responsible savers, the one who saves less may be treated as a reckless spender...and when both are spenders, the one who spends less might be cast as hoarder.

• **Money worrier vs. money avoider.** The partner who worries more—or more openly—about money comes to believe that his partner doesn't take financial matters seriously. The worrier typically is the partner who handles most of the bill-paying and budget-balancing chores. The other partner believes that the continual worrying about finances adds unnecessary tension to the relationship.

• **Planner vs. dreamer.** One partner takes charge of the nitty-gritty details of the family's finances...while the other acts as visionary, ignoring details and thinking big. These roles could be complementary, but more often they leave partners battling over financial priorities and processes.

Example: The planner tries to enforce a detailed budget, while the dreamer makes impulsive purchases that fit the image of how he wants life to be.

• **Money monk vs. money grower.** One partner considers money dirty and corrupting, and doesn't bother investing or seeking raises...while the other believes that earning and saving are worthwhile life goals. Even minor differences here can seem very significant because our basic outlook on money is so closely tied to our core beliefs.

• **Risk taker vs. risk avoider.** One partner's aggressive approach to investing or career planning creates discomfort for the other, who lives in fear that the family's savings will be lost. When risk takers suffer financial setbacks—as most have in the past year—their risk-avoider partners typically blame them for those losses. Risk takers usually are men—but not always.

• **Money merger vs. money separator.** One partner believes that all of the couple's savings and financial decisions should be bundled together...while the other tries to keep some of his money separate from the other partner's. Money mergers often consider their partners' desire for separation a sign of lack of commitment to the relationship. It typically is men who push to merge the family finances.

Example: A wife who does not work outside the home inherits money and wants to keep it separate from the family's money. Her husband is insulted by this request because he has been sharing his income for years.

BRIDGING THE MONEY GAP

A four-step plan for avoiding financial fights with your partner...

1. Consider financial disagreements with your spouse as relationship inevitabilities, not examples of your partner's flaws. We tend to dismiss or demean our partner's financial opinions when they differ from our own. It is these contemptuous responses—and not the financial differences themselves—that turn disagreements into brawls.

Better: Start with the assumption that your partner's financial thinking is both reasonable and closer to your own than you realize. This keeps things friendly and prevents disagreements from escalating.

Examples: Your partner isn't necessarily a spendthrift just because he doesn't save as much as you...or a big risk taker simply because he takes more risks than you...or a money avoider simply because he doesn't fret as openly about recent stock market losses as you do.

2. Create an atmosphere that encourages civil discussion of financial matters. Financial differences are more likely to escalate into fights when they're allowed to fester without discussion. Unfortunately, couples often hesitate to raise financial topics that have led to fights in the past.

Better: Establish a framework for calmly discussing all your financial issues that promotes safety and trust. Set aside perhaps 20 minutes per week for the money conversation. During the session, one spouse shares one of his money concerns for two to three minutes, while the other listens and then repeats what was said. The first spouse then speaks again, and the process is repeated until the first spouse is done. After that, the spouses switch roles, and the second spouse goes through the process. It is important to be empathetic and avoid being judgmental or argumentative.

Example: *Partner 1:* "I'm worried that the stock market will continue to decline."

Partner 2: "I hear that you are worried about further declines. It is perfectly reasonable to have those concerns considering everything that has happened recently."

The more you understand how your partner feels about finances, the more likely you are to sympathize with his feelings, even if you don't agree.

3. Tell your partner what you admire about the way the partner handles money. This positive feedback helps balance the largely negative feedback that most married people normally send their partners about their financial decisions, often without realizing it.

Examples: A risk avoider might tell her risk-taking partner that she admires his ability to put up with declines in portfolio value without panic. A hoarder might tell a spender that he admires her generosity and ability to enjoy life.

4. Take one action every week that fits your partner's financial makeup, not your own. When both partners do this, it can help them moderate their financial views and move toward a middle ground. Expect it to feel uncomfortable at first.

Example: A spender might cancel a purchase and put the money into an investment account instead. The hoarder partner might agree to a discretionary purchase without any complaint.

Over time, if you follow the four steps above, you will lessen tension and conflict with your spouse over money.

Eight Savvy Ways to Help Parents in Financial Need

V. Raymond Ferrara, a Certified Financial Planner and Certified Senior Advisor. He is president and CEO of ProVise Management Group, LLC, a financial planning firm in Clearwater, Florida, *www.provise.com*. He has served on the board of directors of the Financial Planning Association and the Institute of Certified Financial Planners.

Your own financial problems might not be your only financial problems in this difficult economy. If your parents or your spouse's parents are still alive, their money woes might land in your lap as well. There are a number of things that adult children can do to help their parents financially—without sacrificing their own financial futures in the process. *Eight smart steps...*

1. Find out where your parents stand financially. Parents often try to hide their financial problems from their adult children. They're embarrassed or in denial about their predicament...desperate to avoid becoming a burden...or don't think that it's proper to discuss money.

It's in your best interest to find out as soon as possible if your parents are having financial problems. These problems only get worse if not addressed.

Best way to find out: Note changes in your parents' discretionary spending. If they have stopped spending money on things that they have always enjoyed, such as eating out...traveling...giving gifts to their grandkids...or golfing every day, it might signal money problems.

Frame all questions about your parents' finances as part of larger discussions about the world's financial problems…a friend's financial problems…or your own financial problems. At least this way, your parents will not feel singled out or unnecessarily embarrassed about their own plight.

If you suspect problems but your parents seem hesitant to share their financial situation with you…

• Remind them of how they have helped you financially in the past.

• Point out ways in which your financial planning is intermingled with theirs. This makes discussing their financial situation seem like less of an intrusion.

2. Scrutinize your parents' bills for waste. Offering to give them some cash might not be the only way that you can assist your parents through their financial problems. Seniors are often victims of overbilling and outright fraud. Trimming your parents' bills can improve their financial situation without costing you a dime.

It pays to approach this tactfully so that your parents don't think you're trying to stick your nose into their finances without reason.

Strategy: Mention that you recently have given your own bills an audit and discovered a lot of ways that you were being taken advantage of through unnecessarily high charges… illegitimate charges…and double billing. Offer to help your parents go through their own checkbook register, credit card statements and bills. This can frame the issue as "us against them," rather than "I know much better than you how to spend your money."

Examples: Are your parents still renting a phone from the phone company? Are they paying massive interest rates on credit card debt? Are they being billed for services that they no longer need or even receive? Are there charges on their credit card statements that are not theirs? Is there double billing on their medical bills?

3. Help your parents apply for programs designed to help seniors in financial need. Churches, long-term-care facility development directors and elder-law attorneys' offices in your parents' area should be able to point you to local assistance programs for seniors in financial need. Also contact your parents' state or local Department of Health and Human Services (sometimes called the Department of Social Services) to see if they qualify for Medicaid, subsidized heating bills or utility bills or other programs for low-income seniors.

4. Find out if your parents qualify for charity care for uncovered medical bills. Hospitals and other health-care providers will sometimes waive bills for those with limited income and assets. If medical bills are a major component of your parents' financial problems, this is worth investigating.

5. Consider paying your parents' medical bills directly. If you give money to your parents and they use it to pay their medical bills, the gift counts against the $13,000 per person annual gift tax exclusion. Exceed this limit, and you could owe gift taxes.

Much better: The IRS does not treat payments made directly to a parent's doctor or hospital as taxable gifts to the parent. Paying these bills directly is therefore a way to provide more than $13,000 in financial support to your parent in a year without incurring gift taxes.

Paying medical bills directly also can be easier for parents to accept than taking cash from their children outright.

6. Help your parents evaluate the reverse mortgage option. If your parents are age 62 or older and have substantial equity in their home, a reverse mortgage could be an effective way for them to tap the wealth they have tied up in their home without moving out of their home…or feeling like a financial burden to you.

Some parents refuse to consider a reverse mortgage so that their kids can inherit their home. Let your parents know that their well-being is a greater concern to you.

Read up on reverse mortgages at *www.hud. gov.* Shop around before agreeing to terms— reverse mortgage fees and interest rates can vary greatly.

7. Consider lending money to your parents rather than giving it outright. When you make such a loan and you have formal loan documents that record it, by law your money will be repaid from your parents' estate before the estate is divided up among all your parents' heirs.

Proposing a loan also gives you a fallback if your parent refuses an outright gift.

Example: "OK, Dad, I give up. You won't let me *give* you money...so let me *lend* you money instead. There's no dishonor in accepting a loan."

8. Ask your parent to move in with you. Combining your parent's household expenses with your own could save hundreds every month in rent or mortgage costs—more, if it means that your parent doesn't have to enter an assisted-living facility. It also is a more acceptable alternative for many parents than accepting financial assistance from a child.

Of course, this arrangement works only if you have an in-law apartment on your property...or an extra bedroom in your home and a great relationship with your parent.

How to Get Your Overspending Under Control

Marjory Abrams, president of Boardroom Inc., 281 Tresser Blvd., Stamford, Connecticut 06901.

I just read a fascinating article about "clothing diets"—the grassroots movement that involves, say, buying no new clothes for a year or wearing the same six pieces for an entire month. Some people participate to simplify their lives. Others want to save money or break the cycle of overspending—a motivation that intrigued me because of a recent conversation with Olivia Mellan...and after I'd bought some "irresistible" strappy sandals for myself while shopping for shoes with one of my daughters.

Ms. Mellan, a money psychotherapist (*www. moneyharmony.com*), has many clients with overspending problems. As she notes in her book *Overcoming Overspending*, they look for instant gratification, don't plan long-term and fill their lives with things. Mellan herself was once like this, buying clothing whenever she felt lonely or depressed. Others overspend for the thrill of it or to keep up with the Joneses. Men and women are equally vulnerable—a woman may buy clothing, while a man treats people to lunches he cannot afford. This can lead to problems in a marriage.

To help people kick the habit, Mellan suggests strategies similar to those used to treat other addictions...

•**Avoid slippery slope places.** Mellan was enticed into department stores by promotions from her favorite makeup brand. Some other downfall triggers may be eBay or warehouse clubs crammed with "bargains." Ignore these promotions until you really need something—and then buy only what you need.

•**Nurture your soul.** Overspending is indulging at the surface. Indulge yourself at a deeper level—with volunteer work, spiritual activities and creative pursuits. Mellan experienced no urge to overspend while working on a tape for the memorial service of a beloved friend.

•**Set specific short- and long-term goals—** for example, paring down debt by a certain amount or saving for a new roof. Make them realistic (for example, not buying clothes for a month is more realistic than not buying them for an entire year). Reassess your goals every six months.

•**Reward yourself for progress—**but in ways that don't undermine your goals. Visit a museum, or go to a fun festival (*www.festivals. com*). Get together with friends for a sweater swap.

•**Join Debtors Anonymous** (800-421-2383, *www.debtorsanonymous.org*). Membership in this 12-step program is free. All the members keep records of income and expenditures, develop spending plans and benefit from talking about the experiences of others.

Occasionally, even Mellan backslides. I am sure I will, too. But progress does not require perfection.

8

Insurance Information

What the New Health-Care Law Means for Your Wallet: Money-Saving Steps to Take Now

The March of 2010 federal law overhauling the entire system of health care will have far-reaching financial effects for millions of consumers and taxpayers. Here, two top experts describe what this recent law means for you—and how you can best prepare for the dramatic changes to insurance coverage and taxation over the coming months and years...

FOR INSURANCE COVERAGE
Maura Carley, MPH, CIC

• **The new federal insurance pool for high-risk individuals might offer a solution** if you have a preexisting health condition that has made it difficult to obtain comprehensive coverage at a reasonable price. But the pool, slated to start in late 2010, is not necessarily your best solution. More than 30 US states already offer some form of high-risk insurance for people with preexisting conditions. Compare the coverage and costs of your state's options (if there are any) and the new pool after details become available. The Web site of the Department of Health and Human Services (*www.hhs.gov*) will provide details about the new pool in the coming months.

Not every consumer with a preexisting medical condition will qualify for the new pool. Applicants must have been without insurance

---

Maura Carley, MPH, CIC, the CEO of Healthcare Navigation, LLC, a patient advocacy company with offices in New York City and in Fairfield and Darien, Connecticut, *www.healthcarenavigation.com*. She previously served as regional director of Kaiser Permanente's New York Health Plan.

Thomas P. Ochsenschlager, Esq., CPA, vice president of taxation at the American Institute of Certified Public Accountants (AICPA), Washington, DC, *www.aicpa.org*. *Accounting Today* named him one of the 100 most influential accountants for four consecutive years.

for at least six months. If you have managed to hang onto coverage, perhaps by paying for a high-cost, high-deductible plan, it might be safer to remain with this plan or sign up for a state high-risk pool, if available, rather than go for months without insurance to qualify for the new pool.

If your family cannot purchase affordable health insurance because one of your children has a preexisting condition, shop around for coverage again, starting September 23, 2010. Beginning that day, the new law stops insurers from denying coverage to children under age 19 with preexisting illnesses, even if the children never had health insurance before.

Starting in 2014, insurers won't be allowed to turn down any applicants because of preexisting conditions.

•**If Medicare's "doughnut hole" has prevented you from buying some prescribed drugs, relief is on the way.** Previously, Medicare recipients with more than $2,830 in annual drug costs had to pay 100% of drug costs out of pocket up to $4,550. The law provides a $250 rebate to those who reach the coverage gap this year. A 50% discount on purchases of prescription drugs that fall into the gap takes effect in 2011. This discount increases until it reaches 75% in 2020.

•**If you have a Medicare Advantage Plan, consider whether to switch to a Medicare Supplemental Plan** during the next open-enrollment period. The new health-care law is likely to lead to premium increases and/or reductions in benefits for Medicare Advantage Plans, which are offered through private insurers and serve as alternatives to standard Medicare coverage. Medicare Supplemental Plans, or "Medigap policies," also are sold by private insurers, but they supplement standard Medicare rather than replace it. New Supplemental Plans M and N, available through private insurers starting June 1, 2010 are worth a look.

•**If you have a long-term-care insurance policy, keep it.** The health-care law includes an optional long-term-care insurance program, starting in 2011, but the benefits offered by this program are capped at $50 per day—not nearly enough to pay what might cost several hundred dollars per day for long-term care if you are disabled. If you're considering obtaining a new long-term-care policy, don't assume that the best option is to wait until 2011 for this federal plan.

•**If you have an adult child younger than 26, you can provide coverage for that child under your group or family health policy** starting in late September 2010, but explore other options first if your adult child is not already covered.

Currently, each state has its own rules for how long children can remain on their parents' policies. Some force children off the policies when they graduate college...others allow children to remain on their parents' health insurance policies well into their 20s—but only if these children remain unmarried and often only if they are in college or living under the parents' roof. The new rules will not contain these restrictions—although remaining on the parents' plan will not be an option if the adult child is eligible for a group plan through his/her own employer or spouse's employer.

In many states, healthy people in their 20s can purchase private health insurance on the open market for as little as $150 each month,* less than it might cost to keep these young people on family policies. However, these inexpensive individual policies often have high deductibles, zero coverage for maternity care and other restrictions.

Helpful: Starting in 2014, those in their 20s can buy "catastrophic" coverage with lower premiums and very high deductibles.

•**It may be time to make that doctor's appointment if you have put off going** for fear that having any major health problems on your record would make it difficult to obtain insurance in the future. Between the high-risk pool that will be created late in 2010 and the rules that prohibit insurers from turning down applicants because of preexisting conditions, which go into effect in 2014, the new law greatly increases the odds that acceptable coverage will be available to you even if there are health problems on your record.

*Price subject to change.

FOR YOUR TAXES
Thomas P. Ochsenschlager, Esq., CPA

The changes in the Tax Code contained in the health-care law are meant to raise more revenue from high-income people to help subsidize health coverage for middle- and low-income people. *Here's what you can do to minimize your taxes and/or boost your benefits…*

• **If your annual adjusted gross income could be above $200,000 ($250,000 if married and filing jointly) in coming years, sell highly appreciated investments in 2010** to lock in capital gains at today's tax rates (15% for most people…0% for those in the 10% and 15% tax brackets). Starting in 2013, these high-income households will face a new 3.8% Medicare tax on investment income, including capital gains, interest, dividends and annuities. As temporary tax breaks expire, their capital gains tax rate is due to be increased as well, from 15% to 20%, starting in 2011.

Strategy: If you sell appreciated securities, such as stocks, you can immediately rebuy the same securities if you like—"wash sale" rules that take away your tax advantage when you quickly rebuy an investment apply only when realizing losses, not gains.

• **If you're in a cash crunch and need to withdraw money from your health savings account (HSA) to pay non-health–related bills, do so by the end of 2010.** The penalty for nonqualified HSA withdrawals doubles in 2011—from 10% to 20%.

• **If you fund a flexible spending account (FSA) to pay out-of-pocket health costs, rethink how much you should contribute for 2011.** Starting in 2011, most over-the-counter medicines and certain nonprescription health-related items, such as bandages, will no longer qualify as FSA (or HSA) expenses. Also, FSA annual contributions will be capped at $2,500 starting in 2013.

• **If you are a small-business owner considering offering health benefits to your employees, tread with extreme caution.** True, the health-care bill offers tax credits to small businesses that provide health insurance for employees from 2011 through 2014—particularly businesses with 10 or fewer employees

who earn modest wages, on average. Unfortunately, those tax credits do not last forever, and there's no guarantee that the "insurance exchanges" (insurance marketplaces meant to allow small businesses to pool together with others to reduce costs) will be affordable for small-business owners. All cautious small-business owners might hold off on providing insurance to employees at least until it becomes clear how much it will cost to provide insurance through these exchanges. Companies that have 50 or fewer employees face no penalty for not offering health coverage.

• **If you frequent tanning salons, a 10% tanning bed tax takes effect** in July 2010.

What You Don't Know About Health Insurance Could Hurt You Badly— How to Save *Thousands*

Eliza Navarro Bangit, Esq., an attorney who analyzes health insurance contracts and federal and state health insurance laws as a senior research associate at Georgetown University Health Policy Institute in Washington, DC, *http://ihcrp.georgetown.edu.* She's also author of, and contributor to, many research articles on private health insurance.

Millions of people are being forced to find new health insurance coverage because they lose their jobs, their retiree benefits are cut or their premiums soar. But the mumbo jumbo that fills health insurance policies can cost you thousands of dollars in unexpected expenses because you often don't get what the policy seems to promise.

That is because health insurance policies are full of language that is difficult to decipher and important details that are hard to grasp—whether your policy is provided by an employer or it's individually purchased. Since policies are not regulated by the federal government but by each state, there is no mandate as to what they should contain. In recent surveys, more than half of respondents did not understand their current health insurance policies…and people who thought that they had good policies had loopholes, limits and exclusions that they didn't know existed.

The problem has not gone unrecognized. Aside from the health-care reform bill that became law in March 2010, members of Congress have proposed a bill that would require insurers to more clearly communicate to consumers what is covered in a policy—and what is not covered.

Whether you have a health insurance policy already (either through your employer or on your own) or are considering buying health insurance (perhaps because you have recently been laid off), it pays to know what the fine print says and what to do if there are loopholes or limits that could cost you. *What you need to know…*

WHAT TO LOOK FOR

No health insurance plan will pay for everything, but some provide more than others. *Watch for…*

•**Comprehensive coverage.** Seek out the most comprehensive policy you can afford. Look first at the policy's list of covered benefits, which should include hospital stays and expenses, outpatient treatment, doctors' visits, prescription drugs, mental health treatments, rehabilitation care and lab and imaging tests. If a medical service is not mentioned in the policy—for example, outpatient chemotherapy—chances are it is not covered.

Find out which providers and hospitals (especially specialty hospitals) are covered by the policy. Be aware that even the policy that covers what is "medically necessary" may exclude particular services or cap them. A recent study analyzed the estimated out-of-pocket costs for heart attack treatment under several different health plans in California. Although cardiac rehabilitation is standard medical treatment for heart attack patients, one of these insurance policies did not cover this treatment at all.

If you are buying your own policy, review the health plans in your state at eHealthInsurance (800-977-8860, *www.ehealthinsurance. com*) or at Vimo (866-955-8466, *www.vimo. com*). To evaluate different policies, our team at Georgetown University Health Policy Institute has developed a worksheet, available at

http://healthinsuranceinfo.net/managing-medical-bills/worksheet.pdf.

•**How the deductibles work.** This is the amount of money that you will pay for medical care each year before your health insurance kicks in.

When reviewing a policy, check to see if all of your costs for medical care will apply to one deductible or to two—for example, a separate deductible for drug costs. Determine if these deductibles apply separately to individuals and to family members. If you have a high deductible and each family member has a separate deductible, it can be costly. There are no exact guidelines regarding reasonable deductible amounts.

Best: Weigh the health insurance premium against the protection that the policy offers—what are the covered benefits, what is excluded and limited, what is the cost if you get sick.

•**A protective out-of-pocket maximum.** Look for a policy that protects you with an out-of-pocket maximum, the most that you will have to pay for medical expenses in any given year. Add up all your deductibles, copayments and coinsurance to determine the out-of-pocket maximum.

Avoid: Policies that exclude the deductible or any copayments or coinsurance from the out-of-pocket maximum.

In some cases, costs for office visits, prescriptions and mental health outpatient visits are not counted toward your out-of-pocket maximum. If so, then your actual out-of-pocket expenses can be much more—even thousands of dollars more each year—if you get really sick.

•**No caps on lifetime or annual benefits.** The problem with any kind of limit on lifetime or annual benefits is that you could be left on your own to pay for treatment costs that are much greater than you expected. If you get sick, you want to be sure that your policy can easily accommodate big bills. Check to ensure that the policy has no cap on specific kinds of treatment, such as hospital and outpatient medical treatment, doctor visits, drugs and diagnostic imaging tests.

•**The contract, not a brochure.** Ask for the contract, called Evidence of Coverage (EOC), which is legally binding. Insurers may say that the EOC is available only after a purchase, but don't take no for an answer. Examine the contract carefully.

•**Loopholes.** It's hard to catch every single detail, especially since loopholes can crop up anywhere.

Example: A policy offered by AARP began hospital coverage on the second day of the hospital stay. But the first day—when diagnostic tests and emergency procedures are performed—typically is the priciest. AARP has since suspended sales of this policy.

Best: Get a referral for a licensed insurance broker from someone you trust. A broker can help speed up the shopping and application process.

HOW TO CUT UNEXPECTED COSTS

If you do find a loophole or aren't satisfied with your policy, you can...

•**Switch policies.** Very often, it is not until you are using an insurance policy that you find out what it really covers (or doesn't). If you have health insurance through your employer, and several policies are offered, you can usually change policies during the open enrollment, a period of time set up annually when employees can change or make changes to their insurance. If you have your own health insurance policy and you are healthy, you should have no trouble finding another one. But do not cancel your existing policy until your new one takes effect. If you have a preexisting medical condition, insurers in many states can deny coverage (except in Massachusetts, Maine, Vermont, New York or New Jersey), exclude coverage for a specific condition or charge you more. The new health-care reform law will protect people with preexisting medical conditions, but it won't take full effect until 2014.

•**Appeal.** If you have a claim that was denied and you don't think it should have been, you can appeal the decision. Most states require health insurance providers to have both an internal and external (independent) review process for handling complaints and appeals.

The Henry J. Kaiser Family Foundation offers comprehensive information about the process at *www.kff.org/consumerguide/00-intro.cfm.*

Don't Switch Health Plans—Until You Read This...

Charles B. Inlander, a consumer advocate and health-care consultant located in Fogelsville, Pennsylvania. He was the founding president of the nonprofit People's Medical Society, a consumer advocacy organization credited with key improvements in the quality of US health care in the 1980s and 1990s, and is the author of 20 books, including *Take This Book to the Hospital with You: A Consumer Guide to Surviving Your Hospital Stay* (St. Martin's).

I f you think you'd like to make changes to your health insurance, November and December generally are the months to do so. With health-care costs continuing to rise at double the rate of overall inflation, choosing an affordable plan that covers what you need is more important than ever. *What to consider—and where to find help...*

If you're insured through your employer: Most companies with 200 or more employees—and even some smaller firms—offer a number of plans to their employees.

Beware: Make sure that you check exactly what is covered for all of the plans...understand whether there are limits to what is covered... and determine how much you must pay out-of-pocket for each service in each plan. Do not automatically assume that plans that charge the lower premiums are the best deals. More often than not—especially if you or a family member uses many medical services in a year—the deductibles, co-payments and limits on services make the lower-priced plans lousy deals.

Excellent option for younger and/or generally healthy people: Health Savings Accounts (HSAs) are tax-exempt accounts that can be used to pay for current and future medical costs with money contributed by the individual account holder—or, in the case of an employee plan, by employers and/or employees.

Beware: An HSA should be selected only if you expect minimal annual medical use, such as routine checkups. If the coverage is used more than that, your out-of-pocket costs can skyrocket.

If you are a Medicare beneficiary: If you are in the traditional Medicare program and like it, then stick with it. But if the cost of Medicare (currently $96.40 per month* for most participants) and supplemental Medigap insurance (the cost varies but can exceed $300 per month) is too much, consider switching to a Medicare Advantage Plan. These privately run plans usually offer more services (such as vision care and/or prescription drug benefits) than traditional Medicare. You pay the same monthly government premium—and may have to pay an additional premium for extra services. But you do not need to carry a supplemental Medigap policy, so you can save money.

Beware: Many Advantage programs require you to use their networks of doctors and hospitals. If you go outside this network, you generally must pay some or all of the expenses out-of-pocket. In addition, the health-care reform law substantially cuts federal funding for these plans, which will inevitably lead to higher premiums and/or reduced services. To learn about plans in your area, consult the Medicare Web site, *www.medicare.gov/choices/advantage. asp* or call 800-633-4227 (MEDICARE).

If you have Medicare Part D drug coverage: Part D adds prescription drug coverage to the primary Medicare plan. Review your policy annually or you may experience a costly surprise.

Beware: Every year, the insurers can alter prices and even add or drop drugs from their programs! Be sure to read all your Medicare mail to stay up-to-date on what is covered.

Helpful: Use this worksheet, *www.cms.hhs. gov/partnerships/downloads/mpdcpinfowork sheet.pdf*, to determine your prescription medication needs. Then go to the Medicare Web site, *www.medicare.gov*, to compare plans in your state that meet your drug requirements.

*Prices subject to change.

Medicare Drug Plans— Answers to Your Vital Questions

Paul Precht, director of policy and communications, Medicare Rights Center, a nonprofit consumer rights organization in New York City and Washington, DC, *www.medicarerights.org*. He previously served as editor of Inside CMS, an independent newsletter covering Medicare and Medicaid policy.

Medicare Part D, also known as Medicare Prescription Drug Coverage, has been available for more than four years, yet it still continues to cause confusion among seniors. Unlike with the other parts of Medicare, seniors cannot simply obtain Part D coverage through the Medicare system. Instead, they need to sort through an array of complicated private plans, each with its own rules, costs and lists of covered drugs. *Below, Medicare rights expert Paul Precht answers the most important questions about Part D...*

• **What's the best way to pick a Medicare drug plan?** It's usually wise to pick the plan that best covers the prescription medicine that you currently take. While prescription needs could change, chances are the drugs you take today will be the drugs you take in the year ahead.

Differences in coverage and costs can add up to hundreds of dollars each month. To estimate the cost of each plan based on your current drug needs, use the Medicare Prescription Drug Plan Finder tool from Medicare.gov (800-633-4227) or contact your state's Health Insurance Assistance Program—you can find contact information through the Eldercare Locator (800-677-1116, *www.eldercare.gov*).

• **Can I switch plans if my health situation changes?** You generally cannot switch from plan to plan in the middle of a calendar year, but you can switch to a different plan for future years. The open-enrollment period to make changes for the coming year runs from November 15 through December 31. Access Medicare.gov or call 800-633-4227 for details.

Every senior should review his/her coverage well before the end of every year. The costs and coverages of your current plan could be slated to change next year. Your drug needs might have changed or new plans might be available.

Loopholes: Seniors can change Part D plans outside of the open-enrollment period under certain specific conditions, including if any of the following are true...

•They begin receiving government assistance with their Medicare Part D expenses (see below).

•They go into, leave or live in a nursing home.

•They relocate to outside of their current plan's service area (or they relocate within their plan's service area and additional Part D options not available at the previous address are available in the new location).

•**Am I required to sign up for Medicare Part D?** Participation is voluntary—but it is a good idea for most seniors who do not already have drug coverage. It's also smart to sign up and pay the monthly premium even if you do not currently require any prescription drugs. Not only does this provide financial protection in case you do need prescription drugs later in the year—it also protects you from the potentially steep late-enrollment penalty. Seniors who neglect to sign up for a Part D plan when they're first eligible—typically when they turn 65—face a late-enrollment penalty that grows by 1% per month for as long as they delay. That 1% adds up quickly. If you wait four years to sign up, you'll pay 48% more than other seniors for the same prescription drug coverage.

If you do not think you need prescription coverage when you first become eligible for Medicare, sign up for the lowest-premium plan available. In most regions, there are plans that cost only $25 or so per month.*

Loophole: You will not necessarily face a late-enrollment penalty if you have "creditable" drug coverage—at least as good as Part D— from another source, such as an employer's supplemental health plan or the Department of Veterans Affairs. If you later decide to sign up for Part D, however, you must do so within 63 days of the termination of the creditable prescription drug coverage to avoid a penalty.

*Price subject to change.

•**How does the troublesome "doughnut hole" work?** Most Part D plans are designed with a gap in coverage each year during which you receive little or no help paying for prescriptions. This gap, often called the doughnut hole, begins after the plan member has spent a total of $2,830 in prescription drug costs during 2010 (including the amount the plan pays and the participant's copays). Coverage resumes once the plan member has incurred $4,550 in out-of-pocket drug costs, a figure that does not include the amount the plan has paid.

Some plans provide coverage for generic drugs during this doughnut hole, but these plans tend to charge high monthly premiums. Unless your medical condition or current prescriptions make it very likely that your drug costs will climb to near the top of the doughnut hole or above during the coming year, these plans are probably not worth the expense.

•**Can I get help paying Part D costs?** If your income is below $1,354 per month ($1,822 for couples), you might be eligible for state or federal assistance programs that would pay some or all of your Part D expenses, including premiums, copays and doughnut hole costs.

Asset limits for entry into these programs are uniform nationally—although some states do have programs for help with prescription drugs that do not consider assets. You might be disqualified if your total resources, including bank accounts and most types of investments, exceed $12,510 ($25,010 for married couples). Your primary residence, vehicles, personal possessions and certain other resources do not count toward this limit, and asset limits do not apply everywhere.

•**Will Part D cover drugs that I currently take?** Not necessarily. Many plans cover mainly generic drugs, with restricted coverage for brand-name pharmaceuticals. It usually is safe to switch to generics, but these limitations can be problematic for those taking brand-name prescription drugs for which there is no generic equivalent.

Examples: The cholesterol drug Lipitor and stomach acid drug Nexium do not yet have generic equivalents and are not covered by many Part D plans.

What to do: If you currently take brand-name pharmaceuticals, ask your physician to prescribe generic equivalents. If there are no generic equivalents, ask your doctor if there are other drugs in the same class that do have generic equivalents and might be effective for you. If not, in future years, pay higher premiums to enroll in a Part D plan that includes the brand-name drug you need or ask your doctor to contact your plan and file an appeal by explaining why this brand-name drug is necessary for you. Filing an appeal will not affect your premiums, and your odds of success are good if you have your doctor's support.

For more information: Visit the Medicare Rights Center's consumer advice Web site at *www.medicareinteractive.org*.

Your Life Insurance Coverage May Be at Risk: How to Protect Yourself

Thomas J. Henske, CFP, ChFC, CFS, CLU (chartered life underwriter), CLTC (certification in long-term care), partner at the wealth advisory firm Lenox Advisors, Inc., which has offices in New York, Chicago, San Francisco and Stamford, Connecticut, *www.lenoxadvisors.com*.

Many insurance companies are now in trouble, hurt by higher-than-expected claims and soured investments. Even if the government does bail out some insurers, will your insurer be one of them? And even if your insurance company is sound, your policy could be at risk because of plummeting stock values and record-low interest rates.

Key question for policyholders: Is my life insurance policy secure? *Pitfalls...*

• **Your insurer could fail.**

• **Your policy could lapse unless you pay higher premiums.** (You'll get a notice from your insurer.)

• **Both your cash value and your death benefit could shrink.**

• **You may have to pay premiums longer than you expected to.**

With this in mind, now is a good time to check on both your insurer's financial health (go to page 152 for advice on how to do this) and your individual policy's viability. A little research today may save you from a devastating surprise down the road.

INVESTMENT RISK

For many kinds of life insurance products, financial market conditions can have a direct impact on the value of a policy.

With the three basic kinds of "permanent" life insurance—whole, universal and variable—your insurance either accumulates a cash value or includes so-called separate accounts in addition to its face value (the amount of the death benefit). Although each type can come with different bells and whistles, in general, whole-life policies guarantee a cash value and level premiums. Universal-life policies provide flexible premiums and a cash-value account that accumulates tax deferred at a guaranteed minimum interest rate. And variable-life insurance is a hybrid insurance/investment product, that has nonguaranteed separate accounts the policyholder manages, flexible premiums and an adjustable death benefit.

• **Variable life carries the most investment risk, because its separate subaccounts are mutual funds.** Generally, policyholders can choose among 25 to 30 of such accounts, and the premium is determined by the anticipated rate of return. If investment returns drop dramatically and your premiums don't rise to compensate, you may be told by your insurer that you're not contributing enough to sustain the policy long term.

To avoid such a shock, write to the carrier and ask for an in-force illustration (a computer projection of future premiums, cash values and death benefits) incorporating certain assumptions. For example, ask specifically for a projection showing what will happen to your policy if you pay a certain amount per year in premiums for the next 15 years and your subaccount earns 5% or 7% annually instead of 8% or 10%. You will receive a detailed projection showing whether the policy would still be in force when you're 80, 85, 90, 95 or 100 years old and how high your cash value would be. You might need to boost your premiums to sustain the policy.

• **Whole-life policies generally depend on dividends paid by the insurer.** To achieve them, the carrier invests in conservative investments. If that portfolio's returns drop, dividend growth could fall too, meaning your cash value may not be sufficient to fund the portfolio in later years. In addition, many popular whole-life policies were projected to be "paid up" at a particular point in time based on the dividend rate at the inception of the policy. If these dividends have gone down from the original assumptions that were projected, the policy might require additional premiums. Again, ask for a projection to find out whether you'll need to pay more premiums to sustain the policy. A dividend growth assumption of 10%, which was common during the 1980s, is probably too high now.

• **Universal-life policies are highly sensitive to changes in interest rates.** Especially if you bought such insurance in the 1980s, when rates were in the double digits, you may find your policy underfunded today, as rates have dropped to 4% or lower. Be sure you are paying sufficient premiums to sustain the death benefit—by requesting an in-force illustration in writing.

Once you get the in-force illustration from your insurer, study its assumptions and projections. If your policy is at risk of lapsing, discuss options with your insurance professional. As an alternative to boosting or lengthening premium payments, you may be able to modify the policy—for example, by lowering the amount of coverage or postponing the date when you're paid up.

IF YOU SWITCH

Insurers rarely fail, and even when they do, state guarantees protect policyholders up to a point. But if your carrier looks vulnerable or if you can keep your policy from lapsing only with significant premium adjustments, you may decide to switch insurers. If you do, make sure that the insurance professional for the new company completes a detailed comparison form—which is required by regulators for cash-value policies—showing the new and old policies' features in a way that lets you evaluate them accurately.

An independent comparison may help you with your decision. For $80 to $90,* you can request a detailed assessment of a cash-value policy from the Consumer Federation of America's Rate of Return service (*www.evaluatelifeinsurance.org*).

Replacing your life insurance policy can be stressful and expensive. The underwriting process starts from scratch, meaning that you will need a medical exam, and you may not be insurable at your previous rates.

Then there is the IRS. In order to prevent owing income taxes on the old policy's gains, consult your accountant to be sure you are making a Section 1035 exchange. Under this part of the Tax Code, switching life insurance or annuity contracts isn't a taxable event, provided you meet certain requirements.

Unless your insurer is in serious financial distress, in many cases, you will be better off sticking with your current policy and adjusting your premiums if necessary.

STATE GUARANTEES

State insurance commissions regulate the industry and also provide a safety net in the event that a carrier becomes insolvent. Most states guarantee at least $300,000 in life insurance death benefits per policy, $100,000 in cash surrender or withdrawal values for life insurance and finally $100,000 in withdrawal and cash values for annuities. The guarantees are per person per company, and maximums vary from state to state. To see how much your state covers, log on to *www.nolhga.com*, the Web site for the National Organization of Life & Health Insurance Guaranty Associations.

You can build a second safety net by buying more than one policy. That way, you won't exceed the state maximums for guarantees on each individual contract.

*Prices subject to change.

More from Thomas Henske, CFP...

How to Check Up on Your Insurer

Research the financial strength of the company that issued your policy by looking up its ratings. The five principal rating companies—A.M. Best, Moody's Investor Services, Standard & Poor's, Weiss Ratings and Fitch Ratings—have come under fire for underestimating risk at AIG and others in the insurance industry during the credit bubble that preceded the current crisis. As a result, the rating companies have tightened their standards, and they update assessments more frequently.

To obtain a complete picture, you should check all five agencies' ratings of your insurer. You can do this for free on the agencies' Internet sites. Be prepared for different rating systems. (An A.M. Best rating of A++, meaning "superior," equals a Moody's rating of Aaa, meaning "exceptional," for instance. With Weiss, B is "good," and with A.M. Best, B is "vulnerable.")

As a rule of thumb, you want to see a Best rating of A or higher, S&P and/or Fitch ratings of AA or higher and a Moody's rating of Aa or higher. Note that Weiss, the toughest grader, owned by TheStreet.com, is the only rating company that isn't compensated by insurers, which pay the other agencies to get rated.

If your insurer's rating gets downgraded, dig deeper by speaking to your insurance professional or by looking at the company's financials on its Web site. Changes in liquidity, profitability or leverage, or a slowdown in new sales, might explain the downgrade, but they don't necessarily mean that your insurer is in danger of insolvency. Examples of insurers that have recently been downgraded include MetLife Inc., Hartford Financial Services Group Inc. and Prudential Financial Inc., though their ratings remain strong.

QUESTIONS TO ASK YOUR AGENT

•**Is your insurer diversified?** A company that gets 85% of its revenue from life insurance products could be less secure than one that has a diversified product line.

•**Is it on the National Association of Insurance Commissioners' (NAIC) watch list?** An insurer goes on the watch list if it fails to maintain four out of 12 financial ratios within a range specified by the association. Ask your insurance professional to check the watch list for you.

•**Is its surplus diminishing?** Regulators require insurers to maintain deep reserves—if your company is digging into its surplus, that could be a sign of financial stress.

A useful tool is the "Consumer Information Source" area of the NAIC online site, *https://eapps.naic.org/cis*, where you can type in the company name, your state of residence and the type of policy you hold to see relevant news and any recent complaints from consumers.

You Can Get Affordable Life Insurance Even with A Serious Condition

Cancer patients can purchase life insurance at *standard* rates from some companies, under certain conditions. So can people with heart disease and well-controlled diabetes. Insurers offer low rates to people who have mild forms of these diseases and have a strong prognosis for survival.

Example: One insurer requires prostate cancer patients to be at least 60 years old and to have been treated with surgery.

Do shop around—different companies have different requirements, and the underwriting standards change constantly.

Byron Udell, CEO of AccuQuote, a brokerage that works with dozens of insurance companies, Wheeling, Illinois, *www.accuquote.com*.

The Five Words *Never* To Say to an Insurance Agent

J.D. Howard, executive director of the Insurance Consumer Advocate Network, LLC (I-can), a consumer advocacy organization, Springfield, Missouri. He worked as an insurance adjuster for 30 years before founding I-can in 1994. I-can's Web site is *www.ican2000.com*.

Five everyday words can raise red flags when it comes to filing a car, home or health insurance claim, making the difference between quick payment of your claim and a nightmare of delays or even rejection. Don't let a slip of the tongue cost you money.

1. Sorry. An auto accident is an emotional event—be compassionate but stick to the facts. Saying you're "sorry" to other people involved in the accident or to a claims adjuster implies that you are at fault, and it can be used against you. If you do blurt out "I'm sorry," stop there and use a better phrase later, when you give your formal statement. Never give a statement to a claims adjuster at the scene, especially if that person is working for the other party's insurer. Just say, "Not now." Your own insurance company should take your statement after the dust settles, when hidden damage or latent injuries may become evident.

2. Think. Whether you come home to water damage or you have a fender bender, stay composed and report to your insurer factually what you know, not what you think, regarding cause or speed or other matters on which your opinion may be very wrong. Photograph the scene with a camera or cell phone. Even if you don't think you are injured in an auto accident, say, "I'm not sure." If you feel pain, describe it—do not self-diagnose. Never sign a release from the other party's adjuster at the scene.

3. Flood. This word is a red flag for insurers because a typical homeowner's policy does not cover flood damage from rising groundwater. What it typically does cover is described in words such as, "sudden and accidental discharges from plumbing, heating or air-conditioning systems." Instead of saying "flood," tell your insurer something along the lines of, "The plumbing burst, and there's water everywhere." If you think you need flood insurance, check details of how you qualify at the government Web site *www.floodsmart.gov*.

4. Experimental. Most health insurance policies, especially HMOs and PPOs, require prior approval before you receive any medical treatments that aren't common practice (those that are experimental, investigational or part of a clinical trial). Typically these procedures are excluded from coverage. So don't use the term "experimental" with your provider when describing treatment you want to undergo. Rely on your doctor or his/her staff to explain to your insurer why you need the procedure.

5. Whiplash. This term can encompass a range of injuries to the neck caused by sudden impact. When an adjuster hears the term, his knee-jerk reaction is that someone is making up an injury or trying to jack up payments from a claim. Instead, describe your symptoms.

Example: "I can't move my neck."

Better: Wait until your doctor makes a diagnosis, and share that with the insurer.

More from J.D. Howard…

Insurance and Your College Student

Adjust insurance needs for college students. If your child moves away for college—at least 100 to 150 miles—and does not take a car, your car insurance premiums could drop by as much as 30% and the child still will be covered when he/she's home on vacation. Ask your agent if your homeowner's policy covers possessions kept in the dorm room. For students living off-campus, a renter's policy probably will be required. Find out what your health insurance will cover while your child is in college.

What to do: Talk to your insurance agent—and to the administrator of your company's health plan if you have insurance through an employer.

$20 Part That Can Save You Big on Homeowner's Premiums

Washing machine hoses that leak or break are a major cause of costly water-damage incidents that lead to insurance claims. Many insurers offer discounts of up to 10% on premiums to home owners who simply replace rubber hoses with stainless steel burstproof hoses. The better hoses cost about $20* at hardware stores—and may save many times that off your insurance premium.

Best: Use stainless steel hoses in your home, regardless of the insurance considerations.

The Family Handyman, Reader's Digest Rd., Pleasantville, New York 10570, *www.familyhandyman.com.*

*Price subject to change.

"Trouble Detectors" Can Cut Your Homeowner's Insurance Premiums

Insurers sometimes offer discounts for those who install detectors that can head off a problem that may give rise to a claim.

Examples: Leak detectors that warn of plumbing failures and may automatically shut off a water line...temperature sensors that detect freezing after a furnace breakdown that can lead to frozen pipes. Such sensors can be especially valuable in a vacation home that is left unattended for long periods.

Check with your insurer to get its full list of discount possibilities.

The Family Handyman, Reader's Digest Rd., Pleasantville, New York 10570, *www.familyhandyman.com.*

Car Insurance Myths and Realities

There are a handful of myths associated with car insurance. *Below, the record is set straight...*

• **Red cars are no more expensive to insure than cars of other colors.**

• **New-car theft.** Thieves do not prefer to steal new cars—they usually look for older ones that can be broken up for parts.

• **Loan payoff.** Insurance will not pay off what you owe on a loan or lease if you are in an accident and your car is declared a total loss. It will pay the actual cash value of the car, minus your deductible. You can cover the difference between cash value and what you owe on a loan if you have gap insurance.

• **Rental cars.** Insurance will not pay for a rental car while your car is out of service for repairs or if it is stolen—unless you specifically buy rental-car reimbursement insurance.

Kat Zeman, senior writer, Insure.com, a consumer insurance Web site providing instant quotes and purchasing advice.

Should You Get Pet Insurance?

Pet health insurance can be a good buy if your animal is predisposed to certain conditions and the insurer will cover those specific conditions.

Example: Dachshunds often develop herniated discs.

Insurance also should cover trauma, in case a pet breaks a leg or is hit by a car. Treatment can cost thousands of dollars without insurance. Pet insurance usually costs about $1.50 per day.* Read policies very carefully because many limit what they cover and restrict how much they will pay even for covered events. Providers include Purina, the ASPCA, Hartville Pet Insurance and others. The company you choose should be licensed in your state so that you are not left with unpaid bills if the company folds.

Lee Rosenberg, CFP, principal, ARS Financial Services, Inc., Jericho, New York.

*Price subject to change.

9

Tax Time

Terrible Tax Tips Some Advisers Give

Some guidance you get from your tax adviser may be way off base—with serious consequences. *The most common bum steers…*

• **Max your mortgage.** Generally, mortgage interest is tax deductible, so the larger your mortgage, the greater your write-off.

But you still are paying more than you would with a smaller mortgage. Even if you live in a high-tax area, you'll save no more than 40 or 45 cents in tax on every dollar you pay and you will cut your cash flow.

• **Pay estimated taxes in December.** Unless you're an employee and have enough withheld from your paychecks, you're required to pay estimated taxes four times each year. The last payment for a calendar year is due the following January—so for 2010, the final estimated tax payment must be made by January 15, 2011.

Tax pros often tell clients to pay state and local estimated income tax by December 31 instead of waiting until January. Their reasoning is that if you pay this in December, you can deduct the outlay on your 2010 federal tax return. (Your tax adviser also might suggest that you make December 2010 payments for property taxes due in early 2011.)

Such a strategy may work for some people, but if you're hit with the alternative minimum tax (AMT), a prepayment could waste a potentially valuable tax break for next year. Such taxes aren't deductible in an AMT year.

• **Put money in a child's name to save taxes.** Some tax pros suggest that you do your saving

Edward Mendlowitz, CPA, partner in the CPA firm WithumSmith+Brown in New Brunswick, New Jersey, ranked among the top 35 accounting firms in the US by the industry's leading publications, *www.withum.com.* He has more than 40 years of public accounting experience and is author of numerous books, including *The Adviser's Guide to Family Business Succession Planning* (American Institute of Certified Public Accountants).

and investing in a child's name so that interest and dividends will be taxed at a low rate.

Problem: The so-called "kiddie tax" rules limit that tactic to $1,900 of unearned income in 2010. Beyond that, investment income is taxed at the parent's rate. Kiddie tax rules apply until a youngster reaches age 19...and until a full-time student reaches age 24.

Bottom line: Having your child receive more than $1,900 from investments this year will not save you taxes. Even if you limit the child's taxable investment income to $1,900, you would have to give a child $47,500 to earn that much, assuming a 4% yield.

More from Edward Mendlowitz, CPA...

The Surprise Tax Bill From Paying Off Debt

In these credit-crunched times, a lot of people are trying to get out from under debt. Those who pull it off usually are surprised to discover that their debt-reducing strategies come with a tax bill. *Two examples...*

• **Short sale of a home.** In today's market, many home owners are trying to sell a home for less than the mortgage balance.

Required: The lender must agree that the proceeds from the house sale will fully satisfy the outstanding mortgage.

If you enter into a short sale for your principal residence, you won't have to worry about the tax consequences. However, for any vacation home or a rental property, you will pick up "cancellation of debt" taxable income from a short sale.

Example: Bob Brown gets his lender to the agree to the sale of his home for $200,000 when the mortgage balance is $240,000. The difference ($40,000) is taxable income. Under current law (through 2012), Bob will owe no tax if the mortgage was used to buy, build or substantially improve his principal residence. However, Bob will have $40,000 of taxable income if the sale involves a vacation home or investment property.

• **Credit card settlements.** People who have large credit card debt sometimes are able to settle for less than the full amount owed. As with short sales of homes, if someone owes $35,000 and settles the debt in full for, let's say, $20,000, the $15,000 difference is taxable income.

Loophole: This income is not recognized for tax purposes if the debt relief is part of a personal bankruptcy settlement or if the debtor is insolvent immediately before the debt cancellation.

Even in those cases, the lender will send a Form 1099-C, Cancellation of Debt, to the IRS reporting the cancellation of debt as income. To avoid tax, you must complete and attach Form 982, Reduction of Tax Attributes Due to Discharge of Indebtedness, to your tax return.

Also from Edward Mendlowitz, CPA...

Make Family Loans Less Taxing

Be careful when you lend money to a relative. As the saying goes, "No good deed goes unpunished."

You might even owe tax on money that you never even got. Say you lend your daughter $200,000 to buy a house. You charge no interest. The IRS will impute interest income (act as if you had received interest) to you at the applicable federal rate (AFR)—and this will be taxable income. To find the current AFR, go to *www.irs.gov/app/picklist/list/federalRates.html.* *Recent AFRs are...**

• **On loans up to three years,** 0.46% per year.

• **On loans longer than three years and up to nine years,** 1.92%.

• **On loans longer than nine years,** 3.6%.

So if you make a long-term, $200,000 loan to your daughter but charge her zero interest, and you are audited, the IRS will impute $7,200 of taxable interest income (3.6% of the $200,000) to you, year after year.

To avoid these complications...

• **On a loan of $10,000 or less.** No income will be imputed as long as the money is not used by the borrower to make income-producing investments.

*Rates as of September 2010.

• **On a loan of $100,000 or less.** There will be no imputed income as long as the borrower's net investment income from all sources is no more than $1,000 each year.

• **On larger loans, collect interest.** Say you lend your daughter $200,000 to buy a house and charge her 3.6% ($7,200 a year). She will pay less than she would pay for a bank mortgage, and you would collect more than you would earn on a bank account.

Crucial: Both parties should sign a formal loan agreement spelling out the terms of the loan, including a maturity date and the interest rate. Without such an agreement, the IRS could recast the entire transaction as a gift and require payment of gift tax.

Finally, if the loan is secured by a personal residence, a mortgage should be filed with the county clerk. This will enable the person borrowing the money to deduct the interest payments.

Finally from Edward Mendlowitz, CPA...

Tax Breaks for Unmarried Couples

The so-called "marriage penalty" means that spouses with almost-equal incomes may pay more tax on a joint return than unmarried partners pay on two single tax returns. *For unmarried cohabitants, that's not the only tax break...*

• **Dependency exemptions.** One unmarried partner may claim a dependency exemption for the other. (Anyone can be a dependent if he/she is a member of your household.) That exemption provides a $3,650 tax deduction in 2010.

To qualify, the couple must live together for the entire year. The partner claiming the deduction must furnish more than 50% of the other's support.

Also, the dependent's income cannot top $3,650 during 2010. Fortunately, nontaxable income (municipal bond interest, the untaxed portion of Social Security benefits) doesn't count toward that limit.

• **Medical deductions.** When you pay medical expenses for a person you support, you can deduct the person's medical expenses on your tax return. This includes all medical expenses that are normally deductible. You can take the deduction even if the person you support earns more than $3,650.

• **Capital gains.** For assets held 12 months or less, profitable sales are taxed as ordinary income at potentially very high rates. Thus, income taxes are likely to be saved if the higher-tax-bracket cohabitant gives the assets to the lower-tax-bracket cohabitant, who can then sell them. (Be aware of gift tax implications.)

Moreover, single filers with taxable income below $34,000 in 2010 will owe no tax at all on realized long-term capital gains. If one unmarried partner has such low income, the higher-income partner can give appreciated stocks or funds to the low-income partner, who can sell them and owe no tax.

• **Tax-free compensation.** If you run a business or professional practice while your live-in partner has no earned income, hire him. As long as your partner's salary is reasonable in relation to the work he does, you can deduct the salary as a business expense.

Your partner can earn up to $9,350 in 2010, tax free, sheltered by the standard deduction and personal exemption.

These Taxpayers Beat The IRS—and You Can, Too! Recent Rulings Can Save You Money

Barbara Weltman, Esq., an attorney based in Millwood, New York, author of *J.K. Lasser's 1001 Deductions and Tax Breaks* (Wiley) and publisher of the free e-letter *Big Ideas for Small Business, www.barbaraweltman.com.*

The idea of trying to challenge the Internal Revenue Service is more likely to create visions of defeat and punishment than triumph and reward. But some taxpayers do take on the IRS and win—through a ruling by either the IRS or the Tax Court—providing hope and possible tax savings for all of us.

Notable recent taxpayer victories and the lessons they provide...

TAX DEDUCTION FOR AN ADVANCED DEGREE

Lori Singleton-Clarke, a nurse in Bryantown, Maryland, who managed 110 nurses and technicians in a long-term-care facility, deducted nearly $15,000 in one year for online courses to obtain a Master of Business Administration (MBA). She pursued the degree to become more effective in her duties and because she felt that she was at a professional disadvantage working with more highly educated doctors. She took the courses online for convenience, eventually obtaining her MBA from the University of Phoenix. The IRS rejected the deduction, and Singleton-Clarke challenged that rejection in Tax Court, arguing her case at a one-hour trial without the help of a lawyer.

IRS position: The cost of an MBA isn't deductible for a nurse, because an MBA is focused on a different type of trade or business (not nursing). Only the cost of education that maintains or improves a current job or profession is deductible. In fact, after receiving her degree, Singleton-Clarke obtained a new supervisory position at the facility where she had been working.

Tax Court ruling: Earning an MBA does not automatically mean that you are in a new business. It is a general course of study that does not necessarily lead into a new profession. (*Case:* Lori Singleton-Clarke, TC Summary Opinion 2009-182.)

Lesson: When claiming a tax deduction for higher education, you must say whether it is a general degree, such as an MBA, or a degree directly related to the profession that you already are in, such as a master's degree or doctorate in education earned by a teacher. This is different from a degree in law, medicine or other profession that leads to special licensing or certification, which counts as a new trade or business and is not deductible.

Note: If a deduction cannot be claimed, it still may be possible to claim a lifetime learning credit. This tax credit is for 20% of tuition and fees up to $2,000 per tax year and applies to all higher learning.

QUALIFIED WITHDRAWALS FROM AN IRA

Richard Glen Venet, a 48-year-old Michigan resident, was laid off from his position after 22 years and couldn't find a new job for four years. Because he had mounting credit card debts and he was falling behind on his mortgage, he withdrew $110,691 from his IRA to avoid foreclosure on his home. He set aside $22,138 of that amount to cover taxes on the withdrawal but did not pay any early distribution penalty even though he was under age 59½ because the withdrawal was the result of a financial hardship. He used about $80,000 to pay off mortgage and credit card debt and put the rest in his bank account, which he drew on to help pay for his daughter's college education.

IRS position: Venet is liable for the early withdrawal penalty on the entire amount because he failed to show that any exception to the 10% penalty for a distribution before age 59½ applied.

Tax Court ruling: Part of the money that was withdrawn from the IRA is not subject to an early withdrawal penalty, because there is an exemption for withdrawals used to pay higher education costs for a taxpayer or taxpayer's spouse or dependent. Unfortunately, there is no exemption from the penalty for "hardship" withdrawals from an IRA, regardless of financial need. In this instance, $9,300 used to pay for the daughter's room and board at college was exempt from the penalty—but not the rest of the withdrawal. (*Case:* Richard Venet, TC Memo 2009-268.)

Lesson: Even though a taxpayer can lose on one issue, he/she can win on another for a partial victory. In addition to education, there is an exemption for paying health insurance premiums when a person is unemployed or paying unreimbursed medical expenses exceeding 7.5% of adjusted gross income.

CASH FROM GIVING UP LIFE INSURANCE

If you have a life insurance policy that you no longer require or want—for example, you bought it to protect your family but your children are grown and self-sufficient—you may be able to pocket some money by selling the policy to a third party or surrendering the policy to the insurer. Many taxpayers believe that they shouldn't be taxed when surrendering a life insurance policy. And they have been proved right—in some cases.

IRS ruling: Some or all of the funds received when a life insurance policy is sold or surrendered may be free of tax. Whether part of the money you receive is treated as highly taxed ordinary income or as a capital gain or as neither depends on the premiums that you have paid, the type of policy you own and whether you sell or surrender the policy.

If you...

• **Surrender a whole-life policy,** money received from the insurance company up to the amount of the premiums you have paid over the years is not taxed. Money that you receive in excess of the total premiums you have paid is taxed as ordinary income. (Cash surrender value is determined by the policy contract.)

• **Sell a whole-life policy,** your taxable gain is the amount that you have received on the sale in excess of the total premiums you have paid over the years, which might be greater than your gain in a surrender. Part of any such gain on the sale is ordinary income, but part is a capital gain—capital gains are taxed at no more than 15% (0% for those in the 10% and 15% tax brackets). The portion of the gain that would have been ordinary income if the policy had been surrendered instead of sold continues to be ordinary income—any gain in excess of that is a capital gain.

• **Sell a term policy,** all of the gain is a capital gain because there is no cash surrender value in the case of a term policy, which pays a stated death benefit but does not provide anything to the policyholder or to the beneficiary of the policy beyond this benefit. (*Ruling:* IRS Revenue Ruling 2009-13.)

Lesson: You may be able to convert a nonproductive asset—your life insurance policy—into some cash with favorable tax treatment. But before you sell or surrender a policy, it is wise to talk with an estate-planning adviser to determine the tax consequences. You also can learn more about the possible consequences online from the Internet sites of the Insurance

Information Institute (*www.iii.org*) and the National Association of Insurance Commissioners (*www.naic.org*).

Buy a Mutual Fund, Get A Tax Holiday

Tom Roseen, senior analyst at Lipper, a division of Thomson Reuters Inc., Denver, *www.lipperweb.com.* He is author of *Taxes in the Mutual Fund Industry* (Lipper).

Individual taxpayers are not the only ones who are able to carry forward unused capital losses to offset future gains. Mutual funds can, too.

Strategy: When you invest in a mutual fund, buy a fund with a large tax-loss carryforward. If that fund generates future gains, its shareholders won't owe tax on those gains to the extent that they are offset by the loss carryforward.

Example: In 2008, stock sales by the hypothetical ABC Fund resulted in a $100 million capital loss. The fund has $20 million in losses from selling stocks in 2009 and $50 million in gains from its sales of stocks in 2010. The combined $120 million loss carried over from 2008 and 2009 completely offsets the gains from 2010 and leaves the fund with a $70 million net loss to carry forward into 2011.

GAIN FROM LOSSES

Don't invest in a fund solely for its embedded tax loss—you also must consider its track record, its manager's history and its expense ratio, among other factors. However, if you are considering several funds with good records and experienced managers, the fund with the largest tax-loss carryforward may be your best choice.

How to find out: When investigating a fund, ask the fund's representative or your investment adviser about its tax-loss carryforward situation.

You also can look for loss carryforwards in the "notes to financial statements" section of the fund's annual or semiannual report or check the fund's Web site.

Remember that a mutual fund's loss carryforward shelters the fund's realized gains from tax, not your realized gains from your own selling.

If you buy shares in a fund in 2009 and sell them in 2011 for a profit, you'll owe tax on the capital gains. In that case, you would have to provide your own offsetting capital losses—from investments you sold at a loss—to avoid capital gains tax.

Smart: Sell off some assets at a loss in this current bear market to create your own loss carryforward.

How to Take a Paid Vacation!

Marjory Abrams, president of Boardroom Inc., 281 Tresser Blvd., Stamford, Connecticut 06901.

If the economy is keeping you from having a vacation this summer, consider these money-saving opportunities from Albert Ellentuck, CPA, an attorney based in Washington, DC, who is past chairman of the tax division of the American Institute of Certified Public Accountants…

• **Mix business with pleasure.** When you plan your summer vacation, combining business with pleasure travel may yield tax savings. If the primary purpose of the domestic trip is for business, you can deduct some travel, lodging, dining and other costs even if part of the trip is spent sightseeing or relaxing.

Example: You go on a weeklong business trip to Chicago. If you extend your trip through the following weekend to see friends and play golf, you probably still can deduct your airfare and your hotel bill for the business days.

Required: Keep a paper trail. That might consist of e-mail and regular mail correspondence between you and the business associates you see on your trip. If you attend a conference, keep the agenda as well as your notes from the sessions.

Also, keep a diary to log any business entertaining that you do. Keep receipts, with notes about the reasons for all of those expenses, in case you're ever questioned by the IRS.

• **Rent out your house while you're away.** You can rent out a home for up to 14 days per year without having to declare any taxable income. If you live in a popular tourist area or near the site of a major sports event, you might pocket thousands of dollars, tax-free.

Most US Homes Are Overassessed

Property tax assessment cycles have not caught up with the drop in home values, so as many as 60% of properties are worth less than the amount of their assessments. This means that you can challenge your assessment and have a better chance of paying lower property taxes.

What to do: Visit your local assessor's office, and check the statistics on your home for accuracy. Look at property cards for a number of similar homes in the neighborhood—if their assessments are lower, you can argue that yours should be, too. Gather sales-price data for several comparable homes sold in recent months, and use the information to argue that your home's market value has declined.

Caution: If your tax bill comes due before your appeal is resolved, pay the bill in full to avoid having a lien placed on your home.

Kiplinger's Personal Finance, 1729 H St. NW, Washington, DC 20006, *www.kiplinger.com/magazine.*

Get Paid for Using Less Energy

Mark Luscombe, JD, CPA, principal federal tax analyst, and Carol Kokinis-Graves, JD, senior tax analyst, both with CCH Inc., a tax and business law information publisher, Riverwoods, Illinois, *www.cch.com.*

You can get tax breaks these days for leaner and cleaner energy usage. Many states have joined the federal government in offering generous incentives. *How to save the most...*

FED FUNDS

Between the *Emergency Economic Stabilization Act of 2008* and the *American Recovery and Reinvestment Act of 2009,* energy-focused federal tax breaks abound. Even taxpayers who owe the alternative minimum tax (AMT) can claim the breaks. There are no income caps for eligibility.

•**Residential energy credits.** You can get a 30% tax credit for energy-efficient home installations in 2010. The maximum tax credit is $1,500.

Result: If you spend $5,000 on certain "residential energy" items this year, you'll save $1,500 on your federal tax bill. Eligible purchases include insulation, metal roofs coated with heat-reflective material and energy-efficient windows, doors and skylights.

•**Residential power credits.** You also can get a tax credit of up to 30% of the cost for buying and installing equipment designed to power, heat and cool your home efficiently. Eligible items include solar water-heating and photovoltaic (or power-generating) equipment, small wind turbines and geothermal heating pumps for home heating, home cooling and water heating.

There generally is no limit on these residential energy-efficiency tax credits, except for a $500-per-half-kilowatt limit on tax credits for fuel cells used to supply electricity. For more information, log on to *www.energystar.gov* and click "Tax Credits for Energy Efficiency." Also visit the Alliance to Save Energy Internet site, *www.ase.org.*

•**Vehicles.** Tax credits are still available on hybrid vehicles produced by GM and a few other manufacturers. For exact amounts of tax credits, go to the IRS Web site, *www.irs.gov,* and search for "hybrid vehicle credit."

You also can get a tax credit of up to $4,000 for buying a Honda Civic GX, which isn't a hybrid but runs on compressed natural gas. For more information, visit *www.fueleconomy.gov.*

What's more, tax credits will be available on plug-in electric vehicles—which get power from the electricity grid—when they eventually come to the market, possibly in late 2010. For plug-ins, the tax credit will range from $2,500 to $7,500, depending on factors such as battery capacity.

More from Mark Luscombe, JD, CPA...

State Energy Tax Incentives

States also provide tax incentives for purchasing alternative-fuel vehicles and making energy-efficient home improvements. *The states with exemplary programs...*

•**Colorado, Louisiana and South Carolina** provide their own tax credits for alternative-fuel vehicles. Even more states offer tax reductions or exemptions whenever you fill up with alternative fuels.

•**Connecticut's** residents owe no sales or use taxes when they purchase solar energy electricity-generating systems, compact fluorescent lightbulbs or residential weatherization products.

•**Massachusetts, Minnesota, New Jersey, New York and Wyoming** exempt certain solar- and wind-powered equipment from sales and use or property tax.

•**Georgia, North Carolina, Texas, West Virginia and Missouri** provide "sales tax holidays" for energy-efficient purchases.

•**Missouri** allows residents to deduct the costs of qualified home-energy audits and related recommendations from federal adjusted gross income when computing state income tax.

Details: Visit the Database of State Incentives for Renewables & Efficiency at *www.dsire usa.org.*

Prepare for Tax Losses From Natural Disasters

The free IRS Publication 584, *Casualty, Disaster, and Theft Loss Workbook,* helps you to compile a room-by-room list of belongings that may qualify for a casualty loss deduction if disaster strikes. This information also can help speed insurance claims.

Best: Keep this information updated and store it safely in a Ziploc bag in a fireproof safe or offsite—in case of an unexpected event (such as a fire or theft) that could lead to an insurance claim or loss deduction.

The publication is available at *www.irs.gov* or by calling 800-829-3676.

Deductible Braces

If you set up a Section 105 Medical Reimbursement Plan as a sole proprietor who employs family members (even school-aged children who work part-time in home-based businesses), you can deduct items that are not covered by standard health insurance, such as braces, eye laser surgery and hearing aids. Even your insurance copayments and deductibles can be converted into legitimate business write-offs. You will need an accountant to set it up, but it's worth the expense, especially if you're in the 25% tax bracket or higher.

High-tax-bracket example: If you employ two of your school-age children, both of whom need braces—a total cost of $10,000—and pay for the braces within the taxable year, you will save $2,500 in taxes.

Caution: Make sure that your children are actually performing legitimate, business-related work, such as filing or stuffing envelopes, and document it—or the IRS could disallow your deduction. (Minor children under age 18 working for parents are exempt from FICA and Medicare.)

Julian Block, Esq., a nationally recognized tax attorney and author based in Larchmont, New York, www. julianblocktaxexpert.com.

How to Deduct a Car You Donate to Charity

Nancy Dunnan, a New York City–based financial and travel adviser and author or coauthor of 25 books, including How to Invest $50–$5,000 *(HarperCollins).*

To qualify for a tax deduction for a car you donate to charity, you must itemize on your tax return—that means filing the long IRS Form 1040 in addition to filing Schedule A.

The group to which you donate your car must be an IRS-approved 501(c)(3) organization. Ask the charity for a copy of its tax-exempt-status document or check the IRS list in the Cumulative List of Exempt Organizations at *www.irs.gov.* Then contact your charity of choice and make the donation directly. It will advise you on the correct procedure.

The amount of your deduction depends on the value of the vehicle and how it is used by the charity. In most cases, donors can deduct only the amount that the charity receives when it sells your car.

Example: Your car has a fair market value of $2,000 but the charity sells it for $1,000. You can claim only $1,000.

However, if the charity gives the car to a needy person or keeps it to use in its work (to drive people to medical appointments, for example), then you can use the fair market value as listed in the *Kelley Blue Book* (available at your local library or at *www.kbb.com*).

No matter what charity you select, it must give you documentation of the IRS-allowed deduction amount within 30 days of your donation, or, if it sells your car, within 30 days of the sale. Be sure to get a copy of the title showing transfer of ownership.

If you claim a deduction of more than $500, you must fill out Section A of IRS Form 8283, *Noncash Charitable Contributions,* and attach it to your tax return. If your deduction is more than $5,000, you must fill out Section B of IRS Form 8283 and get an independent appraisal.

More information: IRS Publication 561, *Determining the Value of Donated Property,* and IRS Publication 4303, *A Donor's Guide to Vehicle Donations.*

How Long to Keep Tax Paperwork

Wondering how long you need to hold on to various tax and financial documents? *See below…*

• **Tax returns.** Forever, with proof of filing. The IRS has three years from the date you file to audit returns for errors…and six years if it believes you underreported gross income by 25%. But if the IRS claims that it never received your paperwork, it has unlimited time.

• **IRA contributions.** Permanently, especially if you made nondeductible contributions. You may have to prove them to avoid being taxed again on withdrawals.

• **Bank records.** Monthly statements, seven years. If you get canceled checks, go through them and permanently keep ones related to taxes, business expenses, home improvements and mortgage payments.

• **Brokerage statements.** Keep for at least three years after you sell securities and pay capital gains taxes.

Barbara Weltman, Esq., an attorney based in Millwood, New York, *www.barbaraweltman.com.*

Six Ways to Cut Tax Prep Costs

William Perez, EA, a consumer advocate and practicing tax professional who writes a tax-planning blog for the Web site About.com (taxes.about.com). He is president of San Francisco–based Perez Tax Associates LLC, and a former Tax Specialist with the IRS. His Web site is *www.pereztaxassociates.com.*

A good professional tax preparer can save you money in the long run by helping you minimize your taxes, especially if he/she offers guidance throughout the year, not just at tax time. So what's a fair price to pay for this service?

A 2007 study from the National Society of Accountants found that the average bill for a simple tax return including a 1040, Schedule A (Itemized Deductions) and a state tax return was $205,* and $115 without the Schedule A. But your bill might be several times higher if you select a high-end tax preparer—one who specializes in preparing the taxes of high-net-worth individuals who bring in six figures or more each year—or if your return is particularly complex.

Examples: Being self-employed…owning rental property…relocating to a new state…making a lot of investment transactions.

More than 40% of tax preparers charge per form, with the rest charging per hour, per return or based on some combination of these factors. *Before hiring a tax preparer…*

• **Ask for a price estimate.** An experienced tax preparer should be able to provide this once he learns a little about you and your financial situation.

• **Confirm that the tax preparer has experience with any unusual aspects of your return.** If a tax preparer has to conduct research for your return, you'll be billed for that study time.

• **Find out exactly what you get for your money.** A tax preparer might be worth more than average if he provides ongoing advice about trimming your taxes rather than just filling out tax forms…answers quick tax-related questions throughout the year without an extra charge…or handles your entire return personally rather than handing it off to a less-experienced underling. (Avoid tax preparers who outsource returns overseas, where the experience and education of the workers often is low…and the risk of identity theft sometimes is high.)

HOW TO PAY LESS

Here are six ways to save your tax preparer time—and save yourself money. *If your tax preparer charges per form, not per hour, try to use the following time savers as leverage to negotiate a lower rate…*

*Prices subject to change.

163

•**Offer to file an extension.** Tax preparers' time is at a premium from February to April. Some will negotiate lower rates for clients willing to wait until May or June to file. If you're confident you are due a refund, all this costs you is access to this money for a month or two. If you owe money to the IRS, you will have to estimate the amount that you owe and pay your tax bill before April 15 to avoid paying interest and penalties.

•**Organize your financial data the way your tax preparer wants it organized.**

Example: A tax preparer might want a client's tax files grouped into subfolders labeled "House," "Business," "Investments" and "Kids."

•**Trim data-entry time.** Lots of investment transactions mean lots of data entry for your tax preparer. Active traders sometimes can save money by providing their tax preparers with copies of IRS Schedule D, Capital Gains and Losses, from their brokers' Web sites or by creating an Excel spreadsheet with the required data—the name of the security and number of shares, date acquired, date sold, sale price, cost basis and gain/loss—already entered.

•**Avoid gaps in data.** Tax-prep bills climb when preparers must contact clients for missing information. Get a complete list of everything your tax preparer requires before work begins on your return.

•**Confirm that your bill will return to normal when your financial life does.** Your tax preparer's bill may leap in years when you experience significant financial changes—but it ought to settle back down after that. Unfortunately, some preparers unofficially base clients' bills on the previous year's bill. Remind your preparer that the previous bill was out of the ordinary before work begins on your next return.

•**Ask if you can be in the preparer's office to answer any questions while your return is being prepared.** Some tax preparers allow this. Providing on-the-spot answers to your preparer's questions saves time—and your presence greatly reduces the odds that you'll be billed for more time than your return actually took.

IRS to Monitor Tax Preparers More Tightly

The IRS will monitor tax preparers more closely under the recent regulatory plan. Employees of chain tax-preparation firms and independent tax preparers will have to pay a registration fee...pass a competency exam... and have 15 hours of education per year. The rules—which begin taking effect in 2011 and will take several years to implement—do not apply to certified public accountants, enrolled agents or other professionals, who already are subject to standards in their fields.

Doug Shulman, IRS commissioner, quoted in *The Wall Street Journal.*

Beware Fraudulent Tax Settlement Services

Services that claim to help settle tax debts for less than the full amount usually are fraudulent. Only the IRS can agree to let you pay less tax than you owe—and it accepts no more than 25% of so-called Offers in Compromise (OICs). People with OICs may lose all or almost all their savings, property, home equity, cars and future income.

What to do: If you will have trouble paying what you owe, you can request installment payments by filing IRS Form 9465 if the amount is $25,000 or less, or Forms 433F and 9465 if the amount is more than $25,000. If the amount is $10,000 or less, IRS consent is automatic. You will be charged a fee and interest for the plan, plus possible penalties.

Information: www.irs.gov.

Kiplinger's Personal Finance, 1729 H St. NW, Washington, DC 20006, *www.kiplinger.com/magazine.*

The IRS Is Watching You

Tax authorities watch MySpace, Facebook and other sites. State tax agents have found numerous tax evaders by "Googling" them to see what they say about themselves (such as where they live and work). The agents also compare claims of business owners and investors on their personal Web pages against what they report on their returns. The IRS declines to say whether it watches the Internet—but it does share information with the states.

The Wall Street Journal, http://online.wsj.com.

The IRS Is Cracking Down on More Taxpayers! Red Flags That Trigger Audits

Martin S. Kaplan, CPA, who has a private practice based in New York City. He is a frequent guest speaker at insurance, banking and financial-planning seminars and author of *What the IRS Doesn't Want You to Know* (Wiley).

The IRS has been stepping up efforts to make sure that US taxpayers are paying up, especially as the federal budget deficit climbs. About 40,000 more individual tax returns were audited in fiscal 2009 than in 2008—and the number has more than doubled since 2000. For 2010, the tentative federal tax-enforcement budget is up nearly 10% from last year.

There's no way to absolutely audit-proof a tax return. However, there are steps you can take to minimize the chances that the Internal Revenue Service will challenge yours, including ways to make sure that you don't have any of the new potential red flags that the IRS is targeting. *To reduce the chances of an IRS audit...*

REPORT ALL YOUR INCOME

In the current economic climate, unreported income is a major concern of the IRS, especially if you are self-employed and report income on Schedule C of IRS Form 1040. The IRS estimates the annual "tax gap" between what taxpayers should pay and what they actually pay at $290 billion, and has said that underreported income accounts for 80% of this tax gap.

An agent may look beyond your W-2 forms and 1099 forms that report income. He/she may examine all of your checking and savings accounts from December of the year prior to the year that is under examination through January of the following year—14 months in all. You may have to provide that information for your children's bank accounts, too. The agent will be looking for deposits substantially in excess of the income you reported.

You'll be asked to explain any deposits that were not classified as income, such as proceeds from a home-equity loan, account transfers, an inheritance and gifts.

What to do: Make sure that you report all of your taxable income. Go over all of your bank deposits as an IRS agent might, and see if you can account for all deposits in excess of the taxable income you report.

MORE INCOME = MORE VIGILANCE

With income of $200,000 or less, you have about a 1% chance of being audited, according to the IRS. Audits of taxpayers in this income group rose only slightly from 2008 to 2009. With income of more than $200,000 up to $1 million, your chance of an audit triples to about 3%. Audits of such taxpayers rose by 11% from 2008 to 2009. And with income of more than $1 million, your chances of facing IRS scrutiny shoot up to more than 6%. Audits of seven-figure-income taxpayers rose by 30% from 2008 to 2009.

What to do: The higher your income, the more vigilant you must be about avoiding errors, omissions and questionable deductions. There also is more reason to hire a professional tax preparer. And there may be more reason to lower your taxable income by investing in tax-exempt bonds and other means.

DON'T CALL A HOBBY A BUSINESS

Be cautious about reporting as a business any hobby that is only minimally profitable—

an increasingly common practice that the IRS frowns upon because you are not allowed to deduct losses from a hobby (but you can deduct losses from a business).

A true business may lose money, of course. As long as you possess records showing that you made a legitimate effort to create an authentic business, you can deduct the loss. This means running the activity in a businesslike manner—with a business plan, a separate business bank account, good records of income and expenses, etc.

If you report business expenses, including auto, travel and entertainment expenses, that are high in relation to your income, that also could draw extra scrutiny from the IRS. Keep thorough records of income and expenses for your business.

Be aware that you do have to report all income from a hobby. The good news is that you can deduct expenses of the hobby to the extent of that income.

BE CAUTIOUS ABOUT HOME OFFICES

In addition to unreported income, IRS examiners often focus on deductions for a home office. Therefore, filing Form 8829 (Expenses for Business Use of Your Home) might attract IRS attention and trigger an audit.

What's new: When a taxpayer who is audited has filed Form 8829, many IRS districts now are making it mandatory for a revenue agent to physically visit the taxpayer's home by appointment. During a home visit, the IRS agent will look around and take pictures to determine whether there really is a home office, whether it's set up exclusively for business and how large a portion of the home is taken up by the office.

What to do: Consider restricting the square footage you report for a home office to less than 20% of the total space in your home. You might end up with a slightly lower tax deduction than you are technically entitled to, but you may reduce your exposure to an audit. You even may want to avoid declaring a home office at all.

PROVE YOU DONATED

The IRS appears to be taking a much closer look at cash and noncash charitable donations, especially ones that are very large relative to the taxpayer's income. Giving 10% of your income to charity is far above the norm, which is around 2%. So, donating very large amounts relative to your income may be a red flag to IRS examiners. Gifts of property, especially those valued at more than $5,000, often draw scrutiny.

All charitable deductions must be backed up by written verification now, such as a letter from the charity or a bank record of the gift, or, for cash donations under $250, a bank record recording the gift.

What to do: If you really donate substantial amounts and have supporting evidence, such as receipts…letters from the recipient organizations…and/or your bank statements, take the deductions. Avoid making cash donations—it is better to use a check or credit card.

BACK UP HOME BUYER'S CLAIM

New laws made in 2008 and 2009 created tax credits of up to $8,000 for many first-time home buyers and as much as $6,500 for many repeat buyers.

However, the Treasury Department found that about one out of every 10 claims for the tax credit is faulty, for a total of more than $600 million in claims that will not be allowed. The IRS has frozen thousands of tax refunds and initiated more than 100,000 examinations of questionable claims.

Examples: More than 580 people under age 18 (including a four-year-old) claimed the credit, even though they are not eligible. The IRS suspects that some high-income parents (who were not eligible for the credit) had their low-income children claim the credit. Another, perhaps more innocent, mistake might be claiming the credit if your income was over the limit.

What to do: To avoid inviting an audit, be familiar with all of the requirements for the home buyer's credit, and follow them to the letter. For details, log on to *www.homebuyer taxcredit.com*. Make sure to attach Form 5405 and proof of closing to your tax return.

DON'T EXAGGERATE MORTGAGE INTEREST

During the boom in housing, many people refinanced their homes using "cash-out" mortgages, taking out equity in their homes to use for living expenses. In 2009, the IRS announced it would extend a regional project scrutinizing mortgage interest to a nationwide level by December 2011. Their regional project found many people reporting large mortgage interest deductions in relation to their income—a potential audit red flag.

What to do: If you're reporting to the IRS, say, $20,000 in mortgage interest payments but only $25,000 in income, it would be very wise to include a brief statement explaining how you can handle such a big mortgage—for example, that you are tapping your savings to pay the mortgage.

DECLARE OVERSEAS ACCOUNTS

The IRS has announced that it expects to collect $8.5 billion in back taxes from Americans with foreign bank accounts over the next few years. The IRS is pressuring foreign banks to name names. For example, in 2009, the US and Switzerland reached an agreement requiring Swiss banks to provide account information if the IRS suspects any tax evasion from account holders.

What to do: If you own or have authority over a foreign financial account, you are required to file a Report of Foreign Bank and Financial Accounts (FBAR) to the IRS if the aggregate value of all your foreign accounts exceeds $10,000 at any time during the calendar year. Be sure to do it.

Six Reasons to See Your Accountant After Tax Season

Thomas P. Ochsenschlager, Esq., CPA, vice president of taxation at the American Institute of Certified Public Accountants (AICPA), Washington, DC, *www.aicpa.org*. *Accounting Today* named him one of the 100 most influential accountants for four consecutive years.

I f you filed your tax return by April 15, you might think that you won't see your tax pro until next March or April. That may be true—but it also means that you could be missing valuable tax-saving advice. *When to ask your accountant to have an out-of-season meeting…*

• **Change in family circumstances.** If you're getting married, you might ask for advice on setting up a prenuptial agreement, say, or on how marital assets should be titled. Holding an investment portfolio as "joint tenants with right of survivorship," for example, will enable those assets to pass to the surviving co-owner without the time and expense of probate—but may lead to higher income tax after the death of the first spouse.

Divorcing also presents tax traps and opportunities. And, after the birth of a child, a tax pro can advise you on issues from estate planning to life insurance to setting up a college fund.

• **A change in domicile.** Moving, say, from high-tax New York to low-tax Florida can be a huge tax saver. However, your move might turn into a nightmare if your old state insists that you still owe income tax to it even though you no longer live there. (Your heirs might be assessed for state estate tax, too.)

Your tax adviser can help you establish "domicile" in the low-tax state to avoid a possible challenge from your old state.

According to statistics from the Tax Foundation, in 2008,* the average state and local tax burden (total taxes on income, property, sales, gas, cigarettes, alcohol, etc.) was 11.8% in New Jersey—the highest-taxing state.

What residents of the lowest-taxing states paid: Alaska (6.4%)…Nevada (6.6%)…Wyoming (7%)…Florida (7.4%).

• **Loss of a job.** If you are among the swelling ranks of the unemployed, ask your tax professional about ways that you can continue your health insurance and how to document your job-hunting expenses, which might be tax deductible.

Job loss is forcing many people to tap their IRA or 401(k) accounts before age 59½. If this happens to you, your tax pro can suggest tactics to avoid paying a 10% penalty on early distributions. For example, you won't owe this penalty if you use IRA money to pay college

*Latest date for which figures are available.

bills for yourself, your spouse, your child or your grandchild.

● **Major market swings.** With stocks still trading down from their peaks, taking losses now can save you taxes this year and/or in the future. Your tax adviser can suggest "loss harvesting" strategies and explain how to avoid making "wash sales," which would cancel the tax benefit of selling.

At some point, stocks will go up again. Then your tax adviser can suggest tactics for taking capital gains and using appreciated assets for making tax-saving charitable contributions.

● **Year-end tax planning.** November or December might roll around without providing you with any of the above reasons to visit your tax adviser. Even so, it makes sense to sit down with your tax pro.

By year-end, you'll have a good idea of your annual income and deductions. Any changes in tax law for 2010 will probably have been passed. This will enable your adviser to suggest specific tax-saving strategies.

Example: If your adviser determines that you will not be subject to the alternative minimum tax (AMT) this year, he might suggest that you prepay (in 2010) state and local tax due in early 2011. This would accelerate deductions for these expenses to your 2010 tax return.

However, if you will owe the AMT in 2010, state and local taxes won't be deductible for you. Then your accountant may recommend that you put off those payments until 2011, when those outlays may be tax deductible.

Prepare for Next Year's Taxes Now

Think about what worked well this year and what could be improved.

Examples: If it took a long time to gather your credit card statements, keep them in a single place from now on. Set up specific file folders, and drop or scan documents for next year's taxes into them throughout the year. Highlight deductible tax donations in your checkbook and on credit card statements every month. If you use a tax-preparation program, scan tax receipts using a scanner that lets you easily export data to the tax software.

Leslie Walden, a certified professional organizer and founder of It's Time to Get Organized LLC, in Atlanta, which consults with business and residential clients.

The IRS Is on YouTube

The IRS now has a "channel" at the Web video site YouTube.com, where it displays free tax information videos. There are more than 100 videos, with new ones added regularly on the latest tax information.

10

Investment Ideas

Still Scared? Seven Ways To Overcome Your Fears And Get Back into The Market Now

Snap out of it! That is what Cher told a love-struck Nicholas Cage in the film *Moonstruck*. And that's what many financial advisers are telling gun-shy investors who are anything but in love with the stock market right now.

Those investors are asking themselves if it's still a bit early to buy stocks again because they could plunge even more—or too late because stocks have already recovered so much so quickly.

Top investment adviser Allan S. Roth has helpful answers for you, whether you pulled some money out of stocks...held off on putting new money in...and/or have your money in other investments, such as money-market funds, CDs or bonds, that you could consider shifting to stocks.

The seven rules that will help you ease back into the market...

DON'T DELAY FURTHER

1. Start buying stocks right now—even though the market could tank again. Will you be getting in too early? It's possible. But accept the fact that you will never catch the exact bottom of the market—and realize that with market indexes still at levels where they were 11 years ago, there is a high likelihood that the next 10 years will produce good returns for investors.

2. Buy slowly and systematically. I am advising all my clients to invest equal amounts

---

Allan S. Roth, CPA, CFP, founder and president of Wealth Logic, LLC, an investment and financial-planning firm in Colorado Springs that serves clients with investments from $10,000 to $50 million. He is author of *How a Second Grader Beats Wall Street: Golden Rules Any Investor Can Learn* (Wiley). His Web site is *www.daretobedull.com*.

every month, spread out over the next year, in a 401(k), IRA and/or a taxable account.

Reason: This market has been so viciously unpredictable that you will outsmart yourself if you try to time your investments to take advantage of market pullbacks.

3. Invest only money you can keep in the stock market for at least 10 years. In recent times, I've seen many investors who have three-to-five-year time horizons stuck with big stock losses. That's not enough time to bounce back even if the market suffers just one really poor year.

LET GOALS DETERMINE RISK LEVELS

Whether you have new money to invest or just existing holdings, you are faced with the daunting task of reevaluating how aggressive or conservative you want to be and determining how to allocate your investments. *My top suggestions…*

4. Stop trying to figure out your "risk tolerance." For many years, I quizzed clients on how much volatility they could stomach in up and down markets. I pointed out that how we think we will react to pain is often different from how we really react.

Better strategy: Let your financial goals determine the amount of risk you need to take. That way, you let hard numbers—rather than your own ever-shifting comfort levels—shape your plan. Figure out how much money you need to live on in retirement, then what kind of return you must get to reach that amount.

Example: Say you have a $1 million retirement portfolio and you want it to generate $30,000 in annual income in today's dollars for as long as 30 years. You don't have to take much risk—you can achieve that with conservative bonds. However, if you want the same portfolio to generate $50,000 a year, plus adjustments for inflation, you should consider including stocks as well.

Resource: Log on to *www.bankrate.com* and click on "Calculators," then on "Investment Calculators" and then "Retirement Income Calculator" for a calculator that can help you determine your appropriate asset allocation.

5. Stick like glue, in both up and down markets, to the asset allocation you choose.

Consistency is the most difficult part of investing because it requires the most emotional discipline. The average investor will underperform a total stock market index by about 1.5 percentage points annually because of faulty market timing—bailing out after downturns and jumping back in after upswings. (That's in addition to the effects of trading costs and other expenses.)

If you weren't able to maintain your allocation through the past two bear markets, stop fooling yourself. Ratchet down your risk to a level that you can stick with.

Example: I am in my early 50s with 15 years to go until retirement. But my own portfolio allocates 33% to US stocks, 17% to foreign stocks and 50% to bonds. That may seem too conservative, but it means I lost only 16% in 2008, the worst year I am likely to see in my investing life. With a higher allocation of stocks last year, I would have made panicky moves based on fear and instinct and wound up losing much more.

6. Consider using basic stock index funds. The knock against funds that track the Standard & Poor's 500 stock index or other indexes was that even though they are sure to perform well in bull markets, they are exposed to the full fury of bear markets.

Under this common wisdom, "actively managed" funds can protect you in a bear market by going to cash or buying defensive investments—but that's not what happened in this bear market. Many of the best managers made terrible stock choices at the worst time.

I start with a simple, low-cost, three-fund portfolio of index funds as the basic building blocks for most of my clients…

• Vanguard Total Stock Market Index Fund (VTSMX). *Performance:* -0.84%.*

• Vanguard Total International Stock Index Fund (VGTSX). *Performance:* 2.44%.

• Vanguard Total Bond Market Index Fund (VBMFX). *Performance:* 6.15%.

For more information on Vanguard, phone 877-662-7447 or go to *www.vanguard.com.*

Similar index funds are available from other mutual fund networks.

*Fund performance figures are annualized for the 10 years through August 27, 2010.

7. Use the floor-and-ceiling approach to rebalance. Systematic rebalancing—in effect buying low and selling high—is imperative to long-term investment success. However, many investors were too paralyzed to rebalance at the end of 2008 because it would have meant selling bonds and buying large amounts of stocks. A "floor-and-ceiling" approach can help you overcome that paralysis.

How it works: Once you decide your target allocation for different asset classes of stocks and bonds, choose a "floor" (the most that you will let your allocation in any asset class decrease before you rebalance) and a "ceiling" (the largest amount you will allow an asset class to rise). Typically, I use five percentage points.

Example: You have a $100,000 portfolio consisting of 50% in a total stock market index fund and 50% in a total bond market index fund. Say your stock fund loses $10,000 while your bond fund stays even. You now have 44.4% of your money in the stock fund and 55.6% in the bond fund. To get back to your original 50%/50% allocation, you need to sell $5,000 worth of shares in your bond fund and use it to buy $5,000 of stock fund shares. Alternatively, you could use $10,000 in new investment money to buy stock fund shares and keep your bond fund intact.

Don't Fall for What Wall Street Says

Stephen T. McClellan, CFA, an investment analyst for 32 years at leading Wall Street firms. He was ranked on the Institutional Investor All-America Research Team for 19 straight years. McClellan lives in San Francisco and is author of *Full of Bull: Do What Wall Street Does, Not What It Says, to Make Money in the Market* (FT).

Faced with market turmoil, many investors panicked and blindly sold stocks, unloading good companies that could soon rebound. Others have sought to profit from the downturn by turning to shaky junk bonds. While those risky investments might appear cheap, they could sink the next time the market drops.

To avoid losses, move cautiously. Buy solid companies that can grow over the long term. Be prepared to hold these steady performers for years—and don't abandon good businesses at the first sign of a minor problem. As I discovered during a long career on Wall Street, the best stocks can provide healthy returns for investors with patience. Even people in their 60s and 70s may have long-term investment horizons. *Rules that I follow…*

● **Don't buy or sell in reaction to stories in the media.** At a time when so many news articles are frightening, investors may panic and sell—but this can result in irrational choices.

Example: After General Electric cut its dividend in 2009, the papers were full of negative articles about the company's problems. Investors rushed to sell. The stock decreased from a high above 12 in February to a low of less than seven during March. Soon investors realized that the company was still profitable, and the stock began rebounding, rising above 12 in April. Investors who sold based on the headlines suffered sizable losses.

Better: After you see some bad news, wait a few days. Calmly consider the information and make a dispassionate decision based on the fundamental performance of the company and the long-term outlook for earnings.

Likewise, do not be easily swayed by good news. Chances are that whatever story you've heard actually made its way around Wall Street for weeks before the news articles appeared. If that happened, the pros have already pushed up the prices of shares before retail investors learned of the positive developments. If you do see a report of a positive earnings surprise or record earnings, calmly evaluate the news. Watch patiently for days or weeks to decide whether the good news is an isolated incident or the beginning of a long trend.

● **Limit your losses.** When a stock proves disappointing, be prepared to recognize that you made a mistake. If the stock drops 15% to 20%, have the discipline to reassess your position, determine if the business outlook is intact and decide whether you made an error and should cut your losses. By accepting relatively small losses, you can avoid disastrous declines.

• **Don't try to "catch a falling knife."** After a stock has fallen by half or more, it may seem like a good deal. But all too often, the shares keep dropping. When Internet stocks collapsed in 2000, some shares dropped from more than $100 to less than $10. Although Wall Street analysts recommended the shares at the low levels, many of those stocks lost all their value.

• **Emphasize dividend-paying stocks.** When stock prices soared in the late 1990s, many investors considered dividend-paying stocks to be stodgy. But dividend stocks have proven to outperform the market averages over long periods. During the 80 years ending in 2006, US stocks returned about 11% annually on average. More than 40% of that result came from dividends. In the next several years, markets will struggle to recover from the financial crisis, and stock investors will likely achieve only modest single-digit total returns. Dividends will account for a big percentage of returns.

In today's rocky markets, dividends serve as important indicators. Most companies that pay consistent dividends have plenty of cash and are financially sound. And because they provide their shareholders with steady cash payments, dividend stocks are often quite resilient during market downturns.

• **Seek growth of revenue.** Look for those companies that have been increasing revenues steadily. Such businesses are likely to have a competitive edge—and are likely to continue to grow.

Exception: Beware of companies that are reporting rapid annual growth of more than 25%. Such high rates are unsustainable. When the inevitable slowdowns occur, share prices could collapse.

Subpar revenue expansion during a severe economic contraction is reasonable as long as the pace is relatively healthy compared with the competition.

• **Pursue expanding profit margins.** The best companies report stable or increasing profit margins. These are displayed in annu-

al reports and on stock-related Internet sites, such as Yahoo! Finance (*http://finance.yahoo. com*). If a company has been increasing revenues and profit margins for the past five or 10 years, it likely has a unique product or strong management. At the same time, beware of companies with profit margins that are far superior to those of their industry competitors. It may be hard to maintain such high levels.

• **Avoid turnarounds.** Be wary of companies with weak profit margins and declining earnings. While some value investors do favor such troubled businesses, these turnaround candidates rarely succeed. Once the company begins spiraling down, it could appoint new management or engage in large cost-cutting programs. These moves can give the stock a short-term boost. But most often bad news is followed by more problems.

• **Shop for bargains.** Even if a stock's revenues and earnings are growing rapidly, it may not be worth buying if the price is too high. Expensive stocks can drop sharply at the least bit of negative news. To avoid overpaying, focus on stocks with price-to-earnings ratios (P/Es) that are below the current average for their industries. Over long periods, stocks bought cheaply tend to outdo expensive ones. For a rough gauge of the average P/E of an industry, go to the "Industry Center" at Yahoo! Finance, *http://biz.yahoo.com/ic*, and select an industry from the list.

• **Avoid short-term trading.** Once you buy a stock, aim to hold it for at least one year. If the stock continues performing steadily—and does not drop by more than 15% to 20%—stick with it for years. Short-term trading rarely produces good results because share prices can bounce around unpredictably. If you crave excitement, set aside 5% of your assets for short-term trades—and be prepared to lose all this money.

• **Set realistic goals.** During the 1990s' bull market, stock investors routinely enjoyed double-digit annual returns. But in today's difficult economy, profit margins are under great pressure, and stocks are likely to deliver only modest results. If you record 5% to 10% annual returns, be satisfied with your strategy.

Don't take on more risk in hopes of obtaining results that may be difficult to achieve.

• **Stay diversified.** Hold a mixture of stocks and bonds. Most investors should follow the example of T. Rowe Price Capital Appreciation (PRWCX), a mutual fund that keeps about 60% of assets in high-quality stocks and most of the rest of the portfolio in cash and investment-grade bonds. Since the fund started in 1986, it has averaged an 11.04% return* annually, achieving modest returns nearly every year. That consistent showing has enabled the fund to outperform most of its competitors and avoid the worst losses during the recent market downturns.

*Rates subject to change.

Warning: Inflation Spike Ahead! How to Safeguard Your Portfolio

David A. Twibell, JD, director of wealth management for Colorado Capital Bank, Denver, which oversees $1 billion in assets. He is a nationally recognized authority on investing in troubled economic climates. He provides portfolio management services to high-networth individuals, corporations and nonprofit organizations. Twibell frequently comments on inflation for CNBC and *Financial Planning* magazine. For more, go to *www.coloradocapitalbank.com.*

The deep recession has kept a tight lid on the prices of many goods and services. But that does not mean that the danger of rising inflation has been snuffed out for the long term.

As the economy recovers, I expect inflation to rise as well. While the initial increase may be gradual, once the economy begins to pick up steam, it may not be long before inflation is well above the relatively tame 2% to 3% levels typical in the past decade.

High inflation is painful for most people but especially painful for those who plan to retire soon or who already are retired and living on fixed incomes. Although some inflation is good for many companies because it means that they can raise prices, very high inflation hurts stocks because it becomes much more expensive for companies to borrow money and to pay rising raw material and labor costs. It hurts bond investors because as the interest rates rise, old bonds paying less lose value.

Certain investments act as a hedge against inflation because their value tends to rise at a pace equal to, or greater than, inflation. If inflation remains tame, the broad market will do very well and the inflation hedges you add won't be too much of a drag on your returns. If, on the other hand, inflation gets out of control and the stock and bond markets tumble as a result, the hedges will help offset some of the damage. *Among the best inflation hedges…*

COMMODITIES

Commodities include raw materials such as crops, metals (including gold), timber and oil. *They perform well in a growing economy with lots of inflation for three reasons…*

• **US inflation generally coincides with a falling US dollar,** which boosts commodity prices on world markets.

• **Economic growth means a greater demand for raw materials,** which boosts their prices, especially because it takes a long time to ratchet up production.

• **Demand for commodities is rising rapidly** in emerging markets as they develop infrastructure and middle-class consumers emerge.

How much you need: For conservative and moderately aggressive investors, up to 20% of the stock portion of your holdings, although commodity investments can be volatile sometimes. For aggressive investors, 30% or more of your stock allocation.

Reason: If you can withstand more volatility, investing in commodities makes sense not just as an inflation hedge but also as a way to bet on a sector that is likely to outperform the broad market averages over the next few decades. *Investment options…*

• iShares S&P North American Natural Resources Sector Index Fund (IGE), an exchange-traded fund (ETF) that gives you exposure to various sectors of the oil and gas industry, as well as to metals and mining companies. *Recent share price: $31.95.**

*Prices and rates as of August 27, 2010.

• The US Global Investors Global Resources Fund (PSPFX). If you prefer an actively managed fund over an ETF, this one provides broad diversification among commodity subsectors. *Performance:* 3.47%, annualized for the five years through August 27, 2010. *More information:* 800-873-8637, *www.usfunds.com.*

TIPS

Treasury Inflation-Protected Securities (TIPS) are long-term IOUs issued and backed by the federal government. They start out with a fixed annual interest rate, like other Treasury securities. In addition, the government adjusts the amount of principal based on the Consumer Price Index (CPI), although you are guaranteed to receive at least the original value of your investment at maturity—even if the CPI has dropped.

Currently, a standard 10-year Treasury provides 2.65%…while 10-year TIPS yield 1.05%. If you can make do with the lower yield now, you can buy more protection against inflation through a larger investment in TIPS.

How much you need: For conservative to moderately aggressive investors, 30% or more of the bond allocation of your portfolio. For aggressive investors, TIPS should represent no more than 30% of your bond allocation.

Invest in TIPS directly instead of through a mutual fund or ETF because that way you're guaranteed to get your principal back at maturity. (The value of a fund investment can drop.) TIPS are sold with five-, 10- and 20-year maturities. Purchase minimum is $100.

Consider creating a "ladder" of TIPS, including TIPS with five- and 10-year maturities, as well as previously issued TIPS with three- and seven-year maturities that you can buy in the secondary market. TIPS are best for tax-deferred or tax-exempt accounts, such as IRAs, because TIPS in taxable accounts are taxed on the increased principal each year. Buy them yourself without a fee at *www.treasurydirect. gov.*

REITs TOO RISKY RIGHT NOW

Real Estate Investment Trusts (REITs) own properties and trade like stocks. While real estate normally is a good inflation hedge, this is not a good time to bet on a strong real estate recovery. Prices of commercial real estate are likely to decline further before rising again. Therefore, I have no allocation to this asset class now. However, within a few years, the residential and commercial properties owned by REITs likely will start to go up in value—and REITS provide hefty dividends.

When the real estate market returns to normal, you can invest in a diversified ETF, such as the iShares Dow Jones US Real Estate Index Fund (IYR). It has stakes in 75 of the largest commercial REITs.

Recent share price: $50.60.

Yield: 4.44%.

I also would keep an eye on the closed-end mutual fund Alpine Global Premier Properties (AWP) because it gives exposure to areas of the world where real estate will recover more quickly than in the US, such as Asia and Latin America.

Recent share price: $6.

Yield: 8.51%.

SAVINGS BOND ALTERNATIVE

One other way to help cushion your nest egg against inflation is Series I US Savings Bonds. They can be bought for as little as $25 each through *www.treasurydirect.gov.* But these inflation-adjusted bonds have drawbacks.

The bonds have both a fixed annual rate, which was set at just 0.2% for bonds sold between May 1, 2010, and October 31, 2010… and an inflation component (which is adjusted twice a year) that is set at an annual rate of 1.54% for those six months. That adds up to 1.74%.

If inflation does rise—and all the factors are in place for that to happen—these bonds can be attractive, but if inflation remains tame, the fixed-rate, in effect over the 30-year life of the bonds, doesn't give you much.

You can now buy Series I bonds with your tax refund by using IRS Form 8888.

Invest Like Benjamin Graham: How the Legendary Master Beat The Market...and Which Stocks He'd Buy Today

John Reese, founder and CEO, Validea Capital Management in West Hartford, Connecticut, *www.validea capital.com*. He is author of *The Guru Investor: How to Beat the Market Using History's Best Investment Strategies* (Wiley).

We have been going through the worst economic crisis since the Great Depression, so it makes sense that one of the top-performing investment styles now worked well back then, too. In 1929, a young Ivy League business school professor named Benjamin Graham was practically wiped out by the stock market crash. During the years that followed, he developed strict investing guidelines by focusing on hard facts, such as a company's past earnings and the value of its assets, rather than trying to predict its future. This approach led him to solid, conservative companies whose stocks were selling at bargain-basement prices.

While you won't find the next Google using Graham's prudent, deep-value approach, consider that from the 1930s to the 1950s, his portfolio averaged returns of 20% annually, and his protégé, Warren Buffett, is still beating the market today.

Today, I use various screens designed to replicate the stock-picking approaches of investment gurus like Benjamin Graham, who died in 1976. Since its launch in December 2003, my "Graham Portfolio" has produced a 12.7% annualized return versus just a 0.9% annualized return for the Standard & Poor's 500 stock index.*

GRAHAM'S SECRETS FOR FINDING GREAT STOCKS

• **The company should be rich in assets.** Graham liked firms that have a lot more assets, such as cash, than liabilities, such as debt.

*Rates and prices as of August 13, 2010.

Note: You can find information on company assets and liabilities, price-to-earnings ratios (P/Es) and fair value at *www.morningstar. com*.

Reason: The companies that must make large interest payments on their debt can get in trouble very quickly if earnings decline or don't grow as much as expected. To be ultra-safe, Graham wanted his stock picks to have total assets that are at least twice as much as total liabilities. This requirement alone would have let Graham avoid the recent meltdown in the banking sector because financial-services companies carried far too much debt for him.

• **Wall Street's expectations for the company must be low.** Graham compared a stock's price with concrete financial variables, such as earnings. A company's P/E ratio (stock price divided by earnings per share) is a simple indicator of how much a stock costs relative to the company's performance. The higher the ratio, the more expensive the stock is and the less likely it will do well. Graham considered only companies with P/Es of less than 15. That would have protected him from the blow-up in high-P/E real estate stocks in 2008 and tech stocks back in 2000.

• **The organization's stock should be so cheap that it's unlikely to drop much more.** Graham tried to estimate what a company would be worth if it were sold off to a private investor. Today, many stock analysts and brokerage firms provide similar assessments of a stock's "fair value." But since fair value depends on numerous assumptions that could be inaccurate, Graham always required a big margin of safety. He considered only stocks selling far below their fair value, often 30% to 70% less. By paying just $50 for a stock that he thought was worth $100, Graham allowed for unforeseeable events that could alter the business landscape.

MOST ATTRACTIVE STOCKS ACCORDING TO THE GRAHAM PORTFOLIO METHOD

• **Archer Daniels Midland (ADM)** is one of the world's largest processors of wheat, soybeans and other agricultural commodities

175

and a leading manufacturer of corn sweeteners and ethanol.

Recent share price: $30.05.

Why Benjamin Graham would like it: The company has no significant long-term debt repayment due in the next few years. Its expansion into emerging markets will drive growth.

●**Jakks Pacific (JAKK)** produces brand-name toys, such as SpongeBob SquarePants and Hannah Montana dolls, as well as NASCAR toy racing cars, and related products. Its largest customers include Target, Toys "R" Us and Walmart.

Recent share price: $14.39.

Why Benjamin Graham would like it: Jakks has been busy slashing costs to bolster profits and its management has proven adept at finding new blockbuster toys.

●**Magellan Health Services (MGLN)** is one of the nation's largest providers of behavioral health-management services through its network of psychiatrists and psychologists.

Recent share price: $43.88.

Why Benjamin Graham would like it: Magellan is in excellent financial health, and its expansion into radiology and pharmaceutical management should generate strong cash flow in the coming years.

●**Tidewater (TDW)** now operates the largest global fleet of maritime supply vessels, primarily used by offshore energy production firms.

Recent share price: $39.01.

Why Benjamin Graham would like it: Investors are wary of the drop in global energy demand and the company's need to upgrade its aging vessels in the future, so they have pushed the stock price down. Tidewater's P/E ratio is just 8.25 despite the company's exceptionally strong balance sheet and strong position in its sector. It should be able to ride out the slump.

Two Important Market Indicators to Watch

Gerald Appel, president of Signalert Corporation, an investment advisory firm in Great Neck, New York, that manages $225 million for investors. The author or coauthor of more than 15 investment books, he is regarded as one of the patriarchs of technical market analysis.

Marvin Appel, PhD, vice president of Signalert and editor of the market-timing newsletter *Systems & Forecasts*, *www.systemsandforecasts.com*. Marvin, who's Gerald's son, has been a financial consultant to the New York State Legislature.

They are coauthors of *Beating the Market, 3 Months at a Time* (FT Press).

Two simple short-term measurements have proved to be very effective and reliable indicators of the risks associated with investing in the stock market. Following these indicators isn't a way to get rich quick. *But, they can help save you from being too optimistic and getting burned or being too fearful and missing out on potential profits...*

●**10-day high-low average.** This indicator measures the number of New York Stock Exchange stocks hitting new 52-week highs in price divided by the total number making new 52-week highs and lows.

Example: If 100 stocks reach their highest prices of the past year and nine hit their lowest, then the high-low average would be 92% (100 ÷ 109)—where we were recently, down from 99% in early 2009.

Why it is useful: You want to be heavily in the stock market whenever this indicator is rising and hits 90% or more. That's because more and more stocks are participating in the rally, investors are pouring money into the market and it is gaining strength. However, when the indicator drops below 80%, it has historically been a good time to reduce your positions.

You can find these figures each day at *The Wall Street Journal* online market data center (at *www.wsj.com*, click on "Markets," "Market Data Center" then under "US Stocks," click on "New Highs & Lows").

●**VIX.** This is the ticker symbol for the Chicago Board Options Exchange Volatility Index, which is a popular measure of how much fear investors have about the future direction of the S&P 500.

When a large number of traders become fearful and sell indiscriminately, VIX levels rise. The index hit an all-time intra-day high of 89.53 on October 24, 2008. When market conditions improve, stock price movements generally become more orderly and the index declines. The end points of market declines are frequently signaled when the index rises to very high levels, perhaps 40 to 45 or more, and then turn down, indicating a reduction in market instability.

Why it is useful: A gradual decline from levels in the 20s or higher down to levels of 20 or below usually indicates a more stable stock market and may be a bullish signal. However, if the VIX declines to very low levels, perhaps 10 to 12, this often is an indication that investors have become too complacent, and it may be a bearish sign for stocks.

Example: The VIX dropped to as low as 10 in 2007, just a few months before the start of the 2008–2009 bear market. The VIX has been between 18 and 30 (except for the brief spike to 46 in May 2010), which generally indicates a stable market. Investors should get nervous if the VIX drops again to 10 to 12 or rises above 30.

See the latest VIX at *www.cboe.com/VIX.*

Get a Second Opinion

Get a second opinion on investments if you aren't comfortable with your broker's recommendations. Financial professionals often have differing views. It's best to go to a planner who charges a flat fee or hourly rate—as opposed to a broker, who could be compensated on commission. Find a planner through *www.acaplanners.org* or *www.garrettplanning network.com.* A one-time assessment is likely to cost a few hundred dollars.*

George Mannes, senior writer at *Money,* Time-Life Bldg., Rockefeller Center, New York City 10020.

*Price subject to change.

Those Shocking CEO Salaries Can Tell You Which Stocks NOT to Buy

Graef Crystal, leading expert on executive compensation for 50 years. He was director of compensation for General Dynamics and Pfizer and headed the world-wide compensation consulting practice at Towers Perrin. Crystal was a professor at the University of California at Berkeley's Haas School of Business and wrote a syndicated column for *Bloomberg News.* He writes about executive compensation at *www.graefcrystal.com.*

The Obama administration is trying to crack down on pay packages for corporate executives, saying that runaway compensation too often does not reflect shareholders' wishes and frequently encourages excessive risk-taking.

My research over five decades goes a step further, providing evidence that outsized salaries and bonuses often cause executives to focus more on their own needs than on shareholders' needs...to focus on short-term gains rather than long-term goals...and to take steps that can hurt a company's stock market performance. As an investor, it would be wise for you to consider executive compensation as one of the key factors when deciding whether to buy or continue to own a stock.

WHAT THEY'RE PAID

To find out a CEO's compensation, go to *www.forbes.com/ceos* or *http://toomuchonline. org/executive-pay-scorecard.* For more detailed information, go to the company's Web site or to *http://secwatch.com* to obtain a copy of the company's proxy statement (Form DEF 14A). It details the compensation for the CEO and other highly paid executives, including base salaries...bonuses...and payments of company stock and nonstock incentives. In some cases, the statement lists executive compensation at other companies so you can compare.

KEY QUESTIONS

Check how closely CEO pay is linked to performance. *I realize that not everyone has the time to analyze SEC documents, but at the very least, get the answers to these two questions...*

• **Is the award of any stock shares and bonuses contingent upon meeting specific financial targets and goals?** Some part of the CEO's pay should be based on performance to give him/her incentive.

• **Was the CEO rewarded with pay raises and/or bigger bonuses over a period when the stock price was down?** I don't mind if a CEO earns a ton of money for long-term, exemplary performance, but the operative word is "earn."

The wrong answer to either of these questions may be a strong indication that the CEO does not put investors' interests first and that the board of directors is doing a poor job.

Example: Six Flags operates the world's largest regional theme parks. Although it aggressively acquired theme parks throughout the late 1990s and early 2000s and took on crushing debt, it still was a viable enterprise, drawing 25 million visitors a year and generating $1 billion in annual revenue.

Many investors expected CEO Mark Shapiro to turn around the company's sagging fortunes when he came on board in 2005. He sought to clean up the parks and add family-focused attractions, such as Thomas the Tank Engine and Looney Tunes rides. By the end of 2008, however, the stock had lost 98% of its value, falling to less than $1 per share, and it was delisted from the New York Stock Exchange. The company's debt had risen to $2.3 billion.

So what happened to Shapiro? Despite the company's dismal outlook, the board of directors approved a bonus of $3 million in April 2009, saying that Shapiro had exceeded every operational goal in the past three years.

Upshot: In June 2009, Six Flags filed for Chapter 11 bankruptcy protection, likely wiping out its shareholders. That's not my definition of success.

POSITIVE SIGNS

Although there are many criteria to consider before buying any stock—including the stock's performance over various periods of time, its price-to-earnings ratio (P/E) and potential earnings growth—executive compensation programs that align the CEO's interests with those of company shareholders can be a very positive sign.

Each of these companies deserves an "A" for CEO compensation policies and practices...

• **Best Buy Co., Inc. (BBY).** Former CEO Bradley Anderson's pay rose and fell with Best Buy's fortunes over his seven years in the job, until he retired recently.

Example: During 2008, when the stock dropped by 46% and the company cut jobs and offered buyouts for corporate staff, the value of Anderson's payment package dropped by 60%. He was given a salary of $1.25 million, with no stock options, and he did not qualify for a performance-based bonus. The wise compensation policies will continue now that Brian Dunn, the former chief operating officer who began as a salesclerk at Best Buy nearly 24 years ago, has taken over as CEO. Dunn is counting on a continued focus on customer service to distinguish the consumer electronics chain—which benefited from the shutdown of Circuit City—from competitors.

Recent share price: $33.14.*

• **Costco Wholesale Corp. (COST).** CEO James Sinegal, whose tenure stretches back 26 years, was paid just $350,000 plus an $80,000 bonus and 50,000 new shares (worth $3 million) in 2008. This is a modest pay package for a company this successful, and Sinegal deserves every penny because Costco's annualized returns over the past 10 years beat the Standard & Poor's 500 stock index by about four percentage points annually.

Recent share price: $55.31.

• **Gilead Sciences, Inc. (GILD).** John Martin, PhD, CEO for 13 years at this biotech company that develops therapies for infectious diseases, was paid a $1.15 million salary and a $1.65 million bonus in 2008. His compensation is a great bargain for shareholders, who've enjoyed 10-year annualized returns of 27.9% from Gilead Sciences. Martin's pay incentives challenge him to improve company performance.

Recent share price: $34.31.

• **Nordstrom, Inc. (JWN).** Blake Nordstrom, who has been CEO of this high-end retailer for nine years, was paid a salary of only $700,000 and no bonus in 2008, although he also was

*Prices as of August 13, 2010.

awarded 51,847 shares in stock options worth $790,000 at the time. This package is appropriate considering that in the fiscal year that ended January 31, 2009, the company's revenue and earnings dropped sharply amid the retail slump, and the stock plunged 66% (it has since bounced back). Even though this is a family-run business, the CEO runs it with great regard for shareholder welfare. Executives cannot cash in their stock options for at least three years after receiving them and then only if the company's stock returns beat a majority of its retail peers.

Recent share price: $31.05.

Red Flags in Financial Filings

Phrases such as "change in revenue recognition" and "change in depreciation period" in a company's financial filings can indicate an attempt to improve results artificially. Also, unusual definitions of common financial phrases can affect an investor's perception of performance. And, be especially suspicious of phrases such as "substantial doubt" and "materially and adversely affected," which can mean that a company has a severe problem.

What to do: Read financial statements and SEC filings very carefully, paying special attention to footnotes and definitions.

David Trainer, president, New Constructs, a financial-research firm in Brentwood, Tennessee, *www.newconstructs.com*.

Six Stocks to Own for The Next 20 Years

Robert Zagunis, a principal at Jensen Investment Management, Inc., Portland, Oregon. He is comanager of the large-cap growth fund The Jensen Portfolio (JENSX), *www.jenseninvestment.com*.

It used to be that cautious investors could buy shares in powerful companies with seemingly bright outlooks and hold them for many years without worrying. But in these volatile times, it often seems that "buy and run for cover" has replaced the strategy of "buy and hold." Stock prices and dividends of companies ranging from industrial legends General Electric and General Motors to financial giants Citigroup and Bank of America have been crushed. The sectors that are in or out of favor change at lightning speed.

But there is a new generation of blue chips that can withstand today's challenges and that you can count on for 10 years, 20 years and maybe more. *How to choose the best of them…*

THEY HAVE THREE KEY TRAITS

I still believe that holding a good stock for a decade or more is the best strategy for individual investors. Less turnover (trading in and out of stocks) means fewer market-timing mistakes, lower transaction costs and, in taxable accounts, less of a tax headache every year.

But it will take many years for our current economy and financial system to recuperate. That means it's even more important now to select the stocks of companies that can withstand today's turbulence and thrive in years to come, as I do with the fund I manage. *The traits I look for in companies…*

• **Each is a highly profitable cash cow.** Businesses that generate large and predictable amounts of extra cash won't have to take on heavy debt in today's unfriendly capital markets to keep growing. The easiest way to identify these companies is with a financial measurement called return on equity (ROE). This measure indicates how effectively a company uses its assets to generate profits. I consider only firms that have had ROEs of 15% or greater for the past 10 years. To find the ROE of any company, go to *http://moneycentral.msn.com*. Type in the ticker symbol, then click on "Key Ratios" (under "Financial Results") and then "Ten Year Summary." You can also find lists of stocks with high ROE on Morningstar.com's "Premium Screener."

• **Each is able to adjust and do well whether the economy is up or down.** That weeds out the cyclical businesses whose stocks may excel in a growing economy but that struggle in a recession. An all-weather company often uses periods of economic distress, such as the current recession, to gain market share.

•**Each has a strong and enduring edge over its rivals.** A company may have patents that give it a competitive advantage…or it may be able to produce a product at a lower price than anyone else…or its customers may stay loyal because it's too difficult and costly for them to switch.

Requiring these three key traits cuts down on volatility in a portfolio and it eliminates 98% of stocks—including those whose prices are inflated by bubbles, such as the Internet stocks that soared in the mid- to late 1990s only to burst a few years later.

MY SIX FAVORITE STOCKS

Companies with all three key traits…

1. Abbott Laboratories (ABT). One of the world's largest manufacturers of health-care products and pharmaceuticals, it has a wide selection of patent-protected drugs, including Humira (to treat arthritis). Although growth in sales of this best-selling drug has slowed because of the economy, and the stock's price has decreased this year, Abbott's consistent profits are prized by investors. Healthy cash flows have let it increase its dividends for 38 years in a row.

Biggest risk: The expiration of patents on blockbuster drugs and increasing competition from the generic drug industry. Abbott has muted this risk by developing other lucrative products, including nutritionals and those that advance the treatment of vascular disease.

Recent share price: $50.06.*

More information: 847-937-6100 or *www. abbott.com.*

2. Adobe Systems Inc. (ADBE). The graphics software that Adobe provides, including Photoshop, Adobe PDF and Flash, is installed on hundreds of millions of computers around the world and is used to create much of the content we see in print and on the Internet. Adobe is very well positioned to profit from emerging long-term trends in technology, including the increased use of handheld devices and the growth of Internet advertising, Web conferencing and digital cameras.

*Prices as of August 13, 2010.

Biggest risk: Other tech giants developing competing products. Microsoft considered including an Adobe-like program in its most recent version of *MS Office*, but it backed off after Adobe threatened legal action.

Recent share price: $28.01.

More information: 800-833-6687 or *www. adobe.com.*

3. Equifax Inc. (EFX). One of the three major credit-tracking services in the US, Equifax provides information to help credit issuers make lending decisions. Equifax, Experian and TransUnion face little threat of further competition. They also offer identity-fraud protection services and programs to help customers keep their credit records clean. Equifax is the only one of the three that trades primarily on a US stock exchange.

Biggest risk: The US credit market is a mature one, and demand for credit scores may decline over the coming years if fewer loans are made. Equifax will counter this possible slowdown by establishing bureaus in foreign markets where credit scoring has enormous growth potential.

Recent share price: $30.20.

More information: *www.equifax.com.*

4. PepsiCo (PEP). One of the world's largest beverage and snack companies, its brands encompass Pepsi-Cola, Lays potato chips and Doritos corn chips. The company has raised dividends for the past 38 years, including a 7% increase in 2010. PepsiCo's powerful distribution network to stores (it controls 60% of the US snack market) and its ability to adapt to recent consumer trends (healthier, baked snacks…ready-to-drink coffees) will keep it profitable for decades.

Biggest risk: PepsiCo has not been able to displace cola market leader Coca-Cola. However, it has gained more control of the noncola market with the help of its Gatorade and Tropicana brands and recently bought its two largest bottlers for about $6 billion, which gives it greater control of distribution.

Recent share price: $65.56.

More information: 914-253-2000 or *www. pepsico.com.*

5. Praxair Inc. (PX). The dominant supplier of industrial gases in North America and South America, it provides oxygen, hydrogen and other gases for manufacturing products in the aerospace, food, health-care, chemicals and oil industries. Praxair signs its customers to long-term contracts (typically for 15 to 20 years) with clauses that allow it to raise prices if its raw material costs increase. Because industrial gas is a critical component for these customers, Praxair almost always gets paid on time.

Biggest risk: The weakening US economy could damage Praxair, but the company has reduced its dependence on North American revenue to 55% of its total from 65% and is expected to grow quickly in the emerging markets of China and India.

Recent share price: $87.29.

More information: 800-772-9247 or *www. praxair.com.*

6. Stryker Corporation (SYK). As one of the leading medical-equipment makers in the world, it specializes in high-profit orthopedic implants for knees, hips and spines. Stryker is a small company with many specialized patents. The aging of the baby boom population will enable Stryker to raise its prices substantially and increase earnings and cash flow at a double-digit rate for many years to come. Stryker has almost $4 billion in cash.

Biggest risk: Health insurance firms that resist price increases for orthopedic treatment and surgeries. But Stryker is using all its relationships with hospitals and doctors to ramp up its secondary business in operating-room equipment, hospital beds and other medical furniture.

Recent share price: $46.57.

More information: 269-385-2600 or *www. stryker.com.*

Foreign Stocks Are Up And Heading Higher: Experts' Favorite Picks

James Moffett, CFA, executive vice president, Scout Investment Advisors, Kansas City, Missouri. Moffett is also lead portfolio manager of the Scout International Fund (UMBWX), whose 10-year annualized returns of 3.7% put it in the top 11% of all large-cap foreign stock funds, according to Morningstar, Inc. Check out *www. scout-ia.com.*

Leonard Goodall, PhD, CFP, coeditor of the monthly financial newsletter *No-Load Portfolios*, which offers model portfolios of US and foreign mutual funds, Las Vegas. It is one of the top-performing newsletters focused on mutual funds tracked by *The Hulbert Financial Digest* over the past 10 years, increasing 4.8% per year, on average, compared with a loss of 0.9% for the Wilshire 5000 stock index. He formerly was chancellor of University of Michigan, Ann Arbor, and president of University of Nevada, Las Vegas.

I n 2008, investors fled from what seemed like some of the riskiest parts of the world, sending many overseas stock markets sliding even more sharply than US markets.

Recently, numerous investors have regained their appetite for foreign risk and global diversification, seeing a greater potential for economic growth and market gains overseas than in the US. A key index of stocks in emerging markets, including countries such as Brazil, Russia, India and China, has increased 12.9% for the year ending August 27, 2010, compared with a gain of 5.3% for the Standard & Poor's Index of 500 US stocks. However, a key index of stocks in foreign countries overall has fallen 9.7% due to concerns about large fiscal deficits in Greece and other euro-zone countries.

To help you decide what role foreign stocks should play in your portfolio now, check out what two top authorities on global investing have to say…

FOREIGN STOCKS
James Moffett, CFA

Although global stock markets may move in similar directions over the short run, investors will see less and less correlation with the US market over the next 15 years, providing the potential for greater diversification. I expect more robust economic expansion and greater stock increases in countries where few people now have cars, cell phones or even TVs than in the US. And with the US likely to face years of high inflation and heavy debts because of the federal government's massive spending to stimulate the economy, the dollar will sink in relation to foreign currencies. That will help foreign companies, whose profits and stock prices look stronger when converted to weak US dollars.

The key to success in foreign investing isn't to try to hit home runs. Too many investors feel compelled to buy supercharged stocks of companies in the riskiest countries with the fastest-growing economies, such as China and Russia, which do not treat their shareholders as fairly as the developed markets.

The reality is that your overseas portfolio doesn't need a lot of razzle-dazzle to do well. I focus on undervalued, large-cap companies, with strong balance sheets and stable long-term growth potential, that I can hold for at least five years. I also avoid too much risk by limiting my direct exposure to emerging markets. Instead, I invest in the big beneficiaries of Chinese, Russian and Latin American growth.

My favorite foreign stocks now...

•**AmBev (ABV)** is Brazil's largest beverage company, distributing beer brands including Brahma and soft drinks such as the very popular Guaraná and PepsiCo products throughout Latin America. The company—whose management runs it very efficiently—produces a very high core operating profit margin.

Recent share price: $104.31.*

•**Enbridge Inc. (ENB)** is a Canadian pipeline company that transports oil and natural gas to millions of customers in Canada and the US. It derives its oil supply from Alberta's oil sands, the largest oil reserves in the world outside of Saudi Arabia. The company offers steady cash flow, and the stock's recent dividend yield was 3.5%. The stock's annualized return over the past 10 years was 18%.

Recent share price: $48.82.

•**Ericsson Telephone Co. (ERIC)** is the world's leading maker of infrastructure equipment for mobile communications. The Swed-

*Prices and rates as of August 13, 2010.

ish company has the highest profit margins in the industry and a solid balance sheet. The voracious appetite for broadband wireless in China and India will drive record demand in the coming decade.

Recent share price: $10.42.

•**Fresenius Medical Care AG & Co. (FMS)** is the world's largest dialysis company, offering services and products in more than 100 countries. Dialysis helps remove toxins and waste from the blood of patients who suffer from kidney problems. The German company is in one of my preferred global investment sectors—nonpharmaceutical health care. This sector has enormous growth potential as more and more patients in developing nations gain access to treatments, but it doesn't bear the heavy research costs or patent risks of drug manufacturers.

Recent share price: $55.89.

•**Nidec Corporation (NJ)** is a leading Japanese manufacturer of small precision motors and electronic instruments that power products ranging from automatic windows and antilock brakes in automobiles to hard drives in iPods. The company has begun a major push into the Chinese market.

Recent share price: $21.19.

MUTUAL FUNDS
Leonard Goodall, PhD, CFP

My favorite foreign stock funds now...

•**Vanguard FTSE All-World ex-US Index Fund (VFWIX),** launched back in March 2007, continues the Vanguard tradition of providing convenient, diversified exposure to stocks at ultralow costs. Unlike most foreign stock index funds, this one includes both an emerging-markets stake and exposure to Canada. With more than 2,000 stocks, it should be everyone's core foreign stock holding. The fund is up 2.8% for the year ending August 27, 2010.

Expense ratio: 0.40%.

More information: 800-523-7731, *www.vanguard.com.*

•**Oakmark International Fund (OAKIX)** has one of the best long-term records of any actively managed foreign stock fund. All their managers take a careful approach, focusing on stocks that they believe to be big bargains, but they are willing to invest in any country and in any size company where they can find the bargains.

Performance: 5.03%, annualized returns for the five years through August 27, 2010.

Expense ratio: 1.17%.

More information: 800-625-6275, *www.oak mark.com*.

• **The T. Rowe Price Latin America Fund (PRLAX).** If you already have ample international coverage overall but want to be more aggressive about profiting during the global economic recovery, this is the best fund covering a booming region. It offers a modest expense ratio of 1.29% and a seasoned staff of analysts. The fund is dominated by Mexican and Brazilian blue-chip firms, such as wireless telecommunications giant América Móvil and the energy company Brazilian Petroleum Corporation.

Performance: 21.44%, annualized returns for the five years through August 27, 2010.

Expense ratio: 1.9%.

More information: 800-638-5660, *www. troweprice.com*.

Allocation for the Global Recovery

In the coming global recovery, non-US countries, especially countries in the developing world, will grow much faster than the US, and stock market returns in emerging markets will outperform US returns. For the stock portion of an investor's portfolio, I recommend 30% to 35% US securities and 60% to 65% non-US—with up to a quarter of the total portfolio invested in China, Asia (but not Japan), South Korea, Hong Kong and Brazil.

Best: Use either exchange-traded funds or mutual funds to invest in these countries.

Allen Sinai, PhD, chief global economist, Decision Economics, Inc., New York City. Log on to *www.deci sioneconomics.com* for more information.

How to Buy Shares In a Private Company Before It Goes Public

Nancy Dunnan, a New York City–based financial and travel adviser and author or coauthor of 25 books, including *How to Invest $50–$5,000* (HarperCollins).

Shares from privately held companies are unavailable to the public, but employees sometimes have the option of buying in.

Advantage: If you buy shares in a privately held company and it later goes public, you stand to make a lot of money.

There is an online service, SharesPost (*www. sharespost.com*), that matches private companies that want to sell shares (typically to raise cash) with investors who want to buy.

Disadvantages: There is no ready market for selling shares you've bought—usually they must be sold back to the corporation or to other shareholders. You also don't know what a privately held company's shares are worth.

To buy or sell shares, you must be an "accredited" investor, defined by the SEC as a person who has individual net worth, or joint net worth with one's spouse, that exceeds $1 million...or any person with income exceeding $200,000 in each of the two most recent years or joint income with a spouse exceeding $300,000 for those years.

At SharesPost, you can do a free search for organizations with shares for sale.* For a $34 monthly fee, you can post your own listings to buy shares and download company documents. The minimum purchase or sale is set at $25,000.

If you are interested in buying shares of any of the private companies listed, have your lawyer or accountant review the documents and purchase contracts.

*Offer and prices subject to change.

Tricks for Getting Better Prices on Stocks

Sheryl Garrett, CFP, founder of Garrett Planning Network, a network of fee-only financial advisers, Shawnee Mission, Kansas, *www.garrettplanningnetwork.com*. She is coauthor of *Just Give Me the Answers: Expert Advisors Address Your Most Pressing Financial Questions* (Kaplan Business).

Buying low and selling high is the big goal with stocks, but unfortunately, we sometimes end up doing just the opposite. Knowledgeable investors use several automated tricks to help improve their odds. *How these tricks can help you...*

PICKING WHEN TO BUY

A buy-limit order allows you to automatically buy shares of a stock if and when they hit a predetermined price. Stocks often fluctuate 1% to 2% within a day, and fast-moving stocks can drop by as much as 3% to 4% before bouncing back. A buy limit can help you catch the lower end of the price range.

Example: Last year, I decided to invest in Citigroup. I observed that the stock's trading range had moved between $1.17 and $1.70. I put in a buy-limit order for $1.20 per share, which saved me as much as 50 cents a share. That can add up if you are buying hundreds or thousands of shares. Citigroup was recently $3.88 a share.* Of course, if a stock price is shooting straight up day after day, this trick doesn't work, but that's rarely the case.

What to do: Go to *http://finance.yahoo.com*, type in the symbol of the stock you want and you'll see the high and low share-price range for that day. Or if you are dealing with a broker, ask him/her for the day's range. Choose a buy-limit price a few cents higher than the low of the day.

Reason: Stocks often approach their lows of the day and then turn back up. You often will miss executing your order if you set it at or below the low of the day. Use a buy-limit order only if you are willing to miss out on buying the shares altogether—otherwise use a straight

*As of August 13, 2010.

184

market order, which means that you will buy immediately.

PICKING WHEN TO SELL

A stop-loss order permits you to automatically sell shares of a stock if they drop to a predetermined price.

Example: I had a client who bought Bank of America stock in October 2008 for $20 per share. It rebounded to nearly $25 per share, and many investors thought it had avoided the worst of the financial-sector meltdown. But my client wanted to protect some of his profits, so he set a stop-loss order for $22 per share. By March 2009, Bank of America had plummeted to $3 a share. My client had turned a potential catastrophe into a small profit.

What to do: I generally set stop-loss orders at 10% below my purchase price for stable, blue-chip large-caps...20% for smaller or more volatile stocks. This strikes a reasonable balance between not selling on every short-term market swing...and cutting my losses before they really damage my portfolio.

If I put a stop-loss order on a stock and the price rises, I reset my order with my broker every time the stock goes up by 10% or 20% above my initial price.

Example: I bought Google at $380 per share in February 2009 with a stop-loss order of $312. The stock rose to $470 per share by September. I expected it to go higher but wanted to protect my downside, so I set a new stop-loss order for 20% below $470, or $376.

TIME LIMITS

For both the buy limit and the stop loss, you need to indicate the time limit that your order will be in effect. A good-till-canceled order stays in effect until it is executed or until it reaches a specified time limit, which some brokers cap at 30 days. A day order keeps your order in effect only during that trading day, in case you want to reconsider your instructions the next day.

When to Sell a Stock in a Tricky Market

Patrick Dorsey, CFA, director of equity research for Morningstar, Inc., in Chicago, which tracks more than 290,000 investment offerings, *www.morningstar.com*. He is author of *The Little Book That Builds Wealth: The Knockout Formula for Finding Great Investments* (Wiley).

The recession and market losses might make you want to jettison your entire stock portfolio.

Smarter move: Distinguish between stocks with a bleak long-term outlook and those that are likely to rebound. *How to decide when it's time to pull the plug on or pare back a stock you own...*

• **When the changing business landscape undermines the company's competitive advantage.** This could be because of a shift in technology, consumer preferences or government regulation.

Example: Garmin (GRMN) used to thrive as the big leader in mobile global positioning system (GPS) devices, but now other devices, such as cell phones, provide GPS capability in a more convenient and cheaper form, and Garmin is not a leader in that highly competitive arena.

• **When your stock's dividend yield rises to unsustainable levels.** Companies whose dividend is yielding more than 9% or 10% of the share price rarely sustain the dividend. Either the stock goes back up, which means that the yield for new purchasers drops, or more commonly, the dividend is reduced or eliminated. If a major reason for owning the stock was the dividend it threw off, replace it with a stock that has a more stable dividend.

Example: Eastman Kodak Company (EK). Its dividend yield was around 11% when it announced in April 2009 that it was suspending its dividend.

• **You want to upgrade the quality of your portfolio.** Say you own shares in a small technology company whose stock price has been crushed over the past year. Consider selling the stock and buying shares in a high-qual-

ity tech company, such as Cisco Systems, Inc. (CSCO), which is trading at bargain prices. High-quality tech companies don't sell at bargain-basement prices very often, so it's worth taking advantage of the opportunity.

• **When any stock holding grows beyond a certain percentage of your portfolio.** For safety and diversification, it is smart to limit your stake in any stock to 5% of the value of your stock holdings.

Example: Walmart (WMT) stock was up 20% in 2009 while the Standard & Poor's 500 stock index sank 37%. That performance by Walmart could have increased its allocation in your portfolio beyond the limit you set for it.

When to Dump Your Mutual Fund—and How To Pick a Much Better One

Adam Bold, founder of the Mutual Fund Store, an investment advisory firm located in Overland Park, Kansas, *www.mutualfundstore.com*. It is a nationwide network of investment advisers who oversee more than $3 billion on behalf of 25,000 investors. Bold is author of *The Bold Truth About Investing: Ten Commandments for Building Wealth* (Ten Speed).

Ordinarily, I would sell any fund that vaporized 40% of my money in a year. But nowadays, that kind of dizzying dive is the norm rather than the exception. So, how do you decide whether to fire a fund that you had considered one of the keys to your financial future? *My rules...*

WHEN TO DUMP A FUND

The reason that you bought a fund may no longer exist if the manager has changed his/her approach...or that approach is not what you thought it was...or you got in because the fund was hot and now it's about to turn dangerously cold. *Dump the fund immediately if...*

• **It does not fit your risk tolerance.** Many investors who do not think of themselves as aggressive included Legg Mason Value Trust (LMVTX) as a core holding in their portfolios.

They did so even though its legendary manager, Bill Miller, liked to buy volatile growth stocks. That risk was easy to accept when Miller beat the Standard & Poor's 500 stock index 15 years in a row (1991 through 2005). But in recent years, his aggressiveness has cost shareholders dearly. The fund lost 23.7% per year, on average, from the beginning of 2006 through 2008, compared with an 8.4% loss for the S&P 500. The fund beat the S&P 500 by 14% in 2009, but Miller shows few signs of toning down his style.

Alternative: A core large-cap value fund should offer cautious consistency with the potential to beat the S&P 500 Index over long periods. The Wasatch-1st Source Income Equity Fund (FMIEX) may not soar in bull markets, but it has controlled losses more effectively than Miller's fund in bear markets.

Performance: 2.47%, annualized returns for the five years through August 13, 2010.

More information: 800-551-1700, *www. wasatchfunds.com.*

The fund ranks in the top 1% of its category for the past five-year and 10-year periods.

• **Ballooning assets lead to significant underperformance.** Dodge & Cox is a relatively small investment firm that shuns publicity and advertising. Its flagship stock fund, Dodge & Cox Stock Fund (DODGX), swelled to nearly $66 billion in assets because it beat the S&P 500 by an average of more than 11 percentage points annually between 2000 and 2006. The fund used the cash influx to build up staggeringly large positions in financial industry stocks, such as AIG, Fannie Mae and Wachovia. When all those stocks imploded in 2008, smaller mutual funds were nimble enough to get out and limit the damage. Because of the large numbers of shares it is selling, a big fund may take weeks to unwind any losing investments. Dodge & Cox was also forced to quickly sell stocks just to meet redemptions from fleeing shareholders. The fund is still chunky with $38.1 billion in assets as of August 13, 2010. Don't wait any longer. Cut it loose.

• **You purchased the fund as its bubble was about to burst.** It can be very dangerous to pile into last year's big winners—that's often when they are likely to turn into losers.

Example: In 2008, many investors went into long-term Treasury securities because they are backed by the federal government. That popularity pushed interest rates on new Treasuries way down and pushed up the value of older Treasuries, making funds that held them one of the only bright spots of 2008. The Vanguard Long-Term US Treasury Fund (VUSTX) returned 22.5% in 2008 and lost 12% in 2009. And the Wasatch-Hoisington US Treasury Fund (WHOSX) returned 37.8% in 2008, but it fell 22.6% in 2009. If interest rates rise further, the funds could see more double-digit losses. It's time to get out if you haven't done so already.

WHEN TO WAIT BEFORE YOU DUMP

In certain cases, you would be wise to keep a close eye on any underperforming fund you own but not dump it immediately. *Watch it closely if…*

• **It fails to outperform its benchmark index and/or 50% of its fund peers over a two-year period.** After it fails this test, I will watch the fund especially closely for the next 12 months and read the manager's quarterly reports to understand why it is underperforming. I'll sell the fund after this one-year period if its performance continues to fall short of its benchmark or falls behind half its peers.

For instance, the S&P 500 Index is the benchmark for large-cap US stock funds and the Russell 2000 Index for small-cap US stock funds. If an actively managed fund that you own consistently fails to beat its benchmark, switch funds. It does not cost any more to own a good fund than a bad one. Also, if my fund has fallen behind half of its peers, that means there are lots of better fund managers out there who are more deserving of my money. Check relative performance for various periods at Morningstar.com by entering your fund's symbol in the search box, clicking "Search" and then clicking "Performance."

• **A new fund manager takes over.** I believe that the fund horse race is all about the jockey. Performance is unlikely to remain the same if the manager leaves, even when the replacement is an experienced manager with a similar style.

Example: The First Eagle Overseas Fund (SGOVX) and First Eagle Global Fund (SGENX) were run by one of the world's great investors, Jean-Marie Eveillard, starting in 1993. In March 2009, he retired and was replaced by a pair of junior managers whom he trained. It will be difficult to mimic Eveillard's winning formula, which over the years mixed cheap foreign and US value stocks with gold. Through spring of 2010, neither fund's returns were in the upper 20% of funds in their categories. I would sell.

Bond Investors Beware

Financial peril is greatest in 10 states. The Pew Center on the States, a nonprofit research organization, has created a list of states that face pressures similar to those that have threatened California's fiscal solvency.

Hardest-hit states, in addition to California: Arizona, Rhode Island, Michigan, Oregon, Nevada, Florida, New Jersey, Illinois and Wisconsin (*www.pewcenteronthestates.org/beyond california*).

What you can do: Municipal bond investors should shift away from states and municipalities with the weakest credit ratings, according to George Friedlander, a veteran muni bond analyst at MorganStanley SmithBarney. In a recent report, he recommends "a gradual restructuring" of muni portfolios toward bonds with higher credit ratings…bonds from states other than the one you live in for geographical diversification…and bonds funded by revenue from essential services. He says that budgetary pressures at the state and local level are going to be quite severe during the next two years, at the very least, and that there are likely to be some defaults on bond payments. But he adds that it is unlikely that defaults will be widespread.

Cash In Matured Savings Bonds

More than 40 million Series E savings bonds that are over 30 years old and worth more than $16 billion no longer pay interest but remain outstanding. If any belong to you or your family, you can redeem them for cash.

Helpful: The new Treasury Hunt Web site (*www.treasuryhunt.gov*) will let you find expired savings bonds issued in 1974 or later through its searchable database of bonds registered to Social Security numbers. (Bonds issued before then weren't registered to Social Security numbers.) The site also contains useful information about what to do regarding lost and/or matured bonds.

Bob Carlson, editor, *Bob Carlson's Retirement Watch*, Oxon Hill, Maryland, *www.retirementwatch.com*.

A Golden Opportunity

Gold is still attractive even at more than $1,000 per ounce.* Central bankers and politicians around the globe are under pressure to print more money to solve debt problems. That would increase inflation, a good environment for gold. Plus, many experienced investors are now viewing gold not just as a hedge against inflation, but also as a partial replacement for the US dollar as a "reserve currency" if the dollar continues to lose sway—no actual currency is an obvious substitute. Traditionally, conservative investors have thought in terms of 2% to 5% gold holdings. Now, with our debt- and deficit-plagued economy, it's prudent for older US investors to hold up to 10% of their portfolios in gold.

Easiest way: SPDRS Gold Trust (GLD), an exchange-traded fund (ETF).

Robert H. Stovall, CFA, managing director, Wood Asset Management, Inc., Sarasota, Florida, *www.wood asset.com*.

*Price as of August 13, 2010.

Real Gold vs. an ETF

Andy Sutton, founder and chief strategist for Sutton & Associates LLC, an independent investment advisory firm based in Laurys Station, Pennsylvania, *www. sutton-associates.net.*

Are there any advantages to owning gold through exchange-traded funds (ETFs) rather than real physical gold?

Owning shares of gold ETFs, which track the price of gold and trade like stocks on an exchange, is vastly different than holding real gold. If you own shares of a gold ETF, such as SPDR Gold Trust (GLD) or iShares Comex Gold Trust (IAU), you don't actually own the bullion held in depositories on behalf of the fund, and you can redeem your shares only in cash. Trading them is as easy as a click of a mouse.

If it's safety you're after, however, I recommend buying "physical" gold, as this is the ultimate insurance policy for protecting your wealth from events that could upset a paper portfolio. It's the only asset class that's not dependent on the performance of corporations, banks or governments.

Two long-running online sellers of bullion and gold coins, respectively, are Kitco (*www.*

kitco.com) and Swiss America Trading Corp. (*www.swissamerica.com*).

Note: The best place to keep your gold is in a well-secured safe in your home—with all the recent bank failures, there have been sporadic problems with people being able to access safe-deposit boxes.

Barron's Best

In *Barron's* 15th annual ranking of online brokers, top ranking went to ThinkorSwim (*www.thinkorswim.com*), which was acquired by TD Ameritrade last year and offers a variety of tools to aid investors, including a cost-basis and tax-accounting tool. It also was among those top-ranked for options trading. Fidelity (*www.fidelity.com*), which provides 25 Black-Rock/iShares exchange-traded funds (or ETFs) with no sales commission charged, was top-ranked for long-term investing.

Best-ranked for international trading: Interactive Brokers (at *www.interactivebrokers.com*), which offers access to over 80 exchanges and market centers around the world.

Barron's, 200 Liberty St, New York City 10281.

11

Shopping Savvy

Money Guru David Bach Protects You from Today's Most *Infuriating* Money Rip-Offs

oes it feel like you are getting scammed every time you open up your wallet, pay the bills or take a trip? Most companies can't raise prices during a recession because they risk driving away business. Instead, they employ all kinds of sneaky (but legal) ways to take advantage of consumers.

Result: You get gouged by hidden fees, obscure rules, misleading come-ons and billing "mistakes." *My secrets for fighting back against today's most infuriating rip-offs...*

CREDIT CARD CHICANERY

Credit card companies continue to come up with ingenious ways to get your money.

The latest: If you pay part of your bill before the due date and carry over the rest as a balance, it is logical to assume that you are charged additional interest on only the unpaid portion. But more than one-third of banks now calculate interest for the month by basing it on the account's average daily balance for the past two months. In other words, you get charged interest on money that you've already paid back!

How to fight back: Consider dumping or not using any of your cards that have this "double-billing cycle." Check the fine print of your credit card statement. Look in the disclosure box for the entry under "Method of Computing the Balance for Purchases" to see if it says something like "Two-Cycle Average Daily Balance (including new purchases)."

David Bach, founder and CEO of FinishRich.com, a financial coaching and education company in New York City. He is regularly featured on the *Today* show and is author of the best sellers *The Automatic Millionaire, Fight for Your Money* and *Start Over, Finish Rich* (all are from Broadway).

SALES TAX TRAP

In most states, the sales tax you pay on your car repair bill is applicable only to charges for the parts that your car needed and the supplies the repair shop used (for example, lubricants and rags). The labor is not taxable if it's separately stated from the repair parts on the customer's invoice.

Lazy or unscrupulous auto-service facilities may write down just one amount on the bill and charge you sales tax on that total amount. A 5% sales tax misapplied to a big job that included $1,000 of labor takes an extra $50 out of your pocket.

How to fight back: Ask that your bill contain separate charges for labor and parts/supplies. Check that sales tax is charged only on the parts/supplies portion of the bill.

HOSPITAL HIJINKS

Even well-meaning hospital staff can inadvertently jack up your bill. They make suggestions to alleviate your pain, inconvenience or worry without realizing that it will cost you more.

Examples: I knew an elderly man in intensive care who was ready to be moved into a regular room. There were no rooms available. A doctor suggested that it was a slow night in the intensive care unit (ICU) so there was no problem with the patient remaining there. The man felt grateful until he realized that additional costs had been tacked on to his bill—he got charged for spending more time in the ICU. I also heard of a frightened child who was calmed when a nurse gave him a little teddy bear. The teddy bear was billed at $57.50 as a "cough support device."

How to fight back: Be wary of simply accepting extra services from doctors or nurses that are clearly not needed—even if they imply that they're doing it as a favor. Unless you get them to call the hospital accounting department to obtain authorization for a free service, you'll likely get charged according to the usual hospital guidelines, and your insurance company may refuse to cover the additional amount.

GIFT CARD FINE PRINT

Gift cards have become much more difficult and inconvenient to redeem because of restrictions on how they can be used.

Examples: Starbucks gift cards are not accepted at many Starbucks outlets in airports, supermarkets and bookstores. Some Master-Card and Visa gift cards that you buy online charge you a $6.95 delivery fee* and you are allowed to check your balance by phone for free only twice. Many gift-card issuers won't replace the card if you lose it or they require that you know the card's ID number.

How to fight back: Sell your unused gift card for cash, or trade it for a different gift card for a comparable amount. You can now exchange or sell it online at sites such as Plastic Jungle (*www.plasticjungle.com*).

Example: Say you get a $200 Walmart card as a gift, but you don't want it. Plastic Jungle lets you cash it in for up to 92% of the verified card balance or donate it for the benefit of your favorite nonprofit organization. You can also exchange your $200 card for purchasing power at places like Amazon.com. Cards for sale or exchange must have a minimum balance of $25.

Also, understand the replacement rules for your gift card if you lose it. Make a copy of both sides of the card (and make sure the ID number is readable). Report a loss as soon as possible, because you're responsible for any transactions on the card before it's reported missing. If an issuer replaces the card, expect to pay a fee, typically $15.

REBATE HURDLES

In this economy, marketers are using rebate come-ons aggressively. These rebates are very attractive to cash-strapped consumers. So why are four out of five available rebates never redeemed? It's because the manufacturers and stores purposely make the redemption process hard.

How to fight back: When you see an advertised price, make sure that you understand any rebate offer so you can jump through all the hoops to secure your rebate. Keep the box the item came in, as well as copies of the

*Prices and rates subject to change.

receipt and all the paperwork from the rebate offer, until your check arrives. Send in your rebate materials by "certified mail with return receipt requested" if the rebate is sizable ($20 or more). That way, you have evidence that your submission was delivered if the processing company claims that it was never received. Typical cost for certified mail with return receipt is $2.25 to $5.

If you don't receive your check in the time frame promised, call the number on the rebate form and make a fuss.

If the phone call doesn't get you results, send a polite letter, with copies of the rebate material you mailed in, to the manufacturer and the store where you purchased the item.

Write: "My decision to purchase your product was based on your offer of a rebate. My purchase constituted an acceptance of that offer. If I don't receive my rebate check within 30 days, I will complain to the Federal Trade Commission and my state attorney general."

INFLATED RENTAL-CAR BILLS

Rental-car businesses count on harried travelers being too distracted to notice inflated bills.

How to fight back: Return the vehicle on time. Grace periods for late returns are shrinking. If you roll in one second past 30 minutes after the scheduled return, you may well get charged an extra day.

Use every discount available to you. For instance, membership in AAA, AARP, Costco or Sam's Club will qualify you for a 15% to 25% discount at most major rental companies. For additional coupons, visit *www.rentalcarmomma.com* and *www.rentalcodes.com*.

Don't choose the "buy a full tank of gas up front" option, since it's inevitable that you'll return the car with some gas in it, thus giving free gas to the company.

Beware of These Fees Buried in the Fine Print

Daniel S. Blinn, Esq., founder and managing attorney of Consumer Law Group LLC, in Rocky Hill, Connecticut, which represents consumers in individual and class action litigation against businesses, *www.consumerlawgroup.com*. Blinn is board president of Statewide Legal Services of Connecticut, a nonprofit organization dedicated to assisting low-income people with civil cases.

Many companies make it tough for customers to know exactly what they're getting into when they buy a product or service.

That's especially true now when financially aching firms are imposing even trickier terms. *What to look for in the fine print...*

•**Credit card issuers.** Terms buried in the fine print dictate when your attractive promotional interest rate soars to a "default" rate that can be as high as 29%. The increase may occur when you exceed your credit limit or miss or are late with even a single minimum payment.

Also buried in fine print: Late fees, extra charges for purchases from foreign countries, and what protections the company does and does not offer for theft or damage of merchandise charged on the card. Pay particular attention to rules governing cash advances, which are typically stricter than those concerning purchases.

•**Auto dealerships.** Automakers and dealers are offering some very attractive financing terms these days. However, unscrupulous dealers have been known to keep customers waiting up to six hours for loan approval so the exhausted buyer will sign a contract quickly—without realizing all that it says. Always read the contract from top to bottom and beware of phrases such as "subject to loan approval" or "subject to financing." They might mean that the seller can change your interest rate after you sign the contract.

•**Cell-phone service providers.** Cell-phone contracts do disclose that the advertised price for service bears little resemblance to what you will actually pay after various surcharges, taxes and fees are added to your bill. However, that disclosure comes in the form of an asterisk, with a little note below that says the touted price isn't the bottom line. To discover how much more you will really owe, look on the back of the contract or receipt that comes with the phone itself. Also make sure that you understand the cost of sending and receiving anything other than phone calls, such as e-mail, documents or photos.

• **Health clubs.** Many people lose their resolve a couple of months after joining a gym, so health clubs do all they can to collect or lock in payments up front. For example, the salesperson may describe a "low monthly fee" of $25 that suggests you can quit at any time, but the contract clarifies that only $5 of that amount is membership dues. The remaining $20 is an installment payment plus interest on a larger, longer-term membership charge, perhaps amounting to several hundred dollars.

How to Get VIP Customer Service

To get the best customer service, first check your pessimism at the door. Expect great service, and you probably will get it. Be sure to set the right tone from the beginning—the initial 10 seconds of interaction provides the foundation for the remainder of the encounter. Also, make salespeople feel special and empowered. For example, start your question or request with, "I really need your help, and you seem like just the person who can help me." Be forthright about your expectations to eliminate any guesswork on the salesperson's part. Be assertive, but not pushy or rude. Finally, remember that you are a customer, not a master. The salesperson's job is to provide you with a service, not to be your servant.

Chip R. Bell, Gun Barrel City, Texas, and John R. Patterson, Atlanta, customer loyalty consultants and co-authors of Take Their Breath Away: How Imaginative Service Creates Devoted Customers *(Wiley, www.take theirbreathaway.com).*

The Secret to Spending Less and Living Just As Well

Gregory Karp, whose syndicated newspaper column, "Spending Smart," reaches more than six million readers around the country. He is author of *The 1-2-3 Money Plan: The Three Most Important Steps to Saving and Spending Smart* (FT). He lives in Yardley, Pennsylvania, and his Web site is *www.gregorykarp.com.*

Living through a recession doesn't require that you become a full-time cheapskate—but you do have to budget smarter and spend purposefully rather than by accident and habit.

Bonus: By plugging up the leaks of wasteful spending, you can redirect that money to things that are very important to you.

MEDICAL

• **Medication expenses.** The prices of drugs not covered by insurance often vary widely among pharmacies, so you can save hundreds of dollars by comparison shopping. Start online at Destination Rx (*www.drx.com*), which searches for the cheapest prescription prices from pharmacies and other retailers in your area and also makes suggestions that you can discuss with your doctor about cheaper generic options. My favorite bargains come from discount retailers Walmart, Target and Sam's Club, which have expanded their discounted prescription-drug programs to provide 90-day supplies of up to 350 generics for $10 or less.*

• **Eyeglasses.** Pay as little as $8 for prescription eyeglasses, shipping included, from Zenni Optical (*www.zennioptical.com*). The site lets you choose from hundreds of different frames. While they aren't as well constructed as designer frames, they're ideal as a backup pair and to expand your eyeglass wardrobe. Another eyeglass site, EyeBuyDirect.com, has glasses for $7.95 and lets you upload a photo of yourself and "virtually" try on glasses by superimposing frames on your photo.

Important: To order, you'll need to provide your prescription (get it from your ophthalmologist or optometrist). You will also need

*Prices, offers and rates subject to change.

to know your pupillary distance (the distance between the centers of your pupils) to ensure a proper optical fit. Your optometrist should be able to give you that number, but most online retailers also provide instructions for measuring it yourself.

TELECOMMUNICATION

•**Cable "triple-plays."** So many telecommunications companies aggressively push their "triple-play" packages. If you consent to buy cable-TV, phone and high-speed Internet services from the same provider, you get a discount. But this isn't always the best deal. You can often save more buying à la carte from different providers.

Example: As part of my $99 bundled service, I was paying $13 per month for unlimited long-distance phone service. That sounds really good—except that I was only making one hour's worth of long-distance calls, which worked out to 22 cents a minute. I could have gotten an à la carte plan that charged $86 for cable, local TV and high-speed Internet plus long-distance for five cents a minute.

Annual savings: $120.

Best: Analyze your usage pattern, then compare rates from competing cable and phone service providers in your area.

•**Premium TV.** Subscribe to premium channels for only part of the year. This way, you can best suit your viewing habits.

Example: I like certain HBO series that run for only six months each year. I also watch more movies in the summer while network shows are in repeats. I subscribe to the appropriate premium channels only during those time periods. Since I'm not required to choose an annual package, I can add or subtract services at will. I save about $100 a year.

•**Cell-phone service.** Consider a prepaid, pay-as-you-go wireless phone plan instead of the long-term contract. The price for prepaid phones, and minutes to load on to them, has dropped. If you are using your cell phone for less than 400 minutes a month, you can save money with a prepaid phone.

How it works: You can buy a prepaid cell phone at discount retailers, such as Walmart and Target, for $15 to $140, depending on the features you want. These phones come with plans offered by providers such as TracFone (*www.tracfone.com*)...Net 10 (*www.net10.com*)...T-Mobile (*www.t-mobile.com*)...Virgin Mobile (*www.virginmobile.com*). I switched my two cell phones last year and saved $565.

To compare the best of prepaid cell-phone plans, go to ConsumerSearch (*www.consumersearch.com/prepaid-wireless*).

HOUSEHOLD PRODUCTS

•**Books.** Get discounted books when you travel. Buy a book in a Paradies Shop airport bookstore, and return it within six months to another airport bookstore for a 50% refund on your purchase. For more on the Read & Return program, visit *www.theparadiesshops.com*.

For audiobooks, a three-month subscription to *www.audible.com* saves you up to 75% off CD audiobook retail prices.

How it works: You pay $149.50 a year to purchase and download a dozen books. You can choose from more than 75,000 titles, including the latest best sellers.

•**Razor blades.** High-quality razor-blade refills have become shockingly expensive—up to $3.50 per blade—and most people replace them at least every couple of weeks. You could buy cheap disposable razors, but the more expensive razors and blades really are superior. I quadruple the life of my blade by drying it carefully after every use. Blade dullness is caused by rusting more than by contact with whiskers.

•**Clothing.** With so much merchandise backing up due to slower sales, department stores are marking down items as soon as five weeks after putting them on the sales floor.

Note: Shop late in the day on Thursday because that's when stores begin markdowns for the weekend.

Other strategies: Haggle. Retailers want to make sales, so you can negotiate in most situations. If a shirt is missing a button, ask the floor manager for a discount—he/she usually has the discretion to give you up to 15% off.

For shoe deals, go to the DSW site (*www.dsw.com*), which offers thousands of discounted designer brands for men and women, free shipping on orders of $35 or more, and allows you to make returns directly to DSW retail stores to avoid return-postage fees.

FOOD

• **Eating out.** Even many upscale restaurants are offering bargains and using technology to advertise deals.

Good resource: Restaurant.com. You search for restaurants in your area and buy $25 gift certificates for $10 with your credit card, thus saving $15.

• **Supermarkets.** Sales run on a roughly 12-week cycle. That means you can save lots of money by buying enough of any sales item to last for three months.

• **Coupons.** Instead of spending lots of time searching through the Sunday newspaper for products, retain the inserts in their entirety. Write the date on the corner of the front page. When ready to shop, go to CouponMom.com and search its free grocery coupon database. The site tells you the date of the insert where the coupon appears.

Four Easy Ways to Reduce Household Spending

Here are four simple ways you can save money at home... First, use dishrags instead of paper towels. Rinse out after every use, and wash periodically. Second, buy loose tea, and use one-third less than recommended—package labels often call for more than is needed. Third, close all closet doors when not in use—otherwise you are spending money to heat or cool the contents of your closets. Finally, cancel garbage pickup if you pay for a private service, and drive your own trash and recycling to the dump—or take turns with a neighbor so that each of you needs to go only every few days.

Woman's Day, 1633 Broadway, New York City 10019, *www.womansday.com.*

The Ultimate Cheapskate's Five Big Ways to Save $20,000 a Year

Jeff Yeager, dubbed "The Ultimate Cheapskate" by NBC's *Today* show, honed his cheapskating skills during 25 years working with underfunded nonprofit agencies. He lives in Accokeek, Maryland, and is author of *The Ultimate Cheapskate's Road Map to True Riches* and *The Cheapskate Next Door* (both from Broadway). His Web site is *www.ultimatecheapskate.com.*

Nearly all of the talk these days about economizing focuses on how to get what we want but pay less for it. It's all about how to get more for less.

For those of us who are longtime advocates of the "simple living" movement, it seems as if most Americans are missing what may be the golden opportunity of these hard times—coming to appreciate that less can often be more. In other words, we shouldn't be worrying so much about "How can we afford it?" Instead, we should be asking, "Do we really need it?"

Here are five lifestyle changes to consider. They may seem fairly radical to you when you first think about them—but if you adopt even one or two, you'll not only save some serious money, you just might be happier in the end.

1. Cancel your cell phone.

Yearly savings: $1,000 per phone.

The idea is surprising, I know, but just consider this for a moment. Only 20 or so years ago, cell phones were practically nonexistent, and the world seemed to work okay. Today, cell phones are considered a necessity, even though surveys show that we dislike our cell phones more than any other device that we own (including the alarm clock). So if that's truly how we feel, how can giving them up be a bad thing? The average cell-phone plan costs about $80 per month,* and a study recently released by Utility Consumers' Action Network found that the actual average cost of using a cell phone is more than $3 a minute if you don't use up most of your minutes and about $1 per minute even if you do use all of your minutes. As a fairly successful author and a national media personality, I am the poster

*Prices subject to change.

child for this cause, as I have never owned a cell phone, and I get by just fine.

If you can't imagine not having a cell phone, consider a prepaid phone plan. Watch for sales at such stores as Target, Walmart and Radio Shack.

2. Get rid of your second or third car.
Yearly savings: $9,000.

The average American household now owns two or three vehicles. That compares to about one car per household in 1960. AAA estimates that it costs $9,369 per year to own and operate a medium-sized sedan that is driven 15,000 miles annually. The national average cost per mile is 54 cents by the time you factor in depreciation, insurance, repairs, gas, taxes, etc. If your family owns more than one car, what's the worst thing that could happen if you give up one? You could easily save thousands of dollars a year by sharing a single car, coordinating trips, taking public transportation and so on. And Mother Earth will thank you.

3. Prepare more meals at home.
Yearly savings: $2,000.

According to the Bureau of Labor Statistics, the average US family spends about $2,668 every year eating out. I would estimate that you could prepare these same meals at home for about 80% less, or an annual savings of roughly $2,134. The other upside is that old-fashioned family time around the dinner table may make a comeback. An article in *Archives of Pediatrics & Adolescent Medicine* reported that frequent family meals are associated with a lower risk for smoking, drinking and using marijuana among adolescents, as well as a lower incidence of depressive symptoms and suicidal thoughts. And these kids were more likely to have better grades.

4. Wear out your clothing.
Yearly savings: $1,800 per family.

A small fraction of the clothing we throw away in the US is truly "worn out," meaning that it's threadbare, torn or badly stained. Many of us donate unwanted clothing to charity, but even charities have more donations than they can handle, and much of the clothing eventually ends up being thrown away. The problem is that we rarely wear out our clothing—or very

much of anything else—these days. According to some government information, the average family in America spends probably $1,800 on shoes and clothing per year. Clearly most of us have more than enough in our closets to go for six months to a year, or even longer, without needing to buy anything new.

5. Give up college room and board.
Yearly savings: $9,000 per student.

The average cost of student room and board at colleges and universities is about $9,000 per year. A generational shift has occurred here in the US over the past few decades when it comes to kids living with their parents while they attend college. Back in my college days (the 1970s), lots of us—myself included—lived with our parents and attended the local university or community college. Today that arrangement is fairly rare—it's just not "cool" to live with your folks. Of course, in my day, student loans were uncommon, in part because we didn't need to borrow money to pay for room and board. The irony is that these days, many kids graduate with so much debt—tens of thousands of dollars in student loans—that they have no choice but to move back home with their parents after college. Now, back in my day, living with your parents after you graduated really was uncool.

***

More from Jeff Yeager...

Best Negotiating Strategies: How to Get a "Nice Guy Discount" on Appliances, Electronics, Furniture, More

With dollars stretched so tight these days, retail customers are scarce. And when customers are scarce, they obtain bargaining muscle. Shoppers who are willing to negotiate even a little often get better deals.

A survey from the Consumer Reports National Research Center found that more than 90% of consumers who got up the nerve to negotiate on things such as electronics, appliances, furniture and even medical bills reported receiving a discount at least once during the survey period, with most saving $50 or more each time they were successful.

Known as "The Ultimate Cheapskate," I routinely negotiate on a wide variety of purchases—in both good times and bad—frequently shaving 5% to 10% off the asking prices and sometimes 20% or more on big-ticket items. For this article, I tapped my bargain basement brain trust of more than 300 volunteer "miser advisers" for their best negotiating tips.

Our mantra: It does not hurt to ask, but always be both friendly and polite. Also, first impressions are important, so it's best to dress nicely but casually—a slovenly appearance can arouse suspicion, and overdressing suggests wealth and therefore an ability to pay more.

GENERAL STRATEGIES

The first step is to make sure that the person you are speaking with has the authority to negotiate. If not, ask to speak to someone who does. "Is there a manager or someone I can speak with about the possibility of getting a better price on this product?" often does the trick.

For major purchases, including appliances, computers and furniture, do your homework to find out how much an item sells for elsewhere. If you know that an item is cheaper elsewhere, it is usually best to let the salesperson know that you're wise to the fact that his/her price isn't the best around. Even if the retailer already has the best price, there's no downside in asking for an even sweeter deal. As one miser adviser told me, "I've never had anyone raise the price because I asked him to lower it."

It's usually best to state up front the amount that you're willing to pay, adjusted to allow for some haggling.

Example: If you're willing to pay $50 for an item that is marked $60, you might start off with a lowball offer of $40 or $45, with the hope of compromising somewhere around $50.

You don't have to name a price. You can just ask, "Can you do any better on this?" In keeping with the importance of being friendly, many times I ask for (and receive) a "nice guy discount," based solely on the fact that I'm a nice guy. It's as simple as asking, "Can you do any better on the price?" then adding, with a smile, "What about giving me a nice guy discount,

because I'm a nice guy?" If nothing else, I bet you'll get a free smile out of the salesperson.

When asking for a discount based on poor service, damaged merchandise and the like, be honest. Don't fabricate or exaggerate, but politely speak your mind if you are dissatisfied in any way or think that the condition of an item warrants a price reduction. Just say to the person in charge something like, "I'm not trying to be difficult, but I feel I should let you know that the service I received today was disappointing," and provide one or two details. Let the person in charge respond. He/she often will offer some type of make-good concession, but if he doesn't, you can then ask, "Is there anything you can do to keep me as a future customer?"

WHEN THE ANSWER IS "NO"

Be prepared for rejection because the answer often is "no." Handle it gracefully, and don't be embarrassed or get nasty. On major purchases, when the initial response is "no," I generally say, "Is there anything I can do to change your mind?" followed by, "Is there anyone else I can speak with?"

If, in the end, the answer remains "no," I thank the salesperson or manager for his time and tell him that I'm going to shop around. Occasionally (but rarely) he will reconsider as you're headed for the door. You always can slip back later to buy the item if, in fact, you can't do better elsewhere.

FINE-TUNING YOUR STYLE

With these general strategies in mind, here are some of the finer points when it comes to cutting the best deal...

• **Flash the cash.** Offering to pay with cash instead of a credit card often can convince a retailer to knock a few dollars off the price, because that's what you're saving him in credit card–processing fees. And actually showing the greenbacks when you make your best offer sometimes can close the deal.

• **"I can't afford it."** In times such as these, there's nothing wrong with telling a merchant the truth. Do not break out the violins—just come clean and say something along the lines of, "I really like this product, but to be honest with you, my budget is pretty tight these days. Can you do any better on the price?"

• **Watch for sales before and after you buy.** Many retailers will give you the sale price even when an item is not on sale or match a competitor's sale price, sometimes even before or after the fact. Be prepared to go back to a merchant and suggest that you'll return an item for a refund if he doesn't give you the lower sale price. Some retailers have a policy that if an item goes on sale within a certain time period—say, 10 days or two weeks—they will refund the difference.

• **Ask to cancel your service.** Particularly when it comes to dealing with service providers over the phone, politely stating that you would like to talk to someone about canceling your service (cable service, phone plans, credit cards, etc.) usually will get you connected—and pronto—to someone whose job it is to keep you as a customer. This is the person who is authorized to cut you the best deal possible.

• **Never on a Monday.** In my experience, the best deals are made late in the week, particularly on Fridays and especially before holidays or three-day weekends. Everyone is in a good mood and wants to wrap things up, and salesmen often want to meet their weekly quotas. Avoid negotiating early in the week.

• **"Do any discounts apply?"** If you are still gun-shy about haggling, start with this simple baby step—always ask whether any "promotions" or "other discounts" might apply. Ask this when you're in a store or making a catalog purchase over the phone. "Promotions" are special deals that salespeople (particularly at catalog companies) can mention only if the customer asks first. Many merchants also extend discounts to the members of AARP, AAA, warehouse clubs, etc., and even if you're not a member, they sometimes will give you the same break if you ask.

Example: I stayed at a hotel recently and asked if an AARP discount would be accepted. The desk clerk said "no," but she immediately took 15% off the price of my room, explaining that if the hotel did offer an AARP discount, that's what it would be.

Don't Be Shy—Give Haggling a Try

Most shoppers are successful at haggling. More than 65% of consumers surveyed said that they had tried to negotiate a better deal recently. Of those, 88% were successful at least one time—83% in bargaining for hotel rates…78% for airfares…and 62% for credit card fees.

Consumer Reports, 101 Truman Ave., Yonkers, New York 10703, *www.consumerreports.org.*

Buy a Fridge in May, a Computer in August: Our Guide to the Best Times to Buy Just About *Anything*

Mark Di Vincenzo, a journalist based in Newport News, Virginia, who interviewed hundreds of merchants and analyzed years of sales data and industry reports for his book *Buy Ketchup in May and Fly at Noon: A Guide to the Best Time to Buy This, Do That and Go There* (Harper, *www.buyketchupinmay.com*).

The prices of certain products fluctuate by 10% to 75% during the course of a year. Some even vary predictably within a single day or week. Knowing how to correctly time purchases can save you hundreds or even thousands of dollars per year.

APPLIANCES AND ELECTRONICS

• **Best time to buy small appliances and electronics—April.** Many electronics products are made by Japanese companies, which typically introduce new products and discount older ones soon after March 31, the end of their fiscal year.

• **Best time to buy a refrigerator—May.** Merchants often slash fridge prices in May to clear space in showrooms and warehouses for new models, which arrive each summer.

• **Best time to buy a computer—August,** during back-to-school sales. Prices often drop by $50 or more.* Printers and other computer peripherals sometimes are thrown in as well. Exceptions…

• **Buy a television in January,** when discounts are common on units that were not sold at the holidays and on products replaced by newer models unveiled at early January's Consumer Electronics Show. (TVs often are attractively priced during December's holiday sales as well.)

• **Buy cameras in February.** The new models come out in January and February. Get a good deal on a year-old model at a Presidents' Day sale.

• **Buy portable music players in August or September.** These often are marked down in anticipation of the new models, which tend to arrive in September and October.

• **Best time to buy a lawn mower, snowblower or barbecue grill is near the end of its season of use.** Discounts can reach 30% to 40% on grills and lawn mowers between Labor Day and November…with similar savings on snowblowers in March. Merchants do not want to store these bulky and expensive items until their next season.

HOUSE

• **Best time to make an offer on a house— January.** Home buyers face minimal competition during this cold month because house hunting is no fun when the weather is at its worst. Less competition means greater odds that a seller will accept a low-ball bid. The weather is no better in February, but by then sellers are more likely to hold out until temperatures and the housing market begin to heat up in March.

The first Tuesday of January can be the perfect day to make an offer. Home owners will have recently made their month-end mortgage payment, a reminder of the high cost of holding on to an unneeded home. Tuesday also is a perfect day to make offers in slow housing markets because by then home owners realize it's unlikely that other house hunters from the weekend's showings intend to make offers.

*Prices and rates subject to change.

Alternate strategy: Make an offer on Christmas Day. Sellers are happy to receive an offer, even on a holiday, and people are in a good mood on Christmas, leaving them psychologically predisposed to be flexible and generous in their negotiations. Add a message to your offer explaining that the home would be the perfect place to raise your family—we tend to become very family-oriented over Christmas. You will need a real estate agent who is willing to work on Christmas to do this.

CLOTHING

• **Best time to buy thrift shop clothing is soon after area dry cleaners make donations.** Some of the best clothing available at many thrift shops is donated by dry cleaners. These are mostly high-end clothes that the dry cleaners' customers failed to pick up.

Ask a thrift shop employee if the store receives donations from any dry cleaners and, if so, when those donations tend to arrive. Stop by soon after a donation is expected.

• **Best time to buy new clothing is about a month after you first see it.** If clothing hasn't sold six weeks after it appears in stores, the markdowns begin. Ask an employee how long an item has been in stock if you are not sure.

CAR

• **Best time to buy a new car if low price is your priority is October through December.** Dealers often discount the current year's models by as much as 20% late in the year to make room for new models. October and November are the best bets if you're at all picky about what you drive. The prices can be even lower in December, but by then very few desirable vehicles from the current model year are likely to be available.

Whatever month you buy your new car, shop on one of that month's final days. Salespeople and dealerships become more willing to offer attractive deals late in the month because they often need to sell cars to meet monthly sales quotas or earn bonuses.

• **Best time to bring a car to a mechanic for repairs—Thursday.** This is the slowest day of the week at many repair shops. Some shops are willing to offer discounts of 10%

to 20% to customers who are willing to wait until Thursday—if those customers know to ask. But don't expect a Thursday discount at a shop that always is busy. Thursday discounts most likely are given to customers who bring multiple jobs to a shop, so consider holding off on having a minor repair done until additional work is required.

MARKETS

• **Best time to shop at a farmers' market is just before closing time.** Farmers' market merchants hate loading unsold goods back onto their trucks. If fruits and vegetables are already ripe and are unlikely to be sellable in another day or two, point this out. Discounts can be 50%, sometimes more.

• **Best time to buy at an outdoor flea market is on the last weekend of the season.** Outdoor flea markets shut down for the winter in most parts of the country. Sellers often are willing to accept low-ball offers rather than put merchandise in storage for months.

Should You Buy an Extended Warranty?

Consider if and how soon you might need any repairs before getting a warranty.

The chance of requiring repairs within three to four years for a variety of products: Desktop PCs have a 31% rate of repair…laptop computers a 43% rate…lawn tractors, 31%…riding mowers, 32%…side-by-side refrigerators that have an icemaker and dispenser, 37%…self-propelled mowers, 28%…washing machines (top loading), 22%.

Many other major appliances have a 20% or less chance of needing repairs within three or four years. These include gas ranges, 20%…refrigerators with a top or bottom freezer with icemaker, 20%…clothes dryers, 15%…vacuum cleaners, 13%…digital camcorders, 13%…digital cameras, 10%…and televisions, 6% to 8%.

Consumer Reports, 101 Truman Ave., Yonkers, New York 10703, *www.consumerreports.org*.

Comparison Shopping With Your Cell Phone

Use your mobile phone to compare prices. Applications (apps) for various phones let you scan bar codes while shopping and then tell you if a nearby store has the same item at a better price. You can use the information to go to the other store or get the store you are in to match the lower offer. Some apps let you take a picture of a product or the bar code, then search stores to find out where it is carried and at what cost.

Caution: The technology is new and has flaws—for instance, it may send you to a store with low prices, but then the item is out of stock.

Better: Call ahead to find out if an item is in stock. Or search online before leaving home— you can easily compare prices and find out if stores have what you want.

The Wall Street Journal, *http://online.wsj.com*.

Shrewder Shopping at The Supermarket

Teri Gault, founder and CEO of TheGroceryGame. com, a subscription Internet service based in southern California that reports on thousands of sales, specials and available coupons each week for many supermarkets around the country. She is coauthor of *Shop Smart, Save More: Learn the Grocery Game and Save Hundreds of Dollars a Month* (Avon).

Your supermarket is a great place to really save money in this prolonged recession. Supermarkets have become ultracompetitive, enticing customers with aggressive sales, coupons and other sorts of discounts. *My secrets for saving $100 a month per person at the supermarket…*

• **Choose a primary supermarket.** I used to chase sales all over town, but it was a huge waste of time and gasoline.

Reason: Supermarkets that are within the same county tend to have similar sales cycles.

So the same deal you get on spaghetti at one store will be matched by another store at the same time or within a few weeks. Shopping at the same store also lets you familiarize yourself enough to know when a "special" really is special.

• **For certain items, the bargains are consistently better at stores other than supermarkets.** If you use a lot of these items, it may be worth it to make separate stops. For milk, over-the-counter (OTC) medicine and personal-care products, shop at drugstores. For snacks, cereals and cleaning supplies, shop at superstores, including Walmart. For alcohol, eggs, frozen appetizers, kitchen storage containers and cakes, shop at warehouse clubs, such as Costco. For fresh, seasonal produce, try local farmers' markets.

• **Stockpile enough of the sale item for about 12 weeks.** Supermarkets typically cycle their rock-bottom sales over that period through every section of the store. I buy nearly every item in my pantry and freezer at a 30% to 50% discount off regular prices. For example, my favorite cereal goes on sale every 12 weeks. I know I use a box of cereal every two weeks, so every time the cereal goes on sale, I replenish my inventory back to six boxes.

• **Clip coupons for the items you intend to stockpile.** Many people think coupons are primarily for junk food or products that only large families with kids will desire. But over the past couple of years, manufacturers' coupons have been extended to many more meats, vegetables, healthful food, organic food and household products. They also now extend to their customers more "multi-purchase" offers that save $1 to $5* if you buy several different items from the same manufacturer, such as Kraft or General Mills. These offers can usually be combined with coupons.

You don't have to have an Internet connection to track down coupons. Ninety percent of all coupons are printed in the Sunday newspaper supplements.

Bonus: Many supermarkets will double the value of any coupons you use. However, supermarkets that do not double coupons often

*Prices, offers and rates subject to change.

issue their own coupons with a higher face value.

• **Use your coupons on sale items.** The week a coupon appears in the paper is often not when the item is actually on sale at your supermarket.

Reason: Coupons are the first wave of promotion, designed to entice you to buy the item near full price.

Stacking a coupon on top of a sale is how I'm often able to get items for free.

Example: I recently purchased Colgate toothpaste (regularly $2.19 for one 5.8 ounce tube) on sale for just 99 cents. But I had a 50-cent coupon, which my store doubled—so I paid nothing.

• **Buy meat that has been marked down for same-day sale.** Supermarket meat departments put meat on sale on the last day of its "sell-by" date. The meat is safe and palatable until the "use-by" date on the package, which is typically five days after the "sell-by" date. Ask the butcher at the meat counter what time of day perishables are marked down (usually the morning of the "sell-by" date).

• **Watch out for shrinking package sizes.** Manufacturers know that price hikes will drive away consumers. Instead, they maintain the same price but reduce the size of products, hoping that you won't notice. Major ice cream makers have shrunk their standard containers to 1.5 quarts from 1.75 quarts, so you're getting 14% less in every carton. Dial bath soap bars went from 4.5 ounces to four ounces, making them 11% smaller.

Self-defense: Do not look at the total price. Check the tags on the shelf that list the price per ounce or unit cost when comparing similar products. Consider store brands, which typically cost 10% to 30% less than "brand names" and are often the same product made by the same major manufacturer—just with a different label. One of the nation's largest grocery retailers, Kroger, lets you try the store brand and if you don't like it, return it for your money back or the comparable brand-name item.

• **Skip prepared foods, such as cut vegetables, sliced fruit and cheese, and washed lettuce.** The premium you pay, often 100%, is not worth the time you save preparing the food yourself.

An exception: Work-intensive meals. For example, a ready-to-eat chicken on sale costs me only about a dollar more than a raw one, but I save an hour of preparation.

• **Pass on the organic produce unless it really matters.** Fruits and vegetables grown without chemicals or pesticides can cost up to twice as much as regular produce. So I purchase only the ones that as regular produce tend to be the most highly contaminated according to the USDA—apples, bell peppers, celery, cherries, peaches, pears, potatoes, red raspberries, spinach and strawberries.

• **Use your supermarket loyalty cards to save on much more than just groceries.** Privacy advocates have criticized rewards cards because they give grocers access to personal information, such as your e-mail address and what you buy each week. But the advantages now outweigh the dangers. For example, my Vons Supermarket card will give discounts at affiliated businesses in my area, such as oil-change franchises, car washes, theme parks and restaurants. I also get alerts about product recalls. Some supermarkets recently e-mailed club cardholders about the potential danger of peanut products that they had purchased.

Cut Your Grocery Bill 50% Just by Avoiding These Common Shopping Mistakes

Stephanie Nelson, founder of the grocery-shopping Web site CouponMom.com, which has more than two million members. Located in Atlanta, Nelson is author of *The Coupon Mom's Guide to Cutting Your Grocery Bills in Half* (Avery). She saves an average of 50% on her family's groceries, about $100 a week.

Many family budgets have now been stretched to the limit due to the weak economy. Trimming grocery costs is a great way to fight back, but too often shoppers make mistakes and end up paying more than they need to.

Here, the most common shopping mistakes and what to do instead...

Mistake: **Assuming sale prices are attractive prices.** Supermarket sale circulars often contain some great deals—but they typically have many items priced at or near their regular prices as well. The store's desire is that shoppers will snap up any advertised "special" without noticing how little they're saving.

Don't go out of your way to purchase a product unless the sale price is at least 50% below the regular price (or buy-one-get-one-free). If the price reduction is more modest and you're not picky about brands, you probably will get a better deal if you wait a bit for it to go on sale.

Mistake: **Shopping in the wrong department.** Prices on very similar goods can vary significantly from one section of the supermarket to another. *Examples...*

• Cheese can be two times as much in the deli or gourmet section as it does in the dairy section. The brands might be different, but the quality usually is just as good. I compared costs at my supermarket for feta, blue cheese, goat cheese, Vermont cheddar and Parmesan, and I found that the dairy-case versions cost as much as 63% less* than the gourmet-cheese options.

• Also, within a deli department itself, the prices can vary greatly. In my grocery store's deli department, prepackaged sliced cheese is more expensive than the cheese sliced at the counter. *Example:* An eight-ounce package of deli-sliced American cheese sold next to the deli counter costs $4.99, which is $9.98 per pound. I can buy the same cheese if I am willing to take the time to have it sliced for $5.99 per pound ($2.99 per pound when it's on sale).

• Nut prices in the produce, snack and baking sections can differ. I compared the price of pecans, walnuts and almonds sold in one-pound bags in the produce department to the same type of nuts sold in one-pound bags in the baking aisle at the same store. Almonds were 27% less expensive and walnuts were 14% less expensive in the baking aisle. But pecans were 29%

*Prices, offers and rates subject to change.

less expensive in the produce section than in the baking aisle, so you have to check carefully.

• Salsa often is more expensive in the snack aisle than in the condiments aisle. There almost always is at least one brand of salsa on sale, but it tends not to be the one that the supermarket puts on display by the chips.

• Organic foods located in supermarket organic aisles usually are substantially more expensive than those shelved among nonorganic goods elsewhere in the store.

Mistake: **Buying 10 when a store offers 10 for $10.** Unless the store specifically says that you must purchase 10 (or another number that's mentioned) to get the sale price, 10 for $10 means that you could buy one for $1 if you prefer. Stores price items this way because it tricks shoppers into buying more than they want.

At some grocery stores, you don't even have to buy two when the sale is buy-one-get-one-free. If the store's registers ring up each item in a buy-one-get-one-free offer at half price, rather than one at full price and the other at $0, you likely will get the 50%-off price even if you buy just one. Ask at the customer service desk at your supermarket if you are not certain.

Bonus: If your supermarket rings up both items in a buy-one-get-one-free offer at half price and you have two coupons for the item, you can redeem both coupons. (If one rings up at full price and the other for free, you can use only one coupon.)

Mistake: **Assuming products shelved on supermarket aisle endcaps and display islands are special deals.** These locations attract a lot of attention, so supermarkets prefer to fill them with high-volume or high-margin products, not sale items that don't earn them much profit.

Be especially wary if an endcap or island display features several different but related items. One of these might be on sale while all the rest are at regular prices. The supermarket hopes that the brightly colored sale tags on the display will confuse shoppers into thinking that all the items are discounted, which often is not the case.

Example: A display in the fruit aisle includes a sale price on strawberries but regular prices on shortcakes and whipped cream.

Mistake: **Not watching as prices are rung up at the register.** Supermarkets adjust the prices of thousands of items each week. Inevitably, some of those changes are not correctly programmed into their computers.

Watch the register readout carefully as items are scanned to catch mistakes as they happen. Then skim your receipt for any mistakes you may have missed—preferably before leaving the store.

Some stores have a policy that if an item is rung up incorrectly, the customer gets the item for free. This policy may not be publicized, so be sure to ask at your store.

Mistake: **Assuming there's a one-coupon-per-item limit.** Most grocery stores let shoppers use both a manufacturer's coupon and a store coupon on the same item if both happen to be available.

At many BJ's Wholesale Clubs (800-257-2582 or *www.bjs.com*), their shoppers can even use multiple manufacturers' coupons on the same purchase when multiple units of the item are packaged together. (The other major wholesale clubs currently do not accept manufacturers' coupons.)

Example: If BJ's sells applesauce in packages containing three jars, you could redeem up to three applicable coupons.

Some supermarkets will let their shoppers use expired coupons…or even store coupons offered from different stores. These tend to be unadvertised policies, so ask a cashier or at the service desk. (These policies are most likely to be offered by supermarkets that do not double coupons.)

Mistake: **Forgetting to peel off instant-use coupons on packages.** Manufacturers sometimes attach coupons directly to the products for instant savings. Why do they do this rather than just lower the product's price? Because 60% of these on-package coupons are not redeemed. Shoppers either forget about the coupon by the time they get to the register…or erroneously assume that the cashier will peel the coupon off and then ring it up. Cashiers are trained to move fast and might not even notice these coupons, so it is up to you.

Mistake: Thinking the largest-sized package will be the best deal. Frequently, smaller packages cost less per ounce or per unit. This is particularly true with sale-priced breakfast cereal, canned tuna, milk and diapers. Compare the per-ounce or per-unit prices listed on the shelf price tag.

If you have a coupon that is valid for any size, the smallest package usually is the best deal.

Example: A coupon offering $1 off any size of a particular brand of pasta sauce lowers the cost of the $2.50 45-ounce jar to 3.3 cents per ounce…or the cost of the $1.50 26-ounce jar to 1.9 cents per ounce.

Mistake: Not adhering to the five-minute rule when buying prepared foods. Supermarkets charge hefty premiums for the convenience of cooked, cut or washed foods. When the prep time involved is five minutes or less, I find it's worth it to do the prep myself.

Examples: Buy a head of lettuce rather than a bag of washed and cut lettuce. Buy a block of cheese rather than shredded cheese. Buy whole fruit rather than cut fruit.

You'll not only save money, you usually will get better quality. Supermarkets generally slice up older or bruised fruit and vegetables that wouldn't otherwise sell. And cut or shredded foods often spoil faster.

Mistake: Ignoring wholesale club deals that are available to nonmembers. In most states, even if you don't join a wholesale club, the club's pharmacy legally is required to fill your prescription at the member price. (Call wholesale clubs in your region to ask if this is true where you live.)

Costco and Sam's Club pharmacies typically charge substantially lower prices than the chain pharmacies. (BJ's no longer offers pharmacies.) Costco's pharmacy prices can even be checked online in advance (go to *www.costco. com*, click on "Pharmacy," then "Prescription Price Checker"). Phone your local Sam's Club pharmacy for prices.

In some states, wholesale clubs also are required to sell beer and wine to nonmembers at the member price (as well as liquor, if it is offered). Wholesale clubs' beer prices tend to be about 10% lower than those of other merchants…and their wine prices can be 35% lower on their more expensive bottles.

How to Drink *Better Wine* for *Much Less* When You Eat Out

Robin Goldstein, editor of the Fearless Critic restaurant guide series and author of more than 30 travel guides. He is a certified sommelier, former food critic for *Metro New York* and the *New Haven Advocate* and author of *The Wine Trials 2010: The World's Bestselling Guide to Inexpensive Wines* (Fearless Critic, *www.thewinetrials.com*).

Restaurants typically charge three times more for one bottle of wine than you'd pay in any store. It's a massive markup that makes even the mid-level wines seem extravagant.

Inside info: You don't have to splurge on expensive wines—cheaper bottles are often just as good. Many pricey wines receive rave reviews only because human beings are psychologically predisposed to assume that expensive products are better.

Some inexpensive wines are far better than others, of course. *Five shrewd ways to spot the values on restaurant wine lists…*

1. Avoid chronically overpriced varieties. Certain types of wine are simply so popular that the wineries and restaurants can charge a premium for their popularity.

Examples: Champagne—the name used for sparkling wines from a particular area in France—is usually overpriced. Instead, order a Spanish Cava or Pacific Northwest sparkling wine. Instead of California Chardonnay, order a Grüner Veltliner from Austria when you want white wine. It's versatile and almost always a bargain. Instead of Napa Valley Cabernet Sauvignon, if you want a red wine that goes well with meat, ask for an Argentine Malbec or a French Bordeaux from a lesser-known winery. Among all the Italian reds, Brunello is almost always very expensive—order the Sangiovese di Romagna instead. It's made from the same grape, albeit in a slightly different way.

2. Favor countries with weak currencies.

Examples: Wines from Argentina, Chile and Hungary are especially good bargains for US buyers because the value of their currencies has fallen against the dollar.

3. Skip the well-known wineries. Restaurants often charge inflated prices for these—they know many patrons will pay extra.

4. Order wine by the bottle or half bottle, not by the glass. A bottle of wine fills at least four glasses, and yet many restaurants charge much more than a one-quarter of the bottle price for a glass, an additional markup on top of the already steep restaurant wine premium. Worse, wine sold by the glass might be poured from a bottle opened a day or more earlier.

5. BYOB and pay the restaurant's fee for opening a bottle you bring. Paying $10 to $20 to drink your own bottle of wine in a restaurant might seem like a rip-off, but in fact corkage fees often are money savers.

Corkage fees and BYOB policies vary from restaurant to restaurant. Call and ask about the rules before bringing a bottle.

Better Than New

Repaired shoes can be better than new. Materials used in shoe repair often are three to four times better quality than ones used to manufacture shoes—even expensive shoes. Shoe-repair shops use the same high-quality materials on all shoes—better heels, soles and stitching. Shoes also can be completely reconditioned, which includes fixing torn or weakened areas, replacing worn-out parts and restoring color and finish. Simple repairs, such as adding new heels, usually cost around $20.* Reconditioning can cost $100. This is well worth it for a pair of shoes that costs $300, for example, because you would

*Prices subject to change.

be getting virtually a new pair of shoes for a fraction of the cost.

Mary Hunt, editor, *Debt-Proof Living*, Box 2135, Paramount, California 90723, *www.debtproofliving.com.*

Money for Old Gadgets

Sites such as Gazelle.com and MyBoneYard.com will buy old gadgets that you no longer use. Both sites take computers, monitors, cell phones and digital music players. Answer a few questions about the device (its condition, whether you have the original software, cables, etc.), and these sites will quote you a price. Free shipping is offered for most items, with prepaid shipping labels sent by e-mail and boxes mailed to the sender.

Get Cash for Your Cell Phone

At *www.flipswap.com*, you can receive cash for your old phone or donate it to a charity of your choice. Phone values vary from a few dollars to well over $100* for recent, desirable models. Very old phones and those in poor condition get no cash, but they will be recycled. In 2008 alone, Flipswap's program kept the equivalent to 80 tons of solid waste—much of it toxic—out of US landfills.

*Price subject to change.

Sell Your Old Books Online

Type in the ISBN numbers (you can find them on the back cover of the book or on the copyright page) of books that you no longer want at Cash4Books.net, and the site will make an offer on each. When you are ready to ship, you print out a prepaid mailing label (shipping is included), package the books and send them off. Cash4Books.net will send you a check or deposit a payment into your PayPal account within three business days after receiving and processing your books.

When Your Cell-Phone Contract Expires...

When the service contract with your cell-phone provider runs out, you become a month-to-month customer. All provisions of your contract remain the same, but you can leave the provider at any time with no penalty.

You can use the end of your contract as leverage for negotiating better rates and terms. The cell-phone company's retention specialist can give you benefits if you sign up for another two years—extra minutes, a credit on your bill, etc. Shop around and get offers from other service providers. Then call your carrier, say that you are thinking of moving to a new company and ask what the company is willing to do to keep you. If the customer service person is not helpful, ask to speak to a retention specialist.

John Breyault, vice president of public policy, National Consumers League, Washington, DC, *www.nclnet.org.*

Cut Your Energy Bill by $1,500 This Summer

John Krigger, founder of Saturn Resource Management, an environmental consulting, training and publishing company located in Helena, Montana. He has served as a consultant to the US Department of Energy and is coauthor of *The Homeowner's Handbook to Energy Efficiency* (Saturn Resource Management, *www.homeownershandbook.biz*).

You can trim your energy bills by more than $1,500 this summer just by taking these simple steps...

•**Use window fans after sunset.** Outside temperatures can drop quickly once the sun sets, even in the middle of the summer. Turn off your air conditioner, and turn on a window fan. Fans use only a fraction of the electricity of air-conditioning and may make you just as comfortable when nighttime temperatures drop.

Savings: Two fans combined likely use just 5% of the electricity that it takes to air-condition a home. If you can turn off your air-conditioning for 10 hours each night on 100 nights each year, you easily could save $500.

•**Use fans to circulate the air when you do turn on your air-conditioning.** When you shut the windows to turn on air-conditioning, you rob yourself of the cooling power of the wind. Supplement your A/C with fans, and the air moving around the room will make you feel four degrees cooler. Your fans will use a lot less electricity to achieve this four-degree decrease than the air conditioner would. Turn off fans whenever you leave a room—the electricity is wasted if no one feels the breeze.

Savings: As much as 6% of your air-conditioning costs, which for some households is $100 to $200 per year.

•**Draw your drapes or blinds to prevent direct sunlight from heating your home on hot summer days.** White or metallic venetian blinds or opaque roll-down shades can reflect much of the sun's heat back out, reducing or even eliminating the need for air-conditioning.

Savings: As much as 40% to 45% of your cooling bills if you currently have uncovered windows—that could be close to $1,000.

•**Use your pool pump and filter less often.** Pool owners often set their pumps and filters to run between 12 and 24 hours per day—but as little as four hours a day might be sufficient. Experiment with shorter run times until you find your pool's minimum acceptable filter usage.

Helpful: Set a pool's pump and filter to run in the morning and late evening, not between noon and 6:00 pm, when summer electricity demand peaks and rates may be higher.

Savings: Perhaps $20 to $30 per month, depending on how many days of the year your pool is in use.

Where to Find Free Expert Medical Advice

Charles B. Inlander, a consumer advocate and health-care consultant located in Fogelsville, Pennsylvania. He was the founding president of the nonprofit People's Medical Society, a consumer advocacy organization credited with key improvements in the quality of US health care in the 1980s and 1990s, and is the author of 20 books, including *Take This Book to the Hospital with You: A Consumer Guide to Surviving Your Hospital Stay* (St. Martin's).

Even though there is an abundance of health information online, you may not find answers to specific questions related to your personal medical diagnosis or treatment. For those questions, you may want to speak to an expert other than your own doctor, who may not have the necessary expertise and latest information about your condition. The good news is that it's often easy to reach an expert—and, in many cases, that medical information is free! *Clever ways to get information from top-notch medical experts...*

●**Contact a medical school.** Faculty members at medical schools, such as physicians and researchers, know about the latest treatments for rare or complicated medical problems and can be good sources of referrals to doctors and hospitals that specialize in your medical condition. Over the years, I have always found it relatively easy to contact medical school faculty by phone. First, check the listings of medical schools at the Web site of the Association of American Medical Colleges, *www.aamc.org/medicalschools*, and look for the school closest to you (in case you need to meet directly with the expert). When you call a medical school, ask for the chairperson of the department most closely related to your medical condition—for example, cardiology or endocrinology.

Insider tip: When you call, don't go into detail about your medical condition. Instead, get right to your question. For example, you may ask, "Where would you recommend that I get a second opinion for this problem?"...or "Is the treatment my doctor recommended the only option?"

●**Call a teaching hospital.** Because medical students are taught in these hospitals, the physicians who head up the specialty departments are often considered authorities in their field. You can get a list of teaching hospitals in your state at *www.healthguideusa.org/teaching_hospitals.htm*. Follow the steps described above in contacting the specific person best able to help you. Because department heads typically have hectic schedules, chances are you will have to leave a message.

Insider tip: Most of these doctors have private practices, so you should be prepared to schedule an appointment if you have a complicated question or problem. But if you are looking for a referral or source of information (such as studies) about a disease or treatment, the doctor or his/her staff often will get back to you with a suggestion at no charge.

●**Go to your insurance carrier.** You may be surprised to learn that your insurance company may have the answer to your medical question. If you have questions about your medical care, call your insurer's nurse/medical expert hotline. More and more insurance companies are putting in hotlines that allow you to speak to health-care practitioners directly. In addition, members of many health plans can discuss their medical conditions and treatment issues with experts such as nurses, respiratory therapists and dietitians, known as case managers or disease management specialists. Check to see if your insurer has such a program.

Drug-Company Coupons May *Not* Be a Good Deal

The discount and rebate coupons from pharmaceutical companies are mostly for newer, brand-name drugs—but there may be older, equally effective medicines, including generics, that work as well for lower cost. Coupons can be found in newspaper and magazine ads, on drug firms' Web sites and at sites such as *www.internetdrugcoupons.com*.

What to do: Ask your doctor whether a medicine on which a coupon is offered is the most effective and least expensive alternative for you.

The Wall Street Journal, http://online.wsj.com.

The Cost of Health Care Is Negotiable

Don't be reluctant to negotiate your health-care expenses.

What to do: Ask hospitals and doctors for a price break. When choosing a facility, consider cost—an urgent-care center may charge $150* for services that could cost $1,000 at a hospital emergency room. Use generic drugs whenever it's possible—and when one is not available, ask your doctor if you can try a less expensive medicine designed to treat the same condition.

Also: Find out about benefits through your insurance company. Some offer discounts on gym memberships, stop-smoking and weight-loss programs, and other services.

The Washington Post, www.washingtonpost.com.
*Prices subject to change.

Money-Savers for Dog And Cat Owners

We love our pets and want to make sure that they live long, healthy lives. *Here are ways to ensure that they do just that—without breaking the bank in the process...*

•**Catch diseases early.** Watch for changes in a pet's routine, such as more panting than usual or additional water consumption. These can be early signs of disease—which may be easier and less costly to treat than at later stages.

•**Feed them a high-quality diet.** You will keep your pet healthy and save on vet bills.

The first ingredients on the label should be animal proteins, and not byproducts, grains or vegetables.

•**Have grooming done midweek.** Many salons charge 20% less for work done on Tuesday through Thursday.

•**Consider pet insurance.** The cost is about $16/month* for cats and $22/month for dogs. Log on to *www.petinsurance.com* or *www.pet-insurance-info.com* to learn what's covered.

Charlotte Biggs, chief governance officer, Pet Care Services Association in Colorado Springs, www.petcare services.org.

*Prices subject to change.

Tipping Do's and Don'ts

Jodi R.R. Smith, Marblehead, Massachusetts–based author of *From Clueless to Class Act: Manners for the Modern Woman* (Sterling).

In this day and age, tipping has become more of a "requirement" than a "gratuity." *Here's when to tip—and when not to...*

•**If restaurant service is poor, tip around 12%** instead of the normal 15% to 20%. Servers get very low wages and need tips, so giving zero is rude. Tell the restaurant manager if you are unhappy with your dining experience—but do not blame the server for factors out of his/her control, such as the quality of the food.

•**Put money in a tip jar only if someone goes beyond the basics of his job.** There is no need to tip someone who simply hands you a drink or food across a retail counter. But a person who gives your child or grandchild an extra treat deserves a tip.

•**When you pick up takeout food, tipping is not necessary.**

•**If food is delivered, tip about 10%** of the bill even if there is a delivery charge. That charge goes to the restaurant—the tip goes directly to the person who delivers your meal.

Spending Money on Others Makes *You* Happier!

Spending money on others makes you happier than spending it on yourself. In one recent study, high income and greater levels of spending on gifts for other people or charitable donations were equal factors in peoples' reported happiness. In another study, people given small amounts of money reported being happier when they donated it than when they bought things for themselves.

Elizabeth Dunn, PhD, assistant professor, University of British Columbia, Vancouver, Canada.

A Shopping Buddy

Compare product features and reviews at Buzzillions.com. The site currently offers nearly four million product reviews on anything from digital cameras to dog clothing. Reviews are presented in an easy-to-use way.

Example: If you click on digital cameras, the camera reviews are divided into "All reviewers," "Casual photographers," "Photo enthusiast" and "Semipro photographer." Or you can sort by price, type of camera (point-and-click, digital SLR, etc.), manufacturer, store or feature. The site also provides a "review snapshot," which is a compact list of the good and bad features of a product based on its reviews. Once you have decided on a product, you can click a link and go directly to a site where you can buy it.

A Quick Tip

Before wearing new clothes, wash them or run them through a cycle in a hot dryer.

Reason: If several people try clothing on before it is finally sold, it may contain bacteria from respiratory secretions, as well as skin flora, vaginal organisms and traces of fecal material.

To protect yourself when shopping, wear clothes underneath whatever you try on, so that the clothing does not touch your skin. And wash your hands after shopping.

Philip Tierno, PhD, director of clinical microbiology and immunology, New York University, Lagone Medical Center, New York City, and leader of a test of 14 items of clothing for *Good Morning America*.

12

Retirement Riches

How to Design Your *Perfect* Retirement

Large corporations draft up mission statements to help clarify goals and plan for the future. Typically, businesses assemble key directors and staff at a luxury retreat to discuss the company's objectives, values and future plans. The result is a brief mission statement that captures the essence of a company and serves as a road map.

In just a few succinct sentences, these documents describe a business from several different angles...

• **Mission.** What is the company's purpose? What does it do and how is it unique from its competitors?

• **Vision.** Where will the organization be in three to five years?

• **Values.** What are the principles, morals and philosophy that underpin its behavior?

• **Identity.** Where does the company fit into society?

Just as many businesses find these documents indispensable, people nearing or in retirement can benefit from a personal mission statement to "redesign" a period of life that often lasts decades. Retirement does not come with instructions—you must write your own training manual. Unlike prior stages of your life—school, marriage, career—retirement has no predefined roles, no bosses to supervise you and no competitive coworkers to measure yourself against.

The best part of retirement is having control over your time and the freedom to pursue your interests. But you need to devote time and deep thought to figure out what you want now, where you are going and how you will

---

Richard G. Wendel, MD, MBA, Cincinnati-based author of *Retire with a Mission: Planning and Purpose for the Second Half of Life* (Sourcebook). Dr. Wendel is a retired urologist with a business background who volunteers at SCORE, Counselors to America's Small Business, *www.score.org.*

get there. A well-crafted statement can help you develop a plan that will unify your identity, life's purpose and core values. As a retired physician and volunteer at the small-business counseling agency SCORE, I see many people flounder in retirement. That's why a personal mission statement is so important at this stage of life. It will provide the needed structure and strategies to get you where you want to go.

FIVE KEYS TO A HAPPY RETIREMENT

Personal mission statements are just that—personal. Yours will not look like mine or anyone else's. *However, your mission statement needs to address the following five keys to a happy retirement...*

•**Health.** Your number-one priority should be a commitment to a healthful lifestyle. Without it, your retirement plans will be foiled. In preparing your statement, include strategies to promote regular exercise, a more healthful diet and quitting bad habits, such as smoking or drinking too much.

•**Giving back.** Ponder ways to share your intellectual, social and economic capital with others. This could mean becoming a coach or mentor to younger people.

Inheritance issues should also be thought through and included in your mission statement. So many retirees do not give sufficient thought to a fair distribution of family assets, keepsakes and heirlooms. Lack of explicit instructions may create discord and hurt feelings among heirs.

•**Renewing family life.** One of the windfalls of retirement is time available to strengthen family ties. Consider ways to reach out to children and grandchildren, settle old arguments with siblings or aged parents and renew ties with your extended family. You might organize a reunion, dig into genealogy or look up long-lost first cousins.

•**Personal interests.** How often have you said, "I'd like to study guitar or take up woodworking or go to a cooking school, but I just don't have the time"? Well, in retirement, you do. A side benefit of cultivating new interests is a growing circle of friends. One of the most positive predictors of a satisfying retirement is a large social network.

•**Finances.** Money will give you the options and flexibility to carry out your plans, so include a financial strategy in your mission statement.

Best: Consult a financial planner, tax adviser or other qualified professional to be sure that your resources are adequate and to develop strategies for a financially secure retirement.

HOW TO GET STARTED

To write an effective document, you'll need to set aside enough time to sit down and think deeply as you create the bulk of your statement. Naturally, you will add to it and revise it over time as more ideas occur to you...and show all or parts of your statement to some of your family and friends to get their insights. *Start by answering these questions...*

•**How do I stay healthy and active?**

•**How can I share my experience with others?**

•**How will my family relationships be altered?**

•**Which new and old friendships do I wish to nurture?**

•**Which new social and athletic activities might I like?**

•**What do I want to leave to my heirs and charity?**

•**Do I want to work part-time?**

Your mission statement may be just a few succinct paragraphs or it may run to several pages. Just be sure to address your goals, objectives, values and a vision of where you want to be in three to five years. *Some examples to get you started...*

•**Mission...**

•Help my daughter, a single mother, raise her three small children.

•Share my financial-planning expertise by teaching a personal-finance class at a local community college.

•Explore my creative side by signing up for evening painting classes.

•Develop a healthful eating plan.

•Become much more active in my church.

•**Vision...**

•In three to five years, move to Vermont and make new friends.

• Grow my new e-commerce business by 50%.

• Have an established, part-time consulting practice.

• **Values...**

• Always be guided by caring and giving, not jealousy or intolerance.

• Focus on my spiritual life. Practice the habit of gratitude, giving thanks daily for the good things in my life.

• Acknowledge that the human body is my most valuable possession and vow to become the primary caretaker, focusing on a healthful lifestyle.

• **Identity...**

• Replace the accolades received at work with pride in personal development.

• Feel proud of my primary career but excited about new ventures ahead. Enjoy new roles as caregiver, nurturer and homemaker.

• Rejoice in the freedom of retirement.

NOW PUT IT IN ACTION

A well-tailored mission statement may take months or even a few years to evolve. Corporations consider this a living document and so should you. You might tape it above your desk for daily reflection or put it in a drawer for a fresh look. Either way, the personal mission statement will be an indispensable tool in helping you pursue your passions in this new phase of life.

Cell Phone for Seniors

The ClarityLife C900 cell phone has large buttons, oversized text on its video screen, 20-decibel amplification to assist hearing and a one-touch emergency button to contact relatives or another source of help. It also has a built-in flashlight. The cost is about $185.*

More information: Call 800-426-3738 or visit *www.clarityproducts.com.*

*Price subject to change.

Five Amazing Places To Live the Rest of Your Life

Barbara Corcoran, founder of the Corcoran Group real estate company and president of the business consulting company Barbara Corcoran, Inc., both in New York City. She is real estate contributor to NBC's *Today* show and CNBC and cohost of ABC's *Shark Tank* entrepreneurial reality series. Her latest book is *Nextville: Amazing Places to Live Your Life* (Springboard). Her Web site is *http://barbaracorcoran.com.*

Many of today's retirees see retirement as a fresh start—the chance to pursue a creative passion, launch a signature enterprise or further a favorite cause—rather than a never-ending vacation.

For those of us ready to stage a second act, a retirement locale must be more than an affordable place to spend the next phase of our lives. It has to offer stimulating cultural, intellectual and physical lifestyle opportunities.

Here are some top destinations that appeal to a broad range of interests and preferences. *What they all have in common is that they're not full of people who "act old"—they're growing centers of recreation and commerce...*

TOWNS

• **Hot Springs, Arkansas.**

Who: Artists and people of all generations who come to soak in Vapor Valley's thermal waters.

Where: An hour's drive west of Little Rock and near Ouachita National Forest, a sprawling nature preserve.

Why: Hot Springs today boasts music and film festivals plus a large community of painters, potters and sculptors who display their works in dozens of galleries.

How much: The median price of homes is $150,000.*

• **Tempe, Arizona.**

Who: Outdoor types and people who like to volunteer.

Where: A 20-minute drive from Scottsdale and Phoenix.

*Prices subject to change.

Why: Tempe has 300 sunny days per year, 150 miles of bike paths and hundreds of acres of parkland in its busy downtown, around a huge urban lake. It also is home to programs that match over-55 adults with volunteer opportunities, including high school tutoring, as well as second-career opportunities, such as small-business consulting and civic posts.

How much: The median price of homes is $177,000.

• **Eugene, Oregon.**

Who: Environmentally conscious people of all ages.

Where: Approximately two hours south of Portland.

Why: Wind and water supply the bulk of Eugene's power, making it one of the greenest cities in America. Bicycles are the vehicles of choice. Scenery includes wilderness forest and protected wetlands. Home to University of Oregon, Eugene draws youthful souls who give it a smart, independent vibe. This is a good place to start, maybe, an organic-cookie business or alternative bookstore.

How much: The median price of homes is $265,000.

RETIREMENT COMMUNITIES

• **Riderwood in Silver Spring, Maryland.**

Who: A community of 3,000 creative intellectuals, age 60 and up.

Where: A campus 15 miles north of Washington, DC, built in 2007.

Why: Riderwood aims to nurture the mind, offering a theater group, men's chorus, dozens of on-site classes and volunteering opportunities in surrounding neighborhoods.

How much: The entrance fee for a small one-bedroom apartment is $169,000, with a monthly fee starting at $1,600. For a large two-bedroom, two-bath unit, the entrance fee is $330,000 and $2,070 monthly.

• **The Village at Penn State, Pennsylvania.**

Who: Eternal students.

Where: State College, Pennsylvania, which is about halfway between Philadelphia and Pittsburgh.

Why: The Village includes mixed-age housing and a "Life Care" community for people age 62 and up. Penn State students teach free classes to residents of Life Care in return for course credit, and the town of State College has a busy café scene.

How much: Entrance fees in the retirement community start at $181,500 for one-bedroom apartments, with monthly charges starting at about $2,500.

Do-It-Yourself Retirement Planning

Elizabeth K. Miller, CFA, CFP, president of Summit Place Financial Advisors, LLC, a fee-based financial services company, Short Hills, New Jersey, *www.summit placefinancial.com.* Miller is often interviewed by the financial media and is a lecturer at Chautauqua Institution, Chautauqua, New York.

The recent market turmoil probably hurt your retirement savings. You know you could use the advice of a professional, but you do not want to pay the fee in these tough times.

Alternative: The Internet has some excellent resources to help do-it-yourselfers build up their retirement portfolios. *Here are free Web sites to help you answer three important questions...*

• **Am I on track to retire?** To answer this question, begin with a retirement calculator. AARP offers one at *www.aarp.org/money* (go to "Tools" on the left, and choose "Retirement Calculator"). The calculator provides estimate buttons to help you fill in important assumptions, such as future inflation and potential returns on your investments. The results provide a clear analysis, and you can change some of your assumptions. If you use higher investment return assumptions, you won't need to put away as much money as if you use lower returns, so enter these choices carefully. I suggest trying 3%, 5% and 7% to see how your potential returns can change.

• **How should I allocate my investments?** Now that you know how much you need to contribute, how should you allocate your current assets and your future contributions? In these turbulent times, start with a fresh look at your risk tolerance. MSN has a 20-question risk quiz at *http://articles.moneycentral.msn. com/help/tools.aspx* (choose the "Risk Tolerance Quiz" under "Investing"). The results include a basic recommendation for your asset allocation. Go back and change your answers so that you can see how the recommendations change.

Next take a look at an asset-allocation site. Try the SmartMoney One Asset Allocation System, which can be found at *www.smartmoney. com/tools/worksheets*. With this allocator, you can enter your current investments, as well as your future assumptions. The results show you how much you need to rebalance each asset allocation in your portfolio. Try it a few times, changing your choices for "volatility tolerance" and "economic outlook," to see how the recommendations change.

• **What investments should I choose?** Now you are ready to implement your changes. If you need information on investment choices, start at *www.finra.org*. The Financial Industry Regulatory Authority (FINRA) is the largest independent regulatory authority for securities firms in the US (on the Web site, click on "Investors," then go to "Smart Investing"). It offers unbiased educational information on all areas of investing.

If you are ready to choose your investments, try *www.morningstar.com,* which provides independent research on stocks, mutual funds, exchange-traded funds and even some hedge funds. Select the "Funds" tab for the latest news on funds. Then on the left, browse "Investing Ideas" and "Fund Ratings" for ideas for your portfolio. For information on individual stocks, go to the "Stocks" tab or enter a specific stock symbol at the top of the screen.

Women: You Need To Save *More* for Retirement Than Men

After retirement, women live an average of 22 years, compared with 19 years for men. Women must save an additional 2% a year for 30 years to make up for that difference.

But: Women often start saving two to four years later than men, on average, and women invest less—7.3% of earnings, compared with 8.1% for men.

And, one-quarter of women don't contribute to company-sponsored retirement plans at a high enough level to take advantage of the company's matching funds.

Study by Hewitt Associates, human resources consulting firm, Lincolnshire, Illinois.

Annuities Can Repair Your Nest Egg...If You Avoid These Costly Traps

Michael E. Kitces, CFP, CLU, ChFC, director of financial planning for Pinnacle Advisory Group, Inc., a private wealth management firm in Columbia, Maryland, that oversees $600 million of client assets, *www. pinnacleadvisory.com*. He is coauthor of *The Annuity Advisor* (National Underwriter).

Stung by the collapse of the stock market, many retirees and preretirees are turning to annuities to provide guaranteed income for life. Sales of immediate annuities —contracts issued from insurance companies that convert a lump-sum payment into a guaranteed stream of cash flow—have soared recently. Part of the big attraction is that some annuities offer much better returns than bank certificates of deposit (CDs) or short-term government bonds, but there are many dangers amid these opportunities. New products have been designed to counteract the disadvantages, but it is a confusing array. *When it might be wise to consider an annuity—and how to avoid the traps...*

YOU'RE NEWLY RETIRED

In this case, you want a guaranteed payout to start quickly and provide stability throughout your retirement.

The solution: An immediate, fixed lifetime annuity.

How it works: You sign a contract and write a lump-sum check to an insurance company. The insurer invests the money and guarantees to pay you a predetermined fixed dollar amount (on a recurring basis) for the rest of your life.

Example: A 65-year-old who buys an immediate, fixed lifetime annuity today may receive $6,000 to $8,000 every year for each $100,000 invested in the annuity. These payments are partially growth and partially a return of principal.

Drawbacks...

• **A lack of inflation protection.** Without inflation adjustments, the annuity payments may be unable to cover all of your needs in later years.

• **Lack of significant capital appreciation.** The amount you invest in an annuity might provide you with much higher returns if you invested in riskier assets, like stocks, though, of course, there is no guarantee that would happen.

Wise moves...

• **Wait a year or so into retirement before buying an immediate annuity.** At that point, you will have a realistic idea of how much money you need each month.

Example: A 65-year-old man has a $1 million nest egg and needs $40,000 a year in living expenses in addition to Social Security. He'll likely have to invest at least $500,000 in an annuity to receive that much, leaving him $500,000 to invest in a mix of cash and bonds for short-term needs and stocks for longer-term appreciation.

• **Do not use all or nearly all of your retirement money to buy an immediate annuity.** Instead, buy one that, when combined with the Social Security benefits you receive, covers no more than your basic living expenses each month. That way, you'll be able to invest your remaining money more aggressively, if you choose to, without having to tap into it during downturns in the market.

• **Add an inflation rider to your contract if you can.** If your payouts remain the same over time, inflation can eat away at the purchasing power of that money. An inflation rider increases your payments annually to keep pace with inflation. Such a rider is expensive. You can expect your initial payouts to be at least 20% lower than initial payouts without an inflation rider.

Note: Many companies do not provide this option. Companies that do offer this option include The Vanguard Group and New York Life.

• **Consider a "joint and survivor" annuity if you're married.** This type of fixed lifetime annuity stipulates that in the event of your death, your spouse will continue to receive your regular payouts.

Cost: The initial payouts you receive will be at minimum 10% lower than with a single-life annuity.

• **Buy a "life with term certain" annuity.** These annuities provide payments for life but also guarantee a minimum number of payments—so if the "for life" time period turns out to be short, heirs still receive some, and possibly most, of the money back.

• **Create a "ladder" of immediate annuities by purchasing several contracts over a number of years.** The average payouts for annuities tend to rise and fall with interest rates at the time of purchase. Since interest rates are so low now, payouts on annuities will be relatively skimpy. By staggering your purchases annually over the next several years, you make sure that not all of your money gets locked in to a lifetime of lower annual payments.

YOU'RE NEARING OR IN RETIREMENT

You don't need a guaranteed payout now, but you want to be sure that you have payouts when you get older, especially if you might face higher health-care costs or live to a very old age.

Solution: A fixed "longevity" annuity.

How it works: It's like having an immediate annuity that doesn't start for 20 years. You pay for it now and the money grows on a tax-deferred basis until you reach old age, typically 80 or 85. At that time, the insurance company begins to pay you guaranteed, regular income that will continue for the rest of your life.

Example: A 65-year-old woman can typically get a $60,000 a year payout starting at age 85 for an investment of about $71,000.

Drawbacks: Your heirs get nothing if you die before you begin to receive payments, and there are no inflation riders available.

Wise move: Buy the longevity annuity when you retire. My clients typically buy them during their 60s.

Reason: Coverage is relatively cheap at that age.

YOU ARE STILL WORKING

You want to keep your nest egg growing aggressively when you are still working, but you also want to make sure that you have some guaranteed income when you do retire.

Solution: A variable annuity. Variable annuities offer the possibility of better returns than fixed annuities and some level of guaranteed payout.

How it works: You invest one lump sum in stock or bond mutual-fund–like portfolios called "subaccounts." Investing in a variable annuity has a couple of key advantages over simply investing on your own in mutual funds—your money grows tax-deferred…and you may get some form of guaranteed payout at an agreed-upon age in the future, depending on whether and what type of guaranteed income rider(s) are purchased.

Unlike with a fixed annuity, a variable annuity will allow you to access your principal should your plans change. You also typically get a death benefit so that your heirs receive a payout at least equal to the amount you initially invested, minus your withdrawals, even if your investments perform poorly.

The most logical candidates for variable annuities are investors in their 50s who have already maxed out their retirement plan contributions and don't need to convert investments into an income stream for at least five or 10 years.

Drawbacks: Fees are higher and more complex than if you simply invest on your own in mutual funds. Add to that the costs of investing in the subaccounts and the cost of guarantees and riders, and it could easily mean that about 2% to 4% of your total invested amount annually goes to fees. You also face stiff penalties with variable annuities. For instance, if you withdraw your principal within the first seven years, you might pay a surrender fee of 1% to 7% of the money you withdraw after a limited number of penalty-free withdrawals.

Tax liability: You owe ordinary income tax on any investment gains you get as payouts, but no tax on your original principal.

Wise move: Consider buying a guarantee that you can sustain a certain amount of income over time if your principal declines or is exhausted. These guarantees are known as "living benefits riders."

The riders typically come in three varieties: Guaranteed minimum income benefits and guaranteed minimum withdrawal benefits, each of which provides some type of minimum guaranteed amount of future retirement cash flow…and guaranteed minimum accumulation benefits, which may make a policyholder's nest egg whole after 10 years if there are no withdrawals, even if it is worth less than what he/she started with.

Cost: An additional 0.4% to 0.8% in annual fees.

Note: Whichever type of annuity you buy, be sure to set aside money for "liquidity needs," that is, money to cover emergencies.

More from Michael Kitces, CFP…

How to Shop for an Annuity

When you are looking to buy an annuity, keep these two suggestions in mind…

• **Find the best payout.** Fixed and variable annuities are sold through insurance agents, banks and major investment firms. But the contracts themselves are actually issued from life insurance carriers, such as Metropolitan Life and Prudential. Since each insurer uses proprietary formulas to determine their payouts to you, and since annuity prices are not negotiable, it does pay to comparison shop. For example, an immediate annuity with a survivor benefit purchased today for a man age 70 could pay from $516 up to $769 each month based on a lump sum of $100,000.*

Helpful resources: Immediate-Annuities. com compares prices at 20 leading insurers... AnnuityFYI.com represents various insurers and offers educational resources to learn about and compare annuities.

• **Investigate the financial strength of the insurance company that guarantees your annuity.** The current financial crisis as well as the collapse of some insurers has heightened fears about whether the insurance companies we hand our money to will be around in later years to make payments.

Best: Check the health of the annuity issuer with the three main independent rating agencies—A.M. Best (*www.ambest.com*), Moody's (*www.moodys.com*) and Standard & Poor's (*www.standardandpoors.com*). Each of these firms has its own grading scale and research methods. Limit your options to insurers that receive either an A+ from A.M. Best or AA– or better from Moody's and Standard & Poor's.

*Prices subject to change.

Perfectly Legal Ways to Cut Taxes on Your IRAs

Ed Slott, CPA, Rockville Centre, New York, an IRA consultant and publisher of *Ed Slott's IRA Advisor,* a monthly newsletter. He is author of *Stay Rich for Life!* (Ballantine) and a book, workbook and DVD set called *Secrets to Financial Freedom* (Bottom Line Books, see *www.keepyoursavings.com/blp.*) Slott has been the host of two public television specials on estate planning. His Web site is *www.irahelp.com.*

Thirteen million households are eligible to convert tax-deferred traditional IRA accounts to tax-exempt Roth IRAs in 2010. That includes millions who couldn't do so previously because the old rules did not allow people with annual incomes of $100,000 or more to convert.

The new rules eliminating that income cap have raised many questions for those considering such a move. *Here are answers to some of those questions...*

• **If I convert, do I have to convert all the money in my traditional IRAs?** No. You can convert any portion of your traditional IRAs. As a result of the conversion, you will have to pay tax on any amount that you are converting if you never paid tax on it before, but you will never pay tax again on the Roth IRA money, no matter how much it appreciates. You can avoid pushing yourself into a higher tax bracket by spreading the conversions out over several years. And for the amount you convert in 2010, you can declare half on your tax filing for 2011 and half for 2012.

• **What if I have both pretax and after-tax money in my IRAs?** On any Roth IRA conversion, you will owe income tax based on what percentage of your overall IRA assets those pretax dollars represent.

Example: John Smith has two traditional IRAs. One holds $20,000 of pretax dollars and the other holds a $4,000 after-tax contribution plus $1,000 of gains that have never been subject to income tax. Therefore, John has a total of $21,000 in pretax money, which is 84% of his total. So on any Roth IRA conversion, 84% of the amount that's converted will be taxable income.

• **Can I convert money in my traditional 401(k) accounts directly to a Roth IRA, including money that I recently contributed to my 401(k)?** Yes, but only if you are eligible to roll over your traditional 401(k)s to a traditional IRA. Typically, that means that you have left or are leaving your employer. In that situation, you can convert any or all of the money in your traditional 401(k) to a Roth IRA, including money that you just contributed.

• **What if the market crashes again and the value of my converted account plunges?** I will be liable for tax on money that I've lost! There is a tax escape hatch. You have until October 15 of the next calendar year to "recharacterize" the account back to a traditional IRA and not pay tax on the converted money. Then, in the calendar year after that, if you have waited at least 30 days, you can convert it back to a Roth, hopefully with a lower tax bite than you would have paid on the original conversion.

•**Are there still limits on my income that could prevent me from contributing directly to a Roth IRA?** Yes and no. Technically, high-income taxpayers (those having modified adjusted gross incomes of more than $120,000...or more than $177,000 for joint filers) still are prevented from contributing to a Roth IRA in 2010.

But you can get around that. First, contribute after-tax dollars—money on which you already have paid taxes—to a traditional IRA. Then convert that traditional IRA to a Roth. You will pay additional tax only on the amount by which the traditional IRA has appreciated.

Easy Way for IRAs to Invest in Gold

Current tax law prohibits IRAs from holding "collectibles," which generally include physical gold. But, in two private rulings, the IRS has held that IRAs can invest in exchange-traded funds (ETFs) that hold gold without the investment being deemed a collectible. The IRS held the investment in the ETF to be in a security since the IRA has no claim to the underlying gold itself and no way to make the ETF distribute it.

Benefit: ETFs trade on the stock exchanges like stocks.

Caution: Private rulings technically apply only to the parties that received them (the ETFs), but they tend to be persuasive with auditors. See IRS Letter Rulings 200732026 and 200732027.

Bob Carlson, editor, *Bob Carlson's Retirement Watch,* Box 970, Oxon Hill, Maryland 20750, *www.retirement watch.com.*

Should You Pay Off Your Mortgage Before You Retire?

Phillip Storms, principal of Westmont Companies, a Denver-based financial services company specializing in real estate and mortgage planning, *www.westmont companies.com.*

Former generations of Americans almost always paid off their mortgages before retiring. Today, more than a third of all households headed by someone age 65 to 74 still have mortgages.

Having debt means living with financial risk —but continuing a mortgage into retirement often is the best option. *How to decide what to do...*

•**If you can afford to pay off your mortgage in one lump sum without decimating your savings...**consider whether you will benefit more from keeping the money where it is or using it to pay off the mortgage.

If your savings are mostly in stocks: Your investments might earn 6% to 8% per year, on average, although there is no guarantee that your returns won't fall short of that, or even lose value. Meanwhile, your mortgage rate is likely below 6%. Add in the tax deductibility of the interest portion of your mortgage payments, and you might be better off keeping your investments than paying off your mortgage—unless the concept of not owning your home outright in retirement keeps you up at night.

•**If you have a significant portion of your savings in low-interest CDs, money-market funds or conservative bond funds...**it will probably be better to pay off your mortgage.

Traps: If you need to make a large withdrawal from your IRA or 401(k) to pay off a mortgage, that could trigger a big tax bill and rob you of years of tax-deferred investment growth, so try to avoid that step.

Beware: Check whether your mortgage lender will impose a "prepayment penalty." These are most common when mortgages are less than five years old.

•**If you can't pay off the mortgage out of savings all at once...**you have options...

•Accelerate your monthly payments and pay off your mortgage before retirement. If your mortgage is not completely paid off by your retirement date, however, it usually does not make sense to continue the accelerated payments. The early years of retirement are when retirees are most likely to be healthy and eager to enjoy their freedom. It would be a shame to spend these years economizing to make unnecessarily large mortgage payments, only to learn, potentially, that you're no longer healthy enough to enjoy your retirement when the mortgage is paid off.

•Refinance the existing balance to shrink your monthly mortgage payments. By refinancing to a new 30-year fixed-rate mortgage you'll spread your remaining debt over three decades. If your current mortgage has less than 15 years remaining, that could cut your monthly mortgage bill by half or more, assuming that you can find an attractive interest rate. You will have to pay closing costs on this new loan. Still, this is an appropriate alternative if your current mortgage payments are large enough to significantly detract from your quality of life.

When to Use a Reverse Mortgage

Tyler D. Kraemer, Esq., a real estate, finance and estate-planning specialist and principal in the law firm of Kraemer Kendall Benson Rupp Deen LLC, Colorado Springs, *www.k2blaw.com*. He is coauthor of *The Complete Guide to Reverse Mortgages* (Adams Media).

Contemplating getting a reverse mortgage? *In the following situations, it can make sense...*

•**You are facing foreclosure.** In this circumstance, it is nearly impossible to get a traditional home-equity loan, and selling your house outright might leave you owing more than you get from the sale. A reverse mortgage can possibly save you from losing your house if you have significant equity built up. You can never be foreclosed on or forced to vacate your house because you "missed your mortgage payment."

•**Your savings have been depleted to a dangerously low level, and you need the income from a reverse mortgage** to cover health-care costs or other critical monthly expenses. For some retirees, this could provide the time needed for investments ravaged by the recent bear market to recover.

•**You plan to stay in your house for five years or more.** If you sell the house before then and pay back the reverse mortgage loan, then the cost of the loan will seem significant compared to the benefit. If you keep the loan for a long time, you spread the up-front cost over many years.

•**You want to buy a new home but would be forced to use all of your savings to do it.** A federal program called HECM for Purchase allows you to buy a new principal residence and receive a reverse mortgage on it at the same time.

Example: An elderly couple lived in a two-story house valued at $600,000. They sold the home and wanted to buy a one-story home closer to their children for $600,000. Getting a traditional mortgage for the new property wasn't a good option, because they were on a fixed income and didn't want to make mortgage payments each month. They also needed some of the profits from their old home's sale to live on in the future.

Solution: The couple applied for, and received, a reverse mortgage of about $400,000 to buy the new house. That meant that to buy the new home, they had to put down only $200,000, which they acquired from the sale of the old house. The couple makes no monthly payments to the lender—instead, the lender will recover the loan principal plus interest when the home eventually is sold.

BEFORE YOU TAKE THE PLUNGE

Reverse mortgages are complicated. Careful consideration and consultation with your adviser is critical before taking the plunge. In fact, federal law mandates that you attend a session with an independent financial counselor to ensure that you understand all the implications of what you're doing. *Also be sure to...*

•**Comparison shop.** Compare offers, including interest rates, and check the lender's credentials with state regulators and better-business agencies. As with traditional loans, you can save by getting quotes from different lenders. To find reverse mortgage lenders in your state, go to *www.hud.gov* (click on "Resources," then on "Lender Locator").

• **Know the warning signs of unscrupulous lenders.** Reverse mortgages can be tricky, and scams are becoming more common.

Examples: The broker or lender tries to get you to invest your reverse mortgage loan money in costly financial products, such as deferred annuities...or the lender asks you to sign loan paperwork that is not completely filled out.

The bottom line is that reverse mortgages are not for everyone. Spending money on the up-front fees usually makes sense only if you need the cash and you do not have another readily available source.

Secrets of Getting the Most Money from Social Security

Theodore Sarenski, CPA/PFS, CFP, president and CEO of DB&B Financial Services, LLC, an investment and financial-planning organization in Syracuse, New York, *www.dbbllc.com*. Sarenski has made numerous presentations concerning the US Social Security system at the American Institute of Certified Public Accountants' (AICPA) annual conferences and was one of the reviewers of the AICPA's 2005 white paper on Social Security reform, *www.aicpa.org*.

For the first time in more than three decades, in 2010—and possibly in 2011, as well—there will not be a Social Security Cost-of-Living Adjustment (COLA). So today, more than ever, it's important to squeeze as much money as you possibly can out of the system. *Five strategies that can help you...*

• **Delay filing for benefits.** Postpone filing for benefits until age 70.

Example: Say that you are eligible for a $1,000 monthly benefit when you retire at age 62. That's only $12,000 a year. If you wait until age 70 to file, your initial monthly Social Se-

curity checks will increase by 76%, to $1,760. Your future COLA will be higher, in dollar terms, as well.

Downside: If you do not have the money to pay for the initial years of your retirement without Social Security, don't do this. If you delay filing until age 70, but die before age 80, you'll receive less in total benefits than you would have had you filed at 62.

• **Boost spousal benefits with a "start-and-suspend" strategy.** If you earned much more than your spouse during your working years, your spouse should consider filing for "spousal benefits" based on your earnings history once you start receiving benefits, rather than for benefits based on his/her own earnings.

Example: Your spouse's Social Security benefits statement states that he will receive $600 every month starting at full retirement age. Your statement says that you will receive $1,800 per month starting at full retirement age. Rather than filing for benefits based on his own earning record, your spouse has the option of instead filing for spousal benefits, which are equal to 50% of your benefits—in this case, $900 per month.

Unfortunately, having a spouse who intends to claim spousal benefits based on your earnings record can complicate your decision regarding when to file for benefits. You might wish to wait until age 70 to file for benefits in order to collect the maximum benefit, but your partner cannot file for spousal benefits based on your earnings until you file for your own benefits. Plus, while your future wage-earner benefits continue to climb at around 8% each year as long as you postpone the start of benefits up to age 70, your partner's future monthly spousal benefit checks will not continue to increase once your spouse reaches what the government calls "full" retirement age. This is between age 65 and 67, depending on the year of your partner's birth.

Strategy: File for your benefits when your spouse reaches full retirement age, then immediately suspend your benefits by filing SSA Form 521, Request for Withdrawal of Application, with the Social Security Administration to request a "voluntary suspension" of benefits.

(You can find the form at *www.ssa.gov* or by calling 800-772-1213.) Your partner can claim spousal benefits on your suspended account, but the size of your future monthly checks will continue to grow as if you had not yet filed for benefits. End the suspension by contacting the SSA again by age 70, the point at which you will collect the maximum benefit.

• **Switch from spousal benefits to wage-earner benefits.** As described above, a married person can file for benefits based on his own earnings history or for spousal benefits founded on the spouse's earning history. But there's a third option—while you can't file for both at the same time, you can file first for one and later for the other. Doing so could be your best alternative if you and your partner earned comparable amounts during your careers.

Strategy: One spouse—preferably the older spouse if there is an age difference—files for benefits at his full retirement age. When the other spouse reaches her full retirement age, she files for spousal benefits. By delaying the start of her own benefits, this second spouse allows her Social Security benefits to continue to grow at 8% per year, as if she were not receiving any benefits at all.

Next step: This second spouse switches to her own benefits upon turning 70, when the monthly checks reach their maximum. This strategy is particularly advantageous when the spouse who "switches" has reason to expect an unusually long life span, perhaps because of excellent health or family history. The longer this spouse lives, the greater the advantage of maximizing her monthly payments by delaying the start of benefits until age 70.

Example: Let's say you and your spouse would receive $1,000 apiece per month from Social Security if you both filed for benefits based on your own earnings at your full retirement age of 66. Instead, your partner files for benefits at 66, but you claim spousal benefits based on your partner's earnings. This reduces your monthly check to $500—half of your partner's benefit. At age 70, you file for your own benefits. Waiting those four years to file on your own earnings increases your monthly check by eight percentage points per

year, to $1,320. As a couple, you'll come out $14,400 ahead if the "switching" spouse lives to age 80…and $52,800 ahead if the switching spouse lives to age 90.

Caution: This strategy should not be implemented prior to the switching spouse's full retirement age. If you file for spousal benefits any earlier, the monthly Social Security checks will be permanently reduced.

• **Know the rules about remarrying.** A divorced person is entitled to claim spousal benefits based on his former spouse's earnings, assuming the marriage lasted at least 10 years. Remarry before age 60 (or age 50 if you are disabled), however, and you lose the right to claim spousal benefits from the previous marriage. You will be eligible for spousal benefits based only on your new partner's earnings.

Strategy: Consider postponing remarriage until after you turn 60 if your former spouse earned more than your new one and much more than you. When you remarry at age 60 or older, you can claim spousal benefits based on the earnings of your current partner or of a previous partner to whom you were married for at least 10 years.

• **Obtain an interest-free loan from the Social Security Administration.** Would you rather get your hands on your Social Security benefits as soon as possible or maximize your monthly benefit checks by waiting to file? It's possible to do both.

Strategy: File for benefits as soon as you retire, and collect them. But then, before you turn age 70, file SSA Form 521 and repay the benefits that you have received. Then refile for benefits at age 70. This strategy will give you access to your benefits in your 60s…and you will receive maximum monthly benefit checks after age 70, the same as you would have if you had never filed the first time.

The Social Security Administration doesn't charge interest or penalties for utilizing this claim-and-repay strategy, so it's like getting a loan with a 0% interest rate. If you invest your Social Security checks during your 60s, any profit you earn is yours to keep (minus the usual taxes on investment profits, of course).

Warning: If, before you turn 70, you can't afford to pay back the benefits you have received, you will then be stuck with the lower monthly benefit checks for life.

More from Theodore Sarenski, CPA...

How to Pay Much Less in Social Security Taxes

The Social Security system will begin paying out more in benefits than it receives in payroll taxes starting in 2016. The Obama administration has not yet announced its plans for plugging this gap, but any solution is likely to involve higher taxes.

Social Security taxes already are high. Working Americans pay 6.2% of their wages in Social Security payroll taxes—or 12.4% if they're self-employed—on up to $106,800 of income. On top of that, the IRS expects many to pay income taxes on the Social Security benefits that they receive throughout retirement, even though taxpayers in essence already paid income taxes on this money back when they earned wages, a portion of which was diverted into the Social Security system.

Strategies for trimming Social Security payroll taxes and income tax on Social Security benefits...

BEFORE RETIREMENT

Here is what some business owners—and employees who have a degree of control over when they are paid—can do to cut their Social Security payroll taxes...

●**Alternate high-earning years with low-earning years.** Social Security payroll taxes are imposed on only a limited amount of your earned income. In 2010, just the first $106,800 of income is subject to payroll tax. (This figure, called the "wage base," increases in most years with the cost of living.) Certain business owners can take advantage of this by paying themselves significantly more than the wage base in some years and significantly less in other years.

Example: An S corporation owner who ordinarily pays himself $110,000 per year instead pays himself $40,000 in 2008...$40,000 in 2009...and $250,000 in 2010. Because only $106,800 of that $250,000 is subject to the 12.4% Social Security payroll tax in 2010 (the combined rate paid by the owner and his corporation), he saves $14,818 in taxes compared with the three-year even distribution of pay.

Caution: By "stacking" your pay into certain years this way, you may bump a portion of your income into a higher income tax bracket or into the alternative minimum tax—exactly how much depends on your filing status, among other factors.

Tax-saver for employees: If your base pay is significantly below the annual Social Security wage base, but you receive big year-end bonuses that bring you into the vicinity of the $106,800 cap, ask your employer to postpone every other bonus from the end of one year to the beginning of the next, creating alternating double-bonus and no-bonus years. If this results in annual compensation well below the wage base in one year, but well above in the next, the overall Social Security taxes you pay will be reduced.

●**Married couples who work together in family businesses can allocate income unevenly between spouses.** The high-earning spouse's income won't face any payroll taxes above the Social Security wage base.

Note: This strategy makes particular sense when the lower-earning partner expects to eventually claim the 50% Social Security spousal benefit rather than use his/her own Social Security earnings history to determine retirement benefits.

Example: A woman is an attorney in private practice, while her husband acts as her part-time office manager. The business earns $250,000 each year and pays $230,000 to the attorney and $20,000 to her husband. Compared with dividing the income more or less evenly between partners, this frees $123,200 (versus $36,400 if both salaries are equal) from payroll taxes, saving $10,763 per year.

Caution: The IRS might take issue if the spouse's income is clearly far out of line with the work that is performed and thus a blatant attempt to dodge payroll taxes.

●**Family businesses can pay the business owners' children significant salaries.** Those under age 18 are not required to pay any federal payroll tax when they work for their parents, and in many states, they are exempt from state employment taxes as well.

Warning: The child's income needs to be roughly appropriate for the work performed or the IRS could conclude that the parents are illegally hiding their earnings from taxation.

AFTER RETIREMENT

When your income is between $25,000 and $34,000 in a year in which you receive Social Security benefits ($32,000 and $44,000 if married and filing jointly), you must pay income tax on 50% of your Social Security benefits. If your income is more than $34,000 ($44,000 if married and filing jointly), you must pay income tax on up to 85% of your benefits.

These income thresholds refer to something known as "combined income"—your adjusted gross income plus 50% of your Social Security benefits plus nontaxable interest income, such as income from municipal bonds. (For details, see IRS Publication 915, Social Security and Equivalent Railroad Retirement Benefits, available at *www.irs.gov.*)

Good news: Here are three ways to legally reduce or avoid Social Security benefits taxes altogether…

•**Spend down your tax-deferred retirement accounts before filing for Social Security benefits.** If you have lots of tax-deferred retirement savings and wish to avoid benefits taxes—and you haven't started receiving Social Security retirement benefits—do not file for Social Security benefits until age 70. Until then, live primarily off money from your tax-deferred retirement accounts. While withdrawals are taxable income, benefits taxation thresholds are irrelevant if you're not yet receiving benefits.

By the time you near age 70, you might have spent the lion's share of your tax-deferred savings. But because your Social Security benefits increase by 7% or 8% per year for each year you wait to file between age 62 and age 70, your inflated Social Security checks—together with your non-tax-deferred savings and the remainder of your tax-deferred savings—may provide a more comfortable retirement.

Exception: Delaying the start of benefits is a bad idea if poor health or family history suggests that you might not live to your late 70s or later.

Caution: Don't wait until age 70½ to begin making withdrawals from tax-deferred retirement plans, or IRS required distribution rules will tie your hands and force you to make withdrawals in years when they do not make sense from a tax perspective.

•**Avoid the midyear retirement benefits trap.** If you retire in the middle of a calendar year, the income you earned during your final months in the workforce could easily push you over the threshold and make your first year's Social Security benefits taxable. If you retire midyear, wait at least until the following calendar year to file for Social Security benefits.

Exception: Your earned income might not push you past the benefits taxation threshold if you were employed for only a few months of this final year…or had a low salary during this final year.

•**Relocate to a state that doesn't tax Social Security benefits.** State income taxes can exceed 8%.

Solution: Consider retiring to a state that has no state income tax…or which excludes Social Security benefits from taxation.

Those states that do tax Social Security benefits: Colorado, Connecticut, Iowa, Kansas, Minnesota, Missouri, Montana, Nebraska, New Mexico, North Dakota, Rhode Island, Utah, Vermont and West Virginia. (Iowa and Missouri are phasing out this tax.)

Medicare Premiums Rise Above $100 for First Time

Basic Medicare premiums rise 15% for 12 million people in 2010. The increase—to $110.50 per month—marks the first time that premiums will reach above $100. But 73% of Medicare recipients will not face higher rates, because due to federal law, their premiums cannot go up more than their increase in Social Security benefits—which will not go up at all in 2010. There is a move in Congress to block the premium increase.

The New York Times, www.nytimes.com.

Are You Covered by Medicare When Abroad?

Nancy Dunnan a New York City–based financial and travel adviser and author or coauthor of 25 books, including *How to Invest $50–$5,000* (HarperCollins).

Medicare generally does not cover any health care that's outside the US. The government's definition of the US includes the 50 states, Washington, DC, Puerto Rico, Guam, the US Virgin Islands, American Samoa and the Northern Mariana Islands.

Exceptions: Medicare will pay for treatment in Mexico and Canada if you have an emergency while traveling in the US but the closest hospital is in Mexico or Canada...or you have an emergency while traveling to/from Alaska via Canada and the nearest hospital is in Canada.

On a cruise: For you to be eligible for coverage, the doctor treating you must be the cruise line's doctor on that particular ship. If the ship is no more than six hours from a US port, you will get coverage. Medicare will also pay for health services provided by hospital staff if you are subsequently admitted to a US, Mexican or Canadian hospital for an emergency. However, the ship's doctor must have taken care of you on the ship (while the ship met the geographic restriction stated above) and then sent you to the hospital on the same day for the same medical condition.

Good idea: Consider one of the Medicare C through J supplement (Medigap) plans sold by private companies that provide foreign emergency coverage.

More information: 800-633-4227 or *www. medicare.gov/publications/pubs/pdf/11037. pdf.*

Working After Retirement May Keep You Healthy

Postretirement work helps protect against illness.

A recent finding: Researchers who interviewed 12,189 adults found that those who took "bridge jobs"—full-time, part-time or self-employment—after an official retirement had fewer major diseases (such as diabetes, cancer and arthritis) and performed better at daily tasks than those who stopped working.

Theory: The increased physical and mental activity—as well as social interaction—required for working protects against chronic illness and functional decline.

Yujie Zhan, researcher, department of psychology, University of Maryland, College Park.

Volunteer and Live Longer

Seniors were asked if they had spent any time in the past 12 months doing volunteer work for religious, educational or other charitable organizations. Even after researchers adjusted for factors such as chronic health conditions, physical limitations and socioeconomic status—as earlier studies had not—volunteers were less than half as likely to die during the four-year study as nonvolunteers.

Theory: Volunteering encourages social networking, physical and mental activities and self-esteem—all of which contribute to good health.

Sei J. Lee, MD, assistant professor of geriatrics, University of California, San Francisco, and the leader of a study of 6,360 people over age 65.

How to Get People to Really *Listen* to You

Don Gabor, founder of Conversation Arts Media, a communications coaching firm in Brooklyn, New York, *www.dongabor.com*. He's author of *How to Start a Conversation and Make Friends* (Fireside) and *Turn Small Talk into Big Deals* (McGraw-Hill Professional).

One of the biggest frustrations for seniors is feeling marginalized. Your adult children are very busy living their own lives…the grandkids would rather spend their time staring at little screens and moving their thumbs…everyone from young coworkers to store salespeople treats you as though you're a bit out of touch. I used to accept the cliché that older people are ignored by society because their minds are slowing down—until I hit my 60s.

Perhaps my mental processing is not as speedy as it used to be, but I'm just as smart, insightful and prepared to make intelligent decisions as ever.

My conclusion: It is not a physical aging problem that can make seniors feel pushed aside—it is actually a communication problem. *And only we can solve it…*

THE COMMUNICATION GAP

Younger people interact with the world differently than seniors. They like to multitask constantly, putting premium value on processing large amounts of information from a variety of sources and communicating in rapid bursts. Rather than speak to someone for 30 minutes over their phone, they prefer to send 30 cellphone text messages back and forth as they rush about their day. Speed and quantity are more important than the quality of conversations and interactions.

At the same time, older folks are also dealing with unique issues on a daily basis that younger people may not understand or value but that have a powerful effect on the way we act.

Example: Many of us are struggling to maintain a feeling of importance and control as we let go of responsibilities and settle into retirement and downsizing.

Result: We want so much to feel important and independent that we may come off as stubborn and controlling. We are also engaged in shaping and understanding what our life has meant, sifting through our experiences, trying to validate memories that will live on after we die. This intense need to figure out our legacy gives us a tendency to repeat stories, focus in on "unimportant" details and often jump from one topic to another in conversations.

Once you understand these differences between the younger and older generations, it's easier to see why younger family members or strangers might act as if you're invisible or incompetent—and it's easy to lash out when they do. But that frequently serves to alienate us even more.

Much better: Improve your communication style. I'm not suggesting you change your personality or act in ways you do not believe in. Just a few tweaks in how you behave can make a significant difference in being heard. *My secrets…*

• **Present yourself as physically alert and interested.** Body language is powerful, but it is especially important for seniors who must fight the general perception that they're "out of it." *Strategies…*

• When someone smiles at you, smile back and make eye contact. If it's uncomfortable for you to look into someone's eyes, there is a six-inch diameter surrounding the eyes, including the hair, nose, lips and earlobes, where you can rest your gaze and still appear attentive.

• Keep your arms open when you talk with others. Crossing them may feel more comfortable or warmer, but it also makes you look judgmental and skeptical.

• Lean forward slightly when you are seated. Leaning back can give off a strong sense of disengagement.

• **Avoid starting your conversations with negative words.** There is no bigger turnoff to people who phone you than launching into a harangue about how they haven't called you in such a long time…or responding to the question, "How are you?" with "My back is killing me." All you do with such responses is make people perceive you as cantankerous.

Much better: In any conversation, engage in some interesting, positive chat before you express any discontent. And if you want to discuss someone's failure to pay attention to you, broach it in positive terms. Instead of saying, "Would it kill you to pick up the phone more often?" try "It makes me so happy to hear your voice that I wish we could talk more often."

●**Make your point right at the beginning.** Younger people need to move through the world as quickly and efficiently as possible. Instead of processing information from start to finish, they jump right to the end and fill in details later.

Situation: Your gutters are clogging, and you want to take your young neighbor up on his earlier offer to clean them. It may feel natural and friendly for you to build up to your request by mentioning details such as the GI loan you got after WWII to buy the house or how the neighborhood has changed, but this makes your neighbor want to roll his eyes at what he considers minutiae.

Solution: Think of your conversations as newspaper headlines. Even though it may feel abrupt or awkward, present the most important information up front—"I need my gutters cleaned." Then you can fill in any supporting background material (including expressions of thanks).

●**Recognize the negative effect you have when you refuse to make decisions.**

Situation: An adult child is worried about whether it's safe for you to keep driving. You make excuses to avoid talking about it. You're being evasive because you're afraid that your car will be taken from you and you're insulted that your child thinks you could be a danger to yourself and others. A discussion may lead to restrictions on your lifestyle and a compromise of your independence. So, you simply ignore the issue, hoping it will go away.

Your child may interpret your evasiveness as an inability to face reality. This colors his/her overall opinion of you. Since you will not give him any constructive input, his conclusion is that decisions must be made for you.

Solution: Be aware of when you evade difficult decisions and instead make an effort to work toward a real solution. For instance, you can acknowledge to your child that many older people should give up their cars. But you are not yet one of them. Offer to take a driving test or a defensive driving course to demonstrate your competence. Or reach a compromise, such as not driving at night or in bad weather. Making an effort to engage in difficult choices increases your chances of getting your own way on the issues most important to you.

●**Avoid condemning people when you disagree with them.** Aging imparts a certain wisdom that you derive from experience, but many older folks take that as a right to speak what's on their minds whenever and however they want.

Making statements such as, "That's the most ridiculous thing I ever heard," may make you feel as if you've won the argument, but it insults other people. What's more, when family or friends are exposed to a steady stream of your opinions and criticism, it undermines their trust and confidence in you and interferes with their ability to take you seriously.

Much better: Show a desire to understand the other person's point of view. Say, "Well, that may be a great movie, but I didn't particularly care for it." You might even use humor to defuse a tense disagreement. Say, "I don't agree with you, but will forgive you anyway" (with a smile).

Grandparent Visitation Rights

Grandparents have visitation rights in all 50 states. But the provisions of state laws vary widely, and you may have to go to court to have them enforced. The US Supreme Court says that parents have priority in resolving visitation disputes unless they have been alleged to be not fit. Grandparents should attempt to develop and maintain solid relationships with grandchildren that will last even if parents divorce or a parent dies. Negotiate your visitation if possible. Otherwise, consider mediation (for information, contact the American Association for Marriage and Family Therapy at 703-838-9808 or visit *www.aamft.org*). Seek court intervention only if absolutely necessary.

Andrew H. Hook, CELA, member, National Academy of Elder Law Attorneys, Virginia Beach, Virginia, *www.naela.org*.

Surprising Services for Seniors

Joan Rattner Heilman an award-winning travel and lifestyles writer based in New York. She is author of *Unbelievably Good Deals and Great Adventures That You Absolutely Can't Get Unless You're Over 50, 2009–2010 edition* (McGraw-Hill).

Y ou can make your life a lot easier when you take advantage of the many unique privileges and services designed especially to help seniors. Many organizations and businesses today recognize the great potential of marketing to this huge segment of the population and have come up with ways to serve seniors. *Some especially useful ones...*

MAKING A MOVE

Moving from one home to another, maybe downsizing to a condo or an apartment, is a huge job that can be physically and emotionally draining. Senior move managers, organizers who specialize in assisting older people with the problems of relocating, can minimize the stress of this major transition by doing most of the work for you. They can help you pare down your belongings, decide what to take and what to dispose of, recommend charities for donations and help sell unwanted items. They also get estimates from moving companies, oversee the movers, arrange the move date, supervise the packing and unpacking, have the house cleaned—just about anything that you need related to your move. In most cases, you can decide on a package price that includes many services or choose only those that you need and pay by the hour.

Typical package cost: $3,000 to $5,000.*

*Prices subject to change.

Information: National Association of Senior Move Managers (877-606-2766 or *www. nasmm.org*).

TRAVEL COMPANIONS

If you can't or don't want to travel alone, Flying Companions will provide an experienced and insured air traveler who has passed a background check to accompany and assist you when flying anywhere in the world, making the trip as comfortable and hassle-free as possible. The escort does whatever is needed, including making reservations, picking you up at your home or meeting you at the airport, handling airport check-in, getting the two of you through security, handling the baggage, helping with meals and bathroom trips if necessary and delivering you to the prearranged destination, whether it is the airport, a hotel or a residence. The escort will even stay with you, if you like, for an entire vacation. Meanwhile, family or friends will be kept informed by phone or e-mail along the way.

Costs vary depending on a trip's complexity and include round-trip airfare and expenses (such as meals and hotels) for your companion. For example, escorting one person from Ft. Lauderdale to Chicago one-way costs $1,300 to $1,700, which includes two airfares (for you and your travel companion), expenses and the service fee.

Information: Flying Companions (888-350-8886 or *www.flyingcompanions.com*).

FIND A LAWYER

If you're looking for an attorney with a specific area of expertise—real estate, estate planning, bankruptcy, etc.—and you're a member of AARP, you've got easy access to a large directory of qualified attorneys who will give you a free consultation for up to 45 minutes on the telephone or in person. In addition to dispensing advice and helping determine your best course of action, these attorneys have all agreed to provide basic services for members, such as preparing simple wills, powers of attorney and living wills for low flat fees and, except in a few states, give a 20% discount on their customary rates for other legal work.

Information: AARP Legal Services Network directory (866-330-0753 or *www.aarplsn.com*).

13

Estate Planning Essentials

How to Protect Yourself From Inheritance Hijackers: Thieves Are Likely to Be Family

Americans are due to inherit more than $100 trillion in the coming two decades. Unfortunately, billions of those dollars will be stolen before they reach their rightful heirs. Inheritance hijacking is a huge problem, yet it frequently goes unreported. Heirs often do not know or cannot prove that inheritances have been stolen from them.

These would-be heirs lose more than money. They also lose an important final connection to their departed loved ones. An inheritance might have served as a final positive memory of the deceased—instead, the theft of money and/or valuables leaves survivors with feelings of victimization and additional loss.

It's usually not career criminals who steal inheritances. The thief is far more likely to be a family member or someone else trusted by the deceased, such as a caregiver or a financial representative. Often these inheritance hijackers aren't even in financial need. They simply feel entitled to the money or valuables…or are trying to take revenge against another heir for some perceived slight.

BIGGEST THREATS

Inheritance hijacking can take many forms. *Here are five of the greatest dangers and how to protect your estate…*

•**Outright theft.** It is not uncommon for valuables, such as jewelry or antiques, to disappear from the deceased's home before, during or after the funeral. This could be the work

Robert C. Adamski, JD, partner with the law firm of Burandt, Adamski, Grossman & Powell, LLP, based in Cape Coral, Florida, *www.rcadamski.com.* He's handled more than 1,000 inheritance disputes during his 30-plus years as an attorney. He is author of *Inheritance Hijackers: Who Wants to Steal Your Inheritance and How to Protect It* (Ovation).

of a burglar, as criminals occasionally target victims by reading the obituaries and breaking in when the deceased's family members are at the funeral or funeral home. It is far more likely, however, that the missing valuables have been snatched by someone with a legitimate reason to be in the house, such as a family member who wants to grab a treasured possession before all the other relatives get their chance…or an in-home caregiver who takes the items as a sort of do-it-yourself severance payment.

Self-defense: Make a list of valuables, and distribute this among family members. Then move these valuables to a bank safe-deposit box. Alternately, ask a trusted relative to move them somewhere safe right after your death. (Let all other family members know that you have requested this, to avoid any suggestion that this relative is stealing.)

• **Undocumented loans.** A family member requests and receives a loan from an elderly relative, then when this relative dies, denies that the loan existed…or claims that the money was a gift, not a loan. Because family loans rarely are written down, other heirs often do not realize that money is missing…or cannot prove that it was stolen even if they do.

Self-defense: Insist that any loans you make to anyone in the family be fully documented and signed. Keep these loan documents with your other important financial papers. Also, make a copy to store outside your home, perhaps with a trusted relative or your estate-planning attorney. Remember to update loan documents to reflect any repayments made or missed by the borrower.

• **Denigration of fellow heirs.** An heir lies to an elderly relative about the behavior or financial status of other potential heirs in hopes that these people will be written out of the will.

Examples: "Don't trust Jack with money. He has a gambling problem. He'll just waste it." Or, "Sally's a millionaire. She doesn't need your money."

Self-defense: Look for confirmation of any claims about your heirs that affect your asset-distribution plans.

• **Undue influence.** One family member or a caregiver builds a very close relationship with an elderly person in order to coerce or confuse the person into leaving him/her a larger inheritance.

Self-defense: The best defense against being overly influenced by any one person is to try to maintain close bonds with many family members.

• **Forgery.** A family member or trusted adviser prepares a fake will or a fake amendment to a real will that gives the forger a greater share of the estate.

Self-defense: Distribute copies of your will and other estate-planning documents among your heirs. Ask your attorney to keep copies, too. This greatly decreases the odds of forgeries. It also prevents the will from disappearing if one descendant discovers that he has been given less than he thinks he deserves.

Example: A man leaves the lion's share of his estate to his younger son, who is disabled and cannot support himself. His older son destroys the will. By law, when no will is found, each son receives half of the father's estate.

MORE WAYS TO PROTECT YOUR ESTATE

These steps can greatly increase the odds that your assets will reach your intended heirs…

• **Hire a specialist to create your estate plan.** A will and other estate-plan documents that you develop yourself or that are written by lawyers with limited estate experience are more likely to be successfully contested than those created by experienced estate-planning attorneys. Be honest with the attorney about all your heirs. Are any of them the type who might feel entitled to more than you intend to leave them?

• **Discuss your assets and estate plan with your entire family, ideally while everyone is gathered together.** If your whole family knows about your assets and how you intend to divide them before you die, it is much more difficult for one family member to circumvent your plans later.

• **Appoint at least two executors for your estate.** Make one of the two a trust company, a financial planner, an attorney or some other professional not from your family. Appointing multiple executors makes it far less likely that an executor will take advantage of his position to steal from your estate.

● **Give assets to your heirs before you die.** This ensures that the assets wind up where you want them to go…and lets you see your heirs enjoy them. Ask your financial planner or tax preparer how to minimize any tax problems created by large gifts.

● **Insist that the executors of your estate share details about the estate's expenses, assets and financial transfers with all of your beneficiaries.** Your estate-planning attorney can write this disclosure requirement into your will. Such disclosures make it much harder for an executor to hide theft.

● **Reconsider your estate plan before remarrying.** Someone who remarries tends to assume that his latest spouse will treat the children from the first marriage fairly during the estate-distribution process. In reality, such children may end up receiving a smaller share of the estate than the deceased intended—or nothing at all. The new spouse—or his heirs—may put his own financial interests first.

● **Ask your estate-planning attorney about QTIP trusts, bypass trusts, contracts for wealth and other tools** that can help you protect the interests of your children from your previous marriage(s). Also, consider a prenuptial agreement that protects your children.

After the Fact…Making Death Less Taxing

Edward Mendlowitz, CPA, partner in the CPA firm WithumSmith+Brown in New Brunswick, New Jersey, ranked among the top 35 accounting firms in the US by the industry's leading publications, *www.withum.com.* He has more than 40 years of public accounting experience and is author of numerous books, including *The Adviser's Guide to Family Business Succession Planning* (American Institute of Certified Public Accountants).

Al too often, people end up inheriting an estate that owes estate tax.* *Here are tax-saving strategies that a beneficiary can implement after he/she inherits…*

*Though there's no federal estate tax in 2010, it will return in 2011.

● **Use the alternate valuation date.** Estate assets normally are valued at the date of death for tax purposes, but an estate executor can choose to value all the estate assets as of the day that is exactly six months later. The way things have gone with the economy, and are still going, using the alternate valuation date could lead to a smaller estate—and a smaller estate tax bill. If an estate tax return already has been filed, the alternate valuation election may be made on an amended estate tax return filed by the due date of the return (including extensions).

● **Take an executor's fee.** Suppose you are an heir and the executor of an estate that will owe estate tax. You can collect a fee for handling all the paperwork—2% to 3% of the estate assets might be reasonable.

You'll pay income tax on the executor's fee, but the top federal rate is 35%, and many people are in lower tax brackets. The money you remove from the estate would be taxed at 55% (the federal estate tax rate for 2011, unless Congress changes it), so you'll come out ahead.

● **Use the "IRD" deduction.** Estate tax paid on "income in respect of a decedent" can be subsequently deducted on the heirs' income tax returns. The IRD deduction, often overlooked by heirs, relates to money that was earned by the decedent but paid out after his death. The amount of the deduction is based on the estate tax paid on IRD items.

Example: You are the sole heir of your Aunt Sylvia, who dies in 2011 with a $1.4 million estate that includes a $500,000 IRA from which withdrawals are now taxable. Without that IRA, zero estate tax would be due. With the IRA, federal estate tax is $220,000—55% of the $400,000 over 2011's $1 million estate tax exemption.

If inheriting the $500,000 IRA results in $220,000 in estate tax, that's a 44% ratio. Thus, on every $1 you withdraw from that IRA, you can take a 44-cent income tax deduction. That will go on until you have taken $220,000 of IRD deductions, equal to the estate tax paid.

Are You Responsible for Debts of the Deceased? What You Have to Pay... And What You Don't

Gerri Detweiler, credit adviser for the credit education Web site Credit.com, located in San Francisco. She is former executive director of Bankcard Holders of America, a nonprofit consumer education and advocacy group. Based in Sarasota, Florida, she is the author or coauthor of several books, including the e-book *Reduce Debt, Reduce Stress* (Good Advice Press, go to *www.reduce-debt-reduce-stress.com*).

When a family member dies, relatives often wonder if they are responsible for the deceased person's debts. *What you need to know...*

WHEN RELATIVES ARE RESPONSIBLE FOR DEBTS

There are only two circumstances when you are likely to be legally responsible for a deceased relative's debts...

• **You and the deceased are cosigners on a loan or are joint holders of a credit card account.**

• **You are the spouse of the deceased, and you reside in a community property state.** Community property states are Arizona, California, Idaho, Louisiana, Nevada, New Mexico, Texas, Washington and Wisconsin. (Alaska residents can "opt-in" to a community property system.) Ask an estate or probate attorney to determine your liability if you live in a community property state and your spouse left you with significant debts—you might not be liable for all of them.

Example: A surviving spouse in a community property state often is not legally responsible for the deceased partner's debts that predate the marriage.

TRY TO NEGOTIATE

If you are legally responsible for a deceased relative's debts for either of the reasons listed above, you can ask the lenders to negotiate. Some are willing to accept as little as 50 cents on the dollar from surviving relatives, particularly when those relatives have limited assets and income. At the very least, the lenders might be willing to waive any missed payment penalties or interest that has accrued since the borrower's death.

If the lender does agree to accept a lower payment...

• **Obtain this agreement in writing before sending any payment.** Lenders have been known to agree over the phone to accept less than the full amount owed, process the payment, then deny any knowledge of the agreement and insist that the relative still owes the remaining balance.

• **Understand the tax ramifications.** If you are responsible for the debt, the IRS typically considers forgiven debt as taxable income to you.

• **Consider your credit score.** Your credit score could be damaged if you are a co-signer or joint account holder on a debt and the lender accepts less than the full principal owed. Your credit score should not be affected if the debt was in your partner's name and is your legal responsibility only because of community property laws.

MORTGAGE AND CAR LOANS

If the deceased had secured debt, such as a mortgage or car loan, the assets that secure those loans can be reclaimed by the lender unless the estate or surviving relatives make the required payments.

Exception: Some states do shield a portion of the deceased's home equity from creditors. Several states, such as Texas and Florida, provide 100% protection for primary residences.

• **If the amount owed on a secured loan is greater than the current value of the asset,** it might make sense to allow the lender to reclaim it. Be aware, however, that the lender could repossess the asset and continue to pursue additional payments from the deceased's estate (or directly from you if you are a co-signer on the loan or a spouse in a community property state).

• **If the deceased's asset is repossessed,** ask your estate or probate attorney to seek a written agreement with the lender that the returned asset will be accepted as payment in full. If the lender does not agree to this, perhaps it will at least consent to reduce the amount owed.

Important: Look over the deceased's credit card statements...car loan statements...mortgage statements...and other debt account statements for any mention of "credit insurance" or a "credit protection plan." If these are listed, the deceased likely paid for insurance to pay off this debt in the event of his/her death. Unfortunately, relatives often must figure out for themselves that such coverage exists—lenders and insurance companies frequently will fail to disclose the existence of the coverage.

ASSETS LENDERS CAN'T TOUCH

Lenders usually can file claims against the estate of the deceased to collect what they are owed, but not all of the deceased's assets are part of his estate. Assets that can be kept out of the estate might be out of the reach of lenders. *These include...*

•**Life insurance policies and annuities.** Proceeds from these belong to these policies' beneficiaries, not to the deceased's estate.

Exception: Lenders can pursue the proceeds of insurance policies and annuities if the named beneficiary is the deceased's estate.

•**Brokerage accounts.** These generally pass directly to a beneficiary, assuming that a beneficiary has been named.

•**Retirement plans.** Money in 401(k) and 403(b) accounts passes directly to named beneficiaries. Lenders might be able to go after money from an IRA or pension plan, however, depending on your state's laws. Ask your estate-planning attorney for details.

STUDENT LOANS

Federally subsidized student loans are forgiven if the student dies and need not be repaid by the student's estate. They also may be forgiven if the student becomes totally and permanently disabled. Federal loans that are made to the parents of students are discharged if either the student or the borrowing parent dies or becomes totally and permanently disabled.

WHEN DEBT COLLECTORS CALL

If lenders pester you...

•**Request that the lender or collection agency contact you in writing, not over the phone.** This cuts down on annoying phone calls and gives you time to investigate whether these debts are real and whether you are responsible for them.

•**Take careful notes.** Write down the name and company of each debt collector...the time and date of each phone call...and as much detail about each conversation as possible.

The Fair Debt Collection Practices Act makes it illegal for collection agencies to misrepresent debts. If a debt collector tells you that you are responsible for paying your deceased relative's debts when you are not...or that not paying the relative's debts will lower your credit score (almost certainly not true), you might be able to sue. Contact a consumer law attorney to find out if you have a case. (Click the "Find an Attorney" tab on the National Association of Consumer Advocates Web site, *www.naca. net.*) The attorney may take the case on a contingency basis (no fees unless you win, and then the lawyer takes a percentage of what you are awarded).

Note: The Fair Debt Collection Practices Act applies only to third-party debt collectors, not to lenders who are seeking payment of their own loans.

Monitor your credit report if a lender or collection agency claims that you are responsible for a deceased relative's debt. The debt might be illegally added to your credit report. If this occurs, contact the credit-reporting agency and officially dispute this debt. If the debt is not your legal responsibility, you might be able to sue the lender or credit-reporting agency that added it to your report.

Provide for Your Beloved Pet After Your Death

Legally, animals are property and cannot inherit anything, but a *pet trust* lets you—the grantor of assets—use assets to care for a pet. You appoint a caregiver—an individual or an organization—to care for the animal. And you designate a trustee, such as an attorney, to set up the trust and monitor the caregiver to make sure that the assets are being used appropriately. The trust also may include a *remainder beneficiary*, who will inherit any assets that may be left after the animal dies. Consult an attorney for details about trusts in your state.

Jonathan Rankin, Esq., animal-law attorney, Framingham, Massachusetts.

Protect Yourself from Gift Taxes

Blanche Lark Christerson, Esq., managing director, Deutsche Bank Private Wealth Management, New York City, *www.pwm.db.com*. She lectures frequently to professional organizations and is author of *Tax Topics,* a newsletter that covers legislative and regulatory developments, current case law and other tax-related matters (available to Deutsche Bank clients).

Worried about estate and gift taxes? Here's a way to make large gifts to family members and owe relatively low gift tax—or no gift tax at all.

Strategy: Use a grantor retained annuity trust (GRAT) to make the gifts. Today's low interest rates make GRATs especially appealing. However, act soon. The Obama administration has indicated that it wants to make GRATs less attractive, but trusts created before legislation is enacted probably will be grandfathered.

GIVE AND TAKE

A GRAT is a trust used by people who expect to have estates subject to federal estate tax (which disappears in 2010 and returns in 2011) and by others who wish to give away assets worth more than $1 million gift tax free.

How it works: You (the grantor) transfer assets to a trust. You "retain an annuity" and receive a stream of income from the trust during the trust term, which you specify. At the end of that term, any assets left in the trust go to beneficiaries you've named. Most GRATs are "zeroed out" to avoid gift tax, meaning that the annuity pays you back, with interest, the value of what you put into the trust.

Situation: Jim Smith transfers his shares of ABC Corp. worth $600,000 to a GRAT. For four years (the term set by Jim), he'll receive an annuity from the trust in the form of cash or other assets worth 27.16062% of the trust's initial value, or $162,964 per year—the amount it takes to zero out the trust. After four years, his two children will receive whatever is left in the trust.

Zeroing out: When Jim sets up the trust, the IRS interest rate used to value interests in trusts (the "Section 7520 rate" published monthly by the IRS) is 3.4%. That rate is used to determine the present value of Jim's annuity. By using this number, Jim "zeroes out" his annuity, so that its present value equals 100% of the trust's initial value. Therefore, he has not made a taxable gift to the trust.

Result: Although Jim will receive back what he transferred to the trust, along with 3.4% annual interest payments, any appreciation on the assets during the trust's term will pass gift tax free to his children.

CLEARING THE HURDLE

As long as the assets in the GRAT outperform the 3.4% Section 7520 rate, the GRAT will not be depleted and assets of some value will pass to Jim's children after four years.

Payoff: If the currently depressed shares regain lost ground in the next few years, there might be $200,000 or $300,000 worth of ABC shares left in the GRAT by the end of the term of the trust, which will pass to Jim's children, the trust beneficiaries, gift tax free.

ACT NOW

GRATs have been so popular and successful in reducing tax that the Obama administration, backed by congressional leaders, may trim their benefits. Although they could still be zeroed out, GRATs would be required to have a minimum term of 10 years, thereby increasing the chance that you will die while the GRAT is still in effect. In that case, most, if not all, of the GRAT assets would be brought back to your taxable estate.

Simple Guide to Estate Planning for the Widowed, Divorced and Never Married

Alexis Martin Neely, JD, an estate-planning attorney and founder and CEO of the Family Wealth Planning Institute in Redondo Beach, California. She is author of *Wear Clean Underwear! A Fast, Fun, Friendly and Essential Guide to Legal Planning for Busy Parents* (Morgan James) and a regular legal commentator for CNBC, Fox and CNN. For more, go to *http://personal familylawyer.com.*

Deciding what should happen with all your financial assets after you die is one of the most important elements of prudent financial planning—and it can be even more critical if you're not married. That's partly because the "marital deduction," which allows a person to transfer unlimited wealth to a surviving spouse without incurring estate taxes, is not available to single people or to domestic partners.

Another danger for those who are unmarried: While your spouse would be likely to make legal and financial decisions that reflect your values and wishes after you die or are incapacitated, a court-appointed public administrator—the default decision maker when a single person has no adult children and no estate plan—is far less likely to do this.

Critical for any single adult: A sound estate plan that addresses your health-care concerns, provides for the guardianship of any minor children and transfers assets to heirs of your choice while minimizing taxes. *To make sure that your plan covers all the bases...*

FIND A PRO

Inexpensive legal software can give you a head start, providing checklists and questionnaires to help you gather the information that an attorney will need. The best-selling program is *Quicken Willmaker Plus 2010* ($27.99* from Amazon.com). You also can use estate-tax calculators and other tools for free at *www.aarp. org.* However, estate planning is complex, and hiring an experienced attorney to guide you

*Prices subject to change.

through the process will ensure that the documents achieve your goals and are valid. Also, since state laws rule estate plans, an attorney will be familiar with the conditions that apply specifically to your circumstances.

If you are a widow or widower, you may feel most comfortable working with the attorney who handled your spouse's estate. Or find a reputable law firm in your area by searching for one through the National Network of Estate Planning Attorneys (*www.nnepa.com*)... the American Academy of Estate Planning Attorneys (*www.aaepa.com*)...or my Internet site (*http://personalfamilylawyer.com*).

Many lawyers charge by the hour, and they will put together a basic will for as little as $50 to $200 depending on where you live. As a single person, however, you should consider retaining an estate-planning attorney who will take a holistic view of your financial and legal situations and make sure that your interests are protected.

Best: Find a lawyer who will create a comprehensive estate plan for a flat, up-front fee. Such a plan will include not only the total complement of legal documents (such as the will, durable power of attorney and health-care directive) but also advice on tax savings and the best ownership structure for your assets (including setting up trusts and possibly a charitable foundation). For a single person, the cost typically ranges from $2,500 to $4,500 plus $500 to $600 per year for a legal services plan, including annual reviews and updates.

GET THE RIGHT DOCUMENTS

The following are the "four legs" of your estate-planning stool...

•**Will.** Your will is where you detail how and when your assets will be distributed after your death. If your spouse has died or you divorce, draw up a new will right away. It must be signed by the correct number of witnesses, which varies from state to state.

Important: A beneficiary should never be a witness, because that suggests a conflict of interest. To make sure that your wishes are followed, you must name an executor, who may be a close friend or relative or a professional, such as a lawyer or trustee. He or she may choose to serve without compensation, but he typically is paid a fee of 1% to 5% of your estate's value, depending on how complicated the distribution of the estate is.

If you are single but have young children, your will is where you name guardians, which may include one for short-term and one for long-term purposes. In a separate document, you also should name the guardians in case you are incapacitated but don't die. You can do this for free at *http://kidsprotectionplan.com*. People who live alone also should make provisions for the care of pets in their wills.

● **Revocable living trust.** Putting your assets in the trust's name is a good step for most people, particularly if there could be complications, because it allows you to pass the assets on to your beneficiaries without hauling them through the court process called probate.

Example: Jane wants her friend Mary to inherit her assets without interference from her family, from whom she is estranged. She creates the Jane Doe Trust, making Mary its beneficiary, and retitles all of her savings, mutual funds, real estate and retirement accounts in the trust's name. She names herself trustee for her lifetime and appoints another trustee to manage the assets after her death for Mary's benefit. The assets aren't subject to estate or gift taxes in 2010—and Jane's estate plan is difficult to challenge in probate court.

● **Durable power of attorney.** It's especially important for single people to designate an agent who will make health and financial decisions in case of incapacity because there's no "better half" to step into that role. A durable power of attorney lasts from the time you sign it until you die and gives a designee authority to make whatever decisions you specify. These may include choosing a nursing home…signing your checks and tax returns…managing your investments…and selling your home.

Many experts recommend having separate powers of attorney for medical decisions and financial affairs, and in most states, including New York and California, that is required.

Caution: It's a good idea to designate an agent younger than you are, such as an adult child, niece or nephew. You probably want to avoid naming co-agents because if they disagree about an issue, they may end up having to go to court.

● **Living will.** A living will (sometimes called an advance health-care directive) should clarify your wishes concerning end-of-life medical treatment, such as whether you want to remain on life support. This also is where you can specify whether and where you would like to donate your organs after you die. If you do not have a durable power of attorney that covers health-care decisions, you can designate an agent to make medical decisions for you in a living will instead. To be valid, it must be witnessed by two adults who are not relatives or your own doctors. You can download free state-specific living will forms from *www.doyourownwill.com*.

Important: If you store these documents in a safe-deposit box, heirs may not be able to gain immediate access without the authorization contained in those documents. Give signed copies to your lawyer or executor. It also is smart to write an informal "letter of instruction" that lets people know where to find your will and other key documents. You can send this letter out yourself, or your lawyer or executor will send it to your designated guardians, trustees and health-care agents if you are incapacitated or upon your death.

SHRINK YOUR TAXES

Estate taxes are a bit of a moving target. Under current law, no estate taxes will apply in 2010, but in 2011, the exclusion drops to $1 million, and the tax rate is 55%.

To make sure that most of your legacy goes to your heirs and not to the US Treasury, consider making gifts during your lifetime. You can give away a certain amount each year to another person—currently up to $13,000 if you are single, which is half the amount a married couple can give—without paying any gift tax. (There's no limit to how many people you can give these gifts to.)

If you are contributing to a college savings plan for the person, you can donate five years' worth of the allowable amount all at once— that is, you can contribute $65,000 this year but make no further contributions during the next four years.

In addition, you can give away $1 million during your lifetime free of gift tax, but this lowers what you will be able to exclude from the estate tax. You also can give away an unlimited amount of assets to charity and directly pay a beneficiary's tuition and/or medical expenses without owing estate or gift taxes.

More from Alexis Martin Neely, JD...

Check Your Beneficiaries

Certain assets, including the cash value of insurance policies and retirement plans, such as IRAs and 401(k)s, pass to the beneficiaries that you designate by way of documents related to those assets, not what you say in your will. Check that you have filed the paperwork necessary to designate primary and secondary beneficiaries for all such accounts, and if an ex-spouse is a beneficiary, be sure to remove his/her name if that's your intent.

Go Your Own Way: Eight Alternatives to a Traditional Funeral

Joshua Slocum, executive director of the Funeral Consumers Alliance (FCA), a nonprofit consumer-rights organization based in South Burlington, Vermont. The FCA has served as an independent funeral-industry watchdog since 1963. For more, go to *www.funerals.org*.

When a loved one dies, his/her relatives, friends or estate often pay upward of $10,000 for a "full-service" funeral without even considering the alternatives. But there are other options you could instruct your heirs to select if you would prefer a more distinctive "exit strategy" and/or lower cost. *Other options and their costs...*

- **Body donation.** Contact regional medical schools and teaching hospitals. Most accept donated bodies. In some regions you will be referred to a statewide donation program.

Cost: Usually free, though some programs require that donors' families pay body transportation costs.

- **A direct cremation.** This involves simple cremation, without costly memorial services. If your family wants a service, they can have this at home after the cremation, in the presence of your remains. Any funeral home that offers cremation must by law offer direct cremation.

Cost: $500 to $1,000.*

To trim costs...

- Select an "alternative container"—a simple reinforced cardboard or pine box.

- Provide your own urn. The urns sold by the funeral industry are way overpriced. Your descendants are legally entitled to collect your remains in any container.

What to do with the ashes...

- Scatter them. Laws may prohibit the scattering of remains on public lands, at sea or on your own property, although they are rarely enforced and it goes on all the time. Check the law and ask permission if it's private land.

- If you have deep pockets and wish to be more creative with your remains, Space Services Inc. will send a small portion into space on a rocket ($695 and up, 281-971-4019, *www.memorialspaceflights.com*).

- LifeGem will compress a portion of your remains into a diamond ($1,999 and up, depending on carats and color desired, 866-543-3436, *www.lifegem.com*).

- **Direct burial (also known as "immediate burial").** Skip the embalming, viewing and ceremonies. If your loved ones wish to hold a memorial service in your honor, they can do so at home without your body. All funeral homes offer direct burial.

Cost: $1,000 to $2,000, plus the cost of a cemetery plot—ranging from less than $1,000 to more than $7,000.

- **Mausoleum.** Above-ground interment is a popular option among those squeamish about being eaten by worms underground or being burned in a crematorium. However, a mausoleum might be a poor solution. Sealed coffins kept above ground often leak or explode as bodies decompose.

*Prices subject to change.

Be sure that any mausoleum you consider has extensive ventilation and drainage. Take a whiff inside—a bad smell is a bad sign.

Cost: From $4,000 to $10,000. The top crypts in high-walled mausoleums often cost less because they are above a visitor's eye level.

• **Backyard burial.** It usually is legal to bury bodies on private land in rural or semirural regions, though there often are rules specifying how far the grave must be from the nearest home or property line. Your family typically will have to obtain a death certificate, and permits might be required. Contact city or county offices for details. Local zoning laws typically ban private-land burials in urban and suburban regions. Connecticut, Indiana, Louisiana, Michigan, Nebraska and New York require that a professional funeral director assist with all burials, even those on private land.

Drawback: Future property owners might be able to prevent your descendants from visiting your grave, but this varies from state to state. It is unlikely that they could legally disinter your remains.

Cost: Backhoe rentals typically cost several hundred dollars for a day, though family and friends could do the digging by hand if they have the energy. Some regions charge a small fee to record the grave on your property deed…and there might be transportation costs if you don't die at home, unless your family is able to transport the body. (Some states require transport by a funeral director.)

• **Burial at sea.** Members of the military, veterans honorably discharged from the military and their dependents have the right to request burial at sea from a US Navy vessel. Families typically cannot be present for these burials. Contact the Navy's Burial At Sea program for details (866-787-0081, *www.navy.mil/ navydata/questions/burial.html*).

Cost: Free, for veterans.

Civilians will find it more difficult to arrange burial at sea. If your family or friends have access to a boat, they generally can legally bury your body at sea so long as the burial takes place at least three nautical miles from land in water at least 600 feet deep and your body is weighted to ensure that it sinks rapidly to the bottom. The EPA asks for notification of sea burials within 30 days after the burial. Additional restrictions apply in certain regions.

Caution: Some states have laws for the "proper disposal of bodies" that could be interpreted as banning burial at sea. Contact your state's health department for details.

• **"Green" cemetery burial.** Your body is buried in a biodegradable coffin or it is just wrapped up in a shroud…without embalming chemicals or a burial vault…and possibly with no gravestone, except perhaps an engraved indigenous stone. Some green cemeteries are maintained in a natural state, not mowed and manicured.

Cost: About $1,000 at a cost-conscious green cemetery, such as Greensprings Natural Cemetery in Newfield, New York (607-564-7577, *www.naturalburial.org*), but some facilities do charge $5,000 to $10,000.

• **Cryonic freezing.** Your body is frozen, then—theoretically—defrosted when medical science discovers a cure for whatever killed you.

Reality: It is extremely unlikely that science could ever reverse the massive damage done by freezing. Companies offering this service include Alcor Life Extension Foundation (877-462-5267, *www.alcor.org*) and Cryonics Institute (586-791-5961, *www.cryonics.org*).

Cost: At least $28,000, and often more than $150,000, depending in part on whether you want to freeze your whole body or just your head in the hope of being able to transplant it to another body.

14

Terrific Travel

Fulfill Your Travel Fantasies: Go Absolutely Anywhere in the World For Less

Where does a cheapskate go on his vacation? The answer—just about any place he pleases!

Surprised? Don't be. I'm known as "The Ultimate Cheapskate," but my wife and I recently returned from a month-long trip to Spain and Morocco. In fact, over the years, I have traveled to every state in the union and on every continent except Antarctica. And I'm sure we'll get there someday, too.

No, I have not lost my passion for penny-pinching, but I have learned lots of secrets for traveling the world on a minimal budget. When you travel on the cheap, you can travel more often and for longer, plus you get a real feel for the places you're visiting and the people who live there. *Here, my advice for vacationing on a budget...*

• **Beware of guidebooks.** Sure, borrow a helpful guidebook from the library to bone up on the places you'll be visiting (I like the Lonely Planet series, *www.lonelyplanet.com*), but don't use guidebooks to plan your every move. If a hotel, restaurant or tourist attraction is recommended in a guidebook, it's likely to be overcrowded—and overpriced—as a result. Staying flexible and scouting out the best bargains as you go—by asking around, checking local publications, etc.—saves you money and is more likely to give you a taste of how the locals really live.

• **Know when to go.** No matter what time of year you vacation, it is always off-season somewhere. That was key to scheduling our

---

Jeff Yeager, dubbed "The Ultimate Cheapskate" by NBC's *Today* show, honed his cheapskating skills during 25 years working with underfunded nonprofit agencies. He lives in Accokeek, Maryland, and is author of *The Ultimate Cheapskate's Road Map to True Riches* and *The Cheapskate Next Door* (both from Broadway). His Web site is *www.ultimatecheapskate.com*.

recent trip to Spain and Morocco. By traveling in winter and immediately after the year-end holidays, we got the lowest possible rates on flights, ground transportation and lodging. Had we traveled during peak season, we could have afforded to stay only about half as long. And while it wasn't lay-on-the-beach weather, it still was plenty comfortable and the absence of tourist crowds was paradise. Check *www.cheaptickets.com* for a list of when it is least expensive to visit destinations throughout the US and worldwide.

• **Time activities.** In addition to looking for off-season travel bargains, it pays to time your activities to maximize savings. Examples: Hotels catering to business travelers often charge less on weekends. Flights that are very early or late in the day can be cheaper. Check the online sites *www.farecompare.com* and *www.airfarewatchdog.com* to find out the cheapest times to fly. And if you want to splurge on that five-star restaurant while on vacation, consider going there for lunch instead of dinner—it's less expensive but just as good.

• **Maximize frequent-flier and credit card rewards programs.** Redeeming miles/rewards credits can be a great way to cut airfare, hotel and other travel costs. We had enough points on our credit card for one free round-trip ticket to Spain. But with so many different frequent-flier and credit rewards programs these days, it may be hard to figure out which are best for you. Check *www.smarttraveler.com* and *www.creditcards.com/reward.php* for a comparison of different plans.

• **Do not make hotel reservations.** During nonpeak travel times, it can pay to travel without advance hotel reservations, as we did on our Spain/Morocco journey. Especially when traveling overseas, hotels that can be easily reserved in advance often are more expensive chain hotels catering to Americans, and sometimes they charge a premium rate for advance bookings. Discovering bargain-priced, locally owned accommodations usually is best done once you're there, and innkeepers are sometimes willing to discount their rates for "walk-in" guests if they think a room will otherwise remain vacant for the night—it never hurts to ask. Just be polite and say something engaging, such as, "Any chance you might have a lower rate for a tired traveler?" If you like the security of reservations, log on to *www.sidestep.com* to comparison shop.

Consider an alternative to a hotel. *Because lodging is likely to be your single largest expense, consider some creative money-saving alternatives...*

• House swapping (see *www.homeexchange.com*) is increasingly popular for travelers looking to barter lodging rather than pay for it.

• Home renting. Web sites, including *www.vacationhomerentals.com* and Vacation Rentals By Owner (*www.vrbo.com*), have special last-minute deals on many property listings.

• Hostels (go to *www.hiusa.org*) offer safe, clean, friendly accommodations to people of any age and at a price of about 80% less than a hotel in the same location. While most hostels have dormitory-style accommodations, an increasing number offer private rooms and baths at bargain prices.

• CouchSurfing (*www.couchsurfing.org*) is a worldwide network of more than 1.5 million folks who will let you sleep on their couches—or often in a spare bedroom—for free simply because they enjoy meeting travelers. When I travel on my book tours, I use the CouchSurfing network and youth hostels almost exclusively.

• Camping. If you enjoy the great outdoors, camping can save you a bundle, and you may be able to camp for free. Go to *http://freecampsites.net* and *www.forestcamping.com*.

• **Look for meal deals.** On longer trips, we like to prepare most meals ourselves because dining out costs a small fortune. Plus, we love to shop in local markets and use ingredients that we can't find at home, even if it's just local fruits, vegetables, breads and cheeses for a picnic. When you stay at tourist-class hotels, hostels or swap or rent a home, you usually have access to at least basic facilities where you can store and prepare your own food.

If you're not into cooking on vacation and you are traveling the US, buy Entertainment Books (*www.entertainment.com*) for the cities that you'll be visiting. These offer coupon savings on dining and area attractions. You also can get discounted meal gift certificates from *www.restaurant.com*.

Wherever your travels take you, here or abroad, hightail it to the nearest college campus, where you will find many inexpensive dining establishments that cater to cash-strapped students.

• **Split expenses.** Have some extra space at the summer cottage you're renting? Consider inviting along friends or family members to share in the fun—and the fixed expenses.

• **Long-distance ride-sharing** to save money (and driving) getting to your destination also is becoming popular. Check *www.eride share.com* and *www.shareyourride.net*.

• **Remember that membership offers its privileges.** At hotels, restaurants and tourist attractions, and whenever you're buying any type of travel service or package, always ask if any discounts are available, particularly if you are a member of AAA, AARP or one of the increasing number of online travel clubs, such as *www.travelmembershipclub.com*. Membership warehouse clubs, such as Sam's Club and Costco, also offer discounts on travel services. And it might help to flash your business card at hotels and car rental offices to see if they'll give you a discounted corporate rate.

• **Go cheap on souvenirs.** Look for practical items, such as clothing and housewares, that you'll actually use. And don't forget to check out secondhand shops, thrift stores and even garage sales when you travel—you're likely to turn up some one-of-a-kind, bargain-priced souvenirs.

Cruise Deals

For the best deal on a cruise, *book far in advance* on the luxury liners—or *as close as possible to the last minute* on mass-market lines. Those are the times when cruise operators usually offer the best prices and the most extras. *Use a travel agent*—he/she often has special relationships with cruise lines and can get better rates. *Pick your itinerary carefully*—"repositioning" cruises and ones just before and after peak season usually are the best

values. *Choose the cabin category,* then have your agent help you pick the best room on a particular ship. *Book your next cruise while on ship* to get repeat customer discounts.

Travel + Leisure, 1120 Avenue of the Americas, New York City 10036, *www.travelandleisure.com*.

Budget Travel Expert's Ways to Really Get to Know a Place

Pauline Frommer, creator of the Pauline Frommer series of guidebooks (Wiley) for budget travelers and the cohost of *The Travel Show*, a nationally syndicated radio show. The daughter of Arthur Frommer (founder of the famed Frommer's travel guides), she has been traveling extensively since she was four months old. She is a two-time winner of the North American Travel Journalists Association's "Best Guidebook of the Year" award. For more, go to *www.frommers.com/pauline*.

Many travelers never truly get to know the places that they visit. They see the tourist sites, shop at the downtown stores, eat at restaurants near their hotels. This does not provide an accurate picture of the region—and it's a sure way to pay inflated out-of-towner prices.

Here, Pauline Frommer—creator of the Pauline Frommer series of guidebooks—tells how to really get to know an area *without* spending a lot...

INSIDER INFO

• **Peruse the regional newspapers before your trip.** The local newspapers list upcoming area events, review restaurants and offer a glimpse of what's going on in the area. Many newspapers now are available online. You can find links at *www.onlinenewspapers.com* and *www.newspapers.com*.

• **Go on a walking tour, not a bus tour.** Walking tours generally cover smaller areas than bus tours. They also tend to be less expensive than bus tours and move at a slower pace, making it easier to ask the guide questions. Most walking tours take in the traditional tourist sights, but unlike bus tours, some will simply cover an interesting area of a city, taking in many sights that tourists don't know to seek out. And unlike bus tours, they are more likely to have a unique focus. For example, one walking tour might take you to famous movie locations in the region or on the trail of a notorious killer (such as the Jack the Ripper tours in London). Other walking tours might be food-oriented, with the guides taking you to local food stores and restaurants, where you tour kitchens and get to sample as you go. Walking tours often can be found through museums and clubs. Or Google the city you plan to visit and the phrase "walking tours." Good guidebooks often include walking tours.

•**Stay in a bed-and-breakfast, not a hotel.** B&B owners often can provide valuable local tips for their guests, unlike hotel concierges, who sometimes receive kickbacks for steering their patrons to expensive tourist destinations. B&Bs also tend to have a social atmosphere where guests swap valuable travel tips.

Alternative: Rent an apartment or home for your vacation. These properties typically are in residential areas, which provide a truer sense of the region than the hotel district. Online sites such as VRBO.com…HomeAway. com…and Zonder.com connect travelers with property owners. Negotiate your rate—in this economy, many property owners are willing to take less than their asking price or throw in perks, such as free use of the phone.

•**Get lost.** Spend a few hours getting lost. Walk wherever your feet take you (or drive wherever your car takes you). Wandering is not wasted time—it's the best way to discover the parts of town that most tourists miss.

Helpful: Carry a street map so that you can find your way back. Do your wandering during daylight hours to minimize risk.

•**Eat at restaurants in residential districts.** A region's cuisine can be a big part of its culture—but restaurants located near hotels and tourist destinations are almost never the best way to sample it. Such restaurants make money by overcharging out-of-towners who they know will soon leave and perhaps never come back. It is better to patronize restaurants in residential areas, which make money

by serving food so good that local customers turn into regulars.

Web sites Yelp.com…Chowhound.com…and Roadfood.com can steer you to restaurants locals love.

Caution: Don't ask a concierge or cab driver to recommend a restaurant. Low-quality, overpriced restaurants sometimes pay these people to steer business their way.

•**Shop at the local farmers' market…and, when abroad, the local supermarket.** Markets provide an accurate picture of how locals eat and live. They also are an inexpensive place to grab a distinctive meal or snack. Local candies or jarred goods make memorable and inexpensive gifts, too.

CONNECT WITH A LOCAL

One of the best ways to get to know a region is to get to know someone who lives there. *To meet a local resident…*

•**Contact the regional greeters program.** There are organizations in some areas that match local volunteer "greeters" with travelers. Just Google the name of the city/country that you're visiting and the word "Greeters" to find out if there is such a group where you're headed. These greeters might provide guidance on the phone throughout your visit or may spend a few hours showing you around in person.

This service usually is free, but it is appropriate to pay your guide's fee or fare if you visit a museum or take public transit together. You should pick up the check if you share a meal or drinks.

Greeters programs typically can provide a volunteer who speaks English…or even someone with whom you share an interest. When I told the Jamaican greeters program that my passion was cooking, they supplied a greeter who took me to her home and taught me to cook the local cuisine.

Examples of greeters programs…

•New York City's "Big Apple Greeter," 212-669-8159, *www.bigapplegreeter.org.*

•Chicago Greeter program, 312-744-8000, *www.chicagogreeter.com.*

•Toronto Greeter Program, *www.toronto.ca/ tapto.*

•Jamaica's "Meet the People," *www.visitjamaica.com*, select the "About Jamaica" tab, then "Meet the People."

•Japan's Goodwill Guides, *www.jnto.go.jp/eng*, select "Essential Info" from under the "Arrange Your Travel" heading, then select "Guide Services," and scan down to the section labeled "Guide Service/Volunteer Guides."

•South Korea's Goodwill Guides, log on to *http://english.visitkorea.or.kr*, then select "Volunteer Tour Guides" under "Essential Information" on the left.

•**Join a hospitality exchange club.** Members provide local insight for other members who visit their area. In some cases, members even can arrange to stay in the guest rooms of local members' homes for free or for a minimal fee.

Example: The Evergreen Club is a hospitality exchange club for those over age 50. The club has hosts across the US, Europe, Canada and Australia. It also has a few members in India, Mexico and the Caribbean. Annual dues are $60* ($75 for a couple). Guest-room stays typically are $18 per night ($24 for a couple)—less if you agree to host guests in your home (815-456-3111, *www.evergreenclub.com*).

•**Network with a local in your field.** A shared profession is a good excuse to contact someone in a region. Doctors might ask to visit local hospitals so that they can study triage systems or new techniques not yet being practiced in their hometowns. Teachers might visit schools, again to see how the education system works in other parts of the world. Professional networking even could make a portion of your travel expenses tax deductible as a business expense. Ask your accountant for details.

•**Approach a local who is like you for guidance.** Want to know what people in the region who share your interests do for fun? Then ask someone who's likely to share your interests. If you like to read, visit a bookstore and ask a fellow patron for advice...if you love the outdoors, visit a store that sells kayaks or camping gear. To improve the odds of aligned interests, pick someone whose age is similar to your own.

*Prices subject to change.

More from Pauline Frommer...

Before You Go...

Make copies of key documents before you travel. Before leaving home, make two copies of your driver's license, medical insurance cards, bank and credit cards, proof of travel insurance and your passport if traveling abroad. Take one set of copies with you, keeping them separate from the originals and your wallet. Leave another set at home with a family member or friend who can provide them if needed. You can also scan and e-mail a copy of the information to yourself.

Also from Pauline Frommer...

What Types of Travel Insurance Do You Need?

Travel insurance you need, and really don't need...

•**Medical insurance?** Yes, do buy. Medicare and many commercial insurance policies do not provide coverage abroad, creating serious financial risk if you become ill or are injured outside the US. Ask your insurance agent or adviser about your existing coverage and supplemental health insurance for a trip.

•**Cancellation insurance?** Maybe. For expensive trips, such as cruises, safaris and extended tours, this protects against the risk that the trip organizer may go out of business or otherwise default, or that you may be forced to stay at home because of a personal emergency. For inexpensive trips, it's probably not worth it.

•**Flight insurance?** No. Insurance that covers death or dismemberment during a flight may cost almost as much as your ticket, and plane crashes are very rare.

Back Up Your Passport

Have your local copy shop make a laminated credit card–sized black-and-white version of the photo page of your passport. If you lose your regular passport while traveling, you still will have all of your information until you can get a replacement.

Arthur Frommer's Budget Travel, 530 Seventh Ave., New York City 10018, *www.budgettravel.com.*

Time Is Money When Traveling

To see the value of your time on a trip, divide the trip's full cost by the waking hours you will have on it. Seeing that per-hour number before you leave will motivate you to plan to avoid wasting time on the trip.

Examples: Call for reservations to avoid waits, and obtain advance passes to museums that let you bypass admission lines. Learn time-saving local transportation options. Plan what you will do at your destination in advance, and check that sites you wish to visit will be open and available, so you don't waste time improvising inefficiently after you arrive.

Rick Steves, travel author and host on public radio and television, *www.ricksteves.com.*

More Spa for Less

Get more spa services for less money. Call spas when making your travel arrangements to ask about discounts. Make weekday appointments when possible—Fridays, Saturdays and Sundays are busier and often more expensive. Ask if you can get a discount for booking or paying for multiple services ahead of time. If you are traveling with other people, find out about price reductions for parties of three or more—some spas offer them.

Condé Nast Traveler, 4 Times Square, New York City 10036, *www.concierge.com.*

Alternative to Traveler's Checks

Prepaid Travelex Cash Passport cards in the currency of the country to which you are traveling are a perfect alternative to traveler's checks.

Example: Euros or British pounds.

The cards work like debit cards—you use them at ATMs or for purchases while traveling. Your name is not on the card—if it is lost or stolen, your identity is safe.

Caution: ATM withdrawals have a fee of 1.75 euros* or 1.25 British pounds (about $2.50 or $2, respectively)…and to convert any remaining money on the card back to dollars upon return to the US, you will be charged 5.5%. (You also can leave the balance on the card for future trips.)

More information is available at *www.cash passport.com/us.*

Anne Banas, executive editor, SmarterTravel.com.

*Prices subject to change.

Why You Need Two Credit Cards on a Trip

Bring two credit cards on a trip. Use one to pay for everything in order to maximize frequent-flier miles and other bonuses. Use the second credit card for emergencies or if the credit line on the first is used up by "lock" charges that are imposed by many hotels and rental-car companies before a bill is paid. Take some traveler's checks with you for situations when you can't (or don't want to) use your credit card.

Also: Photocopy your credit cards and other important items in your wallet so that you will have account numbers and other key information if your wallet is lost or stolen.

TravelSmart, Box 397, Dobbs Ferry, New York 10522, *www.travelsmartnewsletter.com.*

Where to Get Breaking Travel Alerts

Before you travel overseas, receive travel alerts from the US government. The State Department's "travel" Web pages can tell you much about your destination. Visit *http://travel.state.gov* and click on "Travel Warnings," "Travel Alerts" and "Country Specific Information." You can get even more information from the corresponding travel Internet sites of the governments of Canada (*www.voyage.gc.ca*), Great Britain (*www.fco.gov.uk*) and Australia (*www.smarttraveller.gov.au*). You can also sign up for "news update" e-mails from these sites.

Condé Nast Traveler, 4 Times Square, New York City 10036, *www.concierge.com*.

Get Weather Reports For Locations Around The World

Weather2Travel.com tells current weather and provides five-day forecasts and seasonal climate guides for destinations around the world. If you are about to leave on a trip, it will tell you what weather to prepare for at your destination. If you are planning a vacation, you can learn the normal range of temperatures, chance of precipitation, number of hours of sunshine and more information for your travel dates.

TravelSmart, Box 397, Dobbs Ferry, New York 10522, *www.travelsmartnewsletter.com*.

The True Cost of Your Airline Ticket

The real cost of airline travel is not the quoted ticket price. Airlines add multiple fees to that number—and often reveal them only after you buy the ticket.

What to do: Go to *www.tripadvisor.com* for a fee estimator that adds baggage charges and provides onboard costs of amenities, such as meals and headsets for domestic flights. Visit *www.flyingfees.com*, which tracks fees for 21 airlines and lists the least expensive carriers in some categories. At airlines' own sites, use the search function to find fees, which can be hard to locate.

The Wall Street Journal, *http://online.wsj.com*.

The Three Days It's Cheaper to Fly

It costs less to fly on Tuesday, Wednesday and Saturday. Those days are less popular for travel than others and often have the best rates. Try departing on Tuesday or Wednesday and returning on Saturday.

Kiplinger.com.

Disappearing Airline Booking Fees!

Online airline-booking fees are disappearing as sites such as Expedia and Orbitz try to attract business. Those sites, plus Priceline, Travelocity and CheapTickets, have reduced or dropped booking fees, hoping to attract consumers who use the sites to check itineraries but then buy tickets directly from airline sites. Expedia says it is waiving fees permanently. Other sites may run no-fee specials or keep fees at lower levels.

What to do: Shop around at the travel sites as well as the airline sites to find the lowest prices.

Henry Harteveldt, travel analyst, Forrester Research, Cambridge, Massachusetts.

Avoid the Most Expensive Airports

The most expensive airports to fly from usually are major hubs in medium-sized cities because a single airline typically dominates the market. The average fare per mile at Cincinnati-Northern Kentucky International Airport was recently 48 cents*…at Cherry Capital, Traverse City, Michigan, about 41 cents…at Tri-Cities Regional in Johnson City, Tennessee, and Columbia Metropolitan in South Carolina, 39 cents.

The least expensive of the 407 airports in the study was Ted Stevens Anchorage International at 14 cents per mile, followed by Long Beach and Oakland International, California, each at 15 cents. Fort Lauderdale-Hollywood International and Southwest Florida International Airport in Fort Myers, and Sacramento International all came in at 16 cents/mile.

Best: Shop around for flights to make sure you don't overpay.

Forbes, 60 Fifth Avenue, New York City 10011, *www. forbes.com*.

*Prices subject to change.

What to Do If Your Flight Is Canceled…

When your flight is suddenly canceled, improve your chances of rebooking by calling the airline from your cell phone while waiting in line at the ticket counter. You may get through by phone more quickly than you will reach someone at the airport who can help you. For a list of airline phone numbers, go to *www.tollfreeairline.com*.

National Geographic Traveler, Washington, DC, on the Web at *http://traveler.nationalgeographic.com*.

Weigh Bags *Before* Going to the Airport

If a bag you will check weighs more than 50 pounds, and you can't get its contents under that limit, divide them among two bags.

Why: Airlines impose steep fees, about $50,* on overweight bags. But they often charge less than the overweight fee to check in a second bag. So, you'll pay less to check through two bags than you will with one overweight bag.

Check your airline's baggage fee rules.

Money, Time-Life Bldg., Rockefeller Center, New York City 10020, *http://money.cnn.com*.

*Price subject to change.

Luggage Lessons

If an airline loses your luggage, don't panic—98% of bags reported lost are found.

What to do first: File a claim at the airline's baggage office to begin an electronic search tracing your luggage. If it is not found after three days, file a second claim detailing the bags' contents. If the luggage still isn't found, it will be declared officially "lost" after seven to 60 days, depending on the airline, and you'll be entitled to reimbursement for the amount of your loss.

Limits: $3,300 on domestic flights*…about $1,500 on international flights.

More information: Visit the DOT Aviation Consumer Protection and Enforcement online site, *http://airconsumer.ost.dot.gov*.

Bill Mosley, US Department of Transportation, quoted in *Travel + Leisure*, *www.travelandleisure.com*.

*Prices subject to change.

Sail Through Customs

There's a quicker way to make it through US Customs. The Department of Homeland

Security's Global Entry program allows pre-approved travelers to pass through Customs by swiping their passports at a kiosk, posing for a photo, scanning their fingerprints and answering some basic questions on a touch screen. The kiosks are now available in 20 US airports.

Cost to sign up: $100.*

For information about how to sign up and a list of participating airports, go to *www.cbp.gov* (click "Travel").

Travel + Leisure, 1120 Avenue of the Americas, New York City 10036, *www.travelandleisure.com.*

*Price subject to change.

Airport Food Price Alert

Food prices in the airport are supposed to be comparable to food prices outside the airport in many cities.

Example: Prices at a McDonald's or Starbucks at the airport should be the same as prices at McDonald's or Starbucks in the city nearby.

But prices often are higher. Among airports with policies requiring so-called street pricing are Chicago's O'Hare, New York's LaGuardia and JFK, Houston Bush, Newark Liberty, Boston, Philadelphia, Seattle and Washington Dulles. Lots of other major airports require street pricing plus no more than 10%.

Problem: Enforcement is spotty.

What to do: Bring your own food.

Consensus of business and leisure travelers, reported in USA Today, www.usatoday.com.

Before Driving Away With a Rental Car...

Photograph your rental car before driving off the lot. Take photos of the exterior, interior and trunk to document all visible damage and any missing items. If your camera allows you to add a date to each photo, make sure

that you leave this function turned on and the date properly set. Documenting damage will ensure that you are not liable for anything that you did not cause.

TravelSmart, Box 397, Dobbs Ferry, New York 10522, *www.travelsmartnewsletter.com.*

Rental Car Smarts

If you reserve a rental car and the rental company has no cars at the time of your reservation, the company is responsible for finding you another car, even from a competing agency, and paying any difference in price.

If you reserved a specific car and don't get the one you reserved: Ask for a rate adjustment if the car you receive is smaller than the one you reserved. If it is bigger than the vehicle you reserved, you still should pay the lower rate—but you usually will end up paying the difference in gas.

SmartMoney, 1755 Broadway, New York City 10019, *www.smartmoney.com.*

Rental Car Alternatives

Rent-a-Wreck rents used cars from 157 locations, including 38 near airports. Costs could be 75% lower* than at standard rental firms—but one-way rentals are not available, and weekend promotions from major firms may match Rent-a-Wreck's prices. Cars are in good condition but have more miles than cars from other firms (877-877-0700 or *www.rentawreck.com*). Zipcar gives access to vehicles from Mini Coopers to Ford Escapes for as little as $7/hour. It operates in more than 50 cities in the US, Canada and the UK. Insurance and gas are included in hourly rates, but there is an annual fee of $50 and a one-time application fee of $25. Call 866-494-7227, or go to *www.zipcar.com.*

*Prices and rates subject to change.

Car dealers sometimes rent cars by the day at reasonable rates—for example, some Ford dealers offer rentals. But you have to contact each dealer individually to find out if it offers rentals—and at what price.

Arthur Frommer's Budget Travel, 530 Seventh Ave., New York City 10018, *www.budgettravel.com.*

Beat the Soaring Cost Of Rental Cars

Neil Abrams, president, Abrams Consulting Group, Purchase, New York, *www.abramsconsulting.com.*

While travel costs generally have fallen due to the recession, the cost of car rentals has soared.

Rental car rates, which climbed to historic highs in 2009, are expected to keep climbing according to the Abrams Travel Data Rate Index of major rental brands in representative airport markets.

Why: Rental companies have slashed the size of their fleets, so while demand has fallen, the supply of rental cars has fallen much more—increasing demand relative to supply.

What to do: Don't wait until the last minute to reserve a rental car—you may be forced to pay exorbitant rates or not get a car at all.

To get the best rate: Check prices at off-airport locations (which usually are much cheaper) and at local independent agencies...book on-line through a discount travel site, such as Priceline.com, if you are willing to be locked into a preset price without knowing the rental company you are using...book models that are in lesser demand.

Surprise: Large cars and vans often cost less than small cars because concerns about fuel expenses and the environment have increased demand for the latter. But a large car may provide you a more comfortable trip, with the savings covering the cost of any extra fuel you use.

Hotels and Motels Are Quietly Adding and Raising Fees

The latest hotel and motel charges include valet parking fees even if you park your own car...in-room safe fees...mandatory housekeeping and bellhop tips..."resort fees," which can be 20% of the daily room rate...higher fees for fax and mail delivery, baggage handling and bottled water (up to $12*)...added fees for in-room coffee you make yourself. Ask about all fees before booking to decide whether they will raise your costs too much.

Chris Elliott, host of *What You Get for the Money: Vacations* on the Fine Living cable-TV network and editorial director of the travel site Tripso.com.

*Prices subject to change.

Buy the Vacation Home Of Your Dreams: The Best Places to Find Real Bargains *Now*

Barbara Corcoran, founder of the Corcoran Group real estate company and president of the business consulting company Barbara Corcoran, Inc., both in New York City. She is real estate contributor to NBC's *Today* show and CNBC and cohost of ABC's *Shark Tank* entrepreneurial reality series. Her latest book is *Nextville: Amazing Places to Live Your Life* (Springboard). Her Web site is *http://barbaracorcoran.com.*

If you survived the recession with your finances intact, now might be a great time to buy a second home, possibly one that could become your retirement home. *Below, top real estate expert Barbara Corcoran tells what you need to know to capture a great deal now...*

THE OUTLOOK

Residential real estate has probably started to turn the corner or will within months, but there still are amazing bargains—especially in many regions where people like to vacation and retire. Prices are from 20% to 50% below what homes fetched in late 2007, because inventory has risen dramatically as owners faced foreclosures or sold second homes to raise cash. And interest rates on 30-year fixed-rate mortgages are now hovering around 4.5%.*

You would be wise to search for a home whose value will appreciate strongly while the real estate market recovers…and possibly one that would be very easy to rent out for extra income. *To be sure that you're making a good investment…*

• **Count new cars.** The more late-model vehicles you see in a neighborhood, the more upwardly mobile young people reside there. That indicates the local job market is healthy, and growing businesses help protect property values.

• **Go to town.** Does the area have an appealing town center nearby, with at least a few places to eat and a pretty store or two? If not, look elsewhere.

• **Be a snob.** Make sure the neighborhood has a stock of well-cared-for older homes. A place where all of the houses are brand-new lacks character, gives a cookie-cutter feeling and is unlikely to develop status over the long term.

• **Read the signs.** If you see a "For Sale" sign on every other block, you're looking at an exodus. The area may recover eventually, but its current momentum is downward.

WHERE TO LOOK

For the very lowest in second-home prices, shop around in popular, high-density regions where developers overbuilt during the boom. Las Vegas, Phoenix, Miami and their suburbs are overflowing with vacation houses and condos, some on sale for half their original asking prices. Yet these markets aren't a gamble—they will recover in time. Strategy: Don't be afraid to low-ball. Make offers on several different properties at a time, and let the sellers know that you have multiple options.

Another way you can get a lot for a little: Choose a location with a slightly lower national profile, such as…

*As of August 24, 2010.

CRYSTAL COAST, NORTH CAROLINA

Closest major city: Raleigh, about a three-hour drive northwest.

Why it's a bargain: The beachfront towns of the southern Outer Banks saw rapid development during the early 2000s, but demand slowed with the economy.

Seasonality: Ocean breezes make this an appealing summer vacation spot.

Activities: Deep-sea fishing, windsurfing, golf, nature hikes.

Median house price: About $300,000.*

SOUTH LAKE TAHOE, CALIFORNIA

Closest major city: Sacramento, about two hours east.

Why it's a bargain: Near the Nevada state line, South Lake Tahoe offers real estate prices that are far below those in other California resort areas.

Seasonality: A dry climate, with 300 sunny days out of 365, encourages year-round residence. Many vacationers end up making the town their retirement home.

Activities: Skiing during winter…fishing and boating in summer…nearby casino.

Median house price: $312,000.

SAUGATUCK, MICHIGAN

Closest major city: Lansing, an hour-and-a-half drive to the east.

Why it's a bargain: An annual film festival, busy art scene and reputation as the "Cape Cod of the Midwest" (it is by Lake Michigan) have not yet inflated Saugatuck's real estate prices to outrageous levels.

Seasonality: The year-round population of 1,000 swells up to 3,000 during the summer, when vacationers from Chicago, Grand Rapids and Detroit pour in.

Activities: Beach-going, horseback riding, gallery-hopping.

Median house price: $220,000.

GREAT SMOKY MOUNTAINS, TENNESSEE

Closest major city: Knoxville, slightly over an hour's drive north.

*Prices subject to change.

Why it's a bargain: The cost of living in well-appointed towns, such as Gatlinburg, is well below the national average, and Tennessee has no state income tax.

Seasonality: The altitude in Great Smoky Mountains National Park keeps the temperature and humidity down during the summer, when many vacationers visit.

Activities: Hiking, botany, wildlife viewing, lake fishing, barbecue competitions.

Median house price: $199,000.

TYBEE ISLAND, GEORGIA

Closest major city: Savannah, a half-hour west by car.

Why it's a bargain: By freezing or lowering prices, the recession made this upscale, somewhat old-fashioned seaside community more affordable.

Seasonality: Tybee is a summer destination.

Activities: Deep-sea fishing, kayaking.

Median house price: $550,000.

How to Attract More Renters to Your Vacation Home

Make your vacation rental stand out to increase the chance of renting it despite the recession.

Strategies: Let the customers pay monthly or biweekly instead of 50% up-front…update your online listing to include amenities and show your home in the most attractive way…list driving distances to nearby cities to highlight ease of access…give cost comparisons to hotel rooms in your area…consider allowing long-weekend minimum stays instead of a full week or more…consider allowing pets if you don't currently do so.

Christine Karpinski, director of owner community, HomeAway.com, online vacation-home rental site based in Austin, Texas.

Better Travel When You Have a Health Problem

Neil Shulman, MD, an associate professor in the department of internal medicine at Emory University School of Medicine in Atlanta. He is a coauthor, with Michael A. Silverman, MD, and Adam G. Golden, MD, of *The Real Truth About Aging: A Survival Guide for Older Adults and Caregivers* (Prometheus).

Travel can be stressful for everyone, but it poses particular challenges for those with health problems. *To travel safely…*

• **Carry a "health profile."** Suppose that you have sudden chest pains or difficulty breathing. You might be too sick to discuss your health history with the doctor who treats you.

I advise everyone who travels to put a typed health profile in his/her wallet or purse. The profile should include your name and contact information (along with the phone numbers of emergency contact people)…your medical diagnoses…medications that you're taking… and information about allergies. It also should include your insurance information, doctor's telephone number and, if possible, copies of test results revealing your condition, such as cardiograms and lung tests.

Helpful: Google offers a free service that allows you to store your health information and print out a wallet-size version. See *www. google.com/health.*

• **Get vaccinated.** If you haven't gotten flu vaccinations for seasonal and swine flu, ask your doctor if you need them. Most flu deaths occur in people who have preexisting health problems.

If you're traveling outside the US, you may need other vaccinations as well. Check the online site of the Centers for Disease Control and Prevention, *www.cdc.gov* (click on "Travelers' Health").

Don't wait until the last minute to get vaccinated. Some vaccines take weeks before providing total protection.

• **Manage your medications.** Always pack enough medication to last longer than your trip, just in case there's a delay getting home. Do not count on filling your prescriptions when you're away. Many of the drugs that are readily available in the US may be unavailable in other countries or packaged under different names.

When flying, put all of your medicines (in their original, labeled containers) and medical devices (such as syringes) in a clear plastic bag and carry them with you (don't check them in luggage, which can get lost).

•**Walk around.** One of the main risks of airplane flights (or trips by car, train or bus) is deep-vein thrombosis (DVT). Blood clots that develop in the legs can break free and travel to the lungs. This condition, known as pulmonary embolism, is frequently fatal.

DVT often occurs in those with other health problems, including congestive heart failure. It's mainly caused by immobility because clots are more likely to form when you don't move your legs.

Stretch your legs at least once an hour. On a plane, train or bus, walk up and down the aisle. On car trips, stop and walk for a few minutes. In between walks, rotate your ankles and flex your toes.

Also helpful: Drink at least one extra glass of water every hour or two during trips. It may reduce the risk for clots.

•**Plan for altitude.** If you are going to a high-altitude location, you may feel tired and have difficulty breathing, in particular if you have chronic obstructive pulmonary disease (COPD), anemia or heart disease. Check your doctor about precautions you need to take. You might just need to take it easy for a few days after you arrive. In most cases, you will be advised to drink plenty of water.

If you use supplemental oxygen because of COPD or other lung disease, airlines typically will provide you with all the needed in-flight oxygen equipment (you could be charged a fee). Ask whether you need documentation from your doctor. If you need oxygen when you arrive, be sure to make arrangements before you go.

Travel Headache Help

Many travelers experience migraines or tension headaches when flying.

If you get airplane-related headaches, try an anti-inflammatory medicine, like *naproxen* (Aleve) or *ibuprofen* (Motrin), a few hours before you expect the headache to occur.

Or you can talk to your physician about a prescription for Midrin—a combination of the painkiller *acetaminophen*, the mild sedative *dichloralphenazone* and *isometheptene*, a drug that constricts blood vessels. Take two about two hours before the plane is scheduled to take off and two at least three hours later, with lots of water. These approaches help some people.

Also, stay well-hydrated—drink a lot of water the day before travel and the day you fly, including on the plane.

Alan M. Rapoport, MD, neurologist, David Geffen School of Medicine at University of California, Los Angeles, and founder and director emeritus, New England Center for Headache, Stamford, Connecticut.

Is It Safe to Swim In the Ocean?

It is safe for the vast majority of people to swim in the ocean. However, do take some precautions. In one recent study, 1,303 healthy adults swam at a South Florida beach for 15 minutes. When water samples were analyzed, 37% of them contained *Staphylococcus aureus* (staph) bacteria, which can cause a serious infection. At the highest risk for staph and other bacterial infections are older adults, young children, those with weakened immune systems.

Theory: Some swimmers may deposit staph bacteria—which is present on the skin of many healthy people—in the water. To protect yourself and others, shower with soap both before and after swimming in subtropical waters, including at beaches in South Florida, Southern California and the Caribbean.

Lisa Plano, MD, PhD, associate professor of pediatrics and microbiology, University of Miami.

Homeopathic Remedies For Seasickness

If you feel nauseated and turn pale or greenish when inside the ship but feel better on deck in the fresh air, take *Tabacum*. If symptoms worsen from the slightest motion (even from watching objects move) and from being in the cold open air on deck but ease when you lie on your side, try *Cocculus indicus*. With either remedy, take three 30C pellets (dissolving them under your tongue) at 20-minute intervals until your seasickness is gone or for a maximum of three doses. Do not repeat on subsequent days—either the remedy worked or it didn't. Both remedies are sold at health-food stores.

Edward Shalts, MD, DHt (diplomate in homeotherapeutics), a private practitioner in New York City, and author of *Easy Homeopathy* (McGraw-Hill).

How to Protect Yourself From GI Illness on a Cruise

Philip C. Carling, MD, professor of clinical medicine, Boston University, and the lead author of a study of 56 cruise ships, published in *Clinical Infectious Diseases*.

Gastrointestinal (GI)-illness outbreaks on cruise ships are linked to improperly cleaned restrooms.

Recent results: Restroom cleanliness scores tend to be lower on ships that have outbreaks of the illness. Researchers believe that one passenger or crew member on a ship may come down with the *norovirus*, responsible for most outbreaks, and then substandard hygiene and improper cleaning of restrooms help the disease to spread. The norovirus can survive for weeks on surfaces at room temperature and is difficult to kill. Alcohol hand rubs kill it slowly and incompletely. The only thing that has been shown to work well is chlorine bleach.

According to CruisingHealthy.com almost 80% of all cruise ships that dock at US ports have at least one passenger or crew member with a confirmed diagnosis of GI illness by the ship's medical staff.

Self-defense: Wash hands using soap and water, and avoid contact with restroom surfaces, such as doorknobs, toilet handles and changing tables.

Natural Jet-Lag Remedy

Tart cherries have high levels of *melatonin*, which helps regulate your circadian rhythm and induce sleepiness.

Best: Have one-half cup of dried tart cherries (like Montmorency) or have two tablespoons of any cherry juice concentrate one hour before you wish to sleep on the plane and an hour before bedtime for the three days after you land.

Russel Reiter, PhD, professor of neuroendocrinology, University of Texas Health Science Center, San Antonio.

Better Travels with Your Dog

If taking a long trip by car with your dog, visit your veterinarian for a canine health certificate, which attests to the pooch's good health. Authorities may ask to see one if you are stopped. Also, keep your dog in the back of the car for safety, give the dog a rest stop whenever you take one and have plenty of water available. If traveling by plane, check with the airline—each has its own rules. Carry a small dog aboard if possible in a dog carrier that fits under your seat—many airlines allow this, usually for a $100 fee* each way.

Justine Lee, DVM, veterinary emergency critical-care specialist and associate director of veterinary services, Pet Poison Helpline, *www.petpoisonhelpline.com*, writing in *Prevention*.

*Price subject to change.

15

Friends, Family and Fun!

Beginner's Guide to Twitter: This Free Online Service Can Be Surprisingly Useful...

Everyone seems to be atwitter about Twitter. The free online service allows users to send and receive very succinct messages, no longer than 140 characters apiece. The typical Twitter message, known as a "tweet," might provide a quick update on what you're doing or request help with a problem. Users post tweets to a personal Web page from their cell phones, PDAs or computers. *How Twitter can be useful and how to sign up...*

TWITTER FOR FUN AND FAMILY

To use Twitter in your personal life...

•**Keep friends and family updated on your life when you don't have the time or inclination to call or e-mail.** You might tweet,

"We arrived home safely from our trip"...or, "The car's running again. It was just a fuse."

Real-life tweet: A passenger on a plane that skidded off a Denver runway last winter used his cell phone to tweet about the event moments after it occurred. His friends never had to worry about his safety, because they got his tweet and learned that he was unharmed before the incident was reported in the media.

•**Arrange social activities, even at the last minute.** Rather than place dozens of calls to find someone who is free, send out a single tweet. This tweet might read, "I'm going fishing. Anyone want to join me?"

Real-life tweet: Basketball star Shaquille O'Neal used Twitter to inform his friends and fans that he was sitting down to dinner alone

---

Joel Comm, an Internet entrepreneur in Loveland, Colorado, who has helped to found such Web sites as WorldVillage.com and ClassicGames.com (now Yahoo! Games). He is author of *Twitter Power: How to Dominate Your Market One Tweet at a Time* (Wiley, *www.twitterpower.com*).

in Phoenix. A couple of local basketball fans drove to the diner and hung out with him.

• **Solicit opinions, advice or assistance on short notice.** You could tweet, "Can anyone suggest a good place for dinner in Albany?"… or, "My car broke down in Portland. Can anyone recommend a good mechanic?"

HOW TO SIGN UP

Twitter is easy to use. Visit *www.twitter.com*, click "Get Started-Join!" and follow the simple directions.

E-mail a link to your Twitter Web page to keep friends, family, colleagues and clients posted on your life or business. You can find people to follow by clicking on "Find People" from your Twitter home page.

Warning: Click "Settings," then check the box by "Protect my updates" on your Twitter account page if you want to maintain control over who reads your tweets. Leave this unchecked only if you do not expect to share sensitive information and would like to reach strangers as well as friends. Always be careful. If you are going to be out of town for a few weeks, you may not want to tweet about that if everyone can read your posts.

You also can choose to receive tweets from individuals on your cell phone. Though Twitter is free, your service provider may charge you when you send or receive messages from your phone depending on your plan.

Safeguard Your Snapshots: Best Ways To Store Digital Photos And Videos

Daniel Dumas, associate editor in charge of product reviews at *Wired* magazine and Wired.com, San Francisco, *www.wired.com/reviews*. He previously wrote about portable technology at *Mobile PC* magazine.

Your digital photos and videos could be lost forever if there's a problem with your computer. *The best alternatives for backing up this irreplaceable data…*

252

ONLINE STORAGE PROVIDERS

You can upload photos and videos to servers owned by online photo-sharing companies or other online digital-storage providers. Your photos will be stored in a far-off location, so that they will remain safe even if a fire or natural disaster destroys your home.

Downsides: Uploading numerous pictures or videos over the Internet can be extremely time-consuming, particularly with a slow Internet connection. You might have to pay a monthly fee to store more than a few hundred pictures. Your pictures could be deleted if the company goes out of business or you fail to pay storage fees.

Best for: Those who have fast Internet connections…wish to share photos with far-flung friends and family over the Internet…want the ability to access photos from computers other than their own. *Options include…*

• **Flickr Pro Account.** Yahoo!'s digital photo service, *Flickr*, offers unlimited digital photo and video storage for $24.95/year.* Video clips cannot go beyond 90 seconds each. *www.flickr.com.*

• **Picasa Web Albums.** Google's *Picasa Web Albums* provides one gigabyte of free online storage, enough for perhaps several hundred digital photos. Additional storage is available for a fee. *http://picasaweb.google.com.*

Example: 80 gigabytes cost $20 per year.
Google also offers free Picasa software that helps you organize and edit photos.

• **Shutterfly.** This popular photography Web site offers free unlimited photo storage. Users cannot retrieve their pictures in high resolution online, but they can buy a DVD of their high-resolution images from *Shutterfly*. The price of these "Archive DVDs" varies depending on the quantity of photos involved. *www.shutterfly.com.*

Example: A DVD that has 1,000 pictures is $19.99 plus shipping. Each additional 1,000 images adds $4.99 to the price.

EXTERNAL HARD DRIVES

An external hard drive is similar to the hard drive built into your computer. An external

*Prices subject to change.

drive offers added memory if your computer's hard drive is filling up...or backup storage in case your computer's hard drive fails.

Downside: External hard drives do sometimes fail, particularly if they're dropped even a short distance.

Best for: People who want to store large numbers of photos—even hundreds of thousands—for an affordable price...and want to back up and access photos quickly. *Options...*

• **Seagate FreeAgent.** Seagate makes high-quality drives, and the company has excellent customer service. *http://freeagent.seagate.com.*

Example: Seagate's 2-Terabyte (TB) *FreeAgent Desk* external hard drive has a 500 GB capacity and can hold about 250,000 digital photos and up to 76 hours of video. It can be purchased for as little as $100.

• **Western Digital MyBook.** Western Digital also makes reliable, affordable, easy-to-use hard drives. *www.westerndigital.com.*

Example: Western Digital's *My Book Essential Edition* 2-TB external hard drive can be found for around $190. It has a 500 GB capacity and holds about 250,000 pictures and up to 76 hours of video.

NETWORK ATTACHED STORAGE

Network Attached Storage (or NAS) devices are similar to external hard drives except one unit typically contains multiple drives that can be set to back each other up.

Downside: The NAS devices can be several times more expensive than standard external hard drives...and significantly more complex to set up.

Best for: Those willing to pay a little more for the added safety of "redundant" multidrive storage...and who want easy access to backup files from multiple computers. *Option...*

• **Buffalo Technology LinkStation.** LinkStation is easy to set up and use, though transfer speeds are a bit slow. *www.buffalotech.com.*

Examples: The *LinkStation Pro Duo* two-drive 2-TB model costs around $250. The four-drive, 4-TB *Link-Station Quad* costs around $575.

CDs AND DVDs

Most modern computers feature disc drives that can "burn" files, such as pictures or videos, onto CDs. Many even record onto DVDs. Blank discs are relatively cheap when purchased in quantity—as little as 20 cents apiece.

Downside: Recording onto discs is time-consuming, as is finding the pictures you're looking for later. Your images could be lost if a CD or DVD gets scratched or degrades over the years.

Best for: Those who want to back up a relatively small number of important photos—perhaps a few hundred—and feel better keeping backup in their home rather than at a distant server accessed through the Internet.

Free Classical Music On the Internet

Browse for free sound files of classical music by composer, performer, instrument, period or form (minuet, sonata, etc.) at *www.musopen.com.* The music is free to download and share and can be played on a computer or portable digital music device.

Free "Oldies" Radio

Slacker.com is a free "personal" Internet radio service that has "stations" playing music of the 1940s, 1950s and 1960s and stations for classical, country, jazz, comedy and other genres. It is "personal" in that you can click a song as one you "like," "don't like" or want to "ban," and from then on, the selection of songs you hear will be customized to your taste.

How to Get Free Audio Books

Hundreds of books in the public domain (mostly published more than 75 years prior, including many classics) are available for audio download at *http://librivox.org*, a nonprofit, volunteer-run Web site. You can download books to your computer or portable audio player, and if you choose, subscribe through iTunes at *www.apple.com/itunes*.

Convenient and Personal: Order Paper Greeting Cards Online

Electronic greeting cards can be sent over the Internet, but many people think that they are too impersonal. They can't be sent to anyone who lacks Internet service—and they can't be displayed on a mantle.

New: Jackcards.com lets you order the paper cards you want, then sends them to you with postage applied and in an addressed envelope, ready for you to sign, personalize and mail.

Cost: From $2.94.*

*Price subject to change.

Ticket Tips

If tickets to a show or sports event are too pricey when you first check, try again one week before the event—at that point, prices often start to drop daily and even may go below face value. But seat availability drops, too, so you may not get the seating area you want. Avoid Web sites that claim to offer tickets for popular events at discounts, as they may be fraudulent.

What to do: Shop around at reputable sites such as StubHub.com and TicketZoom.com

not only for ticket prices but also for fees. Some sites charge a service fee in addition to shipping and delivery costs, and all costs vary widely. Tickets are nonrefundable, so be sure you know the total price you are paying before you buy.

Kiplinger.com.

Take Me Out to the Ball Game…for Less!

Like airlines, baseball teams adjust ticket prices based on schedules. Midweek games against less interesting teams usually cost the least. Ticket promotions may be available online—go to the team's online site for details. Season–ticket holders often sell off unwanted individual tickets through Craigslist or Stub-Hub. Bring your own food to the stadium if the team allows it—some do. Find out if your team offers tickets plus unlimited food for a fixed price—at least seven teams offer these arrangements. Spend less getting to and from the baseball stadium by using public transportation instead of your own car.

What to do: Check each team's Web site—promotions vary by team, by game, by time in the season and by day of the week.

CBSMoneyWatch.com.

To Get Free Entertainment— Volunteer!

Inquire if theaters need volunteers to help with concerts, plays or dance recitals you'd like to see. They usually need volunteers to help promote events or to serve as ushers and greeters for the events. Promoters usually are given free tickets, and ushers and greeters get to see the show. You also can try to volunteer at local museums or nature centers to see the exhibits for free.

Consumer Reports Money Adviser, 101 Truman Ave., Yonkers, New York 10703, *www.consumerreports.org.*

Swimmers' Alert

Inhaling just a tiny amount of water while swimming or bathing can sometimes lead to "dry drowning," in which water in the lungs reduces oxygen flow to the brain, causing loss of consciousness or even death. Dry drowning can occur up to 24 hours after being in water. Children and adults who are not good swimmers are at risk, as well as people with underlying lung problems, such as asthma.

Warning signs include persistent coughing, shortness of breath, pain in the chest, extreme tiredness and/or behavioral changes shortly after being in water. If you or a loved one has any of these signs after swimming or bathing, see a doctor immediately. Victims of dry drowning must have a breathing tube inserted so that oxygen can be supplied to the lungs.

Neil Schachter, MD, professor of pulmonary medicine and medical director of respiratory care, Mount Sinai Medical Center, New York City.

Take Advantage of Cheaper Golf Club Memberships

Private golf club membership fees are down 13% from peak years and more than that at some financially troubled clubs. Some also are providing financing deals or giving new members the opportunity to pay their initiation fees over several years. Semiprivate and public clubs are lowering their fees, too.

What to do: Talk to any club in which you are interested, and find out what special deals it is offering.

Kiplinger's Personal Finance, 1729 H St. NW, Washington, DC 20006, *www.kiplinger.com/magazine.*

Herb Garden Advice

To prevent invasive herbs from taking over your garden, don't plant them directly in the ground. Plant each herb in a 12-inch plastic pot (you can sometimes get these for free from nurseries), then plant the pots in the ground. Make sure the rim of the pot is an inch or so above the soil level. The pot will prevent aggressive plants, such as mint, lemon balm, catnip and horseradish, from taking over.

Key: Remember to "deadhead" (cut off new seedheads) regularly to stop any pushy species from self-sowing in the garden.

Sharon Lovejoy, gardening expert and lecturer in South Bristol, Maine, and author of *Trowel & Error: Over 700 Shortcuts, Tips & Remedies for the Gardener* (Workman).

Gardening Self-Defense

Gardeners are at risk for tetanus. The bacteria that causes tetanus, also called lockjaw, is commonly found in dirt and on tools. Gardeners account for more than one-third of the tetanus cases reported in the US each year. Tetanus is rare, but it can be fatal.

Self-defense: Get a booster shot every 10 years.

UC Berkeley Wellness Letter, 500 Fifth Ave., New York City 10110, *www.wellnessletter.com.*

Are These Poisonous Plants in Your Yard?

Backyard plants can be poisonous. More than 68,000 Americans per year are poisoned by plants. Reactions can range from a skin rash or upset stomach to severe gastrointestinal symptoms or even death. Small children and pets are at highest risk.

Common plants that can be harmful: Oleander, datura, castor bean.

Ask a garden center or landscaper for more information.

Amy Stewart, avid gardener and winner of the California Horticultural Society's Writers Award and author of *Flower Confidential* (Algonquin).

Natural Ways to Keep Deer Away

Daniel M. Sherman, principal of Daniel Sherman Landscape Architect, PC, in Valhalla, New York, and chairman of the Piermont, New York, parks commission. His design work has been featured in *House & Garden, The Modern Estate, Westchester Magazine* and elsewhere. Sherman's online site is *www.dansherman landscape.com.*

Deer can do hundreds of dollars' worth of damage to landscaping in a single night of munching.

Fencing can protect your plants, but deer have been known to jump fences as high as eight feet. Plastic netting is unsightly, and deer sometimes push it aside. Some deer-repellent sprays smell bad and may be toxic to children and pets. *Alternatives…*

CHOOSE THE RIGHT PLANTS

No plant is guaranteed deer-proof, but you will minimize the chances of a deer invasion with these…

•**Shrubs.** Avoid holly, rhododendrons, azaleas and euonymus. *Better choices…*

•Boxwood. Though it's often clipped into hedges or topiaries, it provides a pleasing fluffy shape when untrimmed. The Korean boxwood is a hardy ground cover.

•Andromeda. An elegant, mounding evergreen, with narrow leaves and clustered pink or white flowers in spring.

•Spirea. An easy-to-grow, deciduous summer bloomer in pink, red or white.

•Caryopteris. Drought-tolerant, with purple-blue flowers, it tends to freeze back (if not, it should be cut back) during winter and returns in spring.

•**Trees.** Avoid pine and hemlock. *Two better choices…*

•Japanese maple. Graceful with spectacular red, yellow or orange fall foliage.

•Spruce. A classic evergreen, with fragrant silver-blue needles.

•**Annuals and perennials.** Avoid hostas, lilies, impatiens and roses.

Better choices: Lilacs, foxgloves, snapdragons, cosmos and lantana.

•**Other deer-resistant plants.** Pachysandra, an evergreen ground cover…ornamental grasses…fragrant herbs, such as lavender, rosemary, mint and sage.

NATURAL SPRAY

When deer are hungry enough, they may eat even deer-resistant plants. To be on the safe side, use a natural repellent spray as well.

I have had good results with Deer Stopper, a pleasant-smelling liquid made of natural ingredients, including rosemary oil, mint oil and egg. You can buy it at hardware and garden stores, including The Home Depot, or online from the manufacturer (*www.messinawildlife. com*).

Cost: About $13 for a one-quart spray bottle,* which covers 1,000 square feet.

Apply once a month in winter and every other month from May through October.

*Price subject to change.

The Etiquette of Regifting

Give a gift you have received as a gift only if it is like new and you think that the recipient will truly enjoy it. Impersonal items, such as scented candles or a box of chocolates, can be "regifted" as a last-minute hostess gift, but don't regift homemade or unique items, which may be recognized by the original gift giver.

Also: Never put saving a few pennies before a friendship. When in doubt, purchase a new gift.

Anna Post, author and spokesperson, The Emily Post Institute, Burlington, Vermont.

16

Auto Answers

Five Simple Ways to Make Your Car Last 300,000 Miles

When you drive your car regularly, some wear and tear has to be expected. But you can take some important steps to reduce excessive wear—and in the process, save money on car maintenance and ensure that your car runs for as long as possible.

Bonus: The resale value of a well-maintained car always is greater than that of an identical car that did not receive proper care.

KEEP YOUR CAR BATTERY FULLY CHARGED

Most people do not pay attention to a car battery unless it stops working, but keeping your battery at full charge extends its useful life. Repeated charging and discharging can weaken the battery's ability to hold a charge over time.

Your auto battery also becomes depleted when you don't use the vehicle for more than a few weeks. Even though the car is not running and all accessories are shut off, if the battery is connected, there is a gradual draw of current.

What to do: To avoid depleting your battery, don't use the radio, headlights, interior lights and any other accessory when the engine is off.

If your car is not used regularly, consider buying an automatic "trickle charger." This device is connected by cables to the car battery in the car and plugged into a household electrical outlet to provide a charge. I prefer the automatic models, which cannot overcharge your battery because they automatically turn off when the battery reaches its full capacity.

Eric Peters, a Washington, DC–based automotive columnist and author of *Automotive Atrocities! The Cars We Love to Hate* (MBI). His Web site is *http://ericpeters autos.com.*

These trickle chargers are available at auto-parts stores for about $40.

FILL YOUR GAS TANK

A full or nearly full tank reduces the odds that you will need expensive fuel system service in the years ahead. Most gas tanks are made of metal, and a partially empty fuel tank is prone to rust. Rust particles flake off and can clog fuel filters, fuel lines and fuel injectors, leading to costly repairs. In addition, rust can eat through the tank, creating holes. That might take 10 to 15 years, but modern cars often last that long and longer. Replacing a gas tank (and fuel lines) is an expensive job.

What to do: Keep your gas tank as full as possible at all times. Never let it get lower than half a tank.

Bonus: You won't ever have to make an emergency almost-empty stop at a gas station that charges more than an average price for gas.

WATCH YOUR TIRES

Today's tires are much more reliable than tires in the past—so much so that people tend to not think about their tires or check their air pressure.

Result: Underinflated tires are more common today. Tires that are underinflated create more friction than those that have the right amount of pressure. This reduces gas mileage and can cause tires to wear out faster.

With today's high-quality tires, air leakage typically is very slow and might not be noticeable to the eye until the pressure has dropped to dangerously low levels.

What to do: Check your tire pressure. Almost all new cars now have built-in electronic tire-pressure monitors. For older cars, it's wise to check your pressure the old-fashioned way, using a handheld gauge—at least every two weeks. It is best to do this when the tires are "cold" (not warm from driving). Add air whenever tire pressure falls below the carmaker's recommended minimum level. This is listed in the owner's manual or on a sticker on the inside of the driver's door jamb.

OIL CHANGES

Oil's main job is to capture contaminants that would otherwise contribute to the wear and tear of the car's engine.

What to do: Keep the engine well-serviced by always changing the oil at the prescribed time. Don't go longer than one month or 200 to 300 miles past the mileage/date interval.

PROTECT YOUR CLUTCH

The clutch on a car with a manual transmission wears down during the course of normal use, mainly because of friction. Replacing the clutch can cost $1,000 or more, so the longer you can go between clutch jobs, the better.

What to do: Most wear and tear takes place when you start and stop a vehicle and shift gears. To cut back on wear and tear on the clutch, try to minimize stop-and-go–type driving as well as gear changes.

Example: Try to maintain your vehicle's momentum by anticipating changing lights and the ebb and flow of traffic. It is much easier on the clutch to "roll out" in second or third gear than to start from a dead stop in first gear. When you change gears, do it smoothly, not abruptly.

Important: Avoid excessive use of the clutch and "riding" it (partially engaging the clutch, which increases friction and can wear it out).

More from Eric Peters...

Fixing Your Own Car Just Got Easier

If you like to make vehicle repairs yourself, here are a few gadgets, including diagnostic tools, that could make it easier...

• **Battery Monitor ($16.50*).** Know the current state of your car battery at a glance with the simple installation (with basic hand tools) of the Battery Doctor monitor on or near the battery. The device also can act as a surge protector during jump-starting (and recharging). Available from California Car Cover Company, 800-423-5525, *www.calcarcover.com*.

• **Non-Contact Laser Thermometer ($59.99).** Car lovers often need to take the temperature of components in their cars to trace an overheating problem. This handheld tool will save both time and hassle because you can read

*Prices subject to change.

the temperature of things, such as radiators and cylinder heads, just by pointing at them. It also is helpful for diagnosing problems with air-conditioning systems—and can read temperatures from -4° F to 968° F. Available from Harbor Freight Tools at 800-444-3353, *www. harborfreight.com.*

• **Multi Fluid Extractor ($89.99).** Changing the oil can be a messy chore that may require jacking up the car and crawling underneath— unless you have this tool. The pump can suck the old oil out of the engine with a nozzle that slips into the oil dipstick tube. It holds nearly seven quarts of oil. Available from Griot's Garage, 800-345-5789, *www.griotsgarage.com.*

• **POR-15 Super Starter Kit ($19.80).** Any car lover's nemesis is rust—and POR-15 is the best stuff available to stop rust in its tracks. A rust-preventive paint (a favorite of those who restore old cars), it permanently seals existing rust and can protect exposed metal with a virtually indestructible coating that can be drilled and painted. The kit includes enough POR-15 to cover six square feet with two coats, plus metal-preparation treatment, a degreaser, gloves and two brushes. Available from POR-15, Inc., 800-726-0459, *www.por15.com* (click on "POR-15 Rust Preventive Paint").

Also from Eric Peters...

Should You Fill Tires with Nitrogen Instead of Air?

Nitrogen leaks less than air (its molecules are larger) and may prevent tire deterioration that can result from oxidation in air-filled tires.

However, nitrogen is not widely available, so when a tire needs to be refilled, you will probably have to go back to the dealer who sold it to you...if you drive a lot, tires wear out quickly, so you won't have them long enough for the "nitrogen benefit" to pay off. Also, nitrogen is much more costly than air.

Result: Nitrogen is best for light drivers who don't drive far from home and expect to keep tires for many years.

Before You Buy Tires...

Check the age of tires before you buy them. Tires deteriorate with age, so you shouldn't buy a tire that is more than two years old. To find the age of a set of tires, look on the sidewall for a string of letters and numbers that start with "DOT." At the end, there is a four-digit number that tells you the week and the year in which the tire was made.

Example: If the number is 2510, the tire was made in the 25th week of 2010.

Consumer Reports, 101 Truman Ave., Yonkers, New York 10703, *www.consumerreports.org.*

Tire Danger! Don't Overinflate

Overinflating tires can result in sudden tire failure, causing the car to go out of control. Never inflate a tire beyond the tire manufacturer's maximum rated pressure, shown on the sidewall (as opposed to the carmaker's recommended pressure, found in the owner's manual, on the sticker inside the driver's side door or on a label in the glove box).

Example: Most car companies recommend inflation of about 26 pounds per square inch (psi)...most tire manufacturers rate tires for a maximum of 44 psi (as indicated on the sidewall)...so you might inflate a tire to 35 psi.

This additional pressure saves fuel, but your car will ride more harshly and not handle as well and the tires will be more vulnerable to damage from potholes and curbs.

David Solomon, certified master auto technician and chairman, MotorWatch, an automotive watchdog organization, Butler, Maryland, *www.motorwatch.com.*

More from David Solomon...

Pothole Protection

Don't step on the brake when driving over a pothole.

Reason: Hitting the brake as the car goes over a pothole shifts the car's weight forward onto the front wheels. This increases the impact force and can damage the car's suspension and brakes, and alters wheel alignment.

Better: Brake just before a pothole to slow down the car, then release the brake as you go over the pothole and, if necessary, brake right after the pothole.

Also from David Solomon...

Better and Safer Way to Jump a Car Battery

Avoid jump-starting your car battery from another vehicle.

Why: The common practice of getting a battery-to-battery "jump" and then using your car's alternator to recharge your battery is a bad idea. Your car's alternator is designed to maintain the battery charge. It isn't designed for the heavier task of recharging a dead battery and may be damaged. Also, jump-starting can cause damage to onboard electrical components and may cause an explosion.

Better and safer: If possible, use a battery charger plugged into a 120-volt power line to recharge the battery before starting the car.

Don't Ignore the Low-Fuel Light

When a vehicle's low-fuel light comes on, there may be as little as one gallon or as much as two-and-a-half gallons of gas left, depending on the car model. Don't keep driving with the light on. In addition to running out of gas, driving with low fuel increases the risk of clogging fuel injectors with the sediment that builds up in the bottom of the gas tank. That can reduce performance and fuel economy.

Robert Sinclair, Jr., manager of media relations for AAA, Garden City, New York, *www.aaa.com.*

Stop That Car! What to Do If the Brakes Fail... Accelerator Sticks...or a Tire Blows

William Van Tassel, PhD, manager of driver training operations at AAA's national office in Heathrow, Florida, *www.aaa.com.* He is a member of the Transportation Research Board's Committee on Operative Regulation and Education and a sports car racer with the Sports Car Club of America.

Tragically, runaway vehicles were in the news recently, when a series of crashes caused by stuck accelerator pedals led to several deaths in the US and to the recall of millions of vehicles.

Runaway automobiles are relatively rare, but they are possible with any vehicle make and model. They may occur because parts fail or wear out, especially if vehicles are not properly maintained.

If you find yourself behind the wheel of a runaway car, you must act quickly and wisely to avoid a crash. The two most common reactions are to immediately slam on the brakes or repeatedly pump the brakes, but these measures could be ineffective or even detrimental.

The proper response to a runaway vehicle depends on why the vehicle has gone out of control.

UNINTENDED ACCELERATION

Your foot is off of the accelerator, yet your speed continues to climb higher. You hear the engine working harder and feel pushed back into your seat.

1. Shift into neutral. This is easy to accomplish with a manual transmission, however, it might be a little tricky with certain automatic transmissions.

All automatic transmissions allow drivers to shift from drive to neutral while moving (and you don't need to depress the brake as you do this). And some automatic transmission shift mechanisms have "gates," or grooves in the gearshift box designed to help drivers access special transmission modes, such as upshifting and downshifting. But, unfortunately, the gates also could make it more challenging to find neutral in an emergency. If your vehicle has an automatic transmission, practice shifting into neutral with the car parked and running so that you'll be familiar with how it feels in an emergency.

Shifting into neutral disengages the engine from the transmission, preventing further acceleration, but does not slow the engine itself. Even with the car in neutral, you likely will continue to hear the engine revving.

Warning: Some news reports have suggested turning the key in the ignition of a runaway vehicle to the "off" position if finding neutral proves difficult. (Note that this is not an option in vehicles equipped with keyless start/stop systems.) Do this only as a last resort and only after several attempts to shift into neutral have failed. Turning the ignition off will rob most vehicles of their power steering and much of their braking power. Under no circumstances should you ever remove the key from the ignition while the vehicle is in motion, because this locks the steering wheel.

2. Step on the brake pedal as hard as you can. Do this while you are putting the car into neutral—or as soon as you can after putting the car into neutral. Throw all of your weight into it, and keep your weight on the brake. The braking systems of modern vehicles depend on a vacuum created by the engine to generate much of their stopping power. This vacuum largely disappears when the accelerator is stuck and the engine is revving, which means extra force may be required from the driver. Do not pump the brakes. Pumping will not enable you to build up the vacuum you need to slow the car.

3. If the first two steps bring no signs of slowing the vehicle, try to work your toe under the accelerator pedal and lift it up.

4. If you are unable to stop the car after trying the first three steps and are faced with a dangerous situation (such as heavy traffic or a busy intersection), gently guide the side of your vehicle up against a guardrail or other barrier that runs along the side of the road. The friction should slow down your vehicle. Your auto will sustain considerable damage,

but that's better than plowing headlong into something at full speed.

Many people ask about using the parking brake (once commonly known as the emergency brake). It is not recommended in this situation, because this brake is weaker and more difficult to control than a standard braking system.

5. No matter what method stopped your vehicle, do not attempt to drive it afterward. Turn off the ignition, then call a tow truck.

BRAKE FAILURE

You step on the brakes, but your vehicle does not slow or slows less rapidly than usual...and the resistance of the brake pedal feels either much harder or softer than normal under your foot. Brake failure typically is caused by either a hydraulic fluid leak in the brake line or by badly worn brake pads. (If your vehicle has been recalled because of a brake failure problem, check to see whether brake failure instructions have been issued for your specific vehicle.)

1. Tap the brakes a few times. In the case of brake failure, tapping the brake pedal could build up any hydraulic pressure that remains in the vehicle's hydraulic line, increasing the brakes' stopping power. Even drivers with vehicles that have antilock brakes should tap a few times.

2. Engage the parking brake as slowly and gently as circumstances permit. If tapping the brakes does not bring the vehicle to a halt, the parking brake is your best bet. Engaging this brake slowly reduces the odds that the vehicle will enter into a difficult-to-control skid. If you don't engage your parking brake often, practice reaching for it while the car is parked so that you can familiarize yourself with its position.

3. If it appears that you won't be able to stop before colliding with another car or running off the road in a curve, gently guide the side of your car up against a guardrail or other barrier that runs along the side of the roadway.

4. Attempt to coast to a stop on the shoulder or some other safe spot. Then call a tow truck.

TIRE BLOWOUT

You feel a jolt and hear a loud noise…and instantly your vehicle becomes difficult to handle. This often indicates that a tire has blown out.

1. Grip the steering wheel firmly with both hands. It usually will take some effort to keep your car in its lane.

2. Lift your foot off the gas. Resist the urge to brake unless you are in a situation where you absolutely must stop quickly. If a tire has blown out, braking is likely to make your vehicle very difficult to control. It could even put the vehicle into a dangerous skid.

3. Gently apply the brakes only when you think you have the vehicle largely back under control, when there is no longer a sensation of skidding or zigzagging.

4. Guide the vehicle onto the shoulder or some other safe spot, then change the tire or call for help.

HEADLIGHT FAILURE

You're driving at night when suddenly everything goes dark. Headlight failure could be caused by an electrical problem or simply a burned-out bulb.

1. Turn on your high beams. The high beams usually are on a different circuit than the regular headlights and may work even when the regular ones fail.

2. Turn on your parking and/or hazard lights (which are on a different circuit than the headlights in most vehicles). If the high beams do not work, the parking and hazard lights can provide at least enough illumination for you to see the road immediately ahead and to help other drivers see you.

3. Slow your vehicle and come to a stop in a safe spot, such as the shoulder, as soon as possible. Turn on your hazard lights (if they are not already on), then turn off the ignition and call for help.

Car Technology That Can Save Your Life

Eric Peters, a Washington, DC–based automotive columnist and author of *Automotive Atrocities! The Cars We Love to Hate* (MBI). His Web site is *http://ericpeters autos.com*.

Automakers have developed some spiffy new technologies for their newest cars that promote safe driving and help to prevent accidents.

Caution: These state-of-the-art devices can help you avoid accidents, but they are not a substitute for good driving.

Here are several recent accident-avoidance gadgets and systems that are standard or optional in many cars (at this time, these technologies are not sold separately)…

LIMITS FOR TEEN DRIVING

MyKey, developed by Ford, allows a concerned parent to limit the speed of the vehicle that their teen is driving to 80 miles per hour (mph). Although the speed limit throughout much of the US is 70 mph, Ford decided to set the limit at 80 mph in case a driver needs to accelerate to avoid a crash. Nothing limits the MyKey system to teen drivers—it can be used by any driver who does not want to top 80 mph. MyKey can be set up to sound a chime if the driver exceeds 45, 55 or 65 mph.

Bonus: Driving at lower speeds can help fuel economy.

The MyKey system also enables parents to control other in-car functions, including the maximum volume of the sound system, and the car can be programmed to emit warning chimes if occupants aren't wearing their seat belts. An owner-programmable ignition key is the heart of the system.

Available in: Focus compact and Escape SUV. Ford plans to offer MyKey on many other models in the future.

AROUND VIEW MONITOR

Infiniti (Nissan's luxury car division) has developed an unusual "panorama view" backup camera that now is available on certain models and may be available on others in the future. It gives the driver a bird's-eye view (as seen from above) of the perimeter around the car—not just what's behind the rear bumper. Mini-cameras with wide-angle lenses are built into the sides, front and rear of the car.

Around View will work with the vehicle in drive and reverse (at low speeds up to about 5 mph) and can be helpful when maneuvering in confined spaces.

Available in: Infiniti EX and FX SUVs.

Caveat: The image on the LCD monitor is slightly distorted, which can make it difficult to accurately judge exactly how much room you've got to work with. Always check twice before backing up—and proceed slowly.

AUTOMATIC BRAKING/ "ACTIVE" COLLISION AVOIDANCE

Pioneered by Mercedes-Benz, this technology uses radar to detect vehicles and slow-moving objects in the vehicle's path (or excessive closing speed between your vehicle and another car). The system can apply the brakes automatically without getting driver input. In Mercedes-Benz vehicles, such as the E-Class and S-Class sedans, the system works with the cruise control to decelerate and accelerate the vehicle with the ebb and flow of traffic. It can bring the car to a complete stop and resume the vehicle's speed without the driver touching the brake or gas pedal.

The system's designed both as an emergency safety measure—applying the brakes in the event that the driver fails to notice a dangerous situation, such as suddenly stopped traffic ahead—and as a convenience, because it allows "set and forget" cruise control operation.

Available in: Mercedes-Benz E- and S-Class sedans, E-Class coupes and Volvo S80 sedan.

Caveat: This technology may cause the vehicle to brake even when you don't want it to. The system can be turned off by the driver.

LANE-DEPARTURE WARNING

Infiniti pioneered this system, which emits a warning beep whenever the vehicle begins to stray over a double yellow line (and potentially into oncoming traffic) or other painted lines. The system can be turned off by the driver in situations where it would give false alarms, such as when driving across parking lots with painted lines.

Available in: Infiniti EX and FX SUVs and M sedans.

DRIVER ALERTNESS MONITOR

Developed by Mercedes-Benz, this system detects when a driver is falling asleep at the wheel. When sensors note decreased or inappropriate steering, the system emits an audible warning signal to try to wake up the driver. The system can be turned off by the driver.

Available in: Mercedes-Benz E- and S-Class, except the S400 Hybrid.

Caveat: It's possible that the sudden audible warning could startle an already half-asleep driver and cause him/her to jerk the wheel or jam on the brakes. Because the system is new, there is no data yet on its effectiveness.

Important: Always get lots of rest before you drive. Take a leg-stretch/bathroom break every three to four hours—and make an overnight stop after spending eight to 10 hours behind the wheel.

The Safest...and Deadliest Months For Car Crashes

Did you know that October is the deadliest month for car crashes? The risk of dying in a crash in October is 16% higher than in March—the safest month.

Reason: No single cause, though daylight, weather, alcohol consumption and other factors that exhibit seasonal variations all create a joint influence.

Michael Sivak, PhD, research professor, University of Michigan Transportation Research Institute in Ann Arbor, and the leader of an analysis of US crash-death figures from 1994 to 2006, published in *Traffic Injury Prevention*.

Rainy Day Driving

Roads are slickest during the first 10 minutes of a rainstorm—that is when oil on the surface is being lifted and mixed with water—so stay off the road during that time if it is possible. Also, replace windshield wipers at least annually—sooner if they streak and wiping them down doesn't help. And, make sure that your tire treads are deep enough to provide traction on water.

How: Place one quarter in the tread (with George Washington's head down). If you can see the top of Washington's head, the tread is too worn and the tire should be replaced.

Tire Rack, an independent tire tester, South Bend, Indiana, *www.tirerack.com.*

What to Do If You're Stuck in a Blizzard...

If you can drive no further during a blizzard, pull off the highway, turn on your hazard lights and hang a distress flag from your window or antenna. Remain in your car, where authorities can most easily locate you, unless there is shelter nearby. To conserve fuel, run the engine and heater for only 10 minutes an hour to keep warm. Open a downwind window slightly for ventilation, and periodically clear snow from the exhaust pipe to protect against carbon monoxide poisoning. Consume fluids to avoid dehydration. Huddle together, or insulate yourself with maps and blankets. Turn on the inside light at night so that rescue crews can locate your car.

Federal Emergency Management Agency, Washington, DC, *www.fema.gov.*

Protect Your Teen Driver

Teens with their own cars are more likely to get into accidents than teens who share a car with a family member.

Recent finding: 25% of teens who had their own vehicles had been involved in crashes, compared with only 11% of those who shared a car.

Traffic accidents are the number-one cause of death for US teens, resulting in more than 5,000 deaths each year.

Best: Discuss driving privileges with your teen. Establish clear rules, and monitor teens' whereabouts.

Teens who said their parents did this in a supportive, noncontrolling way were half as likely to crash, compared with teens who said their parents were uninvolved.

Flaura Koplin Winston, MD, PhD, scientific director of the Center for Injury Research and Prevention at Children's Hospital of Philadelphia, and leader of a study of 5,500 teenagers, funded by State Farm Insurance Co. and published in *Pediatrics.*

Distracted Driving as Dangerous as Drunk Driving

Distraction can impair driving skill as much as intoxication.

Alarming: In a study, 19% of women and 15% of men driving near schools were distracted—typically by cell-phone use, drinking, eating or smoking.

Safest: Turn off cell phones, and don't take your eyes off of the road, especially in school zones.

Jurek Grabowski, PhD, MPH, director of evaluation and research, Safe Kids USA, Washington, DC, and co-author of a study of 41,426 drivers.

Why You Can't Depend On Your GPS

Your GPS navigating device can lead you astray.

Reasons: GPS units are only as accurate as the map data supplied to them. Not all areas have been fully mapped out, and there sometimes are inaccuracies. Rural regions are the most problematic.

Best: Always trust your common sense over the GPS. Be sure to download the most recent maps to your GPS unit—check with the GPS manufacturer to find out when new map data is available and how to download it. Always carry printed directions as well as the phone number of someone who can help if you get lost.

Nancy Dunnan, publisher of *TravelSmart*, Box 397, Dobbs Ferry, New York 10522, *www.travelsmartnewsletter.com.*

Police Go Undercover to Catch Speeders

Police undercover as work-zone surveyors use radar guns to catch speeders. The devices are made to look like surveying equipment. Some communities are using this and other approaches to issue more tickets and boost revenue.

Consumer Reports, 101 Truman Ave., Yonkers, New York 10703, *www.consumerreports.org.*

Downsides of a Hybrid

A recent study shows that people who drive hybrid autos receive more tickets. Many hybrids are driven in urban locations, where people are more likely to be cited for moving violations. Hybrid owners also tend to drive farther just for pleasure, maybe because they feel less guilty about using fuel—but the extra driving (about 2,000 miles a year) offsets some fuel savings.

Raj Bhat, PhD, president, Quality Planning, which analyzed the driving habits of 360,000 vehicle owners, San Francisco.

Are CPO Cars Worth the Extra Cost?

A certified pre-owned (CPO) car is a vehicle that has been inspected and serviced by a new or used-car dealership according to specific standards set forth by its manufacturer, including overall condition, appearance, mileage and age. (Most CPO cars are two to three years old and are just off their first lease.) CPO cars generally offer buyers more real (as well as psychological) security that the car is in good shape and ready to go.

But, CPO autos will cost more. These cars, which are in excellent condition, can sell for 10% to 20% more than the same car that is in average condition.

If you have the knowledge and wherewithal to inspect a prospective used car (or have it inspected by a trustworthy and competent independent shop), you would probably be able to get a better deal on a car that easily can be cleaned and tuned up.

Eric Peters, a Washington, DC–based automotive columnist and author of *Automotive Atrocities! The Cars We Love to Hate* (MBI). His Web site is *http://ericpetersautos.com.*

Car Buying Smarts

When buying a car, use a credit card for the down payment. That way if the dealer goes out of business before you get the car, you can challenge the charge with the card issuer. Also, do not sign any forms with items left blank—the dealership could falsify information. And, do not drive the car home before all the financial paperwork is completed under the terms to which you have agreed—an unscrupulous dealer may call you back, claiming the financing fell through, to get you to sign new paperwork at less favorable terms.

Consumer Reports, 101 Truman Ave., Yonkers, New York 10703, *www.consumerreports.org.*

What to do: Check your memberships. Some warehouse clubs, financial-services firms and auto clubs offer free or low-cost buying services. If you prefer to negotiate for yourself—but want a strong starting point—visit Web sites such as Truecar.com, Edmunds.com and KBB. com.

SmartMoney, 1755 Broadway, New York City 10019, *www.smartmoney.com.*

Save Hundreds, Even *Thousands,* on a New Car

Get help negotiating a better deal on a new car. Brokers' or buyers' agents will search the Web for the best price and negotiate further with dealers on your behalf for a fee of anywhere from $50 to $1,400* depending on the car. Buying services that are offered by financial firms and warehouse clubs, such as Costco, negotiate bulk discounts with dealers and pass along savings to consumers. These services can save you hundreds or even thousands of dollars.

*Prices subject to change.

Lease Trading Savvy

Lease trading can help you get out of a car lease that you can no longer afford...or obtain one if you need a car for a short term and can find a lease that is almost over. Web sites LeaseTrader.com and Swapalease.com have both been arranging lease exchanges for 10 or more years. Fees to transfer a lease generally range from $50 to $500,* and current lease holders must get permission from the leasing company to give up the lease.

Tara Baukus Mello, automotive expert at Bankrate. com.

*Prices subject to change.

17

Home and Heart

The Secret to a Happy Marriage—Just Ask Yourself This Key Question...

We all are shaped by our *early* experiences—even when we believe that we have traveled a great distance from our families, whether it's in time or geographically. Wherever we are, whoever we have become, we still carry with us the blueprint that we developed as a child about how we are supposed to interact with others—and this can hurt our marriages.

Consider these examples...

Eric is afraid to express his real hopes and other feelings to his wife. He holds back and retreats into a shell because as a child he lived with unhappy, depressed parents. Whenever he tried to speak to them about things that bothered him, he felt they grew even more despondent. Before long, Eric shut down and withdrew, fearful that any assertiveness would hurt the people he loves.

Alison is afraid to become dependent on anyone. Her father habitually failed to live up to his promises, and he disappointed her repeatedly, whether it involved taking her on a trip or just coming home from the office before she went to bed. As a result, she grew up afraid of becoming dependent on men, fearing that they would disappoint her. She did marry but remained emotionally detached from her husband. When their marriage ended badly in divorce, she concluded

Joel D. Block, PhD, a psychologist specializing in couples and sex therapy. A diplomate of the American Board of Professional Psychology, Dr. Block is senior psychologist on the staff of North Shore–Long Island Jewish Medical Center in Glen Oaks, New York, and is assistant clinical professor at Albert Einstein College of Medicine in the Bronx. Dr. Block is author or coauthor of nearly 20 books on love and sexuality, including *Sex Comes First: 15 Ways to Save Your Relationship...Without Leaving the Bedroom* (Adams Media). His Web site is *www.drblock.com*.

267

that the inevitable had occurred—she had been let down once again.

There are, of course, differences in the way people react to the experiences of their families. Not everyone will respond to particular influences in the same way, nor will the connection between current behavior and an earlier pattern always be obvious. *But most people can improve their relationships by taking the following steps...*

• **Look for repeated behaviors that have had negative consequences.** Then think back to your childhood about what might be the real cause of these negative behaviors. Being aware of the issue is a key step in resolving it. Did your parents argue and frighten you so that now you avoid confrontation? Did you get a flood of attention when you were ill as a child and now use illness to get attention from your loved ones? Whatever the childhood pattern, try to identify the adult version of that behavior in your current love relationship.

• **Ask yourself, "What am I doing habitually that leaves my partner dissatisfied?"** If you are not sure how to identify the pattern, ask your partner, "What do I do that you think forms a pattern and interferes with our intimacy?" If your partner's response leaves you feeling vulnerable or defensive, it likely is right on target. Most of us are protective of our childhood patterns.

• **Make a change.** Once you have identified a pattern that is problematic, look for ways to proceed that will foster closeness, not create distance. If you have a pattern of avoiding confrontation, for example, push yourself to invite discussion of difficult issues despite your discomfort. If you typically are negative with your partner, try giving him/her the benefit of the doubt. If you are consistent in doing this, you will find that over time, repeating a new behavior decreases the discomfort associated with the behavior.

• **Soothe yourself.** One very important key to changing a long-standing but ineffectual pattern is learning how to soothe yourself. Self-soothing involves turning inward and accessing your own resources to regain your emotional balance. It is the ability to comfort and care for yourself without regressing into a childhood pattern. A key to self-soothing involves regaining perspective—remind yourself that you are doing something positive (changing a negative pattern) and that the discomfort won't last forever. You also can write about the emotions you are experiencing—often that is very effective at releasing emotional pain.

In addition, it is helpful to recall challenges you faced successfully—this helps boost your confidence.

Example: If you had a difficult time in your marriage after your first child was born, but you and your spouse weathered that challenging period, remind yourself of your ability to work as a team.

• **Take the initiative.** Don't wait for your spouse to change. This "I'll change after you do" attitude typically leads to further deterioration of the relationship.

Example: One partner says, "If you would only make me feel welcome, I would be home more." The other partner says, "If you stopped going golfing so often, I'd be more welcoming when you came home."

While it is easier and more productive when husband and wife work together to change, either one may rein in his or her behavior and thereby disrupt the negative pattern. Take the first steps—your relationship will benefit.

• **Persist.** Long-standing behavior patterns are difficult to shake for all the reasons that maintain the pattern in the first place. Consciously trying to change one's behavior can seem unnatural at first because it goes against the flow. We must risk losing the comforts of our familiar patterns, knowing that the new behavior will be worthwhile in the long run. It will take time to extinguish the old patterns and occasional setbacks are likely, but you will find that it gets easier over time.

More from Dr. Joel Block...

When Communication *Hurts* a Marriage: Simple Solutions to Bring You Closer

The happiest, most passionate couples are those who are emotionally open and not afraid to reveal themselves to each other. Yet the potential for deception always is present.

Those "big" lies, such as having an affair, tend to have the worst repercussions (often divorce). Yet a lifetime of small lies also can erode a relationship.

Examples of little lies: Maybe you bought something that you didn't really need—and lied to your partner about the cost. Or your partner noticed your lingering glance at another person—then you swore up and down that you really didn't find that person attractive.

We tell ourselves that these small lies are harmless—or even beneficial because they are protecting our partners' feelings. But little lies can be just as detrimental to a relationship as telling a whopper. They just take more time to tear couples apart—and are not always easy to detect.

People who tell lies really are protecting themselves by hiding their own true feelings. When the truth is discovered (it almost always is eventually), the other person naturally feels betrayed. *Here, the many kinds of lies…*

INDIRECT COMMUNICATION

Rather than stating clearly what they do or do not want, people tend to talk around subjects that they find uncomfortable. The more afraid you are of rejection or potential criticism, the more likely you are to communicate indirectly. The "lie" is not owning up to what is wanted.

Situation: I once counseled a couple who had been married for 12 years. The husband, who was in the restaurant business, had once been arrested for selling drugs. His wife noticed that he recently had a lot more money. She also observed a spike in their cell-phone bills and a spate of hang-up calls.

She secretly wondered whether her husband was back in the drug world—but rather than confronting him about her fears, she tried to gather information indirectly. She suggested, for example, that she might start spending more time at the restaurant. He said he didn't need extra help, but she kept pressing and their disagreements escalated. Finally, she blurted, "You're hiding something. I know it!"

If a couple is going to argue, they should at least have a disagreement based on an accurate understanding of each other's position. With indirect communication, no one is even sure what the argument is about. In this case, the real problem was the wife's (unfounded) suspicions.

Solution: Openly request information. Had the wife stated directly what she was worried about or had the husband asked why coming to the restaurant was so important, they could have had a real conversation instead of an argument. If you're uncomfortable making a request, say so—"I feel uncomfortable asking you, but…" That's the truth. To circle around it is to avoid the truth.

BROKEN CONTRACTS

How often have you made a promise and failed to keep it? Not keeping your word is a kind of lying that can seriously harm a relationship by undermining trust. Even when the promises are trivial—maybe you agree to start projects but fail to follow through—breaking your word can make everything you say seem unreliable.

There's a concept in psychology known as "secondary gains." It means that someone gets positive reinforcement from negative patterns. We're all guilty of occasional broken promises. Someone who consistently "forgets" may be unconsciously creating emotional distance—forgetting puts the other person off—so that the "forgetter" feels less vulnerable.

Solution: If you are a forgetter, try to understand the secondary gains that arise from disappointing your partner. Just understanding this concept can be a powerful step.

Also helpful: A quid pro quo, which roughly means "a favor for a favor." If someone is persistently forgetful, his/her partner can insist on having something done before giving something in return. While this is a bit adversarial, it's sometimes warranted.

Example: The forgetter asks you to mail his package at the post office. You respond, "Absolutely, just as soon as you clean out the backseat of the car as you promised to do two weeks ago."

WITHHOLDING INFORMATION

We all have the right to privacy, but some partners take this to extremes and withhold important information. This is a form of concealment that borders on lying—and is the opposite of true intimacy.

Situation: A husband might avoid certain issues—for example, his feelings about a mutual friend—because he feels that his wife is critical of his opinions. If he gets in the habit of not saying what he thinks, she might criticize his persistent silence—at which point, he will conclude that his wife is too critical.

Solution: This is a slippery slope and it should be addressed by sharing everything. It is the premise of a good partnership. Sharing private personal thoughts with each other creates intimacy. If sharing is met with harsh judgment, don't withdraw. Talk this out with your partner to clear the way for future non-judgmental discussion.

BLAMING

When something goes wrong, the aggrieved party knows precisely whom to blame. It's the other person's fault. When a person blames someone else, he/she is omitting his part in the issue—that's the lie.

In all of my years as a therapist, I've rarely encountered a conflict that truly was just one person's fault—and blame never makes things better.

The person who is blamed feels defensive. He/she will probably respond with counter-blame and anger.

Solution: Instead of pointing fingers, the partners should avoid the language of blame. Substitute sentences that start with "I" for those that start with "you."

Example: Rather than saying, "You never help in the kitchen," say something like, "I feel resentful when you don't help out."

Unlike "you" statements, which typically lead to adversarial reactions, "I" sentences are more honest and less confrontational. They can lead to understanding rather than a continuation of the disagreement.

SEXUAL SECRETS

Sexual desires are among the most sensitive secrets. A partner might reveal something about his/her sexual desires (or sexual history) and then be judged harshly. It's natural for that person, under these circumstances, to be reluctant to reveal himself again.

At the same time, sharing sexual desires with one's partner can build intimacy.

Solution: When you take responsibility for what pleases you, you increase the probability of being pleased. For a couple to have a satisfying sex life, both partners need to be aware of their preferences. If you find it hard to initiate this kind of conversation, perhaps an opportunity will come up while watching a sexy scene in a movie. "Would that kind of thing be exciting to you?" could be a way to start the conversation.

When Spouses Disagree About Their Kids

Marjory Abrams, president of Boardroom Inc., 281 Tresser Blvd., Stamford, Connecticut 06901.

I have found—on both ends of the parent/child relationship—that disagreements between spouses about their children don't stop as children evolve into adults. Instead of conflict regarding limits on TV or junk food, parents may argue about the "child's" career choice or love relationships.

Such conflict is unavoidable, says Nancy Samalin, director of the New York City–based Parent Guidance Workshops (at *www.samalin.com*). One spouse's style may be authoritarian, the other laissez-faire...one may be more controlling than the other.

Samalin tells parents to agree to disagree. *Important strategies...*

• **Discuss differences, but do it out of earshot of your kids.** You don't always have to present a united front, but by discussing issues prior to talking to your child, you'll be more apt to respect your spouse's point of view.

• **Find a compromise position.** Let's say your adult child loses his/her job and needs to move back home. One parent may want to indulge "his/her baby"...the other may expect the child to be more like a boarder while living in the home. Parents need to discuss their views, then meet with their child to discuss everyone's expectations for the situation and come to an agreement. For example, instead of paying rent, the child could handle some household repairs, cleaning or lawn care.

•**Stay out of the middle.** If your child complains to you about the other parent, tell him that the issue is between the two of them, and encourage him to speak directly to the parent he's complaining about.

Samalin, for her part, sees a parent's role as that of a harbor, not a rescue vessel. You are always there for the boat to sail back in, but you shouldn't steer or chase after it.

Car Seat Caution

Oxygen drops when infants sit in car seats. Blood oxygen levels were significantly lower after healthy two-day-old infants sat in car seats for 60 minutes than when the infants lay in cribs.

Reason: An upright position leads to partial obstruction of the upper airway.

Lesson: A car seat is essential for travel safety but should never substitute for a crib. On long car trips, stop frequently to give your baby a break from the car seat.

Lilijana Kornhauser Cerar, MD, head of the neonatal intensive care unit, University Medical Centre, Ljubljana, Slovenia, and leader of a study of 200 infants.

"Third-Hand Smoke" Harmful to Kids

Even "third-hand smoke" is dangerous to children. There are at least 250 poisonous gases, chemicals and metals in cigarette smoke, and these can cling to the hair and clothing of people who do not smoke themselves but spend time among smokers. Young children may be exposed to these toxins when they are near people who smoke or who have spent time with smokers.

Jonathan Winickoff, MD, MPH, associate professor of pediatrics, Harvard Medical School and Massachusetts General Hospital for Children, both in Boston.

New Treatment for Head Lice

The Food and Drug Administration (FDA) has approved prescription *benzyl alcohol lotion* (Ulesfia) for children six months and older. Two weeks after the second of two 10-minute treatments, one week apart, more than 75% of the people treated with benzyl alcohol lotion were free of lice. Side effects may include irritation of the skin, scalp or eyes. Ask your doctor or pharmacist for details and to compare its effectiveness with other products. In some geographic locations, lice have grown resistant to over-the-counter treatments.

Richard J. Pollack, PhD, department of immunology and infectious diseases at Harvard School of Public Health, Boston.

Why Teen Texting Spells Trouble

Did you know that American teens average 2,272 cell-phone text messages per month?

Problems: Constant texting is distracting and keeps teens from having time to think things through. Texting also can discourage autonomy by making it easy for teens to contact their friends when making even minor decisions.

Sherry Turkle, PhD, psychologist, director, Initiative on Technology and Self at Massachusetts Institute of Technology, Cambridge, Massachusetts.

Teens Need More of This Powerful Vitamin...

Many teens are not getting enough vitamin D.

Recent finding: One in seven teenagers—including more than 50% of African-American teenagers—are deficient in vitamin D. Girls have more than twice the risk for deficiency as boys, and overweight teens have twice the risk of those of normal weight.

Vitamin D deficiency can lead to poor bone development in children and has been linked with cardiovascular disease, cancer, diabetes and other conditions later in life. Teens need to consume at least four glasses of fortified milk daily to get the recommended dietary allowance—and should eat more salmon, tuna, eggs and fortified cereals. Or they should take a vitamin D supplement.

Sandy Saintonge, MD, assistant professor of clinical pediatrics and assistant professor of clinical public health, Weill Cornell Medical College, New York City, and leader of a study of about 3,000 teenagers, published in *Pediatrics*.

New Rules for Applying to College

Howard R. Greene, president and founder of Howard Greene & Associates, an independent educational consulting company located in Westport, Connecticut. He is a former Princeton University admissions officer and coauthor of numerous books, including *Paying for College: The Greenes' Guide to Financing Higher Education* (St. Martin's Griffin). His Internet site is *www.greenesguides.com*.

Many students assume that they can no longer afford private college tuition and are applying only to public universities. Some state schools recently experienced a 40% surge in applications.

Meanwhile, fewer schools can now afford to meet applicants' financial-aid needs. Private colleges have been forced to reduce aid because of stock market losses suffered by their endowment funds...while public schools have had to trim aid because of state government budget cuts.

How should college applicants and their parents respond to all of these new economic challenges?

• **Apply to public *and* private schools—even if you cannot afford private college tuition.** Applying to three to five public schools increases the odds that you'll get into at least one of these affordable choices...and applying to several private schools increases the odds that at least one of them will pull out all the stops to lure you to its campus.

• **Skip early decision if money is very tight.** If you are accepted early decision to a college, you are committed to attend. When you apply to many schools, you can attend the one that offers the most attractive aid package.

• **Apply to state colleges and community colleges in addition to state universities.** State colleges and community colleges often are significantly easier to get into—and offer a backdoor into the state's university system. After two years, apply to enter the state's university system as a transfer student. As long as you have a grade point average of at least 2.5, you likely will be accepted. Your degree will be from the state university, same as if you had attended it for all four years. You probably will save money, as well—community colleges and state colleges usually charge lower tuition than state universities.

• **Defer admission.** Most colleges and universities let accepted students postpone matriculation for one year. This is a viable option for those who are accepted by the school of their dreams but cannot afford to attend. One year later, the college might be able to offer you additional financial aid...your family's finances might have rebounded...or you might have earned enough money working to afford to pay more tuition.

• **Evaluate the financial health of private colleges before applying.** If you do need financial aid to attend a private university, target schools that...

• Still have endowments in the billions of dollars despite recent market losses. (You can lower this minimum endowment to a few hundred million for small colleges with only 1,000 to 2,000 students.)

•Currently provide financial aid to at least 40% of enrolled students (50% or 60% is even better). Such schools likely can afford to provide all the financial aid you need.

Helpful: If you cannot locate these endowment and financial-aid statistics on a school's Web site, call its financial-aid department to request the information.

If you don't require financial aid, consider applying to a few schools that have relatively small endowments and low financial-aid ratios, even if these schools' high standards make them seem as if they are long shots for you academically.

Examples: Elon University, Knox College, Pitzer College and Providence College. Money-strapped schools might be forced to accept some borderline applicants this year simply because those applicants won't require financial aid.

Coed Dorm Danger

Coed college dormitories are associated with more binge drinking. Forty-two percent of college students in coed housing reported weekly binge drinking...compared to 18% of students in all-male or all-female housing. Students in coed housing also were more likely to have multiple sex partners.

Self-defense: Encourage students to opt out of coed housing when single-gender housing is available.

Brian Willoughby, PhD, visiting professor, Brigham Young University, Provo, Utah, and the lead author of a study of more than 500 students from five college campuses, published in *Journal of American College Health.*

When Grown Kids Move Back Home—Living (Happily) Together

John L. Graham, PhD, professor of marketing and international business, University of California, Irvine. He is a coauthor, with Sharon Graham Niederhaus, of *Together Again: A Creative Guide to Successful Multigenerational Living* (M. Evans, *www.togetheragainbook. com*).

In these economic times, more grown children are moving back home. The arrangement could work well for you and your child if you discuss expectations and ground rules upfront.

•**Set a deadline.** If you do not want your child to stay indefinitely, say this. You might want to extend the offer only until the child meets a goal.

Examples: Earning a degree...saving for a down payment on a home...recovering from an illness...or finding a job.

•**Decide if your adult child will pay rent and what expenses he/she will cover.** Many parents don't charge rent as long as the child is pursuing mature goals, such as saving money or getting an education. However, if your money is tight and your child is working, it's not unreasonable to expect him to contribute a fixed sum monthly. Adult children usually pay for any extras they need, such as a separate phone/computer line.

•**Limit babysitting.** Be explicit about your limits in caring for grandchildren who come to live or visit. You may want to restrict it to, say, two mornings or one night a week. If you want the overall experience to be a good one, you will need to respect your child's choices in child-rearing and avoid critical remarks.

•**Knock before entering.** Talk about the appropriate rules for entry into one another's private spaces. Do not open your adult child's mail, read his e-mail or answer his cell phone without his okay. He should extend the same courtesy to you.

•**Talk about whether it's acceptable to discuss each other's health, finances and relationships with other people,** and with whom. Also, make specific agreements about visitors, boyfriends/girlfriends and parties.

• **Split the chores.** Adult children typically clean their own living spaces, do their own laundry and take care of their own pets.

Shared chores that tend to cause stress: Moving heavy trash cans…sorting and picking up the mail from shared mailboxes…and moving the car when parking is an issue. Perhaps alternate these tasks or assign them to the person who doesn't mind doing them.

• **Use a headset.** Families often find it desirable to use headsets for listening to radio, television and music so that they don't need to adjust to one another's taste and preferred volume.

• **Meet regularly.** After your child moves in, meet regularly—monthly is usually about right—with the specific purpose of discussing how the current rules are working. I know a mother, father and grown son who have their meeting on a weekend walk. For larger families, meetings may need to be more businesslike. Keep the meeting short, agreeing in advance on the ending time. The organizer begins by asking everyone what is working well before turning to problems. Encourage compromise and creative thinking on all sides.

Caught in the Middle of a Family Feud? What to Do

Judy Kuriansky, PhD, a clinical psychologist and sex therapist on the adjunct faculty of Columbia University Teachers College in New York City. She is author of five books, including *The Complete Idiot's Guide to a Healthy Relationship* (Alpha). Her online site is *www. drjudy.com.*

Quarreling relatives may try to drag you into the fray. But getting entangled adds to your stress and may strain the family further. *Instead…*

• **Do not become a mouthpiece.** Suppose Mom is angry with your brother, but she is afraid to confront him, so she complains to you. You carry messages back and forth…and

the people directly involved never talk honestly together. When negotiations fail, combatants blame you.

Solution: Say, "I cannot play peacemaker. Please resolve this by talking openly to each other."

• **Try to redirect conversation.** When the squabbler complains, refocus on the steps to resolution—communication, compromise and forgiveness.

• **Refuse to take sides.** Simply state, "I love you both. It upsets me that you're not getting along."

• **Keep your complaints out of the mix.** Adding your own accusations—"You are mad at Sis for not lending you money? I am mad at her, too, for forgetting my birthday"—only compounds the current conflict.

• **Suggest outside help.** If feuders cannot reconcile, urge them to see a therapist, clergy member or lawyer. But don't find a mediator for them—it only deepens your involvement.

Exceptions: A crisis does warrant stepping in.

Examples: When there is abuse…a crime …significant emotional harm to a child…addiction…or any suspicion of suicidal thoughts.

More from Dr. Judy Kuriansky…

If a Loved One Is Emotionally Abused…

Being emotionally abused destroys all self-esteem, making the victim vulnerable to escalating maltreatment.

Examples: Constant criticism ("You are fat, stupid, lazy"), humiliation ("No one here cares what you say"), manipulation ("You pay for dinner, I forgot my wallet again"), intimidation (menacing glares), rejection (icy silence).

To help a loved one…

• **Say what you see.** Be frank—"Your boyfriend insults you incessantly. This is emotional abuse." If your loved one denies it, cite specific examples.

• **Discuss his/her motivations.** Gently explore why she puts up with cruelty. Does she believe that she deserves no better? Fear being alone more than being mistreated? Discuss how past experiences (a hypercritical mother, a job loss) affect her choices now.

• **Place blame where it belongs.** Don't imply that she's weak—the bully, not the victim, is at fault—but do emphasize that she has the power to change the situation.

• **Encourage specific action.** Help her rehearse her response to insults ("I refuse to be spoken to that way") or to manipulative tactics ("It's your turn to buy, so check your wallet before we order"). Urge her to set concrete limits—how much free babysitting she'll do for grandchildren, how often she'll accept her ex's calls, how long she'll give an abuser to reform before severing all ties.

Also from Dr. Judy Kuriansky...

Giving Aid When a Loved One Is Ill

Naturally you want to provide support for a friend or family member who is sick or has had an accident. *Helpful...*

• **Do unto others as they would have done to them—not as you would have done to you.** Does he/she want you to listen as he describes his surgery? Or let him cry on your shoulder? Or does he just want you to watch a funny DVD with him? Follow his lead.

• **Help him to regain a sense of control.** Health problems often make people feel helpless. To counteract this, avoid commands ("You must eat now"). Instead, offer choices ("Shall I feed you now or in an hour?"). Discuss ways to increase his independence—for instance, with cutlery designed for people who have trouble feeding themselves. (For products, see *www.caregiverproducts.com.*)

• **Learn from a reputable source about your loved one's medical problem,** its treatment, potential complications, prognosis. Let the doctors and therapists do their jobs, but be ready to offer an informed opinion or to advocate for your loved one.

• **Do not downplay the situation.** Saying, "There's no need to worry" can be an unrealistic statement.

Better: Acknowledge his fears and reaffirm your loyalty—"It's natural to feel panicked at a time like this. Whatever you need, I am here for you."

What No One Tells You About Caregiving

Vicki Rackner, MD, a board-certified surgeon based on Mercer Island in Washington, and founder of the Caregiver Club, *www.thecaregiverclub.com*, an Internet-based community for caregivers and their loved ones. Dr. Rackner is the author of *Caregiving Without Regrets* (Medical Bridges).

If you've ever taken care of a person who is seriously ill, you know how stressful it can be.

What you may not know: There are greater risks to the caregiver's health than previously recognized.

Troubling research finding: Caregivers are 63% more likely to die within a four-year period than people without this extra burden, according to a study published in the *Journal of the American Medical Association.*

Compared with non-caregivers, people who provide care to a loved one tend to exercise less and eat less nutritiously and are at much higher risk for physical exhaustion as well as depression.

CARING FOR TWO

Family members are responsible for about 80% of the elder care in the US. To meet this challenge, caregivers must care not only for a loved one (and, in many cases, other members of their family), but also maintain their own physical and emotional well-being.

As a medical doctor and longtime advocate for caregivers, I know how crucial it is to tend to your own needs while caring for a loved one. *My advice...*

• **Know what you can (and can't) change.** Every caregiver wants to create a different reality and to "fix" things. If you're caring for a stroke patient or someone with Alzheimer's disease, for example, a little part of you will think that you can prevent the person from getting worse just by working harder. That's simply not true.

There are some things that we can't change. People who think that they can change the natural course of aging or disease are the ones who are most vulnerable to depression, self-recrimination and even alcoholism and drug addiction. You can make a loved one happier by engaging him/her in conversation or planning activities he enjoys—but remember that you cannot change the overall course of his disease.

My advice: Understand that caregiving is usually a long-term process and identify not only what's important, but what's possible.

Example: Suppose that you're caring for someone who is disabled by rheumatoid arthritis. He won't care if the house is perfectly clean. What is likely to matter are the more personal things, such as preparing a favorite food or giving an affectionate touch. You've fulfilled your job every time you create one of these special moments.

• **Learn the "51% Rule."** Most caregivers will do anything for their loved one. They prepare meals, go to doctor appointments, get medications, change linens and clean the house—and then, when they're ready to collapse, there's always something else that needs to be done. This approach doesn't work.

So many caregiving situations require more work than a full-time job. All too often, people strive to be a "super caregiver"…to do everything perfectly, setting aside their own needs. It's not uncommon for caregivers to wind up in the hospital themselves—or, worse, to die before their loved ones.

My advice: Follow the "51% rule"—accept that you will make mistakes and will disappoint your loved one at times (maybe even half the time). You will have to make choices and decisions that are in the best interests of your loved one but may make him unhappy. You may even lose your patience at times. Treat your loved one with respect, compassion and kindness, but accept that you will fall short of perfection as a caregiver.

Important: People who become martyrs while caregiving invariably burn out. They also tend to become worse caregivers because they don't have the emotional reserves to stay focused.

• **Get—and give—help.** A lot of caregivers don't realize that accepting help from others is one of the best gifts you can give those who are closest to you.

For people who feel guilty accepting help without returning the favor, bartering can be a great solution. We all have activities that we enjoy and activities that we do not. Suppose you hate doing laundry but love walking the dog—and one of your friends is great with laundry but dreads going for walks. You can help each other.

My advice: Consider forming a caregivers' bartering community. It might include neighbors or individuals from the church or synagogue. Or you could post an announcement on the bulletin board at your local health-food store or doctor's office to recruit people in similar situations who will trade chores, such as yard work or grocery shopping.

It's easier to ask for help if you know that you'll pay back the favor in your own way—especially if it's an activity you enjoy.

More from Dr. Vicki Rackner…

How to Be Helpful…

With caregiving, not all issues have clear-cut solutions. *Here's my advice for navigating some of the trickier challenges…*

• **Reluctance to talk about health problems.** As a caregiver, you most likely already know—or will learn—intimate details about your loved one's health that the ill person may be reluctant to share.

Example: Many older adults won't discuss bodily functions with their doctors.

My advice: You might say, "Don't you think we should talk to the doctor about this issue? If you want, I'll bring it up so that you don't have to." Most patients will say, "Okay."

• **A doctor's disregard for quality-of-life issues.** I knew a woman who took her elderly father to the doctor because his knee was hurting. The doctor glanced at the knee—then sent them home with a prescription for blood pressure medicine.

The doctor was concerned about this patient's high blood pressure because it raised the man's risk for stroke and heart attack. A "simple" bad knee didn't concern the doctor, even though it was preventing this patient from doing the things he enjoyed.

My advice: Sit down with the person you're caring for and make a list before each doctor visit and include not only the key issues, including drug side effects, the presence of pain or other symptoms, but also your loved one's mood and lifestyle issues, such as his level of social and physical activity. If the doctor won't take the time to discuss all of your concerns, consider finding another doctor.

Caregiver Contracts

Caregiver contracts pay adult children or other relatives to take care of elderly or disabled family members. The arrangements can prevent ill will in the family that might arise if the caregivers work without pay but then are left extra money in a will to compensate for the care they gave.

What to do: Set salaries at reasonable levels —no more than it would cost to get needed assistance from nonrelatives. Also, discuss all agreements with other relatives so that they know about the arrangement to minimize any family tensions later.

Study by AARP, *www.aarp.org,* and National Alliance for Caregiving, *www.caregiving.org.*

Dog Bite Prevention

Half of all children in the US are bitten by a dog before they reach age 12—and the most seriously injured kids are under age seven.

Teach your children to avoid dog bites by showing them proper behavior and explaining basic rules: Never approach a dog you do not know or one that is alone, without an owner nearby. Ask the owner's permission before petting a dog. Do not go near a dog that is sleeping, eating, nursing puppies or playing with a bone or toy. Do not tease a dog in any way—the dog may not realize that you are being playful.

American Humane Society recommendations, published in *Dog Fancy.*

Don't Let Your Dog Eat This!

Jon Geller, DVM, an emergency veterinarian at Veterinary Emergency Hospital, Fort Collins, Colorado. Dr. Geller writes for numerous pet magazines and answers dog owners' questions online at *www.dogchannel.com.*

Dogs in general are not very discriminating eaters. As an emergency veterinarian, I have seen dogs that have ingested cigarettes, batteries, ant bait, rubbing alcohol and silica gel packets, to name just a few.

Most dog owners know that chocolate is dangerous to dogs (it can cause heart rate irregularities), but they may not be aware of other seemingly harmless foods and products that can be toxic. If your dog ingests any of the following, see a veterinarian immediately.

• **Grapes and raisins** have been shown to cause kidney failure in dogs. The toxic ingredient is unclear, but it is currently being studied in the veterinary community (a fungus is suspected). The amount of grapes or raisins that may cause kidney failure is not exactly known, so any amount could potentially be dangerous.

• **Xylitol** is an increasingly popular sugar substitute included in many sugar-free gums, candies and other foods. In dogs, ingestion of as few as three pieces of gum with xylitol can result in rapid, life-threatening hypoglycemia (low blood sugar). Higher amounts may lead to irreversible liver damage and death.

• **Macadamia nuts** could cause weakness, lethargy, vomiting, lack of coordination, tremors and hyperthermia (an increase in body temperature) when eaten by dogs. They are especially toxic when coated in chocolate. Because dogs vary so much in size, it's difficult to determine how many macadamia nuts are dangerous. A small handful could be toxic to a small dog, while a very large dog probably would need to ingest a pound or so.

• **Certain glues,** including Gorilla Glue and Elmer's Probond, contain *diphenylmethane diisocyanate* as the active ingredient. This substance, if ingested, can expand to many times its original volume, forming a foamlike ball in a dog's stomach. For some reason, dogs are attracted to this taste. Signs of a blockage include vomiting and nausea (drooling and licking of the lips), with eventual dehydration and weakness.

• **Cocoa mulch.** Just like chocolate, mulch from hulls of cocoa beans contains *theobromine*, which could trigger a toxic reaction in dogs. Dog owners should use regular mulch in garden areas.

Supplements Your Older Dog Needs

Supplements for older dogs help slow the effects of aging. *Vitamin B complex* (B-1, B-2, B-6 and B-12) counters fatigue. *Vitamin C* reduces inflammation and enhances immunity. *Vitamin E* may help prevent skin disorders. *Coenzyme Q10* and *L-carnitine* improve the strength of the heart muscle. *Dimethylglycine* (DMG) stimulates the immune system and works as an anti-inflammatory for joints. *Alpha lipoic acid* promotes ocular health and slows degenerative neurological conditions.

Best: Talk to your veterinarian about which supplements may be best for your older dog.

Fetchdog.com, an online community for dog lovers, Portland, Maine.

Protect Your Dog from Lyme

Lyme disease is more serious in certain dog breeds. Among golden retrievers and Labradors, Lyme disease progresses more quickly than in other dogs. To protect any dog, use the topical tick-control product Frontline and a Preventic collar—the combination provides almost 100% protection from ticks. If you notice any symptoms of Lyme disease, such as fever, lack of appetite and/or appearance of generalized pain, take your dog to the vet immediately for tests and treatment.

Prevention, 33 E. Minor St., Emmaus, Pennsylvania 18098, *www.prevention.com.*

Heartworm Infection Is Spreading

More than one million dogs in the US are infected with heartworms, which could lead to heart disease and even death. Summer and early fall are the peak seasons for mosquitoes, which transmit heartworms with their bites. Protect your canine by administering a heartworm treatment at the same time every month and getting your dog tested annually for heartworms. Take your pet to the vet immediately if you notice signs of heart disease, such as difficulty breathing, fatigue, coughing and fainting.

USA Today, www.usatoday.com.

Cats Are Calming

Dog ownership has long been recommended to help reduce heart attack risk.

Now: A new study links cat ownership to a similarly reduced heart attack risk—perhaps because of the calming effects of cats.

University of Minnesota's Stroke Center, *www.neurology.umn.edu.*

Cure Hiccups with a Q-Tip and Other Clever Tricks from Japan

Lisa Katayama, a Japan-born freelance journalist specializing in Japanese culture and technology who currently lives in San Francisco. She is the author of *Urawaza: Secret Everyday Tips and Tricks from Japan* (Chronicle).

Japan is well-known for its Urawaza—clever, do-it-yourself tricks for using household products to solve common problems. *Here are strategies that have worked for others—and may just work for you...*

HEALTH REMEDIES

• **Cure the hiccups with a Q-tip.** Briefly touch one end of a Q-tip to the small piece of flesh that dangles in the back of your throat (*uvula*).

Why it works: This triggers your gag reflex, which interrupts the spasms of your diaphragm. No hiccup cure works 100% of the time, but this one is more effective than many others.

• **Clear a stuffy nose with scallions.** People with stuffy noses shouldn't use over-the-counter nasal decongestants too often, as overuse can cause increased congestion. But, scallions can serve as a substitute. Trim the top fronds off of two scallions, then very gently put the thick white root part into each nostril. (*Warning:* Do not shove it high up your nose.) Your nose should start to clear in as little as one minute.

Why it works: Like other members of the onion family, scallions contain chemical compounds that make the eyes water and the nose run.

QUICK FIXES

• **Repair a scratched CD with toothpaste.** Place a small dab of white toothpaste on a cotton ball, and gently apply it over the CD's scratch, starting the cotton ball at the middle of the CD and moving it outward. Use a small amount of water and a second, clean cotton ball to remove any excess toothpaste. Let the CD air-dry.

Why it works: The mild abrasives in toothpaste gently smooth out the sharp edges of the scratch. It's those sharp edges that diffract the CD player's laser beam, causing it to skip. This works only on shallow scratches—deep scratches might be beyond repair.

• **Make older, previously water-resistant cloth jackets water-resistant again with a hair dryer.** Set the hair dryer to high, then slowly move it around the outer surface of the jacket.

Why it works: Many, though not all, waterproof cloth garments are treated with something called "durable water-repellent coating." Over time, the coating starts to deteriorate, decreasing its effectiveness. Heat can reactivate the water-repelling properties.

CLEANING TRICKS

• **Clean pen marks off your hands with a tea bag.** Brew a cup of green or black tea, then rub the used tea bag over the pen marks on your skin.

Why it works: Catechin, a chemical compound found in these teas, combines with the pigments and oils in the pen ink, lifting the ink from the skin. The fabric of the tea bag acts as a mild scrubber.

• **Remove stickers or tape from mirrors or windows with mayonnaise.** Both stickers and tape often leave adhesive residue behind when they are peeled from mirrors or windows. Scraping the residue away can take a lot of effort. Instead, place a dab of mayonnaise on a paper towel, and apply this to the adhesive. After a minute or two, the adhesive residue should give way without much scrubbing or scraping—sometimes it simply wipes away with a paper towel.

Why it works: The vegetable oil in mayonnaise dissolves most common adhesives. In fact, you can use vegetable oil to remove adhesive residue, but the oil's more liquid consistency means it won't stay in place over the adhesive as well.

●**Pick up broken glass with bread.** Hundreds of tiny shards often are spread across the floor when glass breaks. Sweeping never removes them all. Next time glass breaks in your home, sweep away all the larger pieces, then press a few slices of bread onto the broken-glass area.

Why it works: Even very small shards will lodge in the bread.

Warning: Dispose of these slices of bread immediately so that people and pets do not mistake them for food.

●**Clean the toilet bowl with mouthwash.** Pour about one cup of mouthwash in the toilet bowl. After 15 to 20 minutes, a quick swipe with a toilet brush should be all it takes to make the bowl's surface sparkle.

Why it works: The disinfectants in mouthwash are designed to make teeth shine and kill germs, but they are equally effective at polishing toilet surfaces and killing toilet germs.

●**Remove burn marks from a pan with eggshells.** Crush an eggshell, then rub these shell fragments against the burned areas with your fingers. Do not use on nonstick surfaces, because it could scratch.

Why it works: The calcium carbonate in eggshells is an abrasive that does a nice job of scrubbing away burns. The small amount of egg white still present on the shell fragments absorbs the loose particles for a clean, shiny finish.

HELP FOR PLANTS

●**Save a diseased plant with garlic.** Grate a single clove of garlic into two cups of water, then pour this mixture around the base of the plant. This works particularly well for the fungus that often kills basil.

Why it works: Garlic contains a compound called *phytoncide* that can kill many common plant root fungi and inhibit certain other diseases in plants.

●**Lengthen the life of cut flowers with bleach.** Add a few drops of bleach to the water in the vase.

Why it works: The disinfecting properties of bleach inhibit the bacterial and mildew growth that often robs cut flowers of their beauty.

Alternative: Drop a penny minted prior to 1982 into the vase water. The copper kills bacteria. (Pennies minted after mid-1982 are mostly zinc and won't help your flowers.)

Help for Household Blunders

Marjory Abrams, president of Boardroom Inc., 281 Tresser Blvd., Stamford, Connecticut 06901.

Prompted by a conversation with a coworker after he used dish soap in the dishwasher (bad idea—bubble city!), I asked friends and coworkers about their more memorable household blunders. *Some of the situations they got into and their solutions...*

●**Shrunken sweater.** Soak for at least five minutes in a mixture of hair conditioner (use one to two tablespoons) and lukewarm water. Do not rinse. Roll the sweater up in a towel to remove excess water. Then lay it on a dry towel, and gently pull the sweater to reshape.

An oddball alternative: Wear the damp sweater—preferably over an extra layer—until it is dry.

●**Smelly wet clothes.** If you have left washed clothes in the washing machine too long, send them through the rinse cycle again and add one cup of white vinegar.

●**Overflowing toilet.** One new home owner had his plumber reconnect the basement sink and toilet, which the previous owners had disconnected. During the next storm, water gushed out of the toilet and flooded the basement.

Solution: The plumber added a check valve, which is an inexpensive device that prevents backflow.

• **Objects dropped down a drain.** Cover the nozzle of the hose on a wet/dry vacuum—not a regular vacuum cleaner—with the leg from a pair of panty hose. Stick the nozzle into the drain opening, and turn on the vacuum. After the object has been retrieved, run water into the drain to refill the trap.

• **Bleach spots on furniture.** A friend's husband cleaned a living room fan with bleach. When he turned on the fan, bleach sprayed all over the room. The navy blue sofa now has permanent bleach stains. My friend covered them with a decorative throw blanket, but fabric paints, available online and at craft stores, could also make the spots less conspicuous.

• **Bleach spots on clothing.** If it's a garment you really love, try using color remover—usually found near the clothing-dye supplies in department and grocery stores—on the entire garment, and then re-dye.

Alternative: One colleague ended up with an artsy T-shirt by carefully spattering more bleach on the garment.

• **Scratched hardwood floors.** A coworker colors in scratches with matching permanent marker.

• **Stuck candle wax.** Freeze wax-covered candle holders, and then carefully chip off the wax.

Wax on a tablecloth: Place a paper towel over the hardened wax and under the tablecloth, and then iron the top towel. The iron should be at a medium, not hot, temperature.

• **Crayon on the walls.** Apply WD-40, then rub the crayon mark using a damp sponge. After the crayon is removed, clean the area with soap and water, and dry with a paper towel. WD-40 is a multipurpose item. Some people have used it to remove nail polish from hardwood floors…camouflage scratches and remove Rollerblade markings on linoleum or ceramic tile floors…and get gunk off piano keys.

Housecleaning Shortcuts: Do Your Bathroom in Seven Minutes…Your Kitchen in 12…

Jeff Bredenberg, who writes extensively about consumer issues and home management. Based in Oreland, Pennsylvania, he is author of three cleaning books, including *How to Cheat at Cleaning* (Taunton). His online site is *www.jeffbredenberg.com.*

Keeping your house clean doesn't have to take hours. By learning a few tricks and shortcuts, you can have an orderly home in minutes.

THE RIGHT SUPPLIES

Keep your cleaning supplies in a plastic caddy with handles so that you can easily move items around the house as you work. If you live in a multistory home, keep a caddy and cleaning supplies on each floor.

Supplies that you should never be without (all available at supermarkets, discount stores and online)…

• **Microfiber cloths.** Microfiber pulls dirt into the fabric better than standard cotton fiber cloths or paper towels, requiring fewer swipes —often just one—to clean a surface. Between launderings, microfiber is easy to clean—just rinse under warm water and squeeze.

• **Electrostatic cloths.** Treated with chemicals to make them negatively charged, electrostatic cloths pick up dust particularly well. You can buy washable or disposable cloths.

• **Scrubber sponges.** Buy the sponges that provide a white, abrasive surface on one side. The white scrubber pad is abrasive enough to scour tough grime but less likely than other types of sponges to scratch surfaces.

• **Plastic toilet brush.** Unlike wire brushes, plastic won't scratch porcelain. Look for the type that comes with its own stand to catch drips.

• **Duster with an extension wand.** Lamb's wool dusters and disposable dusting heads work well. (With feather dusters, sometimes the feathers break and the sharp ends can scratch furniture.)

●**Flat mop.** The flat style reaches under furniture easily. The removable pad can be washed in the washing machine. Or you can use a Swiffer mop that has disposable moist pads.

●**Cleaning solutions and sprays.** You will need a disinfecting cleaner. Check for both words—"disinfecting" and "cleaner"—on the label. A cleaner without disinfectant may not kill germs, while a disinfectant without cleaner won't loosen as much dirt from surfaces. You also will need glass cleaner and toilet bowl cleaner.

BATHROOM: SEVEN MINUTES

●**Clear counters** by putting toothbrushes, deodorant and other toiletries into drawers and cabinets.

●**Squirt toilet bowl cleaner** around the inner rim of the toilet.

●**Spray disinfecting cleaner on the toilet seat and exterior,** as well as on the sink, faucet, counter and tub.

●**Using a toilet brush, scrub the toilet bowl for 10 seconds.** Flush.

●**Spray glass cleaner on the mirror,** and wipe with a microfiber cloth.

●**Use a damp sponge to wipe (in order) sink and faucets, counter, tub, toilet seat, toilet exterior.** Use a microfiber cloth to wipe chrome so that it doesn't spot.

●**Tear off a six-inch length of toilet paper, and use it to sweep up loose hair and other debris** from floor and corners.

If you have an extra five minutes, add these steps: Toss the bath mat, tub mat and towels into the washing machine. Hang fresh towels. Mop the floor. Empty the trash can. Spray cleaner onto your microfiber cloth, and wipe off the doorknobs and any smudges on the door, light switches and cabinets.

LIVING ROOM: 12 MINUTES

●**De-clutter all surfaces** by putting magazines in racks, DVDs in the TV cabinet and books on shelves.

●**Move all lightweight furniture**—such as chairs, end tables and magazine racks—into the center of the room (to make vacuuming and dusting easier).

●**Dust from the top down.** Walk around the room in a circle, using your duster's extension wand and a stepstool if needed to reach high moldings, shelves and lighting fixtures.

●**Walk around in a circle again,** using an electrostatic cloth to dust those surfaces between your head and knees. Switch to a clean cloth when necessary.

●**Run your dusting wand along all of the baseboards.**

●**Vacuum the perimeter of the room.**

●**Put furniture back in place, and vacuum the center of the room.** Vacuum sofa and chairs with the upholstery attachment. If you have an extra few minutes, mop hard-surface floors.

KITCHEN: 12 MINUTES

●**Clear all counters**—put food away in the refrigerator and cupboards, place utensils in drawers and sweep papers into a basket to sort later. Put dirty dishes in the dishwasher.

●**Wipe counters with a sponge sprayed with disinfecting cleaner.**

●**Spray the sink with disinfecting cleaner, and wipe with a damp sponge.** Dry handles and faucet with a dish towel or microfiber cloth to prevent spots.

●**Pick up stray items from the floor, and put them away.**

●**Take throw rugs outside, and shake for 10 seconds.** Vacuum the floor. If it looks like it needs it, give the floor a quick mopping. Put throw rugs back.

●**Spray disinfecting cleaner onto a sponge and wipe the refrigerator,** stove, microwave and other appliances.

●**If you have a window above your sink,** spray it with window cleaner and wipe with a microfiber cloth.

SMALL APPLIANCES

Cleaning tricks for small appliances...

●**Food processor.** Rinse the bowl to remove most food, then fill it halfway with water. Add a squirt of dishwashing liquid. Close, and turn the food processor on for 30 seconds. Rinse. Let the blades spin for a few seconds to dry.

•**Microwave oven.** Pour two cups of water into a microwave-safe bowl. Place the bowl in the middle of the microwave, and cook on high for five minutes to create steam. Using oven mitts, remove and empty the bowl—the water will be scalding hot. Wipe the inside of the oven with a damp sponge.

•**Garbage disposal.** Put a few lemon, lime or orange rinds in the disposal. Run cold water, and turn on the disposal. Grind until rinds are gone. The disposal will smell clean and fresh.

More from Jeff Bredenberg...

Five Things to Stop Cleaning

Here are five things you really don't need to waste your time with...

1. Grill grate. Instead of scrubbing a grill grate after using it, leave the grill on high with the cover on for 15 minutes. Residue will cook away.

2. Shower curtain liner. Liners are really cheap so laundering them to remove mildew is a waste of time. Just replace your liner every six months.

3. Pillow. After washing and drying a pillow, it's never quite the same. Instead, throw it out, and buy a new one every six months.

4. Making up the bed. Microscopic dust mites—one leading cause of allergies—thrive on moisture in your mattress and bedcovers. Leaving the bed unmade allows moisture to escape.

If you really can't stand an unmade bed, then use a duvet instead of a top sheet and bedspread. Simply shake out the duvet, and you're done.

5. Waxing the car. Newer cars have tough finishes that don't need wax for protection.

How to Clean Green

Elizabeth B. Goldsmith, PhD, professor, department of textiles and consumer sciences, Florida State University, Tallahassee, and the author of *Green Cleaning for Dummies* (Wiley).

Many household cleaners have harsh chemicals linked to health problems, from headaches to asthma to cancer. When all these chemicals go down the drain, they contaminate soil and water. You've probably heard of safer natural alternatives—but may not know exactly how to use them. *What works...*

•**Baking soda.** This alkaline mineral cuts grease, grime and smells. For an all-purpose liquid cleaner, mix four tablespoons of baking soda into one quart of water. For scouring, make a paste of equal parts baking soda and water. To avoid discoloration, do not use on aluminum.

Unclog a drain: Pour in one cup of baking soda, then one-half cup of white vinegar...wait several minutes...flush with very hot water.

•**Hydrogen peroxide.** This safer substitute for chlorine bleach breaks down into water and oxygen.

For laundry: Add one-half cup of 3% hydrogen peroxide (sold at drugstores) to a load of white or color-fast fabrics. Do not use on unbleachable fabrics (check labels).

•**Soda water.** Its *sodium citrate* loosens dirt —so use regular club soda, not low-sodium. Dampen a microfiber cloth to shine appliances and glass. To remove red wine from fabrics or carpet, dampen a sponge with club soda and dab the spot...then blot with a cloth to dry.

•**White vinegar (not cider or wine vinegar).** Its *acetic acid* dissolves dirt and soap scum, deodorizes and kills germs. To clean up sinks, tiles, glass and countertops (not marble), mix one-quarter cup of vinegar with two cups of water. For a nicer aroma, add a few drops of a citrus or floral essential oil. To soften fabrics (not cotton or linen), add one-quarter cup of vinegar to the rinse cycle.

Make Your Own Window Cleaner—Cheap and Easy!

Use what most professional window washers use—just mix one teaspoon of dishwashing liquid in a few gallons of water. You'll also save a good deal of money by not buying commercial window cleaners. Put the solution you make in a spray bottle for indoor use.

The Family Handyman, Reader's Digest Rd., Pleasantville, New York 10570, *www.familyhandyman.com*.

Plant Power

Houseplants help remove the chemicals released into the air by paints, cleaners, glues and other products. The plants' physiological processes help remove some *volatile organic compounds* (or VOCs) during the day, and tiny organisms in the soil remove VOCs when the plant is not as active at night.

Plants that remove the most VOCs: Purple waffle plant, wax plant, asparagus fern, English ivy and the purple heart plant.

Bodie Pennisi, PhD, associate professor, department of horticulture, University of Georgia, Griffin, and the leader of a study that tested 28 common houseplants, published in *HortScience*.

Learn to Repair Things Yourself: Helpful Web Sites

Do-it-yourself home repair not only will save you money, it's also quite easy. *Web sites to help you get started...*

• **Enter your question starting with "How to" at the free Web site *www.findhow.com*.** You will get a targeted response with step-by-step instructions, often including photos or a video.

• **Also check *www.fixya.com*,** for technical support, instructions and repair service.

• **For appliances, go to *www.repairclinic. com*.** This site provides you free diagnostic help and offers live chats with experienced repair people. You can order needed parts directly through the site.

Mary Hunt, editor, *Debt-Proof Living*, Box 2135, Paramount, California 90723, *www.debtproofliving.com*.

18

Life Lessons

C'mon Get Happy: What Works May Surprise You…

The philosophers, psychologists and self-help gurus all provide advice on how we can all get happier— but what actually works? Journalist Gretchen Rubin decided to find out. She devoted a year to "test-driving" happiness strategies and gathered feedback from visitors to her popular Web site. She called her research "The Happiness Project."

Different happiness strategies work for different people, but a few strategies stand out…

•**Seek novelty and challenge even if you value consistency and comfort.** I didn't expect exploring new challenges to make me happier—familiarity and comfort are very important to me—but I was wrong. Trying new things is one of the most effective paths to happiness that I have encountered.

The human brain is stimulated by surprise and discovery. Successfully coping with the unfamiliar can provide a high level of happiness. Repeating what we've done many times before can be comfortable, but comfortable is not the same as happy.

Example: Launching and updating my daily blog have brought me great happiness, though initially I feared that I lacked the necessary technical skills.

Challenge yourself to start something that sounds interesting—even if it's different from anything you've done before or requires skills that you're not sure you have. Take a class…try a new hobby…learn a language…or visit a different town or museum every weekend.

•**Try doing whatever you enjoyed doing at age 10.** The person we are in adulthood has

---

Gretchen Rubin, an attorney and former Supreme Court clerk. Based in New York City, Rubin is founder of *The Happiness Project*, a blog and newsletter, and author of the best-selling book *The Happiness Project* (Harper), for which she personally tested happiness strategies. For more, see *www.happiness-project.com*.

more in common with the person we were at age 10 than we realize. Renowned psychiatrist Carl Jung started playing with building blocks as an adult to recapture some enthusiasm he had felt in his youth. If fishing made us happy when we were 10, odds are it will make us happy today…if playing the drums made us happy then, it probably still will.

Example: I was given a blank book when I was a child and really enjoyed filling it with clippings, notes, cartoons, anything that interested me. So as part of my happiness project, I bought myself a scrapbook and started clipping items from magazines and newspapers to paste into it. I was amazed by how much happiness I still could derive from this.

• **Read memoirs of death and suffering.** Paradoxically, sad memoirs can increase our happiness. These books put our own problems in perspective and remind us how fortunate we are.

Examples: I became much happier with my own life when I read Gene O'Kelly's *Chasing Daylight,* the former CEO's memoir about learning that he had three months to live… Stan Mack's *Janet & Me,* about the death of the author's partner…and Joan Didion's *The Year of Magical Thinking,* about the death of her husband.

It's not that I'm happy that other people have been unhappy. It's just a way of appreciating everything that I do have.

• **De-clutter your home.** Only a few minutes of cleaning up can substantially improve one's mood by giving us the sense that we have accomplished something positive. Cleaning can also create an impression of order that can contribute to serenity. And it helps remove a source of stress—conspicuous clutter is a visual reminder of a responsibility that we have neglected.

Try a brief burst of cleaning the next time you feel overwhelmed or anxious even if you don't think it will work for you. Even people who are not particularly fastidious discover that this boosts their mood.

Examples: For me, cleaning out a drawer…organizing my medicine cabinet…or just making my bed in the morning provides a real boost to my happiness.

• **Be appreciative of people's good traits rather than critical of their bad ones**…be thankful for what they do for you, and stop blaming them for what they don't.

Example: I stopped getting angry at my husband for forgetting to withdraw cash before we went out. Instead, I started taking it upon myself to make sure that we had the necessary cash. I also made a point to be more appreciative of all the things that my husband does do, such as dealing with the car.

• **Enjoy today even if there's still work to do.** Many of us assume it's normal to live with limited happiness until some major milestone is reached—we earn that big promotion, have a family or retire. We tell ourselves, I'll be happy when I achieve my goals.

Example: As a writer, I imagined how happy I would be when the book I was working on was finally published.

Unfortunately, people who pin their happiness on a distant goal usually spend most or all of their lives less happy than they could be. Often they set ever more distant goals as the original targets approach…or they discover that the goal that they thought would bring happiness actually brings added stress. Some never reach their goals at all.

I'm much happier now that I remind myself to be happy about making gradual progress toward my goals, even if the goals themselves remain far in the distance.

Seven Tricks to Stay Positive in an Often Negative World

JoAnna Brandi, trained happiness coach and president of JoAnna Brandi & Company, Inc., a customer-care consultancy based in Boca Raton, Florida, *www. customercarecoach.com.* She is the author of *54 Ways to Stay Positive in a Changing, Challenging and Sometimes Negative World* (JoAnna Brandi & Co.).

Happiness is within your reach. Even if life has dealt you challenging cards, you still can be happy—if you learn the mental strategies that help create positive feelings.

Learning to be positive is well worth the effort. People who have a positive outlook not only enjoy their lives more but have stronger immune systems and live seven to nine years longer, on average. They also tend to exhibit better intuition, more creativity and improved problem-solving abilities.

Ways to become more positive...

• **Trigger the laughter effect.** Our bodies produce biochemicals known as *endorphins* when we laugh, which makes us feel more optimistic. We also can trick our minds into thinking that we are laughing by pretending to laugh. Phony laughter might sound fake to your ears, but it can trigger the same wave of endorphin-driven elation that you would get from legitimate laughter.

• **Count those blessings.** Each night before bed, write down three good things about the day. Drifting off with positive thoughts in your mind can help you sleep better—and getting more sleep will reduce your stress and make you feel more positive the following day.

• **Exercise.** Our bodies quickly get flooded with *adrenaline* when we feel stressed, which can make us feel panicky or combative. Physical activity—even a brisk walk up and down a set of stairs—burns off adrenaline, allowing us to feel positive. There even is evidence that 30 minutes or more of exercise three times a week is as effective at treating depression as the antidepressant Zoloft.

• **Use "What's the good word?"** as a greeting, not "How are you?" Using the word "good" at the start of a verbal exchange encourages people to offer positive responses—and their positive words can help you be positive.

• **Savor the positive.** Our minds seem to rush past the good and ruminate on the bad. Force yourself to slow down and fully appreciate small things that you enjoy. Savor each bite of a good meal...delight in a compliment, and reflect later upon how wonderful it felt to receive it...stop and drink in a beautiful view. Discuss your enjoyable moments with those who share them—talking about experiences helps us absorb them. If no one else is around, call or e-mail a friend, or write about the experience in a journal.

• **Create a list of the 10 most positive experiences of your life.** Label each with the primary feeling that it provided, such as joy, accomplishment, empowerment or enchantment. When you feel trapped by negativity, choose the feeling you most need from this list, then mentally re-create the experience. See what you saw when this experience originally occurred...feel what you felt...and hear what you heard.

Example: A salesman is depressed because of a lost account. He mentally re-creates the experience of winning his company's salesman of the year award three years earlier. He hears his name being announced by the CEO, followed by applause. He feels himself rise and climb the steps to the stage. He feels the trophy in his hand.

Just by recalling the sensory feelings of an experience in as much detail as possible, we can trick our brains into believing that we're experiencing it again, triggering all the same biochemical reactions and moods as the first time.

• **Spend time in nature.** We all feel more positive when we spend 20 minutes or more each day surrounded by nature. Being in nature refreshes the spirit and reminds us that we belong to something larger than ourselves.

When you can't find time for the outdoors or the weather is bad, spend a few minutes enjoying a photo or poster of a nature scene. Remarkably, looking at pictures of nature can have the same uplifting effect on our outlook as actually being in nature.

How to Survive Change You Didn't Ask For

M.J. Ryan, a change expert with Professional Think-ing Partners, a consultancy based in Park City, Utah. She is author of *AdaptAbility: How to Survive Change You Didn't Ask For* (Broadway Books). She is former CEO and editorial director of the publishing company Conari Press and one of the creators of its best-selling series, Random Acts of Kindness. Her Web site is *www. mj-ryan.com.*

Almost half of your retirement nest egg disappeared practically overnight…your employer went out of business…a rou-tine physical turned up a serious health prob-lem. Adjusting to change is particularly difficult when change is both unwanted and unex-pected. Sudden, life-altering events can create a paralyzing sense of lost control and dashed dreams.

Important strategies for surviving unexpect-ed change…

•**Engage in at least one activity every day that you can completely control.** It's normal to feel like a helpless victim when an unwant-ed change turns your life upside down. But you can start to shed these feelings of power-lessness by taking up a hobby or pursuing a goal that involves no one's effort or assent but your own.

Example: A woman whose husband left her dedicated herself to running a marathon.

•**Fake the confidence and skills you need to rebound until you have them.** Pretending we can do something helps our brains form the new pathways required to actually do it.

Example: I used to be quite a terrible networker. To overcome this, I asked myself, *What would I do right now if I were a great networker?* then I pretended that I was one. That got me out the door and talking to folks at networking events. Within weeks, I was no longer pretending—networking started to come naturally to me.

•**Focus on where you want to be a year from now.** It's more useful—and more enjoy-able—to look forward after an unwanted life change than it is to look back. Obsessing over backward-looking questions, including *Why*

did this happen to me? and *What went wrong?,* rarely helps us rebound.

Instead, view the current state of affairs not as a setback, but as a starting point. When your mind drifts back to the way things once were, remind yourself, *This is where I am… Now, where am I going from here?*

•**Celebrate small successes.** Put even your tiniest accomplishments in your mental "win" column. This creates a sense that you're rack-ing up wins, which builds positive energy and forward momentum.

Example: If you lost your job, don't wait until you land a new one to view yourself as a winner—that would only make you feel and act like a loser during job interviews. Set an achievable job-search goal each day, such as calling three potential employers…networking with a colleague in your field…or researching a potential employer. Then celebrate your ac-complishment at the end of the day—Hooray, I made progress—and share it with others if possible.

•**Consider why options might work, even if you suspect they won't.** It's easy to fall into the trap of "yes, but" thinking after un-wanted changes happen to us. When we come up with a possible solution, we immediately think of a reason why this solution will fail and conclude that it isn't even worth trying. The problem isn't that the idea is flawed, but that recent setbacks have put us in a negative frame of mind.

When you think of an option, force yourself also to think, *If I did this, here's how it might succeed…*

•**Help others with their problems.** Help-ing puts our own problems in perspective… proves to us that we can accomplish change… and allows us to take a much-needed mental break from our own worries.

Example: One woman forced out of her home by wildfires discovered that collecting blankets for other victims helped her to stop worrying about her home.

•**Encourage yourself as you would your child in a footrace.** Tell yourself, *You can do it!* and *You're almost there!* Do this out loud or, if you're in public, to yourself. It may feel silly, but hearing over-the-top encouragement really does provide a confidence boost, even when it comes from your own mouth.

● **Schedule 15-minutes for "worry time."** Chronic worriers tend to obsess about all their problems, forcing out any productive thoughts during the day and preventing sleep at night. These people cannot cease worrying entirely, but they can contain their worrying to a specific block of time each day.

Give yourself permission to worry during a particular 15 minutes each day, ideally at the time of day when your worries tend to be at their worst. When you catch yourself worrying at other times, remind yourself that you have a schedule, and promise yourself that you'll get all your worrying done then. Experiment with the best time to worry. If right before bed makes it hard for you to sleep, find another time.

● **Give advice to someone facing a change similar to your own, then take that advice yourself.** It's often easier to analyze someone else's problem than it is your own. Our emotions and ego get in our way when we think about our own lives.

Example: Think about what you would tell a friend to do to get her retirement savings back on track. Then follow your own advice.

● **Remind yourself of your strengths and positive qualities every time you think of your problems.** Those who face unexpected problems tend to think about those problems much more than they think about the tools they have for overcoming them. Whenever any problems come to mind, mentally list all your skills, your friends and any other resources to help you rebound.

How to Connect with Someone Who's Depressed

To try and help a friend who is depressed, ask if everything is okay and just offer to listen to him/her. Ask if you can come over for a visit—if he declines, offer to help run errands with him. You could also suggest going for a walk—it may boost his mood. Don't give your opinion on the situation or say that things will get better or that the situation is not so bad.

Woman's Day, 1633 Broadway, New York City 10019, *www.womansday.com*.

Six Self-Help Ways to Ease Anxiety

Michael McKee, PhD, a cognitive-behavioral therapist in private practice in Scarsdale, New York, and research scientist at the Anxiety Disorders Clinic, New York State Psychiatric Institute, New York City.

Here are six simple ways to ease anxiety on your own—without help from a therapist…

● **Exercise.** Research shows that all kinds of exercise will make you feel a lot more confident and at ease. Aerobic exercise stimulates release of endorphins, neurotransmitters that are the body's natural "feel good" drug. Yoga can calm nerves.

● **Deep breathing.** Slow breathing from deep in the diaphragm (belly breathing) slows racing thoughts and restores a sense of control.

● **Progressive muscle relaxation.** To remove tension from your muscles, clench them tightly for a full five seconds, then slowly release. Do this for individual body parts starting with your toes and working all the way up to your face.

● **Cut back on coffee.** The caffeine in coffee is a stimulant, so if you are nervous, it will make you more so. Switch to green tea—it has much less caffeine. Green tea also provides amino acids that researchers believe have a calming effect on the brain.

● **Limit alcohol consumption.** It stimulates stress hormones, so have no more than one alcoholic beverage a day.

● **Keep a "joy journal."** Write down on a piece of paper a list of all the good things in your life. Take notes during the day of any

289

funny, entertaining or rewarding things that occur. By consciously thinking about them, they will become more meaningful than the more stressful parts of your life.

The "10-10-10" Strategy Can Help You Make Much Better Decisions

Suzy Welch, the author of *10-10-10: 10 Minutes, 10 Months, 10 Years—A Life-Transforming Idea* (Scribner). She is a columnist for *O, The Oprah Magazine* and coauthor, with her husband, former GE CEO Jack Welch, of "The Welch Way," a column in *BusinessWeek*. Based in Boston, she is former editor in chief of *Harvard Business Review*. Her Web site is *www.suzywelch101010.com*.

Most of us have trouble making decisions, especially difficult ones. And when we do make a decision, we often wonder if we made the right one. *Here, noted writer Suzy Welch discusses her powerful new "10-10-10" strategy for making better decisions...*

WHY WE GO WRONG

The human mind is wired to be more concerned with current comfort levels than with long-term consequences. Thus when we make decisions, we often act as if the future doesn't exist—or at least, as if it doesn't count for very much. Psychologists refer to this tendency as "hyperbolic discounting."

Example: A busy man is asked to spend hours working on a project. He says yes—even though he knows that he either will have to sacrifice something more important to him or back out of this new commitment later. He tells himself that he said yes because he wants to help. In reality, he said yes because this nets him thanks and praise, which allows him to feel good about himself right now. Saying no would force him to endure a few minutes of guilt and discomfort.

Some people manage to overcome this tendency and focus on long-term goals—but even these seemingly responsible planners can go wrong. The long-term consequences of our actions often are unknowable. When that's the case, making decisions based on only the perceived long-term consequences means living life based on guesswork. Besides, those who always sacrifice near-term happiness for long-term priorities never get to enjoy today—and there's no certainty that we still will be here tomorrow.

Example: A man worked the four-to-midnight shift for years because it provided extra pay, helping him toward his goal of a secure retirement. He rarely saw his family. He died before reaching his retirement age.

THREE TIME FRAMES

A better way to make decisions is to employ a 10-10-10 strategy. *When faced with a crisis or decision, write down each of your options, followed by the consequences of each option in the following three time frames...*

•**The next 10 minutes.** Which option will make your life easiest and happiest right now and in the immediate future? How unpleasant will the coming minutes (or hours or days) be if you choose a different alternative?

Example: Going along with your spouse's plans avoids a fight, making the coming minutes more pleasant.

•**The coming 10 months.** This often-overlooked intermediate time frame is crucial. Ten months is long enough to be significant...yet close enough to predict with some accuracy.

Example: A man is trying to determine whether to quit his job and start a business. He knows that quitting will feel liberating in the next 10 minutes...but it's very difficult to predict whether his business will be a success in 10 years. This man can weigh whether the long hours and huge risks of starting a business will get him out of bed energized for the next 10 months or keep him up nights worrying...and whether his marriage and his savings will survive 10 months of long hours and limited income.

•**The next 10 years (or longer).** Which option points you toward the life you want to live? Which will stand in the way of your long-term goals?

Example: Overeating now puts you on course to look and feel worse in 10 years than you do today.

Money-wise strategy: When decisions involve spending, consider not only how much you will use and enjoy this purchase in 10 minutes, 10 months and 10 years but also how much the money spent would be worth in 10 years if it were invested. An investment that earns 7% compound interest nearly doubles in 10 years.

If all three time frames point to the same option, then the decision is made. If not, you might have to compromise. You don't always have to sacrifice short-term happiness for intermediate or long-term success, but you do have to be honest with yourself about what you are giving up when you choose near-term gratification.

GET HELP

When you confront major decisions, involve others in this process. Ask friends to supply their honest projections of the long-term consequences of each of your alternatives. Also ask if they can think of any alternatives that you missed.

Don't solicit input just from friends—they often think the same way you do. Also ask acquaintances who have shown that they make choices different from your own. Such people can provide new perspectives.

KNOW YOUR VALUES

To be successful, "10-10-10" should be coupled with an understanding of one's values. So many people have never really considered what's most important to them...or lie to themselves about their priorities. These people are susceptible to the two deadly Gs of decision-making—listening to one's gut and succumbing to guilt.

The following questions can help you get to the heart of what you really want...

• **What would make you feel like a failure at your next milestone birthday?**

Example: One woman struggling to balance a family and a time-consuming business answered, "If I let the business fail."

Many women let guilt convince them that they must put family ahead of career. In fact, working hard is one way to set a positive example for children. Plenty of children grow up happy and well-adjusted even though both of their parents work.

• **What do I want people to say about me when I'm not in the room?**

Example: If you would like people to say that you're a square dealer, you had better disclose the problems with your used car to potential buyers.

• **What do you love about the way your parents lived...and what do you hate?** The way we live our lives can be a reaction to the way our parents lived.

Example: A man who answers, "I disliked the silence in my parents' home," could make decisions in his own relationships that encourage openness.

Solve *Any* Problem in Three Simple Steps

Ken Watanabe, author of the best-selling *Problem Solving 101: A Simple Book for Smart People* (Portfolio). He is founder and CEO of Delta Studio, an education, entertainment and media company in Tokyo, where he is developing an educational TV show and a "brain game" for Nintendo. Formerly, he was a consultant at McKinsey & Co. Check out *www.problemsolving toolbox.com* for more.

Five years ago, Ken Watanabe, a Harvard MBA who worked at one of the world's leading consulting firms, walked away from a lucrative career to write a children's book. He was alarmed that school-age kids in his native Japan were good at memorizing large amounts of information but not very effective at applying it to real-life situations. He wanted to teach them in a fun way to broaden and organize their approach to problem-solving and become more proactive in shaping the world.

But then something unexpected occurred. Watanabe's 110-page book became a phenomenon with adults in Japan...and the country's best-selling business book of the year. Since then, it's been published in a half-dozen countries around the world, including, most recently, the US.

Here are Ken Watanabe's secrets to problem-solving...

THE THREE STEPS

Good problem-solving isn't an innate talent. It comes from a way of thinking using a set of techniques that you can practice and improve upon. Most people rely too much on their instincts when they try to solve a problem, especially when they feel flustered or overwhelmed. They tend to grasp at the first or second solution that pops into their heads, even if it doesn't seem completely adequate.

I developed a simple, structured approach that works for addressing almost any kind of problem, big or small. In fact, I've used the same approach helping my Fortune 500 company clients as I do trying to fix the pepper shaker in my kitchen.

• **Step 1.** Identify your problem and the root difficulties that cause it. People tend to think about their situations in such vague, universal terms that they get overwhelmed.

Example: You feel stressed and unhappy because you never have enough money each month. Stress and unhappiness are symptoms, not underlying problems that you can take action to remedy. You have to analyze more deeply. Is the actual problem that you're not earning enough money? Or is it that you're spending too much each month?

To identify problems, I find it very helpful to think of myself as a doctor trying to cure a patient. I list potential causes for a problem, arrive at a hypothesis for the most likely cause and focus on addressing that cause.

• **Step 2.** Come up with multiple solutions. List as many as you can, no matter how improbable. This often leads you to creative and unexpected solutions. Even if you think a particular solution may be the right one, get into the habit of challenging this conclusion. Ask yourself, *What are the shortcomings of this solution? Is there a better way?*

• **Step 3.** Prioritize your actions and implement a plan. After you select a solution, you

need to follow through on it and be prepared to modify it—or replace it—until the problem is resolved.

MY FAVORITE TOOLS FOR SOLVING PROBLEMS

I find that jotting down my thoughts and creating graphic representations of them are essential to breaking down problems into manageable parts and making sure that I explore every possible avenue...

• **The Logic Tree.** This is useful for clarifying your problem and its root causes.

How it works: Write your problem in a box on the left side of a piece of paper. Ask "Why?" you have that problem. For each answer, draw an arrow to the right, and put it in a box. Now ask "Why?" for each of the answers in the boxes. Keep repeating the process until you have identified all of the possible root causes of the problem.

The Logic Tree also can help you to brainstorm a variety of solutions to a problem after you've identified the root cause.

Example: Say that you have determined from the first Logic Tree that the root cause of your money problems is that you don't track your spending well enough. Start a new Logic Tree for possible solutions. In a new box on the left side of a piece of paper, write "I need to track my money better." Then ask "How?". Answers might be "Get help" and "Do it myself." Put these in boxes. Then ask "How?" again. One answer to your "Get help" box might be "Visit a CPA once a month." One answer to the "Do it myself" box might be "Buy money management software."

• **Pros and cons box.** This is useful for evaluating which competing solutions are the best ones. The box allows you to line up and compare the benefits and drawbacks of possible solutions at a glance.

How it works: Draw three columns. Label the first "Possible Solutions," the second "Pros" and the third "Cons." List each solution, and fill in its corresponding pros and cons. You can further refine the process by marking each pro and con entry using a star system. Three stars is very attractive or very unattractive depending on whether it's in your pro or con list, two stars is moderately attractive/unattractive and one star is marginally attractive/unattractive.

Count the stars. If they are in the pro column, more stars is good. If they are in the con column, more stars is bad.

MY PEPPER SHAKER PROBLEM

I had an expensive new pepper shaker that I had to shake and shake just to get enough pepper out. It was a small problem, but one that annoyed me. I thought about throwing it out and buying a new one, but that seemed like a waste. So, I decided to find out whether thinking through the problem in a structured way would allow me to find a more satisfying solution. A pepper shaker, of course, is trivial, but the process used to solve the pepper shaker problem can solve any problem.

In this case, identifying the problem was easy—I wasn't getting enough pepper from my pepper shaker.

•**Possible root causes…**

•I need too much pepper on my food. I rejected this because I really like pepper.

•I wasn't shaking the shaker long enough or hard enough. I dismissed this cause because one or two vigorous shakes should be sufficient.

•The small openings on the top of the pepper shaker were too small. Yes, this seemed like the most reasonable cause.

•**Possible solutions…**

•Buy a new pepper shaker that has larger openings. I had already rejected this idea.

•Increase the amount of pepper that was coming out of the shaker. Yes, but how?

I had to continue generating more refined solutions.

•**Possible refined solutions…**

•Increase the number of holes in the shaker. I didn't want to do this, because it would ruin the look of my pepper shaker.

•Make each existing hole bigger. No, again for the same reason.

•Use more finely ground pepper. Yes, that seemed like the smartest, most practical idea.

I then put the solution into action. I called the store to check whether it carried finely ground pepper—it did, so I bought it.

Got a Problem? Sleep on It

If you take a nap that includes rapid eye movement (REM) sleep—the kind that includes dreams—you might come up with an answer that you did not think of while awake. People who napped with REM sleep did better on word-association tests than ones who napped without REM sleep or who did not nap. Dreams help the mind put together concepts in new and more creative ways—a useful problem-solving tool.

Sara C. Mednick, PhD, assistant professor of psychiatry at University of California in San Diego, www. saramednick.com.

Stop Trying to Multitask!

Studies show multitasking is *not* efficient. You get more done faster and with fewer mistakes by doing one thing at a time. Focusing on one task also reduces stress and protects short-term memory.

David E. Meyer, PhD, director of the Brain, Cognition and Action Laboratory, University of Michigan in Ann Arbor.

Donald Trump's Six Secrets to Keeping Your Edge in Life

Renowned real estate developer and entrepreneur Donald Trump, chairman and president of the Trump Organization, New York City. He is also the author of *Think Like a Champion* (Vanguard, *www.trumpthinklikeachampion.com*).

At an age when most people have contemplated retirement and are slowing down a bit, Donald Trump, age 64, is busy ramping up his activities. In addition to developing hotels and golf courses around the world (including in the Dominican Republic, Dubai, Washington, DC, and Scotland), he has had resounding success with the Miss Universe and Miss USA pageants, founded the online education company Trump University, gotten his golf handicap down to three, written another best seller, *Think Like a Champion,* and concluded the 2010 season finale of his TV program, *Celebrity Apprentice.* The series has received terrific ratings and will soon be entering its 10th season.

Even in trying times, the charismatic, outspoken Donald Trump manages to stay energetic and stimulated by life. And as we all know, money alone can't do that for you. Below, Trump tells us how he stays so productive and keeps challenging himself. *Here are his six secrets...*

1. Relentlessly confront your fears. You can't let fear—fear of the new, fear of growing old, fear of failure—settle into place in any part of your life. Fear has a way of making all problems bigger than they are. The trick is to recognize your fears and then zap them with a problem-solving attitude, faith in yourself and hard work.

Example: I owed billions of dollars in the early 1990s, and many people thought I was finished. Major newspapers were announcing my demise. The big difference is that I didn't believe that I was finished for one second, no matter what people thought. I simply refused to give in to the negative circumstances and kept working to overcome my challenges.

Useful exercise: Rename your fears. Call them "concerns." Just using a different word can affect your approach and reactions. "Fears" create blocks that will only hinder your best creative thinking. "Concerns" can be broken down into units of thought and dealt with in an orderly and persistent manner.

2. Make your communications short, fast and direct. As someone on the receiving end of conversations with people who don't know how to edit themselves, I know what agony means. I think to myself, *How long is it going to take for this person to get to the point?*

People are very, very busy today. They are overloaded with information. Don't drone on and on. Don't force people to sort through it all to get to the important stuff, the good stuff. More often than not, your listeners—whether it's your family, business associates or those in a social setting—will be grateful for your ability to get to the essence quickly for them.

In any conversation, I give myself an internal deadline. I say as much as I can in as few words as possible. If you practice this technique every day, whether it's relaying a message to someone, writing a letter or ordering lunch, it will become natural for you—and you will accomplish more.

3. Put bad news in perspective. The way you handle difficult situations in life says a lot about who you are. The same event can wipe out one person but make another more tenacious. When I'm in the midst of difficult times, I ask, *Is this a blip or a catastrophe?*

This question reminds me that most problems are temporary if you keep your equilibrium and maintain your momentum. Realize that there will always be blips but that you never know when the tide is going to turn, provided you are paying attention and still working toward something worthwhile.

Example: I was scheduled to make a brief appearance on a boat docked in New York City and then get off before it departed on an evening-long cruise around Manhattan. I was about to leave when I noticed that the boat was already in the middle of the river! I wasn't too happy about this turn of events, but it wasn't the end of the world. Instead of fuming and complaining, I adjusted my mood and treated it as an unexpected adventure. I actually had a memorable evening, met some fascinating people and got some great ideas.

4. Don't take yourself so seriously. Over the years, I have been offered a lot of TV commercials and turned most of them down. But my favorite one allowed me to display a self-deprecating attitude that I think took people by surprise. It is a commercial for Visa. I am shown on the top of Trump Tower in Manhattan holding my credit card when a gust of wind blows it to the street below. Next, I am seen rummaging in a dumpster in search of my lost card. A well-dressed passerby remarks, "And I thought he was doing so well."

I do take my work seriously—but the ability to laugh at myself keeps my perspective intact, adds an element of fun to my endeavors and makes people realize that I am complex, concerned about more than just ambition.

5. Never let one person determine your well-being. Several years ago, the now notorious hedge fund manager Bernie Madoff approached me in Palm Beach, Florida, where we both owned property. He said, "Why don't you invest in my fund?" I had enough going on in my own businesses, and I didn't know much about him, so I declined.

I know a lot of very smart people who became victims of Bernie Madoff's unscrupulous scheme and had their futures compromised.

Money is not a prerequisite to live an active, exciting life, but it does provide security, confidence and comfort. The takeaway here is that you must be careful with your financial transactions no matter how much you like or respect a person. Never bet the ranch on one person or one person's idea. Spread your money around with numerous people and organizations. Though we have no guarantees in life, we can take precautions.

6. Turn your passions into productive activities. One thing that I've learned about life is that it should be a series of discoveries. Remember how exciting it was to learn to ride a bike? If you can capture that kind of excitement as you age, you will never "stop"—you will always be on your way to finding where you are meant to be in life. Remember, whatever you do at this point in your life, it's better to love it. Enthusiasm on a big scale equals passion, and passion is what gives you the resiliency to take yourself to amazing places.

Example: I love playing golf, so when I was looking for new real estate projects, I wanted to build the world's greatest golf course. I spent five years reviewing sites around the world and turned down more than 200 possibilities. Finally, I found a dramatic, 1,400-acre landscape in Aberdeen on the north coast of Scotland with miles of spectacular oceanfront and sand dunes of immense proportion. The location had sentimental meaning for me—I have Scottish roots, and my mother's first language was Gaelic. I knew this was the right place, but the scope of development and the cost, one billion pounds, was such that no one thought I would get approval to go ahead. In fact, building this course became such a saga that the BBC hosted documentaries on it and HBO did a feature. We're now moving ahead.

Good-for-You Friends

Judy Kuriansky, PhD, a clinical psychologist and sex therapist on the adjunct faculty of Columbia University Teachers College in New York City. She is author of five books, including *The Complete Idiot's Guide to a Healthy Relationship* (Alpha). Her online site is *www.drjudy.com*.

Some so-called friendships drain energy and increase stress. *Here's how to nurture relationships that nourish you...*

• **Identify toxic behaviors.** It's not always easy to recognize or admit that someone you care for isn't a true friend.

Warning signs: He/she often turns conversations to herself ("You argued with your son? I had a fight with my son, too")...acts envious ("How could you get promoted again when I'm stuck in this dead-end job?")...constantly asks favors or implies that her time is more valuable than yours...or speaks ill of others (she probably badmouths you, too). Weeding out such negative relationships frees up time for healthier ones.

• **Evaluate commendable qualities.** Consider which of your current pals deserves to be dearer. For clarity, use a scale of one (never) to 10 (always) to rate a friend's character in the following areas.

Support: You can share your deepest emotions and count on her in emergencies.

Loyalty: She celebrates your successes and defends you against criticism.

Trust: She tells the truth and keeps promises she makes.

• **Nourish friendships that you want to flourish.** Invite friends to share experiences you are passionate about, such as attending concerts or serving soup to the needy. Suggest everyday activities to do together—running errands, walking your dogs. When you can't get together, phone to say, "I'm so glad we're friends."

More from Dr. Judy Kuriansky...

The Power of Nighttime Dreams

As you fall asleep, imagine yourself already living out a big dream, decorating your dream house, hugging your dream mate. Your unconscious mind will work through the night to make that vision come true...and you will wake with new inspirations about how to turn your dream into reality.

The Six Keys to Fulfilling Friendships

Jeffrey Zaslow, who is based in Southfield, Michigan, and writes a column on life transitions for *The Wall Street Journal*. For 14 years, he wrote an advice column for the *Chicago Sun-Times* after winning the competition to replace Ann Landers. He is a coauthor of the best-selling book *The Last Lecture* (Hyperion). His most recent book, *The Girls from Ames* (Gotham, *www.girlsfromames.com)*, also is a best seller.

The girls from Ames are a close-knit group of women, now in their 40s, who met as girls in Ames, Iowa. As the 11 women moved away, pursued careers, married and had children, they maintained a powerful bond that endures today. *The Ames friends share a number of unspoken ground rules that are crucial to maintaining trust and connection in any friendship...*

1. Work at staying connected. The friends are in e-mail contact with one another nearly every day, hitting "reply all" to keep the whole group in the loop. They get together as a full group at least once a year and in smaller groups several times a year.

2. Root for one another. They celebrate one another's successes, sending cards, flowers and congratulatory messages. Sometimes they feel envious, but they don't undercut one another. They recognize that friendship is not a competition and take pleasure in one another's good fortune.

3. Don't gloat. They don't boast about their incomes or their spouses' incomes. When they talk about their children's achievements, they do not do it in a competitive or domineering way.

4. Show up for important events. In 1986, Sheila, one of the 11 friends, died in a fall. The women were in their 20s, spread across the country, and only half of them could afford to travel back to Ames for the funeral. Those who didn't attend still regret that they weren't able to show support for Sheila's family or get closure.

Years later, when Karla's teenage daughter died after a long illness, every Ames girl came to the memorial service.

The friends make a point of being present for the landmark events in one another's lives, from weddings to serious illnesses and funerals.

5. Be flexible and understanding. These friends recognize that people's needs and capacities ebb and flow. While they do expect loyalty and goodwill from one another, they don't demand constant attention. If an e-mail or a phone call isn't returned right away, they don't get resentful or worry that they're being snubbed. They give one another room to live full lives and be busy and tired.

They also are generous when one member of the circle needs more attention than usual. When Kelly was going through a divorce, the others listened for as long as she needed to talk.

6. Protect all confidences. Secrets shared among group members stay within the group. Disagreements with one another get hashed out within the group—they don't complain to spouses or to other friends.

Example: The biggest disagreement the girls hashed out with one another was how much to share of themselves in the best-selling book about them. Some girls shared more private details about themselves (and the relationship and their friends) than others were comfortable sharing. There were times when feelings were bruised, and they had to reach a consensus on how much from their diaries and letters they were willing to share for inclusion in the book.

Can People Count on You? Even Little Mistakes Can Do Big Damage to Your Credibility

Sandy Allgeier, a certified senior professional in human resources (SPHR) based in Louisville, Kentucky. She previously served as director of human resources for Providian Corporation, a Fortune 500 company. She is author of *The Personal Credibility Factor: How to Get It, Keep It, and Get It Back (If You've Lost It)* (FT Press). Her Web site is *www.sandyallgeier.com.*

If people don't trust you, they won't hire you, do business with you or spend time with you. Most of us try to be true to our word, but it's easy to make accidental, seemingly minor missteps that cause others to have doubts about our reliability. *Among the most common...*

• **Breaking appointments or arriving late.** Some people see nothing wrong with rescheduling appointments or arriving 20 minutes late. But this form of not keeping promises makes others doubt whether we can be trusted.

Situation: You tell a friend that you are so looking forward to seeing him/her—then reschedule three times. Or whenever you meet your friend, you're always late. Even if your reasons are valid, your friend might wonder whether you truly value the relationship.

Strategy: If you are chronically late, allow more time in your schedule for the activities that tend to take longer than you expect. And, if you are chronically rescheduling appointments because of "emergencies," reevaluate what constitutes an emergency or incorporate open time into your schedule so that you can cope with emergencies without canceling other commitments.

• **Being messy or disorganized.** Some disorganized people chronically fail to live up to their responsibilities simply because they lack a system for keeping track of them. Others manage to get things done despite their cluttered desks or homes—but people who aren't messy often assume that messiness is a sign of unreliability.

Situation: If your neat boss knows that your work space is disorganized, he is more likely to view any small error in your work as a sign that your job performance is messy and unreliable, too.

Strategy: Keep your work space neat, particularly if you have a tidy boss, colleague or client who has access to it.

• **Allowing personal matters to intrude on work time.** If friends or family members call or e-mail you regularly during your workday, your bosses, colleagues and clients might question your commitment to work.

Situation: Your boss notices that you often make long personal phone calls and concludes that you can't be trusted to work hard without close supervision.

Strategy: Ask friends and family members to call you only on your personal cell phone. Check your cell-phone messages at lunch and during breaks.

• **Failing to follow through on "minor" promises.** Most of us have more trouble living up to our minor promises than our major ones. We mean to live up to all of our promises, but small ones are easily forgotten. Though our memories, not our morals, are to blame, those around us still might question whether we can be trusted.

Situation: Borrow $10,000 from a friend, and you will certainly remember to pay back the loan. Borrow $10, and the debt might slip your mind.

Strategy: If minor matters often slip your mind, jot down your promises, commitments and debts on a calendar or planner as soon as you make them.

• **Keeping people in the dark about a decision-making process.** People tend to feel deceived or ignored when others make decisions that seem to go against what has been promised.

Situation: A construction company allows their employees to purchase leftover building materials at low prices after projects are completed. One time, surplus materials could not be made available because a client requested the surplus. The employees were not told this and assumed that the boss had gone back on his word.

Strategy: Let those affected by your decisions know why you are making those decisions, even when you have every right to make the decisions without letting them know.

● **Exhibiting body language that doesn't match your words.** People do not hear only what we say—they also subconsciously monitor our facial expressions and gestures. When our words do not match our body language, they sense that we can't be trusted.

Situation: You tell a friend that you are excited about her business idea, but you're tired and distracted and your body language conveys disinterest.

Strategy: Your body language will match your words if you always pay complete attention during conversations—and if you're being honest when you speak.

● **Thinking out loud when others think you're making decisions.** You might be talking yourself through the options, but those listening could mistake your musings for decisions—then question your honesty when you later choose a different path.

Situation: You chat with a friend about taking a vacation together. The friend mistakes this preliminary chat for a firm commitment.

Strategy: Preface your thinking out loud with phrases such as, "I'm just talking through ideas here," or "I need to confirm that this is feasible."

Shine at Small Talk

It's savvy to get comfortable with appropriate small talk. People dislike silence. Have topics at the ready by staying informed about what is happening in the world...in your profession...in your neighborhood. Avoid health, sex, politics and religion.

Barbara Pachter, president, Pachter & Associates, a communications training firm in Cherry Hill, New Jersey, *www.pachter.com,* and author of *When the Little Things Count...and They Always Count* (Da Capo).

The Key to More Peaceful Relationships

An easy way to more peaceful relationships is to stop assuming that you know what someone else is thinking. Whatever you think another person is thinking, you are wrong. Assuming and acting on what you think another person is thinking leads to misunderstandings and upset. If we remember and accept that we're all different and we see the world in our own ways, relationships improve and we are happier.

Andy Feld, entrepreneur based in Morrison, Colorado, and author of *Wake Up! Your Life Is Callng* (iUniverse). His Web site is *www.andyfeld.net.*

How to Calm an Angry Person

Redford Williams, MD, the director of the Behavioral Medicine Research Center at Duke University Medical Center in Durham, North Carolina. He is also author of numerous books, including *In Control* (Rodale), and a coauthor of the video-learning program *Williams Lifeskills—Managing Stress & Anger System,* available from *www.williamslifeskills.com.*

When someone is angry, our instinctive reaction typically is to get defensive (if the person is angry at us) or to give advice (if he/she is angry at someone else). These responses are not useful, as they do not resolve the situation and even may inflame him further. *More effective...*

WHEN YOU ARE NOT THE TARGET

The best way to calm someone who is angry at someone else is to let him vent. Don't interrupt or tell him why he shouldn't be angry or that he should let it go. Don't talk about the time you got mad about the same thing—this implies that your reaction is more important than his.

When he has talked himself out, acknowledge his feelings—whether or not you agree with his views.

Example: "Wow, you're really angry with your boss. I can see how upset you are."

After listening and acknowledging, ask if there is any way you can help. In many cases, the other person will say that you have helped simply by listening. You also might be able to assist with brainstorming and problem-solving. But if you try to solve the problem before hearing the person out or without his approval, he most likely will feel angrier.

WHEN THE ANGER IS DIRECTED AT YOU

When someone lashes out at you, the primitive part of your brain is activated. This creates the impulse to defend yourself from the attack by telling the other person he is wrong or irrational or by getting angry yourself.

Instead, before responding, pause for a few moments and silently ask yourself these four questions…

1. Is this situation *Important?*

2. Is my reaction *Appropriate?*

3. Is the situation *Modifiable?*

4. If so, is taking action *Worth it?*

To remember the four questions when you are under stress, use the partial acronym I AM WORTH IT. I stands for *Important*…AM stands for *Appropriate and Modifiable*…WORTH IT, of course, stands for the last question.

● **If the answer to all four questions is "yes,"** then assert yourself by telling the person the following…

● Exactly what he is doing.

● How it makes you feel.

● What, specifically, you would like him to do differently.

Keep your voice fairly quiet and your tone neutral. Describe behavior, not motives or personal characteristics.

Example: My wife used this technique when I came home in a bad mood at the end of a tough day. Virginia was preparing dinner. On the kitchen counter was a big stack of mail-order catalogs that she had promised to look through a few days earlier. I snapped, "What are these damn catalogs doing here?"

Virginia didn't say a word for about 20 seconds. Then she replied calmly, "Redford, you just walked into the kitchen and barked, 'What are these damn catalogs doing here?' (She told me what I had done.) I came home early to make dinner, and now, I am feeling hurt, unappreciated and, frankly, angry at you. (She told me how it made her feel.) Would it be possible for you to come home at the end of the day and not have the first words out of your mouth be something critical?" (What she would like me to do.)

I turned around, walked out of the kitchen, came back in and said, "Mmm, smells so good. What's for supper?"

When I first arrived home, Virginia could have fueled an argument by snapping back, "What is the matter with you, coming home and criticizing me?" Instead, during those 20 seconds of silence, she asked herself the four questions. Then she made a specific observation and a request for change.

If you need to respond to an angry outburst in a setting where expressing personal feelings is not appropriate—for example, at work—use a results-oriented word, such as "helpful."

Example: "Bill, you just told me that my marketing idea for the new product is the stupidest thing you ever heard. I need to let you know that calling my suggestion stupid isn't helpful. If you could give me some of the reasons you think it won't work, I'd appreciate it."

● **If your answer to any of the four I AM WORTH IT questions gets a "no"**—focus on controlling your reaction. Don't say anything to the person. Instead, if the situation isn't important or can't be changed, say to yourself, "Hey, it's not that important," or "There's nothing I can do to change this guy." If requesting change isn't appropriate or worth it, you can distract yourself by thinking about something pleasant or doing something else...or by taking a few deep breaths and thinking the word "calm" as you inhale and "down" as you exhale. This is not the same as passively giving in. You are evaluating the situation and making a rational decision.

Tricks to Keep Your Cool

Marjory Abrams, president of Boardroom Inc., 281 Tresser Blvd., Stamford, Connecticut 06901.

Tears come easily to a friend of mine. It doesn't bother her when she is around family and friends—but she hates crying at work. Other people I know "lose it" by shaking with nervousness, blushing with embarrassment or revealing other emotions that they would rather not display. Rhonda Scharf, an Ontario-based consultant who specializes in workplace effectiveness (*www.on-the-right-track.com*), told me that looking at someone between the eyes rather than directly at his/her eyes can help you stay calm. Distraction also works. *For example...*

• **Wiggle your toes.** It relaxes muscles, fights off tension and requires conscious thought—which keeps anxiety and other negative feelings from settling in.

• **Focus on your breath.** If your heart starts racing, Scharf suggests concentrating on how air moves in and out of each nostril. Alternate focusing on your left and right nostrils.

MORE HELP FOR EMBARRASSING RESPONSES

• **Tears.** Scharf sometimes finds herself on the brink of tears when she is unusually frustrated or angry. To stop the tears, she puts her index finger at the base of her nasal septum (the divider). It looks as if she is simply stifling a sneeze. Giving yourself a long pinch on your arm or leg may work, too.

• **The shakes.** Place your hands behind your back. Tightly press the thumb of each hand against the index finger of the same hand to release pressure. Don't hold any objects—this can make your shakes more noticeable.

• **The sweats.** Scharf notes that sweating is outside conscious control. Medical treatments may help people whose lives are disrupted by excessive sweating.

Among the options: Prescription antiperspirants...anticholinergic medications, such as *glycopyrrolate* (Robinul)...or Botox injections in the palms of the hands and/or underarm area.

• **Blushing.** Blushing also is an involuntary physiological response. Being worried or self-conscious about it makes people blush even more. Yet, most likely, it is much less noticeable to others than you think it is.

Consider the thoughts that went through your mind as you blushed. Think of positive thoughts to replace the negative ones.

Example: A person often blushed when his boss called attention to a mistake he had made. His negative thought was that he was no good at his job. Replacing it with a thought about, say, a recent workplace success could help him keep from blushing the next time around.

It takes practice to stop negative thinking—but the positive self-talk that replaces it can work wonders in keeping emotions in check.

Seeing a Shrink for the First Time?

If you are going to a psychiatrist for the first time, here's what to expect... Be ready for a comprehensive rundown of your previous history—medical and emotional as well as psychiatric—before discussing your current problems and concerns. Try to be as candid, unguarded and as complete as you can. Provide as many medical records as possible. Have a list of all medicines you currently take, plus those you have taken in the past—especially psychiatric medicines—and include notes on what worked and what did not. Be prepared to discuss social, family, educational and work history...living situation...marital and sexual history...and any risky behaviors, from unprotected sex to failure to use a seat belt.

Richard O'Brien, MD, spokesperson for the American College of Emergency Physicians and clinical instructor, Temple University School of Medicine, Philadelphia.

A Time to Grieve

Give yourself time to grieve after losing a loved one. Grief is a slow process. *Also...*

•**Don't shut others out.** Friends and family will want to help you, perhaps by cooking and performing other needed tasks for you. Allowing them to assist you will reduce your stress and make them happy that they are able to help in your time of need.

•**Keep yourself healthy.** Remember to take care of your body and your mind by getting enough sleep, watching your diet, exercising and finding time to relax.

•**Seek support.** You will feel less alone after talking with others who also are grieving or after reading books and visiting Web sites by and for people who have lost loved ones.

•**Keep your loved one alive through your memories.** Remember all the good times you shared. Look through photo albums and videos, and share stories about the person with others.

Redbook, 300 W 57th St., New York City 10019, *www.redbookmag.com.*

Cell-Phone Games Are Great for Your Brain

Cell-phone games are better for your brain than crossword and sudoku puzzles because they have a timing component.

As you age, your brain faces more challenges with short-term memory and the cognitive tasks of paying attention and juggling multiple abilities. It's important to challenge these skills, and playing games against a clock provides a better brain workout than puzzles and board games.

Cynthia R. Green, PhD, president of Memory Arts, LLC in Upper Montclair, New Jersey, *www.memoryarts.com.*

How Computer Use Harms and *Helps* Your Brain

Gary Small, MD, professor of psychiatry and biobehavioral sciences and director of the Center on Aging, the Memory & Aging Center and the Geriatric Psychiatry Division at the Semel Institute for Neuroscience & Human Behavior at the University of California in Los Angeles. He also has published more than 400 scholarly articles focusing on memory, aging and Alzheimer's disease and is coauthor of *iBrain: Surviving the Technological Alteration of the Modern Mind* (HarperCollins). He's on the Web at *www.drgarysmall.com.*

The average American uses the Internet for 26 hours each month—writing e-mails, searching for facts or simply shopping online. But does all this online activity help—or harm—our brains?

Gary Small, MD, a top authority on brain function, explains that computer use has both positive and negative effects...

YOUR BRAIN ON THE INTERNET

"Use it or lose it" has long been the motto for brain health. And according to new research, processing and responding to a shifting influx of information on the computer appears to dramatically increase mental activity.

Important new finding: When 24 adults both with and without computer experience had their brain activity measured while they searched the Internet for information, the experienced users' brains were twice as lively as the others'. The increased activity was most striking in the brain's prefrontal cortex—the region that weighs complex information and makes decisions.

But the newcomers caught up quickly. After spending just an hour a day on Internet searching for five days, their brains were just as active, when retested, as their more experienced counterparts'.

ONLINE SOCIAL SKILLS

New technology means a world of new opportunities to socialize. For example, so-called "social media" outlets, such as Facebook (*www.facebook.com*), MySpace (*www.myspace.com*) and Twitter (*www.twitter.com*), make it possible to easily communicate with friends and acquaintances, including many you've never actually met.

The more you "socialize" online, the more adept at it you become, as brain circuits engaged by the activity grow stronger. This type of social activity engages the "thinking center" of the brain, as well as areas involved in language and memory functions.

The potential cost: When you spend long hours in front of the computer screen, you have less time for face-to-face conversations, which communicate a far richer stream of information than digital messages can. Facial expression, eye contact, tone of voice as well as body language convey subtleties of thought and feeling that are otherwise lost.

In fact, face-to-face conversation activates the brain more broadly and deeply than does computer communication—speaking, listening and interpreting nonverbal signals engage the neurons in areas such as the *anterior cingulate*, the *insula* and parts of the *frontal cortex* that can weaken from disuse.

Self-defense: Become aware of the hours you spend online and be ready to set limits. Spend more *physical* time with people you care about—for example, schedule family dinners to reconnect with each other. To engage your brain even more fully, make special note of nonverbal communication when you're with people. For example, what are people saying by the way they stand and gesture?

TOO MUCH AT ONCE?

Today's computer technology makes multitasking almost inevitable. Streams of information are constantly converging as e-mails and the lure of the Internet compete for our attention. Hopscotching back and forth grows easier with practice. Presumably it strengthens the part of the brain that lets us leave one task and focus in on another—an area behind the forehead called the *anterior prefrontal cortex*.

The potential cost: Getting used to the staccato thinking style of dancing between tasks may make it more difficult to focus attention long enough to really think through a concern. Some experts have suggested that symptoms of attention deficit hyperactivity disorder (or ADHD) in adults—such as distractibility, impulsivity and inability to concentrate—may be due, in some cases, to brain shifts that occur in response to the continual bombardment of information delivered by technology.

You may think that you're getting more tasks done by multitasking, but in fact the brain is far more efficient when allowed to concentrate on one thing at a time. Studies have indicated that mental efficiency decreases during multitasking, and tasks take longer to complete than they do when done sequentially.

Self-defense: List your tasks in their order of importance, and arrange your schedule accordingly. Set aside times when you focus on paying bills or returning phone calls—turn off your e-mail if it distracts you.

Also helpful: When possible, take "power naps." A Harvard study found that a 30-minute nap renews the neural pathways depleted by multitasking and reduces overall fatigue.

BRAIN-BUILDING TECHNOLOGY

Research shows that regular mental stimulation can spur new connections between neurons and improve memory.

Solving crossword puzzles in the newspaper, for example, and learning new subjects may slow brain aging—or even lower the risk for Alzheimer's disease.

Used wisely, your computer also can help promote brain health. For example, there are Web sites that feature games and puzzles specifically designed to challenge the brain at varying levels of difficulty.

My favorite Web sites: www.brainbashers. com (created by a math teacher in England, this free site provides puzzles, riddles, games and optical illusions)…and *www.braingle.com*

(this site will e-mail you a free brain teaser each day and allows you to chat online with other brain teaser enthusiasts).

Also, brain scans show that searching the Internet for information may take more brain power than reading and can be a great mental exercise.

Are You Addicted to the Internet?

Kimberly Young, PhD, director of the Center for Internet Addiction Recovery in Bradford, Pennsylvania, and author of *Caught in the Net: How to Recognize the Signs of Internet Addiction—and a Winning Strategy for Recovery* (Wiley). She is professor of management sciences at St. Bonaventure University in St. Bonaventure, New York, and serves on the board of *CyberPsychology, Behavior and Social Networking*. For more, go to *www.netaddiction.com.*

The Internet has become so central to our lives that it has become tricky to determine how much time on the Internet is too much. We shop online…pay bills… check sports scores…play video games…visit chat rooms…and write blogs. In a nationwide telephone survey of 2,513 adults, researchers at Stanford University found that about 69% were regular Internet users—and a significant percentage of subjects showed signs that their habits were out of control…

- **13.7% found it hard to stay away from the Internet for days at a time.**
- **12.4% stayed online longer than intended very often or often.**
- **8.7% attempted to conceal nonessential Internet use from their family, friends and employers.**
- **5.9% felt their relationships suffered because of excessive Internet use.**

WARNING SIGNS

To help determine if you are addicted to the Internet, ask yourself the following…

- **Is it hard for me to cut back on my online activities?**

- **Do I often choose online activities over time with friends or family?**
- **Does it interfere with keeping commitments,** such as preparing dinner, walking the dog or paying bills?
- **Do I miss sleep or meals because I'm so engaged online?**
- **Have people commented on how much time I spend on the Internet?**

If you answer "yes" to any of the questions, take steps to cut back.

BREAKING THE HABIT

Learning moderation is the key. *Strategies…*

- **Change your timing.** If you log on first thing in the morning, wait until after breakfast or lunch instead. If you tend to stay up too late while on the computer, establish a limit that you must turn it off at, say, 8:00 pm.
- **Set limits.** Limit session time (set a kitchen timer or alarm clock) or the number of sessions per day or week.
- **Put reminders near the computer, saying, "Are you done yet?"** or "Do you know where your wife is?"
- **Cultivate offline relationships.** If you're constantly socializing online, look for ways you can have fun and feel connected in person instead.
- **Consider whether you have been using the Internet to avoid other issues.** Perhaps you are bored at work or not happy in your marriage. Focusing on the Internet is a way to avoid dealing with the problem. You may need to address any underlying issues more directly through counseling.

Helpful: If technology is interfering with your day-to-day life, get help. Contact the Center for Internet Addiction (814-451-2405, *www.netaddiction.com*).

A Simple Memory Trick

In a study of 57 adults (average age 72), participants were told to push a computer's "F1" key once while performing a list of cognitive and perceptual activities. One group also was asked to touch the top of their heads when they pressed the key.

Result: Those who had touched their heads were much more likely to remember having hit the F1 key.

Theory: It is easier to recall having completed a habitual task if it is accompanied by some kind of motor task, such as touching your head or crossing your arms.

If you have trouble remembering whether you've completed a daily activity (such as taking pills): Try making a specific motion each time you perform the task.

Mark McDaniel, PhD, professor of psychology at Washington University, St. Louis.

Do You Doodle?

In a recent study, people who doodled while listening to one boring phone message remembered 29% more about the message than those who didn't doodle.

Jackie Andrade, PhD, professor, School of Psychology, University of Plymouth, UK, and leader of a study published in *Applied Cognitive Psychology.*

Eat Less, Remember More

Overweight people who reduced their calorie consumption by 30% a day scored 20% higher on a word-based memory exam than they had before dieting. The dieters had lower levels of glucose and insulin in their blood—factors linked in earlier studies to improved brain function.

Study of 50 people, average age 60, by researchers at University of Münster, Germany, published in *Proceedings of the National Academy of Sciences.*

Foods for a Better Memory

Oranges are a great source of folate, which boosts recall and information processing. Strive for one medium-sized orange per day. Black beans are rich in fiber and vitamin B-1, which helps memory by synthesizing *acetylcholine,* the neurotransmitter that is crucial for memory. Aim for one-half cup a day. Sage improves recall for up to four hours after consumption. Add one teaspoon of sage-infused olive oil to canned or homemade soup, or use it in a meat marinade.

Natural Health, One Park Avenue, New York City 10016, *www.naturalhealthmag.com.*

Yum! Chocolate Makes You Smarter

In a recent finding, volunteers found mental arithmetic easier after they were given 500 mg of *flavanols,* compounds found in chocolate that increase blood flow to the brain. They also were less likely to feel tired or mentally drained while doing mental calculations. Dark chocolate has the most flavanols.

Crystal Haskell, PhD, associate director, Brain, Performance and Nutrition Research Centre, Northumbria University, England, and lead researcher of the study.

Mineral for the Mind?

Animals given magnesium supplements experienced improvements in memory and learning skills.

Implication: This mineral could possibly help prevent cognitive decline in humans.

Massachusetts Institute of Technology, *www.mit.edu,* and Tsinghua University, *www.tsinghua.edu.*

19

Business Brainstorm

Jonathan Pond Tells What to Do *Now* in Case You Lose Your Job

Nearly eight million US jobs have disappeared since the recession began in December 2007. Don't wait for the pink slip to show up before you start preparing for the possibility of joblessness. Even if you remain employed, you'll feel less stressed—and enjoy life more—knowing that you are prepared.

Steps to take now...

WHEN LAYOFF IS POSSIBLE

• **Calculate a bare-bones household budget for at least half a year of unemployment.** Based on that budget, build up an emergency fund that you keep in short-term investments, such as money-market funds and three-month certificates of deposit.

What is the absolute minimum you require each month to get by? Add up your mortgage payments...utility bills...insurance premiums...minimum debt payments...the lowest grocery costs that would keep your family fed...and any other expenses that cannot be avoided or delayed.

Multiply this monthly minimum by six. If your current emergency fund falls short, eliminate or slash all noncrucial spending until this savings goal is reached. If the job market looks particularly bleak in your industry—say, auto manufacturing or journalism—don't stop at six months. It could take a year or longer to find a new job, particularly if you must retrain in a different field.

Opportunities: Not eating out...dropping entertainment costs, such as premium cable

Jonathan Pond, a financial adviser based in Newton, Massachusetts. He has hosted 19 public television specials about personal finance and is author of 10 books on money management, including his most recent *Safe Money in Tough Times* (McGraw-Hill). His Web site is *www.jonathanpond.com.*

channels…and eliminating all new clothing purchases.

Helpful: Selling a portion of an investment portfolio is another way to build an emergency fund—but selling stocks means locking in losses…and, unlike cutting costs, it does not provide practice at living frugally, an important skill.

• **Postpone all big-ticket purchases.** Avoid buying a new car or remodeling your kitchen. Vacation locally.

• **If you own a home, apply for a home equity line of credit (HELOC).** Your chances of getting approved for a HELOC, whose initial rates averaged 4.8% in late-August 2010, are much better while you're still employed. But you may need at least 20% equity in your home to qualify. Tap this HELOC only if absolutely necessary.

• **Start looking for a new job before you need one.** Network with contacts at companies that are hiring while you are still employed. This will help you to hit the ground running if you do lose your job. It also improves your odds of being viewed as an attractive applicant—unemployed job seekers may seem desperate and unappealing to employers.

• **Sign up for employer-subsidized education or training.** Your company might have programs that help employees pay for business school or job training. Enroll in such a program before you're laid off, and the training could help you land your next job.

• **Warn your spouse or partner about the dangers.** This isn't the time to bear your family's financial burdens alone. Your partner can help you trim spending—and can start looking for a job if he/she doesn't have one.

• **Raise the subject of emergency loans with family members.** It isn't fair to spring loan requests on loved ones without warning.

WHEN LAYOFF IS LIKELY

If you are virtually certain that a layoff is coming soon…

• **Make only the minimum required payments on your debt if you have not saved up enough for your emergency fund.** Your priority now is to increase your savings, not

to pay down debt. If you will have trouble paying the full amounts due, your mortgage and car loans should be your first bill-paying priorities, then utilities and finally unsecured credit card accounts. Not paying credit card bills will damage your credit, but not paying your mortgage or car loan could lead to losing those assets.

• **Ask your employer to lower your tax withholding.** Reducing withholding increases your liquidity at a time when your access to cash is crucial. If you're laid off, your income tax bill will be lower next April anyway.

• **Reduce your retirement plan contributions.** You could face penalties if you need to pull money out of a retirement plan to pay bills while you're unemployed.

• **Move up all doctor appointments.** You might lose at least some types of medical coverage or find that coverage is more expensive when you are laid off.

• **Prepare a negotiating strategy for a severance package if that's a possibility where you work.** You might be able to negotiate for better terms, if you are prepared when the ax falls. Be prepared to explain why you should receive more severance than other terminated employees.

Example: You could convince key clients to join you at another firm.…therefore, it would be in your company's interest to convince you to sign a "noncompete agreement" restricting your ability to solicit former clients or work in the sector at all for a period of time.

Also, if you or a family member has a serious health condition, negotiate to keep your health insurance benefits for as long as possible. If your job skills are out of date, negotiate for career retraining.

Smart Move If a Layoff Is Likely

Volunteer for a pay cut if you think you may otherwise be laid off. Let the boss know that you are willing to work—and be content—at a lower salary than your current one. Make your proposal in a believable manner—for example, by saying that you do not consider salary a measure of self-worth. In the current economy, it may be better to continue working for less money than to risk being laid off at a time of rising unemployment.

Tyler Cowen, PhD, professor of economics, George Mason University, Fairfax, Virginia.

Negotiating Better Severance: What Companies Hope You Don't Know

Jason Stern, Esq., an attorney based in New York City, who specializes in severance negotiation. He previously served as a judge and hearing officer in New York City. His Web site is *www.severanceattorney.com*.

Severance packages have become much stingier as employers strive to fit large-scale layoffs into ever-tighter budgets. At the same time, obtaining attractive severance packages is more important than ever for terminated employees because finding a new job can take many months in this economy.

Laid-off employees often fear that the initial offer will be withdrawn if they attempt to negotiate, but this almost certainly will not occur. Employers do not provide severance out of kindness. They do this in exchange for the employee's signature on an agreement not to sue for wrongful termination. Obtaining that signature has value to the company.

To get all you can if you are let go...

DON'T SIGN RIGHT AWAY

• **Do not sign any severance agreement when it first is presented to you.** Tell the human resources (HR) representative that you need time to review it with an attorney. Using this phrase is an excellent negotiation tactic even if you do not expect to hire an attorney. If the HR rep acts upset that you intend to involve an attorney, point out that the company

certainly has its attorneys review such documents. Then scan the final paragraphs of the agreement—there's usually a clause near the end stating that the company encouraged you to consult with an attorney. If you see this, point it out to the HR rep.

A warning: If your employer encourages you to resign rather than get laid off, politely decline unless you are offered a substantially improved severance package for doing so. Resigning may deprive you of your right to collect unemployment insurance...or to sue for wrongful termination.

WEIGH YOUR PRIORITIES

Which component(s) of the severance offer would you most like to improve?

• **Cash.** Many companies now offer only one to two weeks for every year you have worked for the company. It is reasonable to request a month of severance pay per year.

• **Pension benefits.** If you are within five years of retirement age, ask the company to continue funding your retirement account until that time.

• **Health insurance premiums.** If you expect to use COBRA (*Consolidated Omnibus Budget Reconciliation Act*) or a similar state program to remain on your employer's health insurance plan, ask your employer to pay some or all of the insurance premiums.

With the government picking up 65% of the premium costs for 15 months for eligible individuals who lost their jobs prior to June 1, 2010, I would say that all these terminated employees should have asked their employers to pick up the remaining 35% for 15 months. Employees with valid claims against the company and employees with more than 10 years of service really should request the standard 18 months of paid COBRA premiums.

• **A written waiver of your noncompete agreement.** A noncompete (or noncompetition) agreement prohibits an employee from working in a related business. Other employers might be wary of hiring you if you don't have a waiver of this agreement—even though your former employer probably cannot legally enforce your noncompete agreement after laying you off.

307

•**Office equipment.** Keeping the company laptop or BlackBerry can help you with your job search.

Helpful: Offer to let the company's technician wipe clean the computer's hard drive.

•**Vacation days.** Ask to be paid for any unused days. Some states require employers to pay for unused vacation time. Sick days have less protection than vacation days. Most states do not require employers to pay for unused sick days.

•**Reference letter.** Decline to sign any severance agreement until you receive a "mutually acceptable" letter of recommendation—a tactic that typically yields a far more favorable recommendation.

EVALUATE YOUR NEGOTIATING POSITION

You might have a lot more leverage than you realize…

•**Have you been offered any severance benefits that you don't need?** Ask the HR rep to estimate the value of these benefits, then try to trade them for severance benefits that are of greater use to you.

Examples: COBRA insurance premium payments may be of little value to you if you have access to a spouse's insurance plan. Outplacement services are of no value if you intend to retire or already have another job lined up.

•**Is there any hint of discrimination in your firing?** Women who have young children or who are of childbearing age…employees past age 40…and minorities should consider whether their group seemed to be singled out for termination or whether the workplace was hostile to them. If so, the threat of a lawsuit could make your former employer more open to negotiation on the severance package.

•**Have other terminated employees been offered more than you?** This is no time to be shy about talking with peers about money. If others got more, you probably can, too.

•**Do you have a friend in upper management?** The HR rep is likely to treat you well if you can convince a highly placed executive to call and tell him/her how valuable you have been through the years. HR employees worry about their jobs, too—they won't want to risk

angering any high-level executives by treating their friends poorly.

•**Did you receive favorable performance evaluations throughout your employment?** Bring copies of these with you when you meet with the HR rep. Better-than-average employees typically receive better-than-average severance packages.

Laid Off or Fired? This Free Resource Can Help

TheCanned.com is a free Web resource for those who were recently fired. It has information about unemployment benefits and health insurance as well as finding a new job. It features a list of job sites and reviews of those sites, plus blog posts on many subjects dealing with unemployment and finding a new job.

Nella Barkley, president and cofounder, Crystal-Barkley Corporation, career-coaching firm in Charleston, South Carolina, and coauthor of *The Crystal-Barkley Guide to Taking Charge of Your Career* (Workman). Her Web site is *www.careerlife.com.*

Tax Breaks for the Jobless

Edward Mendlowitz, CPA, partner in the CPA firm WithumSmith+Brown in New Brunswick, New Jersey, ranked among the top 35 accounting firms in the US by the industry's leading publications, *www.withum.com.* He has more than 40 years of public accounting experience and is author of numerous books, including *The Adviser's Guide to Family Business Succession Planning* (American Institute of Certified Public Accountants).

As unemployment now hovers around 10%, you or a loved one could lose a job. *If so, don't fall into these tax traps or overlook these tax savers…*

Tax trap: If your previous employer provides you with severance pay or payments for accumulated vacation and sick time, you'll owe income tax on all those amounts. The same is true for unemployment compensation.

Ask to have 15% to 35% withheld from your employer's disbursements, depending on your tax bracket. Opt for voluntary withholding or make the required estimated tax payments to cover unemployment compensation.

TAX SAVERS

• **When looking for a new job, your job-hunting expenses should be tax deductible.** Those outlays are considered miscellaneous itemized deductions, which are deductible to the extent that they exceed 2% of your adjusted gross income.

• **If you have highly appreciated employer stock in your 401(k) account, take a distribution of the stock** instead of rolling over the stock to an IRA. This way, when you sell these stock shares, you'll pay favorable capital gains rates (rather than income tax rates) on the appreciation.

Trap: If these shares are transferred to your IRA, this break will be lost.

If you go through your severance pay and need cash…

• **Avoid tapping your traditional (tax-deferred) IRA or 401(k)**—you'll probably owe income tax on your withdrawal and perhaps a 10% surtax if you're younger than age 59½. If you've converted a traditional IRA to a Roth IRA, withdrawals of earnings before five years and age 59½ may draw a 10% penalty.

To generate cash, sell securities trading below your purchase price held in a taxable account. Not only will you avoid taxable income by taking a loss—you'll also be able to deduct up to $3,000 of net capital losses on your 2010 tax return.

Unemployment Insurance Update: Extended Benefits, Tax Relief, More

Rick McHugh, Midwest coordinator and staff attorney in the Ann Arbor, Michigan, office of the National Employment Law Project, a national advocacy organization for employment rights, *www.nelp.org*. An expert on unemployment insurance law, McHugh has been widely quoted in national publications and has written and testified extensively on this topic.

Millions of Americans are likely to be jobless this year. For many of them, unemployment insurance (UI) will be a financial lifeline while they hunt for work. The good news is that the *2009 American Recovery and Reinvestment Act* has provisions that boost the compensation that laid-off workers collect.

Here's what you need to know now about unemployment benefits…

WHAT YOU GET

Generally, states aim to replace half of your prelayoff wages up to a maximum amount set by individual states. Currently, Mississippi provides the lowest maximum weekly benefit of $235, while Massachusetts offers the highest maximum of $629 per week. In addition, UI recipients got an extra, federally funded $25 per week under the recovery act. (The extra $25 is still available through 12/11/10 for those currently receiving it, but the program expired for those making new unemployment claims after 5/29/10.)

Typically, state unemployment benefits last up to 26 weeks. However, the federal Emergency Unemployment Compensation program provides unemployment pay for those who have exhausted the standard 26 weeks. After the 26 weeks expire, federal unemployment payments can last up to another 53 weeks (depending on the unemployment rate in the state).

In addition to these extensions, another 13 or 20 weeks of benefits are available under the Extended Benefits program in about two dozen states. Therefore, people out of a job can qualify for up to 99 weeks in some states.

(This program is slated to expire on November 30, 2010.) The number of states probably will increase. Your state agency's Web site will tell you how many weeks of extensions are available in your state.

WHO QUALIFIES?

Although UI is meant to help those who involuntarily lose their jobs anywhere in the US, every state sets its own rules. In addition to those laid off for economic reasons, some individuals who have been fired or who quit can receive unemployment benefits depending on where they live. If you are out of work for any reason other than a layoff, don't assume that you don't qualify. Instead, file a claim and review your state unemployment agency's decision. If you are turned down, file an appeal.

All states recognize that there can be valid job-related reasons for quitting.

Examples: A big cut in pay and/or work hours…material change in job duties or working conditions…or sexual harassment.

In some states, you also may qualify for unemployment payments if you quit a job for a wide range of "compelling" personal reasons. The most lenient of these states include Alaska, Arizona, California, Pennsylvania and Rhode Island. Most other states either do not accept personal reasons or put varying degrees of restrictions on what qualifies as a "compelling" personal reason.

Some common examples of valid personal reasons: To care for an ailing relative…to escape domestic violence…to move with your spouse who is transferred within a company. (In some states, you qualify even if you move because your spouse gets a job with a different employer.)

Most states use a standard of "misconduct" to determine whether to pay benefits to those who have been let go for noneconomic reasons. Generally, those who are fired for "poor performance" do not lose benefits. All states try to decide whether the reasons for a discharge indicate "willful" misconduct or "reckless" conduct on the employee's part, and in those cases, benefits often are denied. On the other hand, when the employee is fired because he/she simply could not perform up to the employer's expectations, benefits are paid. And in most states, being fired for missing a few days of work for valid reasons is not grounds for denying benefits, especially if the employee called in and can document the reasons for missing work.

Part-time workers qualify as long as they've earned (over a 52-week period) the minimum required amount set by the state, which tends to be between $400 and $4,000. Various states have different job-search requirements for UI recipients to remain eligible. In some states, recipients can look for just part-time work, while in others, they must look for full-time work.

HOW TO FILE

Contact your state's UI agency. You can file your initial claim either by phone or, in many states, through the agency's Web site.

Because of the large number of claims during this recession, most states are encouraging workers to file on the Internet whenever possible. Filing information for every state is found on the US Department of Labor's site at *www.servicelocator.org/OWSLinks.asp.*

Look for work, and be prepared to document your efforts. Report any earnings, even if you have temporary work. Each state uses its own formula for adjusting your benefits according to how much money you earn while collecting benefits.

THE APPEALS PROCESS

All states provide written notices when they grant or deny benefits. The notice will state how many days you have to file your appeal. Appeals must be in writing and filed as instructed on the notice.

What to do: Always open your mail from the agency immediately. Read the entire decision. Allow sufficient time for delivery if you are mailing your appeal. Clearly express that you are disagreeing with the unfavorable decision and include your name and identifying information, but do not feel that you must cover everything. Save that for the hearing.

Important: File benefit claims while your appeal is pending, or you will not get paid for those weeks even if you win your appeal.

The most important stage of appeal is your hearing before an administrative law judge or hearing officer. You will get prior written notice of the date, time and place. Many states conduct hearings by phone.

Take the time to review the notice. Think about the issues that the notice says will be considered at the hearing. Speak clearly, and remain focused on the issues at hand. For example, in a discharge case, the issue is not whether your former employer should have fired you. The issue is whether the reason is valid for disqualifying you from benefits.

Free Money to Go Back to School

Gen Tenabe, coauthor with his wife, Kelly, of *501 Ways for Adult Students to Pay for College* (SuperCollege). He is cofounder of SuperCollege, which offers resources and tools for college-bound students of all ages, *www.supercollege.com*. He lives in Belmont, California.

When the going gets difficult, many adults go back to school. With unemployment rising and industries shrinking, workers are finding that they need to boost their skills, retool their careers and, in some cases, start over—and that means heading back to the classroom.

These days, adults have more educational options than ever. College admissions officers tell me that in the last 12 to 18 months, they have seen an explosion in the number of applicants over age 35. At the same time, retraining courses just for adults, which help those who are unemployed learn new skills needed to return to work, are cropping up at community colleges, community centers and even on the Internet.

Problem: The need for more education hits when many people, especially those who have lost their jobs, have the most trouble bearing the cost of tuition.

Here is how you can pay for the training you need…

GO FOR THE FREE MONEY

Scholarships aren't just for teens—they defray adults' tuition bills, too. For most scholarships, there are no limitations due to age. That means you are eligible for much of the same free money that high school seniors are hunting for! There also are both need- and merit-based scholarships specifically for adults. *To find money…*

•**Search the Internet.** Free Web sites to search for scholarships include FastWeb.com and SuperCollege.com, the Web site my wife and I founded. Once you locate a scholarship for which you might be eligible, contact the sponsoring organization for details on how to apply and deadlines.

Many colleges and universities also offer scholarships specifically for adults who are returning to school. A visit to the college or university's Web site will provide a list of all the available scholarships.

•**Check out professional organizations.** Adults have the advantage when it comes to applying for scholarships and grants through professional and trade associations. Unlike the teens going off to college who have no idea what they are going to do, adult students usually know exactly why they're going back to school and can easily show the commitment that these groups look for.

Start with the local trade and professional associations in your area to see if they offer scholarships.

Examples: Members from the Kentucky Farm Bureau, an organization of farm families, are eligible to get a variety of grants. The San Diego Foundation offers several scholarships for adults.

Also look into national organizations.

Example: The American Association of University Women Educational Foundation offers a grant of $2,000 to $12,000* to college-educated women who want to advance or change their careers or reenter the workforce.

FILL OUT THE FAFSA

The only way for you to determine if you qualify for need-based aid from the institution that you'll be attending and/or for federal loans is to fill out the Free Application for Federal Student Aid (FAFSA), which schools use to determine a student's financial need. For more information, visit *www.fafsa.ed.gov*.

*Figures subject to change.

Almost everyone qualifies for some kind of federal loan, so it's really worth doing all the paperwork.

New: Federal guidelines are now making it easier to repay federal student loans.

Important: Federal student loans usually carry lower interest rates than those from private lenders, such as banks. And because they are guaranteed by the federal government, your credit rating won't be taken into consideration—a potential plus in these troubled times.

Note that the FAFSA now contains a question about whether the student is a "dislocated worker" (someone who has been laid off, for example), which may help you qualify for more aid money from your state.

MONEY FROM YOUR STATE

Your state may provide grants for state-sponsored retraining classes and other skill-building programs. States that have been hardest hit by the recession tend to have the most active and generous programs.

Example: In Michigan's displaced workers program, the participants are given up to $5,000 annually to cover their tuition and other costs.

Best sources: Go to *www.career.onestop.org*. Sponsored by the US Department of Labor, it has links to all of the state retraining programs and new information for workers looking for "reemployment." Also, to help unemployed adults who are returning to college, the Obama administration has created a Web site, *www.opportunity.gov*, which includes information about paying for college.

MONEY FROM YOUR EMPLOYER

Tuition assistance from your employer is a huge benefit for workers who qualify. Often the employee must show how the educational program will improve his/her job performance.

Examples: McDonald's and Starbucks offer generous tuition assistance to both part- and full-time employees.

"LIFE CREDIT"

The fewer classes you have to take, the less you'll pay in tuition. Schools routinely waive requirements for certain classes if you can show

that your previous professional background or life experience taught you material similar to the course's curriculum. An accountant seeking advanced training, for instance, might be able to skip basic finance courses.

There are several types of standardized exams, including the College Level Examination Program (CLEP), available through the College Board (*www.collegeboard.com*), which will test you on, and gives you credit for, knowledge that you already have. Schools don't use any set formula to assign such credit, so you need to work closely with the admissions officer to determine what's best for you.

The Secret to Finding A Job When "There Are No Jobs"

Richard Nelson Bolles, a leader in the career development field for more than 30 years. He is author of *What Color Is Your Parachute?*, the best-selling job-hunting book of all time (revised annually). His latest book is *The Job-Hunter's Survival Guide: How to Find Hope and Rewarding Work, Even When "There Are No Jobs"* (both published by Ten Speed). He lives in the San Francisco Bay Area. His Web site is *www.jobhuntersbible.com*.

Finding a job is difficult enough in this economy, but many job hunters reduce the odds of their success by using common job-search strategies that often fail. *Here's what doesn't work so well—and what does…*

COMMON STRATEGIES

Five popular job-search strategies that *do not* work for the majority of those who try them…

•**Mailing out résumés and submitting or posting résumés online.**

Odds of success: 7%.*

Problem: Employers receive huge numbers of unsolicited résumés. Virtually all of these are filed away without a second look.

*The "odds of success" percentages cited in this article are based on industry studies and other sources. They reflect the percentage of job hunters who eventually find work by pursuing the strategy.

Might work if: Your résumé is handed to an employer by someone the employer knows and trusts—particularly if this individual adds a personal recommendation.

• **Responding to ads in professional or trade journals.**

Odds of success: 7%.

Problem: Employers tend to place ads in these journals only for low-wage jobs and other positions that they have had trouble filling. Also, because most trade journals are national, jobs listed there often require relocation.

Might work if: You have a specific skill set that is difficult for employers to find and you are willing to relocate.

• **Responding to ads posted on Internet jobs sites.**

Odds of success: 10%.

Problem: Employers tend to post jobs on Internet job sites only as a last resort, because such ads tend to bring a flood of responses from many inappropriate or low-quality applicants. A significant percentage of jobs posted on employment Web sites are outright scams, and competition tends to be very fierce for the legitimate openings.

Might work if: Your field is information technology (IT). Attractive IT jobs often are advertised online because employers recognize that tech-savvy employees tend to use the Internet for everything.

• **Responding to ads running in the local newspapers.**

Odds of success: Between 5% and 24%, depending on your salary requirements.

Problem: Most employers consider newspaper classifieds an out-of-date way to find good applicants. Few bother to list attractive jobs there anymore.

Might work if: You're willing to work for close to minimum wage. Many low-paying jobs still are listed in local newspapers.

• **Working with an employment agency or search firm.**

Odds of success: Between 5% and 28%, depending on your salary requirements.

Problem: With the economy struggling, employers don't see the need to pay search firms to find qualified applicants—there are more than enough coming in to them. Also, there is little evidence that agencies do a particularly good job of finding work for clients.

Might work if: You are looking for a low-wage office position, such as a secretarial or clerical job.

BEST WAYS TO FIND WORK

Five job-hunting strategies that offer excellent chances for success, ordered from least to most successful...

• **Networking for leads.**

Odds of success: 33%.

Advantage: Employers love to hire based on personal recommendations from employees and trusted contacts—it vastly improves the odds that the applicant will be talented and suitable.

Limitation: The success of your networking depends on the size and quality of your network. Don't give up if at first no one you know has heard of a job. Continue to expand your network when you are unemployed by asking your contacts to put you in touch with their contacts...and remaining active in your community.

• **Knocking on doors unannounced at employers of interest.** Express an interest in the company or sector, and ask for five minutes of the boss's time.

Odds of success: 47%.

Advantage: It is more common than you might think to find an employer who is about to list an opening, and he/she might hire you without even interviewing other candidates. Small-business owners tend to be go-getters who respect the moxie of those who knock on doors and ask if there is a need for their skills and experience.

Limitation: You must anticipate that you likely will be rejected to your face. Also, this knock-on-doors strategy does not work well at large companies, where it's difficult to get a meeting with an executive without an appointment. Stick to smaller companies with 50 or fewer employees. Midafternoon is the best time to do this. Dress in attire appropriate to that business.

•**Calling companies of interest that are listed in the local Yellow Pages (or white pages business section).** As with the strategy above, ask for the owner, very briefly explain your background or relevant skills, then ask if he/she knows anyone in the industry in need of someone like you...or if you could come in and talk with him about the industry. To present yourself in the best light, review your skills before each call and remind yourself that you would be a productive, useful employee.

Odds of success: 69%.

Advantage: This is a great way to get to know businesses in your region. You could be hired for a job that has not yet been advertised.

Limitation: This is ineffective with large companies that have computerized phone systems and operators who make it difficult to reach those in charge.

•**Partnering with other job hunters.** Put together a group of job hunters who agree to keep an eye out for opportunities suitable for others in the group. Meet at least weekly. To build your group, team up with job hunters you know or go to job fairs to meet attendees who may want to join your group.

Odds of success: 70%.

Advantage: More eyes looking for opportunities can mean more opportunities coming your way. And working with a group makes it harder to slack off on the job search.

Limitation: This works best when members are looking for employment in fields that call for different skills and career goals, so they are not in competition for the same jobs.

•**Taking inventory of yourself,** then targeting the employers where you ought to be working. Spend at least a weekend considering which of all of your skills you most enjoy using...in which fields you would most enjoy putting those skills to work...which organizations have these jobs to offer...which people at those organizations have the power to hire you...and how best to approach them.

Odds of success: 86%.

Advantage: Job hunters who utilize this systematic process tend to appear more con-fident to employers, which makes them more appealing hires. They also are better able to explain why they would be an asset to the organization.

Limitation: It takes time to do this properly. The secret is to define your skills and the type of work you wish to do in as much detail as possible. In poor economies, many job hunters assume that they must cast a broad net and look for any available job. These people come off as desperate. The most successful job interviewees write a detailed inventory of what they have to offer an employer and analyze times when they were successful before they actually go to an interview.

The Secrets to Getting a Great Job If You're 50+

Linda Wiener, age issues expert at Monster.com and a consultant to AARP, the Conference Board and the Department of Labor on mature workforce issues. Wiener resides in Portland, Oregon. Her Web site is *www.exploringcareersinaging.com*.

For people who have not looked for a job in a long time, there are some big changes.

For one thing, the Internet's now replaced classified newspaper ads as the main place to find job listings. So, if your Internet skills are rusty, take a course to get up to speed. Your local community college, adult-education program, even the public library, may have free or low-cost workshops. *Here are some answers to other questions that you may have about looking for a job today...*

•**Assuming that I am Web-savvy, what's my first step in a 21st-century job hunt?** Businesses today are very choosy—hiring for specific jobs and looking for the employee who is a perfect fit. In this environment, it's important for any job seeker to take a hard look at him/herself. You must *know yourself* well to *sell yourself* as the best person for a position.

Your job hunt starts with self-assessment—taking an inventory of your skills, knowledge and personality traits.

Examples: Do you prefer to work alone or as part of a team? Do you thrive in a fast-paced office or in a calmer environment? What are your skills, and do you have the references, certifications or experience (even volunteer work) to prove it? Can you transfer those skills to another field?

•**What are the best tools for self-assessment?** Your local state-sponsored career center may offer free testing, career counseling, training referrals, job postings and other employment-related services. To look for a center near you, go to *www.careeronestop.org*, a US Department of Labor–sponsored career Internet site. *Also...*

•Some community colleges offer free career advice.

•Check out the list of free and fee-based interest surveys and skills-assessment tools at The Riley Guide (*www.rileyguide.com*), an excellent introduction to Internet job searches developed by a research librarian. (Go to *www.rileyguide. com/assess.html.*)

•Read a copy of Richard Nelson Bolles' book *What Color Is Your Parachute?* Updated annually, it is still one of the best books for discovering who you are and what you want. His companion Web site, *www.jobhuntersbible.com*, is a thorough introduction to online job-hunting techniques.

•**Once I have figured out what I want, where do I look for jobs?** Check the large online job boards, such as Monster.com and Careerbuilder.com, as well as sites that target specific industries. (The Riley Guide is an excellent starting place. Click on "Sites with Job Listings.") *Also...*

•Some Web sites cater to the needs and interests of older workers, so check out the listings at AARP.org, PrimeCB.com, RetirementJobs.com, YourEncore.com and Workforce50.com. Idealist. org, although not specifically for older workers, is also a good site.

•Investigate sites of local companies that interest you—information on employment may hide under "About Us" or "Company Information." Do not look only at companies with job openings posted. Target any organization that looks interesting, because many jobs—some say as many as 80%—are not listed. That's the so-called hidden job market.

•**What are some more 21st-century get-your-foot-in-the-door strategies?** To uncover those hidden jobs, you have to really pound the pavement. Go on informational interviews, where the goal is to get information on a field, find leads and expand your network. You are picking someone's brain, not asking for a job.

Start by asking for leads from friends, family, former coworkers, alumni offices and professional associations. Make a list of people who do the work that interests you, then contact them to ask for 20 minutes to get their advice and more referrals. Networking with insiders is also the best way to uncover part-time jobs, which are often not posted or advertised.

Exception: The public sector—local, state and federal government job listings—often include part-time options. Check *www.usajobs. gov* for federal listings or your local and state government Web sites.

•**How is the application process different these days?** Networking and getting personal referrals to hiring managers is still the fastest way to get hired, but if you do find a tempting job online, you will most likely apply for it online, too. It is critical that you use the language from the job posting in your application because computers scan applications for key terms, such as "excellent communication skills" or "proficient in *Microsoft Office.*" Job titles have changed, too, so use up-to-date terms. If you worked in personnel, today you would call that human resources.

Caution: Employers also scan for key words in résumés. Therefore, do not use italics, boldface, unusual fonts or other fancy formatting that might cause a computer to miss your key words.

•**Should I disguise my age or decades of experience on my résumé?** If an employer really cares about your age, there's little you can do to disguise it. Instead, focus on your strengths. Do include any former experience relevant to the position you are seeking regardless of how long ago it was, but leave off the dates of your college degrees if you graduated more than five years ago. Tailor the language in your résumé and cover letter to the job posting. And before you start contacting people, be sure that the recorded greeting messages for your cell-phone and home voice mail are professional. The same goes for any of your own e-mail addresses given to potential employers.

Note: You still need a hard (paper) copy of your résumé to leave behind at an interview (with a cover letter) if you are responding to a Web posting.

•**What about the job interview? Has that changed?** Be prepared for *behavioral interviews,* where you're asked questions such as "Tell me about a time when you participated in a team—what was your role?" or "Tell me about a time when you were juggling multiple projects—how did you handle them?"

To prepare for tough interview questions beforehand, Google "most difficult interview questions." You'll see toughies such as "Why should we hire you?" and "How are you different from the 19 other people who can do this job?" Practice the responses with a close friend who can give you objective feedback. (Monster.com offers job seekers virtual interviews at *http://resources.monster.com/tools.*)

•**How else can a 50-plus worker nail an interview?** Come ready with your own list of questions, such as "What qualifications does your ideal candidate have?" That gets to the heart of the perfect-fit question, and if you've done your research, you can craft an answer that puts you in the best light. Drop a comment about a class you took in the latest software in your industry. Also address worries about your retirement plans by asking, "Are you concerned that I might retire soon?" Reassure the interviewer that you love your work and are in it for a long run. Tell the interviewer that you intend to keep working for some time and have no plans to retire any time soon. Finally, don't forget to ask for the job!

•**So what hasn't changed?** You still have to write thank-you notes, by letter or e-mail, to everyone who helps you and to hiring managers or decision makers who interview you. And, be sure to ask permission before listing people as references.

Little Mistake That Can Cost You a Job

A single typo in your résumé may cost you a job. Forty percent of executives claimed that one mistake in a résumé or cover letter would cause them to turn down an applicant. Seventy-six percent said that two mistakes would stop them from hiring someone.

Self-defense: Proofread all job-related materials very carefully, including anything you post online.

Max Messmer, chairman, Accountemps, a specialized staffing firm that surveyed 150 senior executives from the nation's 1,000 largest companies, Menlo Park, California.

The Five Words *Never* To Say During a Job Interview

Paul Powers, EdD, a management psychologist located in Wellesley, Massachusetts, who has more than 25 years of experience in career counseling. He is also former chairman of the Massachusetts Board of Psychologists and was the original "answer man" for job seekers on the job search site Monster.com. He is author of *Winning Job Interviews* (Career). His Web site is *www.drpaulpowers.com.*

Job hunters greatly outnumber openings these days, so even a seemingly minor slip of the tongue can cut short your employment opportunities. *The five words that can undermine your job chances…*

•**Crisis.** Job applicants often trumpet their ability to respond calmly and intelligently to workplace challenges. Trouble is, when they use the word "crisis" to describe a past professional challenge, they send exactly the opposite message. Epidemics and hostage standoffs are crises—an employer's budget crunch or public relations headache is not. Calling an ordinary workplace situation a crisis just makes you seem like an alarmist—the sort of employee who will blow problems out of proportion and infect those around you with panic. You'll seem more poised and reliable if you instead use words such as "challenge" or "problem" to describe these situations.

• **People person.** Interviewers often cringe inside when applicants describe themselves as "people-oriented" or "a people person." This is like saying that your worst flaw is that you work too hard—it's such a cliché that it will make you seem uninteresting or evasive to an experienced interviewer. Worse, "I'm a people person" is so general and unverifiable that it tends to be offered up by applicants who have no real skills or accomplishments to discuss. Saying something similar could cause the interviewer to subconsciously associate you with this group of people even if you have an impressive résumé.

If interpersonal skills are an important part of what you have to offer, find a more specific, less clichéd way to convey this. You could identify your specialty as "conflict mediation," "coordinating teams" or "soothing upset customers." Cite specific examples of the times that you have used this skill successfully.

• **Can't.** Using negative words and phrases such as "can't," "there's no way" or "impossible" during an interview could make you seem like a negative person. Few qualities turn off potential employers faster than negativity. If you must tell an interviewer that what he/she wants is impossible or that you need a larger salary or budget than he is proposing, find a way to phrase this in a positive way.

Example: The interviewer says that the company is looking for someone to expand its Web site, but your experience tells you that the budget or time frame being discussed is insufficient. Rather than say, "It cannot be done," or "That's not going to work," you might say, "Let's discuss some of the options we would have for getting that done." Mention outsourcing certain functions or focusing initially on only the most important elements of the project.

• **Irregardless.** This is not really a word at all. The correct word is regardless. If the interviewer is a stickler for proper grammar, using this nonword may create the impression that you are ignorant. Another frequently misused word that could hurt your chances is "literally,"

which frequently is used by people who mean figuratively.

Example: "I was literally putting out fires all year." No, you weren't—unless you were a firefighter.

• **Fired.** Interviewers often ask applicants why they left their previous jobs. It's fine to say your position was eliminated in a workforce reduction or that you were laid off, but never say that you were "fired." Though you might consider "fired" and "laid off" synonymous, the former has a much more negative connotation—that you messed up—in most people's minds.

Turn What You Know Into Dough: Earn $1,000 A Month in Your Spare Time

Loral Langemeier, CEO of Live Out Loud, Inc., both a coaching and seminar company that has offices in Nevada and California. She regularly appears on the *Dr. Phil* TV show as a money expert and is author of many books on finance, including the best-seller *The Millionaire Maker* (McGraw-Hill) and, most recently, *Put More Cash in Your Pocket* (Harper). Her Web site is *www.live outloud.com.*

If you want more cash, consider starting a part-time business. Almost everyone has the skills and time required to launch a business that's capable of generating an extra $500 to $1,000 per month.

With a part-time business, the smart strategy is to get it up and running within a week or two for no more than a few hundred dollars. *How to do it…*

LOW-COST BUSINESS IDEAS

Identify skills that you already possess that could be turned into a service-oriented business. *Possibilities…*

• **Tutoring.** Tutor younger kids or help high school students prepare for their SATs or ACTs. Teachers, past teachers, professors and those with degrees from prestigious universities are particularly likely to attract clients.

- **Auto care/repair.** If you are handy with cars, offer auto-maintenance and basic repair services.

- **Computer.** Provide tech support to individuals or small businesses. Set up computer networks, solve problems, optimize computer performance or create and manage Web sites.

- **Foreign language.** If you're fluent in a foreign language, tutor those who want to learn it or students struggling with their foreign language classes.

- **Handyman.** Home maintenance and repair services always are in demand.

- **Music/acting.** Tight budgets are forcing many public schools to cut back on music and theater programs, creating openings for private tutors.

- **Photography.** Offer portrait or wedding photography services.

- **Sewing and alterations.** Alterations are on the rise as people choose to repair, not replace, clothing.

- **Sports.** Help promising young athletes to hone their abilities. Those who played a sport professionally or for a prestigious college program are most likely to attract clients.

- **Woodworking.** High-quality handcrafted wooden bowls and other carved kitchen items can fetch attractive prices in boutiques and at arts and crafts fairs.

If you do not have a particular skill that is likely to be in demand, there are service businesses that do not require extensive training or skills (though experience is, of course, helpful). *Possibilities include...*

- **In-home elder care**
- **Child care/day care**
- **Lawn and garden care**
- **Carpooling/driving services**
- **Pet walking/pet sitting**
- **House-sitting**
- **Housecleaning**

BUSINESSES TO AVOID

Certain businesses are best avoided by people seeking to earn extra cash with little risk...

- **Retail stores.** Retailing typically requires an expensive inventory, long hours, employ-

ees and leased commercial property. Retailers must compete with Internet sellers and massive chains.

- **Franchises.** Profitable franchises charge big up-front franchise fees that part-time business people typically cannot afford.

- **"New idea" businesses.** It takes lots of time and marketing dollars to convince consumers to spend their money on something that they have never spent it on before. The failure rate for such businesses is very high. More than 482,000 applications for US patents were filed in 2009—only a few of these will be successful. It is better to offer a service that people already understand.

SETTING PRICES

Contact companies that provide similar services in your region, and inquire about their rates without mentioning that you intend to enter the same business. Avoid the inclination to undercut the competition's prices. Offering the lowest price for a service creates the impression that your services are less valuable. It is better to charge comparable prices and explain why your services are superior.

Examples: Establish that your qualifications are more extensive...or offer a money-back guarantee.

Exception: Offer lower prices to customers who sign up for extended service packages. Committing customers to long-term arrangements can help beginning businesses build reliable cash flow. It also is a way to make your service seem like a bargain without creating the impression that it is low quality.

Example: Someone starting a part-time car-maintenance business could offer a discount package to customers who sign up for a full-year auto-maintenance program.

MARKETING YOUR BUSINESS

The most cost-effective marketing tool is word of mouth...

- **Visit local businesses that offer related but not overlapping services.** Tell the owners or managers of these businesses what your business does. Ask if you can post a flyer in their windows or leave a stack of flyers on the counter.

Examples: Someone starting a house-sitting or lawn-care business could contact real estate agents.

• **Consider sharing a storefront location.** Ask area businesses that are in some way related to your intended field if they have extra space that they are willing to sublet to you. This can be much cheaper than renting your own space, and you'll have an inside track on that existing business's customers.

Example: Someone starting up a sewing and alterations business could sublet space at a dry cleaner.

• **Contact organizations that work with your intended customer base.**

Example: If you intend to provide tutoring or music lessons to students, contact local schools and youth clubs.

• **Volunteer your services to nearby nonprofits.** It's a good way to make contacts and show off your skills.

• **Offer satisfied customers a discount on their next purchase if they refer someone** who also becomes a customer.

TAXES, LICENSES AND INSURANCE

Don't worry about taxes at first. New businesses typically have 90 days from the date they start taking in money to get tax payments squared away. It is better not to get bogged down in such details sooner than necessary, but do ask your accountant if you need to charge sales tax on any of your goods and/or services. Don't worry about hiring a lawyer or incorporating your business until your business is up and running.

A few details do need to be sorted out before your business gets going...

• **Contact your town or county offices to find out if you need any licenses or permits.**

• **Set up a separate checking account for business expenses and receipts.**

• **Ask your insurance agent about professional liability insurance,** particularly if your business involves anything that could cause injury or trigger a lawsuit.

• **Contact your auto insurance provider if you plan to use your personal vehicle for business.** Your existing policy is unlikely to cover business use.

Surprising Lessons From the Richest Man In Town

New York City–based W. Randall Jones, founder of *Worth* magazine. He spent two years traveling the US visiting 100 places in all 50 states to interview the wealthiest man or woman in each for his book *The Richest Man in Town* (Business Plus).

Some of the richest people around did not depend on the stock market (or an inheritance) to achieve their wealth. And often what they did went against the common wisdom.

W. Randall Jones, founder of *Worth* magazine, tracked down the richest men and women (*average net worth:* $3.5 billion) in 100 American cities and towns to find out how they achieved their financial success and to explore what the rest of us can do in these difficult times to benefit from their examples. *Among the surprising lessons...*

• **Don't set goals.** The conventional wisdom says that extensive career and business planning are crucial, but the richest man in town is more likely to believe that planning inhibits success. Most of these rich men and women don't plot a course that is more detailed than "get up each morning and do better than the day before."

• **What is wrong with goals and plans?** Too often, those who set them feel obliged to stick with them even when changing circumstances render the plans obsolete. Being ready to adapt to changing circumstances is a better policy.

Example: Jim Oelschlager, the richest man in Akron and founder of the investment company Oak Associates, Ltd., says that the only business plan he ever had was "answer the phone if it rang."

One day, a manager at his employer at the time, Firestone, asked him to manage its pension plan. This experience allowed him to create a series of successful mutual funds later on.

Despite the challenge of suffering multiple sclerosis, Oelschlager was able to take advantage of the best opportunities that came his way even when they were not what he expected. Over the years, Oak Associates has profitably expanded—and Oelschlager also started CyGem, an information technology company, and Oak Air airline charters. Oelschlager believes that if he had moved his company in the direction he wanted to go rather than the direction that client feedback led him, "we would have failed miserably."

• **Don't seek out glamour.** The best types of businesses for wealth creation tend to be those not generally considered very lucrative or glamorous.

Examples: James Haslam, the wealthiest man in Knoxville, Tennessee, and owner of Pilot Travel Centers, LLC, made his money in truck stops…Bruce Halle, the richest man in Scottsdale, Arizona, and founder of Discount Tire, made his by selling vehicle tires…David Green, the richest man in Oklahoma City and founder of Hobby Lobby Creative Centers, became a billionaire through an arts-and-crafts supply business.

The trouble with sectors that are associated with glamour and extreme wealth is that there already are many very intelligent people trying to make their fortunes there. Big money can be made in Hollywood…with computer technology…or in real estate—but those fields are so crowded with established players that the person who makes that money probably won't be you. It is better to find a sector where others see less potential…but where you have your greatest skills.

Example: Hartley Peavey, the wealthiest man in Meridian, Mississippi, and the founder of Peavey Electronics, loved playing music but realized that there were so many talented would-be musicians in the world that the odds were stacked against his finding success as one. Peavey was very good at building things, so he made his fortune by building instruments and amplifiers rather than playing guitar, which he also still enjoys.

• **Foster relationships in your off hours.** Due to the recent recession, how to spend off hours is the furthest thing from most of our minds these days. We are too worried about our careers to take much time away from business…and too worried about our depleted savings to treat acquaintances to fancy dinners.

The richest man in town knows that playing golf, tennis or poker…attending fund-raisers and parties…and going out to dinner are not just things to do for fun. Off-hour socializing is when networks are formed with other local business-people and trust is built with colleagues and potential clients.

Example: Dan Duncan, the chairman of the energy company Enterprise Products Partners and the richest man in Houston, says that socializing with other business-people is vital because "I want them to call me first when they want to do a deal."

• **Don't try to create WEALTH—try to create value.** Even when the economy is weak, potential customers still have needs. And they appreciate value, especially if they are spending far less than before. If a business can serve those needs and offer value in good times and bad, wealth should eventually follow.

The richest man in town typically did not set out to become fabulously wealthy. More often, he saw a problem that he could fix or a market that was poorly served and decided that he had a better solution.

Example: There were plenty of antivirus software programs on the market when John McAfee, the richest man in Rodeo, New Mexico, and founder of McAfee Software, unveiled his program in the 1980s. But while the other antivirus software designers tried to sell their products and worried about illegal copying, McAfee gave away his software for free so that it would benefit as many computer users as possible. McAfee's program soon dominated the market, and he made his fortune by selling upgrades.

Build Your Business in Bad Times—Without Slashing Prices

Jaynie L. Smith, president of Smart Advantage, Inc., a marketing/management consultancy based in Fort Lauderdale, Florida, *www.smartadvantage.com*. She is author of *Creating Competitive Advantage: Give Customers a Reason to Choose You Over Your Competition* (Broadway Business).

Business people often feel compelled to lower their prices when the economy struggles or risk losing their increasingly cost-conscious customers. Fortunately, most customers do not make their buying decisions based primarily on price, even during recessions. They make their decisions based on value. To thrive in times such as these, you must convince customers and prospects that your company offers the best value, even if you do charge a slightly higher price. *Here's how...*

• **Determine your competitive advantage.** Competitive advantage is something that you do better than your competition. It also must be something that customers and prospects value.

Helpful: Family businesses often trumpet the fact that they are family owned...and that they have been in business for many decades. Market research shows that these factors are not important in most purchasing decisions.

Exception: A long track record or family ownership might be valued by buyers in sectors known for fly-by-night operators, such as the Florida home-construction industry following a hurricane.

• **Prove your advantage.** So many companies claim to provide high-quality products, customer service and value that buyers tend to ignore these boasts. To gain customers' attention, you must prove it. The best way to do this is to present your business's advantage in a quantifiable, nonclichéd way. *Examples...*

• "96% of our customers become repeat customers."

• "Our 10-year, 100% satisfaction warranty is the longest and most comprehensive in the business."

• "Our technicians are on call 24 hours a day, 365 days a year."

• "99.8% of our products are still working properly five years after installation."

• "An industry-leading 98% of our deliveries are made on time."

• "Our products are made in the US. Our call center is located in the US."

• **Promote your competitive advantages in all your advertising**...on your packaging...on your Web site...even on the product itself.

Example: A surgical-glove maker lists its gloves' technological advantages on the back of the gloves themselves, to increase the odds that doctors and nurses will notice the difference and complain if hospital purchasing managers switch brands.

If you have more than one type of customer, each might have a very different priority and respond to a different competitive advantage.

Example: A siding company might promote "install times 25% shorter than our leading competitors" when selling to contractors ...but change the message to "broadest range of colors—150 to choose from" when selling directly to home owners.

• **Train all employees well.** Make sure that every employee in the company understands that maintaining the company's competitive advantage is a part of his/her job. You will lose all credibility with your customers if you claim an advantage, then fail to deliver it.

Smart Management in Tough Times

If you cannot give employees more money and want to motivate them, focus on three psychological needs—a desire for autonomy, feeling of competence and sense of belonging to the team. This means giving workers more flexibility with doing their jobs...telling them that they are doing well regularly, not just during performance reviews...and encouraging them to work together as team members instead of competing with one another.

Paul P. Baard, PhD, a professor of communication and management and an organizational psychologist, Fordham University Graduate School of Business, New York City.

You Can Get a Raise Even in This Economy... Here's How

Mary Jeanne Vincent, a career expert and strategist located in Monterey, California, *www.careercoachmjv. com*. She managed career centers for Drake Beam Morin, the world's largest outplacement company, before starting her own firm. Her column, "Career Talk," appears in the *Monterey County Herald*.

Many employees won't ask for raises this year, and many job seekers will simply accept any salary they are offered. However, even in this economy, many people can obtain raises or negotiate salaries above an initial offer. *Here's how...*

DETERMINE YOUR VALUE

At Yahoo, the "Calculate Your Salary" tool provides reasonable estimates of how much employees in particular kinds of jobs earn (Log on to *www.hotjobs.yahoo.com/salary*). Also, ask the friendly contacts in your sector what they would consider an appropriate salary given the economy. Hard work and competence are not enough to secure a raise or higher starting salary during a difficult recession. Your employer must believe that you create value in a unique way and that you could not be easily replaced.

Various examples of what to stress: Your productivity or monthly sales are significantly and demonstrably higher than the company average...you have repeatedly found ways to cut corporate expenses...you have the skills and background to fill multiple roles for the company, providing much needed flexibility in times of layoffs...you have close relationships with important clients or potential clients in the sector.

EASE INTO SALARY TALK

•**Seeking a raise.** You risk appearing out of touch with today's reality and insensitive to your company's situation if you come right out and ask for a raise. Instead, ask your boss for an opportunity to discuss your recent job performance and your goals. Schedule this discussion for shortly after you accomplish something that clearly brings value to the company. During this meeting, discuss how you improve the company's bottom line. Prepare one sheet summarizing all your major accomplishments. Segue into a discussion of your compensation.

•**Applying for a new job.** Discuss salary after you've been offered the job. Companies use the question, "What are your salary needs?" to weed out those who ask for too much and those who ask for too little. Employers often assume applicants are underqualified when they request significantly less than expected. Instead, say, "I'm sure we can agree on salary if I'm the right person for the position. First, I would like to discuss the value I can bring to this company."

SUGGEST ALTERNATIVES

In case you are told that a raise or higher starting salary is impossible in this year, consider how your employer could reward you without stretching the budget. *Options...*

•**Negotiate a bonus to be paid in the company's next fiscal year,** when there might be more room in the budget.

•**Agree on a raise that begins at a predetermined date in the future,** assuming performance goals are met.

•**Request extra vacation time...**a flexible work schedule...or the right to telecommute.

•**Ask for a company cell phone...**laptop ...car...or a bigger office.

•**Obtain a better job title** or assignments.

Helpful: If your company is struggling, do not wait for your boss to tell you that a raise isn't possible. Explain at the start of your compensation conversation that you're willing to explore other forms of compensation, which sends the message that you are looking out for the company's interests during these difficult times.

Mediation Magic

To mediate a dispute, first set ground rules for the debate—no bullying and no leaving until the conflict gets resolved. Let both sides express their views in front of each other. Don't play the detective or dig for details, which could compromise your objectivity. Use nonverbal cues, such as nodding your head, to communicate your objectivity and that you are actively listening to both sides. Finally, find the common ground, or try to establish a compromise that meets the needs of both sides.

Psychology Today, 115 E. 23rd St., New York City 10010, *www.psychologytoday.com.*

It's True! Web Surfing *Increases* Productivity At Work

Employees who browse the Internet for fun at work are nearly 10% more productive than those who do not, as long as the time they spend browsing is less than 20% of the total time in the office. Taking a short break lets the mind rest and leads to higher overall concentration.

Study of 300 workers by researchers at The University of Melbourne, Victoria, Australia.

Study Says Taking an Exercise Break *Improves* Performance

Exercise during workdays helps to boost productivity.

Recent study: More than 70% of employees who exercised before work or during lunch reported improvements in time management …workload management…ability to deal with workday stressors…and mental and interpersonal performance compared with days they did not exercise. They also were less stressed.

Helpful: Start a lunchtime walking group at work.

Jo Coulson, PhD, research associate, department of exercise, nutrition and health sciences at University of Bristol, UK. Her study results were published in the *International Journal of Workplace Health Management.*

How to Protect Your Reputation If You're Bad-Mouthed on the Internet

Nino Kader, president of International Reputation Management, a public relations and marketing firm based in Washington, DC, *www.irm360.com.* He previously was a management consultant and company spokesperson for BearingPoint (formerly KPMG Consulting).

A lawyer in Washington, DC, got into an argument on the street. The person he argued with then put a one-sided account of the incident on his blog. Four years later, this blog posting still was one of the first things potential clients found when they searched this lawyer's name on Google.com, costing the lawyer business.

You might laugh off what people write on the Internet—but others won't. Recruiters and employers search the Internet to learn more about applicants and employees. Potential clients search online for reviews of products and services before buying.

Someone with a grudge could slander you on his/her blog…a rival for promotion in your company could create a fake Facebook page for you to make it appear as if you have a wild personal life…a dissatisfied customer (or competitor posing as a dissatisfied customer) could bad-mouth your company on a product-review Web site. *What to do…*

EXPLORE YOUR ONLINE REPUTATION

• **Use Google.com to conduct an Internet search of your own name.** Put your name in quotation marks, and search any alternate versions that you use as well.

Examples: Search "John Smith," but also "Johnny Smith"…"John A. Smith" and "J.A. Smith" if you use these.

•**Search the name of your business and your main products,** too, if applicable.

The first two pages of Google listings that pop up for your name are what matter most. So few people use the search engines other than Google…and most Google users do not explore beyond the second page of listings.

•**Set up a Google Alert (*www.google.com/ alerts*) for your name (in quotation marks).** You'll receive e-mails whenever new Internet postings that include your name appear. This is a free service.

FIX PROBLEMS

If there is false information about you online, e-mail the Webmaster (or blogger) of the site on which these falsehoods appear. (The Webmaster usually is listed on the bottom of the Web page.) Provide proof that the information is incorrect, if possible, and ask to have it removed.

If the Webmaster or blogger refuses to remove negative information, ask if he/she will add your response to the posting. This written response should be calm and well-reasoned, not angry.

Example: "My company does stand behind its products. Mr. Jones was not allowed to return his purchase because it had been chewed up by his dog, something he failed to mention in his post."

BURY PROBLEMS THAT CAN'T BE FIXED

Posting positive and/or neutral information about yourself on the Internet can help push any unfixable negative postings much further down in the Google listings—ideally off of the first two pages. *Some options…*

•**Develop pages for yourself on the free professional networking Internet sites,** such as LinkedIn.com, Facebook.com and Naymz. com. A recent Google feature also allows you to create a personal profile page (*http://google. com/profiles*).

•**Develop a Web page using your name as the domain name.** Domain-hosting companies, such as GoDaddy.com and Hostway. com, can help you register a domain name and set up a simple Web page for as little as $10 per year.* Sign up for at least two years—Google ranks sites higher when they control their domain names for more than one year. If you don't intend on using this Web site for commercial purposes, select an ".org" domain rather than a ".com"—Google tends to rank the ".org" sites higher. (You do not have to be a not-for-profit to purchase an ".org" domain.) If you have a common name, you might have to add a middle initial, a middle name or a dash between your first and last name to find an available domain. Post some biographical information on this site.

•**Start a blog.** Include your name in the blog's name. Blogger (*www.blogger.com*) can help you set up a free blog in just a few minutes. Post to the blog at least once every few weeks, and do not decrease the frequency of posts or your blog will fall in Google's rankings. Add a link on your blog to your Web site and to other blogs that cover similar topics—it will help your blog's ranking if those sites and blogs also link back to you.

•**Get your name into press releases,** positive news stories and positive blog postings on other people's blogs.

Example: Send e-mails to bloggers who cover your area of expertise, and ask if they have any interest in interviewing you for their sites.

SHARED NAMES

If you have a common name, most of the postings on Internet sites that mention your name will have nothing to do with you. This should not be a problem if it is obvious that these postings refer to someone else. If, however, someone with a problematic online reputation shares not just your name but also your profession or your hometown, his reputation could be confused with yours. *If so…*

•**Create a LinkedIn.com page or Web site** that describes who you are in a way that clearly differentiates you from this person. If possible, include a photograph.

*Price subject to change.

• **Consider using another version of your name,** perhaps one that includes your middle initial or middle name.

Why Stuffing Anger at Work Can Be Deadly

Holding in anger at work doubles heart attack risk.

Recent finding: Men who did not speak up when they felt unfairly treated on the job were five times more likely to have a heart attack than men who vented their frustration.

Constanze Leineweber, PhD, psychologist, Stress Research Institute, Stockholm University, Sweden, and leader of a study of 2,755 employed men, published in *Journal of Epidemiology and Community Health.*

Tricks to Keep from Dozing Off at the Wrong Time

Marjory Abrams, president of Boardroom, Inc., 281 Tresser Blvd., Stamford, Connecticut 06901.

No matter how much sleep I get at night, it sometimes is difficult for me to stay awake and alert during long meetings, lectures, movies and the like. It's not a very nice way to spend "date night" with my husband, and it's embarrassing when I struggle to keep my eyes open at work.

Staying alert on the job would seem especially critical for private investigators and not so easy to do during hours-long surveillance in the middle of the night. Vito Colucci, Jr., who has handled many high-profile cases in Connecticut, says that you cannot relax even for a minute during surveillance activities. To stay awake, he sits forward in his seat rather than leaning back. He may crack open a car window while waiting for someone to leave a building. (If you are at a meeting or social event, you can ask to have a window opened.) Sometimes he throws water on his face—you could excuse yourself to do the same in the restroom. Colucci also stays alert by observing hairstyles, clothing, architectural features and other details around him. With five children (now all adults), he has attended his fair share of school graduations, recitals and other activities that did not always keep him enthralled. To keep from dozing off, he would observe the people around him and make up stories about them.

Air-traffic controllers also must be constantly vigilant. Denise Spencer, a controller at the Seattle Air Route Traffic Control Center, finds that physical activity helps. She stands up at her station, drums her fingers (or a pen) on the counter, taps her feet. When air traffic is light, she may work on her posture. Sitting up straight instead of slouching works both the mind and the body, she says. Looking up weather for random airports helps to keep her mind engaged. She also stays physically active outside the job. Her three children keep her on the go, and she exercises regularly.

One friend doodles at meetings to stay alert. A recent study from the University of Plymouth in England found that people who doodled while listening to a tape had 29% better recall than the other participants, on average. Researchers theorize that doodling can keep you from daydreaming while not distracting you from the main activity. Unfortunately, my friend was reprimanded by her supervisor, who thought that the doodling distracted other people. Instead of doodling, another friend makes lists during boring meetings. Though his coworkers may think he is taking notes (sometimes he does that, too), he actually is listing top baseball scorers, his favorite bands, etc., while still listening to the discussion.

Five Simple Ways to Make Work More Fun!

Filomena D. Warihay, PhD, founder and CEO of Take Charge Consultants, Inc., located in Coatesville, Pennsylvania, which provides comprehensive organizational planning and leadership development services. She is also author of *Joy Rules! 30 Lessons to Help Leaders Harness Heart Power at Work* (available through *www.takechargeinc.com*).

Many of us are feeling stressed out, overworked and so underappreciated in today's "do more with less" workplace. A difficult economy means that more than ever, we need the relief that a joyful environment can bring—and a happy workplace is good for business.

When work is fun, creativity is unleashed… cooperation and collaboration are enhanced… and productivity soars. In counseling executives for more than 33 years, I have found that companies where spirits are high get consistently better bottom-line results. *Here's how to bring more joy to the workplace…*

1. Smile more. Studies have indicated that smiling causes changes in the brain and blood that not only make you feel happy but also create positive feelings in others.

2. Use enthusiastic language. Crisp, zesty words, including "Great"…"Wow"…"I love it!" liven things up.

3. Don't wait to celebrate. Trying to meet a specific target or complete a project? Mark small gains along the way by rewarding your team with a thank-you note, small gift or pizza lunch.

4. Brag. When your team does well, broadcast the news in a memo (send a copy to the boss), an item in the company newsletter or an article in a professional journal. Develop offbeat symbols of recognition, such as the 400-pound gorilla award (stuffed gorilla) for overcoming seemingly insurmountable obstacles…or a painter's hat with a star on it for a star team member.

5. Promote silliness. Enliven meetings or team-building activities by bringing in Silly Putty, Koosh Balls, little puzzles and tiny Slinkies to encourage out-of-the-box thinking. Five minutes of play can raise spirits and performance.

Get More Comfortable at Your Desk

If you are at your desk for a large part of the day, you might as well get comfortable. *Here's how…*

• **Set the top of your computer monitor just above eye level,** about an arm's length away, to limit eyestrain.

• **Tilt your keyboard away, not toward you**—angling it toward you bends your wrists back, leading to carpal tunnel syndrome and tendonitis.

• **Set your keyboard height at 24 to 25 inches, also to limit wrist strain**—do not put the keyboard on top of your desk, which usually is 29 inches high.

• **Minimize overhead lighting to reduce glare and eyestrain.** Use lamps that throw light only where you need it instead.

• **Use an angled footrest,** which will encourage you to lean back in your chair for better back support.

Alan Hedge, PhD, director, Human Factors and Ergonomics Laboratory, and professor of ergonomics, Cornell University, Ithaca, New York.

20

Self-Defense Savvy

Could Terrorists Be on Your Plane? The Safest Airlines and Other Ways To Protect Yourself

The attempted bombing of Northwest Airlines Flight 253 on Christmas Day 2009 once again turned Americans' attention to air terrorism. Per mile traveled, flying still is safer than driving, but the dangers of terrorism are real. *Here's what air travelers can do to reduce the odds that they will become victims...*

● **Choose your airline carefully when flying overseas.** It isn't just US citizens who often are targeted by terrorists—it's US airlines and flights headed to the US. All four planes involved in the 9/11 attacks belonged to US air carriers...the Christmas bomb attempt was on a Northwest Airlines flight...and the 2001 shoe bomber was aboard an American Airlines flight. British, French, Russian, South Korean and Indian flights occasionally are selected by terrorists as well.

To reduce your odds of falling victim to a terrorist attack on an international flight, favor airlines that are not typically targeted by terrorists...and that are based in countries that seem unlikely to be singled out for political reasons. These include Germany's Lufthansa, Australia's Qantas and Japan's ANA (All Nippon Airways) and Japan Airlines.

Caution: The risk for terrorist attack currently is greatest on flights from foreign countries to the US. These flights offer terrorists a way to target American victims without having to evade US airport security, which is considered

Mary Schiavo, Inspector General of the US Department of Transportation from 1990 to 1996. Her 1997 book, *Flying Blind, Flying Safe*, highlighted problems with America's aviation security prior to 9/11. Schiavo is a licensed pilot and a former professor of aviation at Ohio State University. She currently heads the aviation litigation team for Motley Rice, a law firm based in New York City and Charleston, South Carolina.

to be among the tightest in the world in the wake of 9/11.

• **Choose flights on smaller aircraft when possible.** Terrorists prefer to target large airplanes. The biggest planes flying now include the Boeing 747, 757, 767 and 777 and most Airbus models. They offer many hundreds of potential victims. Big planes also have much larger fuel tanks than smaller planes, making them potentially more damaging to targets on the ground in 9/11-style attacks.

It is possible to make most flights of 1,000 miles or less on relatively small planes. More than half of all domestic flights in the US now are on regional jets built by Bombardier (which have just 50 to 100 seats) or Embraer (37 to 122 seats). Flying these smaller planes on longer flights requires making a connection.

• **Lean toward small US airports rather than large ones.** Security was very poor at some small American airports prior to 9/11, but that's no longer the case. Security now is much tighter at all domestic airports. In fact, security can be tighter at smaller airports because security personnel at these facilities often have more time to screen each passenger and examine each bag.

• **Report any suspicious activity to the crew.** Suspicious activity by fellow passengers may include individuals spending long periods of time in the lavatory…congregating near the cockpit…having quiet gatherings among themselves…taking an inordinate interest in the flight crew…and/or possessing any suspicious items.

• **Reserve a seat near one of the plane's exits…but not necessarily a wing exit.** It's almost always safest to be seated near an exit in an emergency—passengers near exits get out first. If there is a terrorist with a bomb onboard, however, passengers in the seats near wing exits might be at increased risk. Terrorists generally try to detonate bombs near aircrafts' fuel tanks, some of which are located in the wings. Naturally, it's safer to be farther from the bomb.

Note: Passengers seated close to the wings have the greatest responsibility to be on the alert for suspicious activity by fellow passengers seated near them.

• **Avoid traveling to, from or through all countries that are not in compliance with the International Civil Aviation Organization's safety standards.** On the Internet site of the US State Department (*http://travel.state. gov*), select "International Travel," choose the country, then click "Aviation Safety Oversight" to find out if there is a potential problem.

Example: The US Department of Homeland Security's Transportation Security Administration has warned that it cannot assess the security of airports in Albania, Azerbaijan and Venezuela, among others.

• **Exercise the greatest caution when there has not been a recent terrorist attack.** Most travelers become cautious right after an attack, but history tells us that terrorists wait months, or even years, between attacks on airliners in the hope that security personnel and travelers will let down their guard.

Strategies to Save Your Life—from Veterans of The NYPD and FBI

William F. McCarthy, PhD, president of Threat Research, Inc., an international security-management consulting company in Alexandria, Virginia. He is a 21-year veteran of the New York City Police Department (NYPD) and served as commanding officer of the NYPD Bomb Squad, the largest civilian bomb unit in the US. His Web site is *www.threatresearchinc.com.*

Robert C. Quigley, executive vice president of Threat Research, Inc. He is a 28-year veteran of the FBI and served as the chief of the FBI Bomb Data Center, where he represented the US in an international network of bomb experts. He is also a member of the Association of Threat Assessment Professionals.

Mass-shooting incidents, while a rare occurrence, have increased over the past decade since the infamous Columbine High School shooting back in 1999. In November of 2009, at Fort Hood, an army psychiatrist opened fire, killing 13 people and wounding 30 others. And in August 2010, a man shot and killed eight people, as well as himself, at a beer distributor in Connecticut.

Studies by law enforcement agencies have shown a marked change in how mass shootings typically unfold, notably the movement of the shooter within and between locations, engaging in indiscriminate deadly violence to innocent bystanders. This scenario, whether a criminal or terrorist undertaking, has been labeled the active shooter phenomenon. Typically, the shooter is willing to die.

NEW POLICE RESPONSE

The traditional police response to mass-shooting incidents had been one of containment—establishing the perimeter, possible negotiation and possible forcible entry by highly trained Special Weapons and Tactics (SWAT) personnel. But this specific response has been proved ineffective in dealing with a "hit and run" attack on large numbers of people in multiple locations.

A new law-enforcement response has been developed that focuses on confronting the active shooter(s). First responders are currently trained to go directly after the shooters, temporarily bypassing injured victims. This aggressive police response places survivors at additional risk during the assault.

HOW TO PROTECT YOURSELF

The nature of these shootings requires us all to...

•**Be aware.** First and foremost, the most effective deterrent to crime and terrorism is substantial awareness of your environment. Distracted people are the most vulnerable. Be aware of your surroundings, noting anything out of the ordinary. Pay close attention to your senses.

•**Take action.** If something seems unusual and suspicious, move to a safer area (for example, one with better lighting, more people, visible security, clearly signed exits). If you hear the sound of gunfire, try to sense its direction and specific location. If you can safely exit the area in the opposite direction, do it.

•**Take cover.** If exiting a threatened area is impossible, look for a nearby "safe room" with a substantial door that locks. Place large items against the door for additional protection, and take cover low behind furniture and cabinets. If no safe room is accessible, take cover behind a substantial barrier, such as a concrete wall, steel elevator or escalator or a large plant container.

•**Call for help.** Call 911 or another emergency number. Report your location, the nature of the shooting incident, the number of persons at your location and whether any are injured. Try to maintain contact with authorities so that you can be updated on any actions that law enforcement is taking.

•**Remain hidden.** It is critical to remember that you are in a chaotic, violent environment, where any rapid or unusual movement may place you in a shooter's line of fire or crossfire with police. Stay in a hidden, protected posture until the police declare an end to the incident.

•**Do not open doors or leave your hiding place until you are sure it is safe to do so.** You must be suspicious of any requests to open your security perimeter—these could be coming from the shooter.

•**Help others.** In today's environment, the injured typically will not be tended to until the shooter is captured or killed. So it is important that you try to assist any injured people within your zone of safety.

Crime Is Up: How to Be Your Own Bodyguard

Irene van der Zande, cofounder, executive director and instructor at Kidpower Teenpower Fullpower International, a not-for-profit organization that has taught personal safety and self-defense techniques to children, adults and seniors since 1989, Santa Cruz, California. For more, go to *www.kidpower.org*.

F ace-to-face crimes, including muggings and assaults, are up an average of 33% nationally in this shaky economy. We all need to become our own bodyguards when we're out and about. Most of us know the basic safety advice, such as always being aware of our surroundings. *Here are more tactics to stay safe when you're out in public...*

• **Program your cell phone with the local police number on speed dial in case there's trouble.** Police have told me that this often yields a faster officer response than 911 because a 911 operator has to route the call to a police officer. Check with your local police department to find out which would be faster in your region.

• **Always lock your car.** This seems like a no-brainer, but you would be surprised at how many people forget to do it. Lock your car even if you're just sitting in it for a few moments in a parking lot before you drive off.

• **Carry mugger's money if you are in a high-risk location,** such as a bad neighborhood or a tourist spot in a foreign country. Keep a wallet with $20 to $50 in small bills that's easily accessed, separate from all your other valuables.

• **Press the panic button on your car key to set off the car alarm if someone frightens you.** Many alarms can be triggered from at least 45 feet away, sometimes 100 feet or more. The very loud noise can deter would-be attackers.

• **Place your valuables down and move away if you are asked to give up your wallet or purse.** This increases the distance between you and the assailant.

• **Yell orders if you feel your life is being threatened.** If you give up your valuables, but the person says, "You're coming with me," or starts to attack or pull you, yell clear messages, such as, "Stop," and "Leave me alone," to the attacker. Then, if there are others around, yell, "Call the police," or "Call 911." Don't yell, "Help." The word "help" makes people afraid for their own safety and unsure of what to do.

Example: Late one night, an elderly woman's car broke down in a bad neighborhood. While she was waiting for the tow service, five young men got out of their cars and started threatening her. She screamed to a woman she saw, "Call the police." She then yelled at her attackers, "Stop right there! Get back in

your cars and leave. The police are on their way." The men took off.

• **Know two easy moves that target the most vulnerable spots on the body** in case you must physically defend yourself. *Yelling, "No!" while you perform these moves helps give you more power...*

• The Eye Strike. Squeeze your fingers together (like a bird's beak), and jab them hard into the attacker's eyes. You also can claw your fingers like a rake across the eyes.

• The Groin Strike. Stand with your feet apart, and lift up your knee so that your thigh strikes between the attacker's legs and your knee jabs into his groin.

These moves are not meant to disarm or overpower an attacker, which is difficult to do. You just want to buy yourself enough time to break away from his grasp. If you can manage to get a few feet away from him—all the while screaming—chances are high that he will flee to avoid being caught rather than chase you.

How to Deal with "Phony Cops"

Lt. Sean Cooney, public information officer, Stamford Police Department, Stamford, Connecticut.

Con artists who impersonate police officers on the highway can trick drivers into pulling over on the side of the road to be robbed or assaulted. Most vulnerable are drivers traveling alone, especially women, at night.

Self-defense: Be very suspicious if you have done nothing wrong (you are not speeding, your car's headlights and tail lights are working)...and if the car that pulls you over is unmarked or you can see that it is marked but in dilapidated condition. *Then, if suspicious...*

• **Call 911 or the local police number using your cell phone,** tell them where you are and ask if they have a patrol car in that area. Stay on the phone until another officer arrives.

• **Put on your flashers or turn signal—then drive at a reasonable speed** (avoid looking like you're trying to get away) to a gas station, restaurant or other lit, populated area.

●**Lock all your doors, and keep them locked.**

●**After you have stopped, roll down your window just enough to talk and show your license and registration** but not enough to allow anyone entry to the car.

●**Ask the police officer for his/her photo identification and badge** before providing your own information or following any of his instructions.

●**Ask for a backup officer in a marked car to be sent to the scene.** An imposter will almost always leave at this point.

●**If the "officer" refuses or misbehaves at this point, drive on,** telling the "officer" that if he wants to go ahead and lead you to the police station you will follow.

Why You Should Always Keep a Baby Photo In Your Wallet...

A baby picture can protect your wallet. In a recent study, 88% of people who found wallets with pictures of a smiling baby returned them...compared with 53% of people who found wallets with a photo of a cute puppy...48%, a happy family...and 28%, a contented elderly couple.

Richard Wiseman, PhD, professor, psychology department, University of Hertfordshire, UK, and leader of a study in which 240 wallets were planted on the streets of Edinburgh.

Wait! Before You Open That E-Card...

Creators of computer viruses and other malicious programs use electronic greeting cards (e-cards) to infect recipients' computers.

Danger: Reading an infected e-card could install malicious software on your computer.

Best: Never open an e-card unless it is from a named person you know. Malicious e-cards usually are marked as coming from an unnamed person, such as "a friend" or "secret admirer." Don't open any e-card from a stranger or one that contains a spelling or grammatical mistake in the subject line.

Internet ScamBusters, Boone, North Carolina, *www. scambusters.org.*

What *Never* to Say on Facebook...MySpace...or LinkedIn

Rob Douglas, an information security consultant located in Steamboat Springs, Colorado, and the editor of IdentityTheft.info. He served as a consultant for the Federal Trade Commission on Operation Detect Pretext, a sting designed to catch information thieves. He previously was a private detective in Washington, DC.

Many users of social-networking Web sites unknowingly put themselves at risk. The Web sites such as Facebook, MySpace, LinkedIn and Twitter promote the impression that we are chatting with only our trusted friends, family members, colleagues— but there could be identity thieves, burglars or stalkers taking note. *Here's what not to reveal on social-networking sites...*

●**Addresses and birth dates.** Disclosing your home address or your place or date of birth could make you a target of an identity thief. Your home address even could attract a burglar or stalker to your home. If you are throwing a party and need to provide directions to your home, do this through e-mails that are sent directly to invitees, not through these Web sites.

If a social-networking Web site requires that you include your address or birth date in your profile, supply slightly inaccurate information.

●**Year of graduation from high school or college.** Knowing graduation dates helps scammers pretend to be former classmates, a common way to win victims' trust. Also, potential employers could use your graduation date to estimate your age, then reject you if they consider you too old. This violates age discrimination laws but would be almost impossible to prove.

• **Business contacts.** Professional networking Web sites, such as LinkedIn, typically let people on your contact list see the names and IDs of everyone else on your list. An unscrupulous competitor, a dissatisfied customer or a former employee could send damaging messages about you to everyone on the list. Or a competitor could target your clients if they are among your contacts.

Helpful: LinkedIn allows users to block access to their contact lists. Click "Account & Settings," then "Connections Browse" and select "No, hide my connections list."

Also, look over your contact list every six months, and remove anyone who you wouldn't want knowing the details of your personal or professional life…and anyone who you are not 100% certain is who he claims to be.

• **Mother's maiden name.** Web sites and financial companies often use your mother's maiden name to confirm your identity, so it's prudent to keep that name as confidential as possible.

• **Avoid discussing current or former pets by name on social-networking Web sites as well.** Pet names are another common security question.

• **Your plans for travel and schedules of groups you belong to.** If you mention the dates of an upcoming vacation on a social-networking Web site…or that you've joined a book group that meets every Wednesday at 7:00 pm, you might unwittingly have told a burglar when your home will be vacant…or made it easier for a stalker to follow you.

Helpful: If you post your travel plans on a social-networking site, at least add a sentence suggesting someone else will be in the home…or that the property is well-secured.

Example: "I found a great dog-sitter, and I'm showing him how to use our new alarm system this afternoon."

• **Your valuables.** Do not discuss your expensive art, antiques or jewelry. It could make you a target for a burglar.

• **The name of your doctor, dentist or other health-care providers.** If a scammer learns where you receive medical treatment, he might attempt to obtain your insurance information. This could all be sold to someone who lacks health insurance, who would then attempt to pose as you to obtain treatment.

How to Check Up On *Anyone*: Inside Secrets of a Private Investigator

Vito Colucci, Jr., who has run Colucci Investigations in Stamford, Connecticut, for the past 21 years. He is a former member of the Stamford Police Department, where he worked as a narcotics detective and undercover organized crime investigator. He helped uncover organized crime ties within his own department. He is author of *Inside the Private Eyes of a PI* (Courtland House). His Web site is *www.coluccipi.com.*

A spouse is behaving oddly—is he having an affair? The woman taking care of your aging parent seems honest—but is she? An old friend has disappeared from your life—whatever happened to him?

Private investigators often are hired to answer these questions, but usually it's possible to answer them on your own. *Here, Vito Colucci, Jr., a leading PI, shares his secrets…*

IS MY PARTNER CHEATING?

• **Common warning signs that a partner is having an affair…**

• Suddenly working lots of overtime, particularly in the evenings.

• Hiding cell-phone bills, perhaps by claiming that an employer wants them sent directly to the office.

• Suddenly taking greater interest in physical appearance, perhaps by exercising or buying new clothes.

• Picking fights in the evenings, then storming off for hours.

- Frequently closing off Internet sites when his/her partner approaches.

These are just warning signs. *To find out if your spouse is having an affair...*

- **Watch the money.** Look for receipts in pockets, wallets, purses or hidden in drawers. Read credit card and checking account statements. Do your partner's purchases indicate that he/she is eating in romantic restaurants... checking into hotels...or shopping at jewelry stores? Is he making large cash withdrawals?

- **Follow Internet activity.** A software program such as Spector Pro ($99.95,* 888-598-2788, *www.spectorsoft.com*) tracks everything your partner does on the family computer. Is he visiting dating Internet sites...sending intimate e-mails...reserving rooms in hotels... or shopping for romantic gifts online? These programs also can be used to monitor your children's Internet usage.

Warning: You have a legal right to install surveillance software on a shared family computer, but not on a partner's individual computer or a laptop owned by your partner's employer.

- **Turn your partner's BlackBerry or Windows Mobile smartphone into a tracking device.** Brickhouse Security's Executrac Mobile GPS Tracker software lets you use a computer to track where your partner (or teenager or employee) goes ($29.95 plus $19.95 per month, 800-654-7966, *www.brickhousesecurity.com*). If your partner does not have a smartphone or BlackBerry, you could provide one as a gift.

Free alternative: Automatic highway toll-payment systems, such as E-ZPass and Fas-Trak, provide monthly or quarterly activity reports. Write down where your partner claims to be at given times, then compare with the toll reports.

- **Confirm location claims.** If you doubt your partner's claim that he/she is on a business trip or working late at the office, phone that location—not your partner's cell phone—and ask for your partner. If your partner is there, explain that you were unable to get through to his cell phone and provide a legitimate reason for calling.

*Prices subject to change.

Example: "Did I leave my credit card in your car? It's not in my wallet."

CAN I TRUST THIS PERSON TO WORK IN MY HOME?

Whether you are hiring a housekeeper, a nanny for your kids or a caregiver for your aging parent, you want someone you can trust.

- **Vet the applicant's references, not just the applicant.** Some dishonest applicants ask friends or family members to pose as former employers and provide glowing reviews when new employers call. To combat this, don't ask references just for their opinions of the applicant—also ask questions that get at the details of the working relationship. Compare the references' answers with what the applicant told you.

Examples: When did you hire this person? How long did he work for you? What were his specific responsibilities? With nannies, also ask how many children were cared for and their ages.

It's unlikely that the reference will have all of the details straight if the recommendation is phony.

If the reference is local and you have the address, drive by the home—does it look like the house of someone who can afford to hire in-home help?

- **Have a criminal background check conducted.** Here, you do need to hire a private investigator. Expect to pay $100 to $200 for a nationwide search. There are Internet companies that provide criminal background checks for less than $20, but these are unlikely to be comprehensive.

- **Install a hidden camera.** Logitech's Spy Video Security Master System is a great way to keep tabs on your in-home help while you're out. It's easy to install, and the camera is well-hidden in an innocuous desk clock ($329.99, 800-231-7717, *www.wilife.com*).

Warning: Do not hide a security camera in a bathroom or anywhere where an employee might be expected to undress. Doing so could get you sued for invasion of privacy. If you hide a camera in your parent's shared nursing-home room, make sure that roommates' beds aren't visible in the frame.

WHATEVER HAPPENED TO MY OLD FRIEND?

Finding a long-lost friend can be challenging, particularly if the name is a common one …or if she has married and taken the spouse's last name.

• **Search on the Web.** Google the name. Try nicknames, too. If you know additional information—a profession or lifelong hobby, for instance—try adding this to your Google search.

Example: If you remember that your old friend was always passionate about distance running, search "Larry Smith" and "marathon" or "10k."

Also check the social-networking site Facebook.com (click on "Find Friends" at the bottom of the sign-up page).

• **Search for family members.** If you can't find your friend, try looking for his relatives. They might be easier to find, and they'll likely know where your friend is. Look up your friend's last name in the phone book of his former hometown, then call those who share the name to see if they are related.

• **Search the local newspaper for obituaries for your friend's parents.** Obits often list the names and current hometowns of surviving relatives.

• **Contact professional organizations and licensing bodies related to your friend's line of work.** They might have a database of members.

How to Stay Safe When Disaster Strikes

Charles B. Inlander, consumer advocate and healthcare consultant based in Fogelsville, Pennsylvania. He was the founding president of the nonprofit People's Medical Society, the consumer advocacy organization credited with large improvements in the quality of US health care in the 1980s and 1990s, and is the author of 20 books, including *Take This Book to the Hospital with You: A Consumer Guide to Surviving Your Hospital Stay* (St. Martin's).

It's human nature to tell ourselves that disasters strike other people—not us. But for a reality check on such thinking, just ask those affected by Hurricane Katrina. Since the tragic 2005 hurricane, the federal government has worked with hospitals, nursing homes, assisted-living facilities and other health-care providers to help them be prepared for disasters. Today, many of these facilities have plans and backup systems that will enable them to respond to and survive a storm, flood, earthquake, prolonged power failure and other disasters. But do you have a personal plan of action? This is especially important if you or a loved one has a medical condition that requires daily care. *Steps you should take to develop your own disaster survival plan…*

• **Put it in writing.** Write out a plan of what you will do in case of a disaster and use it for planning purposes and as a checklist to review in the event of an emergency. Note all the ways that you and anyone you might be caring for can get out of the house quickly or to a safe location (such as the basement).

Smart idea: Place emergency phone numbers (including those for public utilities, friends and relatives) in several rooms of your house in case you are trapped in one area.

• **Get a cell phone.** Keep a fully charged cell phone in an easily accessible location in case your land-line phone doesn't work or you need to leave your home.

Smart idea: If you don't already have a cell phone, buy an inexpensive phone but do not sign up for cell-phone service. All cell-phone users are able to call 911 without subscribing to a provider's wireless service.

• **Keep the right equipment and supplies on hand.** If you or a loved one uses an oxygen machine, be sure that you have several large tanks of portable oxygen in the house in case of a power failure. Keep flashlights, a portable commode, extra blankets, bottled water and anything else you might need if you lose lights and heat or air conditioning.

Smart idea: Keep your daily medication in sealed plastic bags to prevent water damage. If your medication requires refrigeration, make sure you have a portable cooler in the house and keep ice packs in your freezer. Check in advance with your pharmacist for the best way to store refrigerated medication during an extended power outage.

•**Remain in touch.** Make sure family and friends are aware of your medical status. If your medical condition limits your ability to evacuate your home, family or friends can alert authorities.

Smart idea: Contact your local police department today to alert them that you need to be checked on if a power failure or disaster hits your area. Ask for the officer who serves as the community liaison.

•**Take action early.** Don't assume that you can weather a predicted blizzard or any other threatening event. Phone a family member or friend to help you or a loved one evacuate at the first warning (if there is one).

Smart idea: If no family member or friend is available, call the police or fire department or your local Red Cross or county government and ask for help.

If a disaster strikes, you'll be glad you followed these steps.

Thousands of Earthquakes Hit the US Each Year: What to Do If the Ground Starts Shaking

Gavin Hayes, PhD, a research seismologist with the United States Geological Survey's National Earthquake Information Center (USGS/NEIC), Denver. The NEIC is the US government's data center and archive for earthquake information. Dr. Hayes specializes in earthquake research and real-time response to large earthquakes. For more, go to *www.earthquake.usgs.gov.*

Major earthquakes in Haiti and Chile in 2010 left hundreds of thousands of people homeless, injured or dead. Virtually ignored amid news of these disasters was a much smaller earthquake in Oklahoma. The Oklahoma quake was thousands of times less powerful than the ones that struck Haiti and Chile, and it caused no serious injuries. Yet it, too, offers a powerful warning—earthquakes can affect many parts of the US.

Major earthquakes are rare across much of the US, but in some ways, this rarity increases the danger. In regions where major earthquakes are possible but not common, many buildings are not constructed to withstand severe shaking…and many residents know little about earthquake safety.

AMERICA AT RISK

In addition to California, US regions known to be at risk for major earthquakes include…

•**Western Oregon and western Washington State.**

•**The greater Mississippi River region—from northern Mississippi up to southern Illinois.**

•**Eastern South Carolina.**

•**Nevada, particularly in the western part of the state.**

•**Utah, western Wyoming, western Montana and eastern and central Idaho.**

•**Much of Alaska.**

•**Big Island of Hawaii.**

Many other locations have lesser but still significant earthquake risks, including northeastern New York State, the North Carolina/Tennessee border area and parts of Colorado, New Mexico, Arizona, New Hampshire and Oklahoma. To get maps detailing earthquake risk regions, log on to *www.earthquake.usgs.gov/hazards.*

STAYING SAFE DURING AN EARTHQUAKE

If you are indoors…

•**Take cover under a table, desk or another piece of sturdy furniture.** If such furniture is not available, drop to your knees and cover your head with your arms.

•**Select a spot that is not near windows…exterior walls…a masonry chimney…heavy upright furniture,** such as a bookshelf or china cabinet…or below anything heavy or made of glass that's hung from a wall or ceiling.

•**Remain in an interior doorway during a quake only if you are in an older brick or adobe building.** Doorways often are the strongest part of older brick and adobe structures. Doorways offer no safety benefits in most other buildings.

•**Do not attempt to exit a building during a quake.** The risk of getting struck and

335

badly injured by falling window glass or other debris while exiting exceeds the risk that you will be injured if you take cover inside.

What to do if an earthquake strikes while you are…

•**In bed.** Remain in the bed and protect yourself as best you can with your covers, pillows and arms.

•**Outside.** Move to an open area away from power lines and buildings. Stay away from chimneys.

•**In an office building.** Get under the nearest desk. Steer clear of file cabinets, which can topple…and plate-glass windows, which can shatter.

•**In your car.** Pull over to the side of the road, park and engage the parking brake. Ideally, avoid parking on or under overpasses, near heavy highway signs or light posts, or in areas where the road has been cut into a hillside—quakes often cause falling rocks.

Warning: If a power line falls on or near your vehicle during an earthquake, remain inside the vehicle until emergency crews arrive to help, even if this takes hours. If the wires are live, the current typically travels along the outer shell of your vehicle, leaving you safe inside—but you could be electrocuted if you attempt to get out.

WHAT TO DO IMMEDIATELY AFTER A QUAKE

Aftershocks tend to be most frequent in the hours and days immediately following an earthquake but can continue for weeks after the quake.

•**If you smell smoke, notice fire or the building you are in is damaged structurally, account for everyone who was in the building, then exit quickly.**

•**If there is no fire and the building appears to be sound, conduct a quick building inspection…**

•If you smell gas or see damage to a gas line, shut off the gas.

•If there's any reason to believe that the home's wiring has been damaged, switch off the electricity.

•**Never linger near the exterior of a building following an earthquake**—an aftershock could cause falling debris.

•**Check on your neighbors.** Emergency crews often are overwhelmed following major earthquakes. It's up to neighbors to help one another.

•**Do not shout for help (unless you hear any voices close by) if you're badly injured,** trapped under furniture or trapped in a collapsed building. Instead, bang a piece of debris against something metal if these things are within your reach. The banging sound will carry farther, and unlike shouting, it will not quickly deplete your energy or fill your lungs with the thick dust that clouds the air after a building collapse.

PREPARING FOR EARTHQUAKES

Below are simple, inexpensive steps that anyone living in an earthquake region should consider…

•**Relocate heavy or glass items currently hung above beds and frequently used seats.** These include mirrors and artwork framed under glass. Secure heavy furniture to a wall.

•**Reposition your bed if it currently is located very near a masonry chimney.** The chimney might be hidden behind wallboards on upper floors.

•**Have rigid gas lines replaced with flexible lines,** and have your gas water heater strapped to the wall.

•**Purchase and plug in emergency lights** that turn on automatically when the power goes out.

•**Get to know your neighbors, particularly if you are elderly or disabled** and could have trouble getting out of your home after an earthquake.

•**Put together an emergency kit** including bottled water…flashlights…extra batteries…a battery- or crank-powered radio…canned food…several days' supply of medications…and a fire extinguisher.

•**Select a meeting point for your family to gather if you are separated.**

Index

O

Olive oil, in Mediterranean diet, 101
Omega-3 fatty acids, 7, 62, 91–92, 93. *See also* Fish
Osteoarthritis, 37, 51, 97. *See also* Arthritis
Osteoporosis, 27
Ovarian cancer, 113–14
Over-the-counter (OTC) medications, 12, 40, 61–62. *See also* Medications

P

Pain
  cherry juice to reduce, 80
  creams for treating, 61–62
  cursing to reduce, 98
  mammograms causing, 116–17
  pet therapy for, 98
  post-surgery, 32–33, 46
  prolotherapy for, 99
  vitamin D link to, 98–99
Pancreatic cancer, 24
Papaya, for gastrointestinal health, 60–61
Parkinson's disease, 4–5, 26–27
Peas, benefits of, 92. *See also* Beans; Lentils
Perfectionism, health link to, 87
Peripheral artery disease (PAD), 18
Pets
  aging, 278
  bacteria from, 56
  bite prevention in, 277
  cost-saving tips for, 207
  disease prevention for, 278
  estate planning for, 231–32
  health benefits from, 98, 278–79
  health insurance for, 154, 207
  toxic substances for, 277–78
Photos, storing electronically, 252–53
Physicals, frequency of, 1
Pistachios, and cancer risk, 96
Plant sterols and stanols, in cholesterol treatment, 50, 91
Plants. *See also* Gardens
  in gardens, 255–56
  for removing harmful chemicals, 284
  therapeutic power of, 48, 65–66
Plastics, health links to, 21, 110
Pneumonia, 3, 8–9, 28–29
Police officers
  criminals impersonating, 330–31
  and speeders, 265
Pomegranate juice, 97, 118
Popcorn, health benefits of, 106
Potassium, blood pressure affected by, 10
Prediabetes, 19–20. *See also* Diabetes
Pregnancy, 111
Problem solving, 291–93
Procrastination, in debt-free living, 127
Property, unclaimed, 134
Property tax assessments, 160
Prostate cancer, 117, 118
Proton-pump inhibitor (PPI) drugs, for acid reflux, 29
Psyllium, for IBS, 121–22
Pulse rate, heart attack risk link to, 12
Pumpkin seeds, as mood booster, 103. *See also* Depression

R

Radiation, 22–24, 96, 116
Raisins, vs. grapes, 105–6
Real Estate Investment Trusts (REITs), 174
Rebate redemption process, 190–91
Red yeast rice extract, for high cholesterol, 91, 92

Reflexes, health link to, 95
Regifting, 256. *See also* Gift card restrictions
Reputation, protecting, 297–98, 323–25
Résumé, proofreading, 316. *See also* Unemployment
Resveratrol, benefits of, 88–89
Retirement. *See also* Aging; Longevity; Seniors
  accounts, 126, 129, 158, 216–17, 309
  annuities, 213–16
  do-it-yourself planning for, 212–13
  locations for, 211–12
  mortgage payoff before, 217–18
  planning life after, 209–11
  services during, 226 (*see also* Medicare; Social Security)
  for women vs. men, 213
  working after, 223
Rheumatoid arthritis, 37–38, 97, 98. *See also* Arthritis
Rights, of hospital patients, 31–33, 41–42

S

Saccharin, as sweetener, 72–73. *See also* Sugar
Safety. *See* Self-defense
Salt
  blood pressure affected by, 9–10
  depression link to, 28
  reducing intake of, 105
School. *See* Students
Seasickness remedies, 250
Selenium, after surgery, 48
Self-defense
  face-to-face crimes, 329–30
  lost wallets, 331
  mass shootings, 328–29
  natural disasters, 334–36
  online, 331–34
  police officer impersonators, 330–31
  terrorism in air travel, 327–28
Seniors. *See also* Aging; Longevity; Retirement
  cell phones for, 211
  communication tips for, 224–25
  false dementia diagnoses in, 26
  in financial need, 140–42
  services for, 226 (*see also* Medicare; Social Security)
Severance packages, 306, 307–8. *See also* Unemployment
Sex
  better, at any age, 107–9
  finding partner for, 109
  heart disease risk and, 110
  high cholesterol and, 110
  medications affecting, 108, 109, 111
  plastic exposure impacting, 110
  urinary tract infections and, 36
  vibrators benefiting, 109
  yoga for improving, 109
Sexually transmitted diseases, 111, 118–19
Shingles, and stroke risk, 15
Shoes, 124, 204
Shootings, self-defense during, 328–29
Shopping. *See also* Credit cards; Debt; Money
  best times for, 197–99
  for cell-phone rates, 205
  extended warranties, 199
  for free medical advice, 206
  hidden fees in, 191–92
  lifestyle change tips for, 124, 194–95
  with medication coupons, 206–7
  negotiation in, 193, 195–97, 205, 207, 266
  price comparison, 199

research before, 208
for restaurant wines, 203–4
rip-offs, 189–92
smarter, in recession, 192–94
at supermarkets, 199–203
VIP service while, 192
Showers
  bacteria growing in, 29
  for workout recovery, 80
Sinus infections, chronic, 57–59
Sleep
  for cold prevention, 57
  correct amount of, 2, 64
  darkness for, 117–18
  difficulty getting to, 18–19, 64
  dreams during, 293, 296
  for heart health, 92–93
  nighttime bathroom trips, 21
  warding off, 263, 325
  weight loss link to, 68–69
Sleep apnea, 9
Smoking, 26, 46, 97, 271
Social networking, 251–52, 302, 331–32. *See also* Friends
Social Security, getting the most from, 219–22. *See also* Medicare; Retirement; Seniors
Soda, kidney disease link to, 27
Soy, breast cancer link to, 105, 117
Spices, fighting bacteria, 106
Spirituality, 52, 82–83
Spontaneous physical activity (SPA), 86
Spouses, spending habits of, 125, 138–40. *See also* Marriage
Sprouts, boosting antioxidants, 57
St. John's wort, affecting surgery, 47
Statin drugs. *See also* Cholesterol
  alternatives to, 90–92
  flu complications and, 60
  natural treatments combined with, 50
  pneumonia risk link to, 29
  for resistant high cholesterol, 5–6
  for women vs. men, 4
Stevia, as sweetener, 72–73. *See also* Sugar
Stocks, as cash source, 125. *See also* Investing
Stress. *See also* Anxiety; Depression; Mental health
  of bill paying, 126–27
  heart disease link to, 14
  kissing to lower, 66
  longevity affected by, 82
  stroke risk and, 15–16
Stroke
  antidepressants link to, 18
  assessing risk of, 18
  menopause link to, 112
  research findings on, 16–18
  sleep trouble and, 18–19
  supplement for preventing, 88
  symptoms, 17
  tea and risk of, 94
  triggers, 15–16
  in women vs. men, 3–4
Students. *See also* Children and teenagers
  college costs for, 138, 195, 272–73, 311–12
  insurance coverage for, 153
  loan forgiveness and, 231
Sucralose, as sweetener, 73. *See also* Sugar
Sugar
  addiction, 102–3
  American consumption of, 22, 102
  research on, 71–73
Supermarket shopping tips, 199–203